8 75

FUNDAMENTALS
OF
MATHEMATICS

This book is in the

ADDISON-WESLEY SERIES IN MATHEMATICS

ERIC REISSNER, *Consulting Editor*

FUNDAMENTALS
OF
MATHEMATICS

---

by

ELBRIDGE P. VANCE

Oberlin College

ADDISON-WESLEY PUBLISHING COMPANY, INC.

READING, MASSACHUSETTS · PALO ALTO · LONDON

Second printing, August 1963

PREFACE

The entire approach to the study of mathematics has been constantly changing in recent years. Although some people have objected to the current trend of unifying or integrating subjects previously taught separately, it is my conviction that such a system seems most efficient. In this way the student acquires a real feeling for mathematical thought and processes common to all fields of mathematics, in addition to the true integration of the fundamental material itself. This conviction has led me to write this book.

One of the aims of the book is the education of the student in the nature of mathematics as a logical system. He must realize that precise definitions are important, that explicitly stated hypotheses are necessary, and that any system of mathematics consists of these definitions and hypotheses, together with results which have been derived by logical reasoning. The second aim of the book is more specific. A unified treatment of the basic ideas of algebra, trigonometry, and analytic geometry is presented, together with a substantial introduction to calculus. Such material is fundamental to any student's training, whether he wishes to continue in mathematics, the natural sciences, and engineering, or whether his interests lie in the social sciences or economics. With the mastery of the material covered in this book, the student should be well prepared to study mathematical logic, finite mathematics, statistics and probability, or continue in calculus.

In writing this book I have been influenced by the Committee on the Undergraduate Mathematical Program of the Mathematical Association of America, the Commission of Mathematics of the College Entrance Examination Board, and the Advanced Placement Program of the College Entrance Examination Board. Although much of the material covered will show this influence, the basic outline of the contents is mine. It has been written so that the moderately well-prepared secondary-school student should have no difficulty with the material; and it can be covered in a five-hour freshman course running a full year. The number of hours can easily be reduced if the preparation of the student is strong.

There are several unusual features of the book. A brief discussion of the one-dimensional coordinate system leads naturally to the ordinary rectangular coordinate system. The definition of the circular functions in terms of this system is the basic unifying link between trigonometry and analytic geometry, and makes it possible to use many simpler, more direct methods. The analytic rather than the computational part of trigonometry has been emphasized, although the latter has been included.

v

A definite distinction has been made between conditional equations and identities. An explicit and detailed treatment of determinants is included. Mathematical induction is introduced carefully and used in several important later proofs. A definite distinction is made between functions and relations. The notions of limit and derivative are treated carefully, consistent with their use in later courses. Integration is introduced as the inverse process of differentiation, a method entirely appropriate at this level. Every effort has been made to present intuitively each new concept before any detailed rigorous discussion.

Many of the problems which appear at the end of each article help to unify the subjects and introduce important concepts and theorems to which later reference is made. Some problems necessary for the continuity of the discussions are marked with an asterisk, and should always be assigned. Answers for the odd-numbered problems appear at the back of the book. Included in the Appendix are tables of powers and roots, four-place tables of the circular functions, logarithms, and the logarithms of the circular functions, as well as the American Experience Table of Mortality.

I wish to express my appreciation to my colleagues who have given advice and suggestions. I am also indebted to several anonymous reviewers and to the staff of Addison-Wesley Publishing Company for their valuable assistance in producing this book.

Any errors that may occur are, of course, my responsibility and I hope that readers of this book will not hesitate to bring them to my attention.

E. P. V.

January, 1960

CONTENTS

CHAPTER 1

NUMBERS AND ELEMENTARY OPERATIONS

The basic quantitative procedures of science involve counting and measurement. Counting characterizes a collection of objects by a number. Measurement assigns a number to some property of an object. Counting and measurement are far from simple concepts, and both have been the subjects of many studies in the field of scientific methodology. The important thing for us in the present study is the fact that both counting and measurement lead to numbers, and through the use of numbers, it is possible to obtain much insight into the workings of nature. We shall begin with the classification of the various types of numbers and then we shall introduce some basic operations and notions which are fundamental in all fields of mathematics and science.

1–1 Numbers. The first numbers encountered by everyone are the numbers 1, 2, 3, ... We refer to these as the *positive integers*. These numbers, together with the *negative integers*, -1, -2, -3, ... , and the zero integer 0, constitute the complete *set of integers*. When any two integers are added, subtracted, or multiplied, the result is an integer. That is, if a and b are integers, $a + b$, $a - b$, and ab are also integers. The zero integer has the special properties that for any integer a, $a + 0 = a$, $a - 0 = a$, and $a \cdot 0 = 0$.

Next, in forming quotients of integers, the rational numbers are introduced. For any numbers a and b, where b is different from zero, then a/b is defined as the number c which, when multiplied by b, gives a. This number c is called the *quotient* of a and b, and is defined by the equation $cb = a$. Fractions of the form $a/0$ are not defined. We therefore say that $a/0$ does not exist, and division by zero is not permitted. If a and b are integers, then c, the quotient of two integers, is called a *rational number*, and the entire set of all such quotients is called the *set of rational numbers*. The numbers $5/3$, $-13/2$, and 1.414 are rational numbers. Any integer n, say 3, is a rational number, since $n = n/1$. The number 1.414, which is an approximation for $\sqrt{2}$, is a rational number, since

$$1.414 = \frac{1414}{1000}.$$

Any rational number may be written as a decimal; indeed a rational number may be identified by the fact that its decimal expansion either

1

terminates or, if unending, is periodic.* Numbers which are nonperiodic and unending when expressed as decimals are not rational. For example, the nonterminating decimal 0.1010010001 ... is not rational. Others which are not rational are the numbers $\sqrt{2}$, π (the ratio of the circumference of any circle to its diameter), and e (the base for logarithms used in calculus), since none of them can be expressed as the quotient of two integers. None of these numbers, therefore, has an unending periodic decimal expansion.

The entire set of numbers expressible as decimals (terminating or not) is called the *set of real numbers,* and those in this set which are not rational form the *set of irrational numbers.* Any irrational number can be approximated by a rational number. For example, the rational number which approximates $\sqrt{2}$, correct to three decimal places, is 1.414. The rational number 22/7 is a common approximation for π, while a more accurate one is 3.1416. The sum, difference, product, or quotient (division by other than zero) of any two real numbers is a real number. The set of all real numbers may be classified as follows:

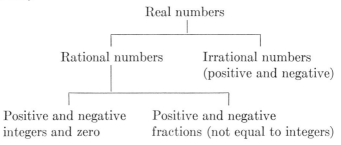

We shall deal primarily with real numbers in this book, but other types of numbers will arise from generalizations or extensions of real numbers. In Chapter 17, for example, we shall discuss the set of complex numbers, which includes imaginary numbers as well as real numbers. However, unless otherwise stated, all numbers will be regarded as belonging to the set of real numbers.

1–2 Equality. The two main types of equations in mathematics, the identity and the conditional equation, have many of the same properties but differ in meaning. Let us distinguish between them.

DEFINITION 1–1. *An* identity *is a statement of equality which holds true for all permissible*† *values of the letters involved.*

---

* Periodic, in this sense, means that the digits repeat either from the beginning (0.161616 ...) or after a certain stage (3.2454545 ...).

† The permissible values are all those values for which each term (Article 1–4) of the equation has meaning.

Each such identity will be denoted by the symbol ≡, in order to emphasize its nature. The following simple examples will help to clarify the concept.

ILLUSTRATION 1. $x + 2 + 5 - 4 - x \equiv 3$ holds for all values of x.

ILLUSTRATION 2. $x^2 - 4 \equiv (x + 2)(x - 2)$, where x^2 represents x times x, holds for all values of x. This statement may be checked by substituting any value for x in both sides of the identity, and is proved in Article 1–5.

The conditional equation is more commonly used.

DEFINITION 1–2.   *The* conditional equation *is a statement of equality which holds true for some, but not all, permissible values of the letters involved.*

One is usually required to solve such an equation, that is, to find all possible values (the solution) for which the equation is true. Later we shall discuss the solving of equations, but now let us consider the following examples.

ILLUSTRATION 3. $x + 2 = 4$ is a conditional equation, since it is true only for $x = 2$.

ILLUSTRATION 4. $x^2 - 7x + 12 = 0$ is a conditional equation, since it is true only for $x = 3$ or 4. Any other value substituted for x in this equation will not satisfy it.

The use of the symbol ≡ for an identity and = for a conditional equation emphasizes the distinction between the two types of equalities.

1–3 Fundamental operations and assumptions. In algebra, as in arithmetic, there are definite rules or laws. The basic properties of the operations on real numbers, addition and multiplication and their inverse operations, subtraction and division, are familiar to the student. These operations are based on the following fundamental assumptions, which hold for all real numbers. The usual symbols for grouping two or more numbers as a single quantity (i.e., parentheses, ( ), brackets, [ ], or braces, { }) apply.

The commutative law for addition. The sum of two numbers is the same in whatever order the numbers are added. That is,

$$a + b \equiv b + a. \tag{1-1}$$

The associative law for addition. The sum of three or more numbers is the same in whatever manner the numbers are grouped for adding. That is,

$$(a + b) + c \equiv a + (b + c) \equiv a + b + c. \tag{1-2}$$

The commutative law for multiplication. The product of two numbers is the same in whatever order the numbers are multiplied. That is,

$$ab \equiv ba. \tag{1-3}$$

Here, a and b are called *factors* of ab.

The associative law for multiplication. The product of three or more numbers is the same in whatever manner the numbers are grouped. That is,

$$a(bc) \equiv (ab)c \equiv abc. \tag{1-4}$$

The distributive law. The product of one number and the sum of two or more other numbers is equal to the sum of the products obtained by multiplying each of the other numbers by the first number. That is,

$$a(b + c + d) \equiv ab + ac + ad. \tag{1-5}$$

There exists an *identical element* for addition and for multiplication. That is,

$$a + 0 \equiv a, \quad \text{and} \quad a \cdot 1 \equiv a. \tag{1-6}$$

There also exists an *inverse element* for addition and for multiplication. That is,

$$a + (-a) \equiv 0, \quad \text{and} \quad a\left(\frac{1}{a}\right) \equiv 1 \quad \text{if} \quad a \neq 0.* \tag{1-7}$$

We also recall that if a and b are numbers such that $ab \equiv 0$, then either $a \equiv 0$ or $b \equiv 0$ and, conversely, if either $a \equiv 0$ or $b \equiv 0$, then $ab \equiv 0$. These two statements may be combined:

$$ab \equiv 0 \text{ is equivalent to } a \equiv 0 \text{ or } b \equiv 0. \tag{1-8}$$

Each number in the system of real numbers may be positive, zero, or negative. If a and b agree in sign, $a + b$ is equal to the sum of the numerical values† and keeps the common sign, while ab and a/b are positive numbers. However, if a and b differ in sign, $a + b$ is equal to the difference of the numerical values and has the sign of the numerically larger number. In this case ab and a/b are negative. When a is not zero, a and $1/a$ agree in sign. Also, a and $-a$ differ in sign, that is, $a \equiv -(-a)$.

---

* $a \neq 0$ denotes the fact that a is not equal to zero. This condition is only necessary for the second part of (1–7).

† The *numerical value* of a number is the size or magnitude of the number without regard to sign. A more detailed discussion of this concept appears in Article 3–1.

ILLUSTRATIONS. $2 + 3 = 5; -3 - 4 = -3 + (-4) = -7.$

$-6 + 5 = -1; 4 + (-7) = -3; 7 - (-4) = 7 + 4 = 11.$

$3(-4) = -12; -3(4) = -12; (-3)(-4) = 12.$

PROBLEMS

Find the sum, difference (first number minus the second), product, and quotient of the numbers in Problems 1–12.

1. 25 and 11	2. 7 and -5	3. -24 and 8
4. -12 and -8	5. 0 and -4	6. 6 and 0
7. 1/2 and 1/3	8. 4/7 and $-2/3$	9. $-9/7$ and $-5/4$
10. $-9/8$ and 11/5	11. 0 and $-5/4$	12. $-2/3$ and 2/3

13. Using the first five equations in this chapter, show that

(a) $a(b + c) \equiv ba + ca$,

(b) $(b + c + d)a \equiv ab + ac + ad$,

(c) $(a + b)(c + d) \equiv ac + ad + bc + bd$.

14. Show by a proper selection of numbers that (a) subtraction is not commutative, (b) division is not commutative.

15. Under what conditions will $-ab$ be (a) positive, (b) negative, (c) zero?

1–4 Addition of algebraic expressions. Any combination of symbols and numbers related by the fundamental operations of algebra is called an *algebraic expression*.

ILLUSTRATION 1. $5a + 6b$, $2ax^2$, and $(6x + 5y)2x$ are algebraic expressions.

Any algebraic expression consisting of distinct parts connected by plus or minus signs is called an *algebraic sum*. Each distinct part, together with its sign, is called a *term* of the expression.

ILLUSTRATION 2. In the algebraic sum $2x^2 - 3y^2 - 5$, $2x^2$ is one term, $-3y^2$ another, and -5 is a third term.

In a particular term consisting of two or more factors, any one of the factors or the product of any set of the factors may be called the *coefficient* of the product of the other factors. For example, in the term $2x^2y$, 2 is the coefficient of x^2y, $2x^2$ is the coefficient of y, and $2y$ is the coefficient of x^2. Frequently it is convenient to distinguish between numerical coefficients and letter-symbol coefficients. In determining the sum or difference of two algebraic expressions by combining similar terms, coefficients are used.

ILLUSTRATION 3. The sum of $2x - 3y + 5$ and $x + 2y - 1$ is

$$(2x - 3y + 5) + (x + 2y - 1) \equiv 2x + x - 3y + 2y + 5 - 1$$
$$\equiv 3x - y + 4.$$

ILLUSTRATION 4. The difference between $2x - 3y + 5$ and $x + 2y - 1$ is

$$(2x - 3y + 5) - (x + 2y - 1) \equiv 2x - 3y + 5 - x - 2y + 1$$
$$\equiv x - 5y + 6.$$

We have stated that algebraic expressions are called algebraic sums whether addition or subtraction is involved. If the expression consists of just one term, it is called a *monomial*. The algebraic sum or difference of two terms is called a *binomial* and, in general, an algebraic expression consisting of a sum of any number of terms is called a *multinomial*. The expression $2x/3y^2$ is a monomial, while $3x^2 - 2y$ is a binomial.

EXAMPLE 1.   Simplify   the   expression $4x - [2x - 3y - (x + 4y)] + (x - 8)$ by removing parentheses or brackets. Then combine similar terms.

Solution.

$$4x - [2x - 3y - (x + 4y)] + (x - 8) \equiv 4x - [2x - 3y - x - 4y] + x - 8$$
$$\equiv 4x - 2x + 3y + x + 4y + x - 8$$
$$\equiv 4x + 7y - 8.$$

The removal of parentheses (or any symbol of grouping) preceded by a minus sign requires changing the sign of each term within the parentheses, but parentheses preceded by a plus sign may be removed without changing the expression in the parentheses.

EXAMPLE 2.   Find   the   value   of $-2xy + 3x - 4y$ when $x = 3$ and $y = -2$.

Solution. Substitute 3 for x and -2 for y:

$$-2(3)(-2) + 3(3) - 4(-2) = 12 + 9 + 8 = 29.$$

PROBLEMS

In each of the following, (a) find the sum of the expressions and (b) subtract the second expression from the first.

1. $2a + 3b - 4$ and $a - 2b + 3$ 2. $a - 2b + 3c$ and $2a + 4b - c$
3. $4x + 3y + z$ and $2x + 3y - 2z$ 4. $2x + y + 5$ and $3y - 2z - 4$
5. $2(x - 3y)$ and $-5(2x + y)$ 6. $-(x + 2y - z)$ and $3(x - y + 2z)$

In each of the following, remove all symbols of grouping and combine like terms.

7. $x - (2y + 3x) - 2y$

8. $3x - (2y - 4x) + 6y$

9. $(2x - 3y) - (8x + 6y + 4)$

10. $(2x - 3y) + (y - 4z) - (z - 3x)$

11. $8x + [(3x - 2y) + (6x - 9) - (x + y)]$

12. $3y - [2y + 3x - (2x - 3y)] + 4x$

13. $2x - \{3y - [5x - (7y - 6x)]\}$

14. $9x - (2y - 3x) - \{y - (2y - x)\} - [2y + (4x - 3y)]$

In each of the following expressions enclose the last three terms in parentheses preceded by a minus sign.

15. $a^2 - b^2 + 2bc - c^2$ 16. $16 - x^2 + 2xy - y^2$

17. $4x^2 - 4y^2 - 4y - 1$ 18. $9x^2 - 9y^2 - 6xy - x^2$

In each of the following expressions enclose the coefficients of x within parentheses preceded by (a) a plus sign, (b) a minus sign.

19. $cx + dy - ax - by$ 20. $5x - ax + 3 - 4x$

21. $ax - by + bx - ay$ 22. $6x^2 - 8x + 3y - 7y^2 + 6x - 4$

Find the value of each of the following expressions for the given values of the letters.

23. $3x + 4$ when $x = 1$ 24. $x^2 - 7x + 10$ when $x = 2$

25. $3x^2 - 2x + 1$ when $x = -2$ 26. $-3x^2 - 4x + 3$ when $x = -4$

27. $2x + 3y$ when $x = -2, y = 3$ 28. $4x - 3y$ when $x = -1, y = 3$

29. $2x^2 - 3xy + y^2$ when $x = 2, y = -3$

30. $3x^2 + 2xy - 4y^2$ when $x = -3, y = 1$

1–5 Multiplication of algebraic expressions. When the factors of a product are equal, the product is called a *power* of the repeated factor. We shall introduce a symbol to stand for such a product. The symbol a^2 represents the product $a \cdot a$. Similarly, $a \cdot a \cdot a$ may be represented by a^3 and, in general, we have:

DEFINITION 1–3. *If n is a positive integer, the symbol a^n, the nth power of a, is the product of n factors each equal to a. Thus*

$$a^n \equiv \underbrace{a \cdot a \cdot a \cdots a}_{n \text{ factors } a}. \qquad (1\text{–}9)$$

In the symbol a^n, a is called the *base* and n the *exponent* of the power.

ILLUSTRATION 1. $2^5 = 2 \cdot 2 \cdot 2 \cdot 2 \cdot 2 = 32$.

From this definition certain theorems on exponents follow.

THEOREM 1–1. *If n and m are positive integers, and a is any real number,*

$$\boxed{a^n a^m = a^{n+m}.}$$ (1–10)

Proof.

$$a^n \cdot a^m \equiv \underbrace{a \cdot a \cdot a \cdots a}_{n \text{ factors } a} \cdot \underbrace{a \cdot a \cdot a \cdots a}_{m \text{ factors } a} \equiv \underbrace{a \cdot a \cdot a \cdots a}_{n+m \text{ factors } a} \equiv a^{n+m}.$$

The reader should also prove the theorems:

THEOREM 1–2. *If n and m are positive integers, and a is any real number,*

$$\boxed{(a^n)^m \equiv a^{nm}.}$$ (1–11)

THEOREM 1–3. *If n is a positive integer, and a and b are any real numbers,*

$$(ab)^n \equiv a^n b^n.$$ (1–12)

ILLUSTRATION 2.
$$3^2 \cdot 3^4 = 3^6 = 729,$$
$$a^4 \cdot a^7 \equiv a^{11}.$$

ILLUSTRATION 3.
$$(2^3)^2 = 2^6 = 64,$$
$$(a^5)^3 \equiv a^{15}.$$

ILLUSTRATION 4. $(2 \cdot 3)^3 = 2^3 \cdot 3^3 = 8 \cdot 27 = 216.$

When no exponent is written, the exponent is understood to be 1.

We are now able, using these theorems and recalling the distributive law, Eq. (1–5), to perform the multiplication of two algebraic expressions.

EXAMPLE 1. Multiply $(2x - 3y)$ by $(3x + 4y)$.

Solution. Each term of the second binomial must be multiplied by the first binomial. [See Problem 13(c), Article 1–3.]

$$(2x - 3y)(3x + 4y) \equiv (2x - 3y) \cdot 3x + (2x - 3y) \cdot 4y$$
$$\equiv 6x^2 - 9xy + 8xy - 12y^2.$$

If we combine similar terms, we have

$$(2x - 3y)(3x + 4y) \equiv 6x^2 - xy - 12y^2.$$

In such problems it is sometimes convenient to arrange both multinomials in ascending (or descending) powers of one letter, write one below the other, carry out the multiplication, and add the products.   Consider the following example.

EXAMPLE 2. Multiply $x^2 - 2y^2 + xy$ by $2x - y$.

Solution.
$$
\begin{array}{l}
x^2 + xy \quad\ - 2y^2 \\
\underline{2x\ -\ y} \\
2x^3 + 2x^2y - 4xy^2 \\
\underline{\quad\ -\ x^2y -\ xy^2 + 2y^3} \\
2x^3 +\ x^2y - 5xy^2 + 2y^3
\end{array}
$$

PROBLEMS

Perform the indicated operations by using the laws of exponents.

1. $a^2 \cdot a^7$ 2. $3x^4 \cdot 2x^3$

3. $3x^3 \cdot x^4 \cdot x^5$ 4. $(-3)^4 \cdot (-3)^5$

5. $y^{13} \cdot y^{11}$ 6. $(2^3)^4$

7. $(a^5)^4$ 8. $(3b)^5$

9. $(5c)^3$ 10. $(3a)^4$

11. $(2a^3)^5$ 12. $(x^4)^n$

13. $(a^r \cdot a^s)^t$ 14. $(x^{2m} \cdot x^{3n})^4$

15. $(2x^n)^n$

Perform the indicated multiplications and collect similar terms.

16. $(4x - 3)(3x + 6)$ 17. $(x + 3)(2x - 5)$

18. $(5a + 2b)(5a - 2b)$ 19. $(4x + 2y)(4x - 2y)$

20. $(3x - 2)(2x + 5)$ 21. $(r^2 - s^2)(r - s)$

22. $(x - 2y)^2$ 23. $(x^2 - xy + y^2)(x + y)$

24. $(2x + 3x^2 - 1)(3x - 2)$ 25. $(x^2 - 2x - 2)(x + 2x^2 - 4)$

26. $(-xy + 2x^2 - 3y^2)(x^2 - 4y^2 + xy)$

27. $(x - 1)(x + 2)(x - 3)$ 28. $(x - 2)(x + 3)(x + 2)$

29. $(x^4 + 2x^2y^2 + 4y^4)(x^2 - 2y^2)$ 30. $(a^{2n} - 7a^n + 10)(a^n - 1)$

31. $(a^{2n} - 7a^n + 10)(a - 1)$

32. $(x - 2x^2 + 5 - x^3)(3x - 4 + x^2)$

33. $(x^{2n} + 2x^ny^n + y^{2n})(x^{2n} - 2x^ny^n + y^{2n})$

34. $(x^n - y^n)^3$ 35. $(x - y)^4$

1–6 Division of algebraic expressions. Before we are able to divide one algebraic expression by another, we must establish an additional theorem on exponents.

THEOREM 1–4. *If $a \neq 0$ and n and m are positive integers,*

$$\frac{a^n}{a^m} \equiv \begin{cases} a^{n-m} \text{ if } n \text{ is larger than } m, & (1\text{–}13) \\[2mm] \dfrac{1}{a^{m-n}} \text{ if } m \text{ is larger than } n, & (1\text{–}14) \\[2mm] 1 \text{ if } m = n. & (1\text{–}15) \end{cases}$$

Proof. This result is established by writing

$$\frac{a^n}{a^m} \equiv \frac{\overbrace{a \cdot a \cdot a \cdots a}^{n \text{ factors } a}}{\underbrace{a \cdot a \cdot a \cdots a}_{m \text{ factors } a}}.$$

ILLUSTRATION 1. $\dfrac{x^8}{x^3} \equiv x^5; \dfrac{x^4}{x^{11}} \equiv \dfrac{1}{x^7}; \dfrac{x^6}{x^6} \equiv 1.$

We are now prepared to divide any multinomial by a monomial. This is done by dividing each term of the multinomial by the monomial and finding the algebraic sum of the resulting quotients.

EXAMPLE 1. Divide $12x^3y^4 + 18x^4y^2 - 36xy^3$ by $3x^2y^2$.

Solution.

$$\frac{12x^3y^4 + 18x^4y^2 - 36xy^3}{3x^2y^2} \equiv \frac{12x^3y^4}{3x^2y^2} + \frac{18x^4y^2}{3x^2y^2} - \frac{36xy^3}{3x^2y^2}$$

$$\equiv 4xy^2 + 6x^2 - \frac{12y}{x}.$$

We have defined (Article 1–4) an algebraic expression as the sum of algebraic terms. Any algebraic term is an *integral rational* term in certain letters representing numbers if it consists of the product of positive integral powers of these numbers and a factor not containing them. For example, ax^2y and $\sqrt{3}\,x^4y^{3/4}$ are integral rational terms in x, and ax^2y and $\sqrt{3}\,x^4y^3$ are integral rational terms in y. The term $by^{1/2}$ is also integral rational in x, since it satisfies the definition. Any multinomial in which each term is integral rational is called an *integral rational expression* or *polynomial*.

ILLUSTRATION 2. The multinomial $3 - 5x^3 + \frac{3}{5}xy^2$ is a polynomial in x and y. However, $-5/x^3$ is not integral in x, and $5\sqrt{x}$ is neither integral nor rational in x.

The degree of a term which is *integral rational* in some letter is defined to be the *exponent* of that letter. Thus ax^2y and $3x^4y^3$ are terms of the second and fourth degree in x, but first and third degree in y. *The degree of an integral rational term in two or more letters* is defined to be the sum of the exponents of those letters. Thus the degree of ax^2y in x and y is $2 + 1 = 3$, while the degree of $3x^4y^3$ in x and y is 7. *The degree of a polynomial* in certain letters is that of its term (or terms) of highest degree in those letters.

ILLUSTRATION 3. (a) $2x + 1$, $x^2 - 7x + 10$, and $3x^3 + 5x^2 - 6x$ are polynomials of the first, second, and third degree in x, respectively. (b) $3x^2y^5 + 4xy^3 - 7x^3y^2$ is a polynomial of the third degree in x, fifth degree in y, and seventh degree in x and y.

Now let us consider the division of one polynomial by another. Our method will follow that used in arithmetic. If we divide 28 by 9, the quotient is 3 and the remainder 1, and we write

$$\frac{28}{9} = 3 + \frac{1}{9}.$$

To divide one polynomial by another:

1. Arrange each polynomial in descending powers of some common letter.

2. Divide the first term of the dividend (the polynomial to be divided) by the first term of the divisor. This step gives the first term of the quotient.

3. Multiply the divisor by the first term of the quotient, and subtract the product from the dividend.

4. Using the remainder thus obtained as a new dividend, repeat this process, thus finding the second term of the quotient.

5. Continue the process until a remainder is obtained which is either zero or is of lower degree in the common letter than the divisor. If the remainder is zero, the division is exact.

The work should be arranged as shown in the example.

EXAMPLE 2. Divide $3x^3 - 4x^2y + 5xy^2 + 6y^3$ by $x^2 - 2xy + 3y^2$.

Solution.

$$
\begin{array}{l}
\text{(Dividend)} \quad \underline{3x^3 - 4x^2y + 5xy^2 + 6y^3} \,\big|\, \underline{x^2 - 2xy + 3y^2} \quad \text{(Divisor)} \\
\qquad\qquad\quad\; 3x^3 - 6x^2y + 9xy^2 \quad\;\;\; \big|\, 3x + 2y \quad\;\;\; \text{(Quotient)} \\
\qquad\qquad\qquad\quad\; 2x^2y - 4xy^2 + 6y^3 \\
\qquad\qquad\qquad\quad\; 2x^2y - 4xy^2 + 6y^3 \\
\qquad\qquad\qquad\qquad\qquad\qquad\;\; 0 \quad \text{(Remainder)}
\end{array}
$$

This result may be expressed in the form

$$\frac{3x^3 - 4x^2y + 5xy^2 + 6y^3}{x^2 - 2xy + 3y^2} \equiv 3x + 2y.$$

EXAMPLE 3.   Divide $5x^3 - 14x + 3$ by $x - 2$.

Solution. Since no x^2 term appears in the given dividend, the coefficient of that term is zero and we have

$$
\begin{array}{r|l}
5x^3 + 0x^2 - 14x + 3 & \ \ x \ \ - \ 2 \\
\underline{5x^3 - 10x^2} & \ \ 5x^2 + 10x + 6 \\
 10x^2 - 14x + 3 & \\
 \underline{10x^2 - 20x} & \\
 6x + 3 & \\
 \underline{6x - 12} & \\
 15 &
\end{array}
$$

This results in

$$\frac{5x^3 - 14x + 3}{x - 2} \equiv 5x^2 + 10x + 6 + \frac{15}{x - 2}.$$

A notation frequently used for a polynomial in x is the expression $P(x)$, read "P of x" (this expression does *not* mean P times x); likewise, a polynomial in x and y might be denoted $Q(x, y)$.   In this notation, if $P(x)$ denotes the dividend, $D(x)$ the divisor, $Q(x)$ the quotient, and $R(x)$ the remainder of a division of two polynomials in x, our result could be stated

$$\frac{P(x)}{D(x)} \equiv Q(x) + \frac{R(x)}{D(x)}, \qquad (1\text{--}16)$$

or

$$\boxed{P(x) \equiv Q(x) \cdot D(x) + R(x).} \qquad (1\text{--}17)$$

Similarly, for division of two polynomials in x and y,

$$P(x, y) \equiv Q(x, y) \cdot D(x, y) + R(x, y). \qquad (1\text{--}18)$$

ILLUSTRATION 4.   In Example 2 of this article,

$$P(x, y) = 3x^3 - 4x^2y + 5xy^2 + 6y^3, \qquad D(x, y) = x^2 - 2xy + 3y^2,$$
$$Q(x, y) = 3x + 2y, \qquad R(x, y) = 0.$$

In Example 3,

$$P(x) = 5x^3 - 14x + 3, \qquad D(x) = x - 2,$$
$$Q(x) = 5x^2 + 10x + 6, \qquad R(x) = 15.$$

PROBLEMS

Divide:

1. $9xy^2 - 6x^3$ by $3x$
2. $4x^2y^3 - 24xy^4$ by $2xy^2$
3. $6x^3 - 9x^4y$ by $3xy$
4. $-15x^2y^3 + 20x^3y^2$ by $-5x^2y^2$
5. $3x^2y - 4xy^2 + 6x^3y^3$ by xy
6. $7x^3y^2 - 14x^5y^3 + 28x^8y^5 - 21x^7y^6$ by $7x^3y^2$

Divide, finding the quotient and remainder, and write out the result of each problem in the form of Eqs. (1–17) or (1–18):

7. $x^2 - 7x + 10$ by $x - 5$
8. $2y^2 - 5y - 6$ by $2y - 1$
9. $3x^2 - 13x + 4$ by $x - 4$
10. $2x^2 - 5x - 12$ by $2x + 3$
11. $2x^3 - 7x^2 + 11x - 4$ by $2x - 1$
12. $y^3 - 4y^2 - 2 + 5y$ by $y - 1$
13. $x^2y - 6x^3 - 12xy^2 - 6y^3$ by $2x - 3y$
14. $2x^3 - 11x^2y + 13xy^2 - 4y^3$ by $x - 4y$
15. $4x^3 + 5 + 4x^2 - 13x$ by $2x + 5$
16. $4x^3 + 5x - 6$ by $2x - 3$
17. $5x^3 - 2x^2 + 3x - 4$ by $x^2 - 2x + 1$
18. $4x^2 + x - 6x^3 + 3$ by $3x^2 + 5$
19. $x^6 - y^6$ by $x - y$
20. $x^7 - y^7$ by $x - y$

The process of division for polynomials in x (or any one letter) may be greatly simplified when the divisor is in the form $x - a$. This process, known as *synthetic division*, will be illustrated by using the problem of Example 3. Writing only the coefficients, we have

$$
\begin{array}{rr|rrr}
5 + \;\;0 - 14 & 3 & 1 - & 2 & \\
5 - 10 & & 5 & 10 & 6 \\
\hline
10 - 14 & & & & \\
10 - 20 & & & & \\
\hline
6 & 3 & & & \\
6 - 12 & & & & \\
\hline
15 & & & &
\end{array}
$$

We next omit those coefficients that are definite repetitions: the first term in the 2nd, 4th, 6th, ... lines and the second term in the 3rd, 5th, 7th, ... lines. Compressing the remaining terms, writing the first coefficient, 5, in the third line, and noting that the 1 of the divisor can be omitted, we have

$$
\begin{array}{rrrr|r}
5 & +0 & -14 & 3 & \underline{-2} \\
 & -10 & -20 & -12 & \\
\hline
5 & 10 & 6 & 15 &
\end{array}
$$

The coefficients of the quotient are also omitted, for they appear as the first three coefficients on the third line, while the remainder, 15, appears as the last number.

The final step of simplification is to replace the subtractions by additions, that is, to change the signs in the divisor (-2 to 2) and in the second line. Thus

$$
\begin{array}{rrrr|r}
5 & +0 & -14 & 3 & \underline{2} \\
 & 10 & 20 & 12 & \\
\hline
5 & 10 & 6 & 15 &
\end{array}
$$

This arrangement represents the synthetic division of $5x^3 - 14x + 3$ by $x - 2$. It yields the quotient $5x^2 + 10x + 6$ and the remainder 15.

Let us summarize the process of synthetic division. To divide a polynomial $P(x)$ by a binomial $x - a$, arrange on a line (in order of descending power) the coefficients of $P(x)$, inserting zero for the coefficient of any missing power of x, and write a on the right. Bring down the first coefficient of $P(x)$ to the first position on the third line. Multiply this first coefficient by a, writing the product in the second line under the second coefficient of $P(x)$. The sum of this product and second coefficient is placed in the third line. Multiply this sum by a, add the product to the next coefficient of $P(x)$, again writing the new sum on the third line, and so on, until a product has been added to the final coefficient of $P(x)$.

The last sum in the third line represents the remainder. The preceding numbers represent the coefficients of the powers of x in the quotient, arranged in descending order. The quotient is a polynomial of degree one less than the degree of $P(x)$.

EXAMPLE 4. By synthetic division, find the quotient and the remainder of $2x^4 + 3x^3 - 4x^2 + 5x + 6$ divided by $x + 3$.

Solution. In this example $x - a = x - (-3)$, so that $a = -3$.

$$
\begin{array}{rrrrr|r}
2 & +3 & -4 & +5 & +6 & \underline{-3} \\
 & -6 & +9 & -15 & +30 & \\
\hline
2 & -3 & 5 & -10 & 36 &
\end{array}
$$

Thus the quotient is $2x^3 - 3x^2 + 5x - 10$, and the remainder is 36.

The process of synthetic division will be very useful in later work.

PROBLEMS

By synthetic division, find the quotient and the remainder in each of the following divisions.

1. $3x^2 - 2x - 4$ by $x - 3$ 2. $2x^3 + 3x^2 - 7$ by $x + 1$
3. $x^3 - 2x^2 + 9$ by $x + 2$ 4. $x^3 + 4x - 7$ by $x - 3$
5. $x^4 - 2x^3 - 3x^2 - 4x - 8$ by (a) $x - 2$, (b) $x + 1$
6. $2x^4 - x^3 - 18x^2 - 7$ by (a) $x + 3$, (b) $x - 3$
7. $3x^4 - 7x - 20$ by (a) $x - 2$, (b) $x + 2$
8. $2x^4 - 3x^3 - 20x^2 - 6$ by (a) $x - 4$, (b) $x + 3$

Use synthetic division to find the quotient and remainder in the following divisions and express the answer in the form of Eq. (1–17).

9. $x^3 - 2x^2 + 3x - 4$ by $x - 3$ 10. $2x^3 + x^2 - x + 4$ by $x + 1$
11. $x^4 - 5x^3 + x^2 - 6$ by $x - 1$ 12. $x^3 + 3x^2 - 2x - 5$ by $x + 2$

1–7 Special products. There are certain special products which occur so frequently in algebra that they have been classified. These are given below. The letters in the formulas may stand for any algebraic expression. The reader should not only verify each by actual multiplication but also memorize them, so that he can recognize both the product from the factors and the factors from the product.

$$a(x + y) \equiv ax + ay. \tag{1–19}$$

$$(x + y)(x - y) \equiv x^2 - y^2. \tag{1–20}$$

$$(x \pm y)^2 \equiv x^2 \pm 2xy + y^2.* \tag{1–21}$$

$$(x + a)(x + b) \equiv x^2 + (a + b)x + ab. \tag{1–22}$$

$$(ax + b)(cx + d) \equiv acx^2 + (ad + bc)x + bd. \tag{1–23}$$

$$(x \pm y)^3 \equiv x^3 \pm 3x^2y + 3xy^2 \pm y^3. \tag{1–24}$$

$$(x \pm y)(x^2 \mp xy + y^2) \equiv x^3 \pm y^3. \tag{1–25}$$

In the following illustrations the reader should determine which of the above formulas is used.

ILLUSTRATION 1. $(2x^2 - 3y)(2x^2 + 3y) \equiv (2x^2)^2 - (3y)^2$
$$\equiv 4x^4 - 9y^2.$$

---

* The sign $\pm$ is read "plus or minus." If the upper (lower) sign is used in the left member, it is also used in the right.

ILLUSTRATION 2. $(x + 2)(x + 5) \equiv x^2 + (2 + 5)x + 10$
$$\equiv x^2 + 7x + 10.$$

ILLUSTRATION 3. $(3x + 4y)(2x - 3y) \equiv 6x^2 + (-9 + 8)xy - 12y^2$
$$\equiv 6x^2 - xy - 12y^2.$$

ILLUSTRATION 4.

$(x + y - 1)^3$
$$\equiv [(x + y) - 1]^3$$
$$\equiv (x + y)^3 - 3(x + y)^2 + 3(x + y) - 1$$
$$\equiv x^3 + 3x^2y + 3xy^2 + y^3 - 3x^2 - 6xy - 3y^2 + 3x + 3y - 1.$$

Here $(x + y)$ is considered first as one term.

ILLUSTRATION 5.

$$(3x + 2y)(9x^2 - 6xy + 4y^2) \equiv (3x + 2y)[(3x)^2 - (3x)(2y) + (2y)^2]$$
$$\equiv (3x)^3 + (2y)^3$$
$$\equiv 27x^3 + 8y^3.$$

PROBLEMS

Find the following products.

1. $2a(3x - 4y)$ 2. $-3x(2x + 7y)$
3. $-7xy(3x^2 + 4y)$ 4. $4x^2yz(z^2 + xy + yz)$
5. $(2x - 3y)(2x + 3y)$ 6. $(7x + 5y^2)(7x - 5y^2)$
7. $(x + 2y)(x - 2y)(x^2 + 4y^2)$ 8. $(x - 3)^2$
9. $(2x + 7y)^2$ 10. $(3x^2y - 5z^2)^2$
11. $(x - 2)(x - 5)$ 12. $(2x + 3)(x - 5)$
13. $(xy^2 - z^2w)^2$ 14. $(\frac{1}{2}x + \frac{2}{3}y)^2$
15. $(4x - 3y)(7x + 3y)$ 16. $[(x + 1) - z][(x + 1) + z]$
17. $(2x + 3y + 3)(2x + 3y - 3)$ 18. $(2x + 3y + 4z)^2$
19. $(x - 2y - z)^2$ 20. $(2a + b)^3$
21. $(x + 2)(x^2 - 2x + 4)$ 22. $(x - 3)(x^2 + 3x + 9)$
23. $(x + 3y + 2z - 4w)(x + 3y - 2z + 4w)$
24. $(4x - 2y - 3z + 3w)(4x + 2y + 3z + 3w)$
25. $(a - b + c - d)^2$ 26. $(2a + 3b - c - 4d)^2$
27. $[2(x + 2y) - 3][2(x + 2y) + 4]$ 28. $[2(x - 3y) + 5][3(x - 3y) - 2]$
29. $(2x + 3y)^3$ 30. $(5x - 3y)^3$

1–8 Prime numbers, factors, and factoring. All positive integers except the number one may be classified as either composite numbers or primes. A positive integer is called *composite* if it can be expressed as the product of two or more positive integers (neither of which is 1), that are its factors. In certain cases some of these factors may be equal.

For example, 4, 6, 9, and 12 are composite, for $4 = 2 \cdot 2$, $6 = 3 \cdot 2$, $9 = 3 \cdot 3$, and $12 = 3 \cdot 2 \cdot 2$. In fact, every even integer greater than 2 is composite.

A positive integer is called a *prime* if it is different from one and is not composite. In other words, it can be expressed as a product of two positive integers only in the trivial way in which one factor is itself and the other the integer one. Examples of prime numbers are 2, 3, 5, and 7.

The *decomposition* of any composite number, that is, the expressing of such a number as a product of prime numbers, is most important. Such a decomposition is always possible, since each factor which is composite can be expressed as the product of smaller factors and ultimately the factors will all be prime. Thus, $60 = 12 \cdot 5 = 4 \cdot 3 \cdot 5 = 2 \cdot 2 \cdot 3 \cdot 5$. Moreover, a decomposition is unique,* although the proof of this fact is too advanced for this discussion. Specifically, a composite number can be expressed as a product of prime factors in one and only one way, except for the order of the factors. Thus 60 can also be expressed as $15 \cdot 4 = 5 \cdot 3 \cdot 4 = 5 \cdot 3 \cdot 2 \cdot 2$. Two integers are called *relatively prime* or *prime to each other* if they contain no common prime factors.

The process of factoring an algebraic expression is similar to that of finding the factors of a composite number. This process, which is *usually* restricted at this elementary stage to factoring polynomials with rational coefficients and to factors completely free from irrational numbers, is frequently performed by reversing the processes considered in Article 1–7. Such a factorization is considered complete when each algebraic factor is a prime factor, that is, an algebraic expression that cannot be factored without violating the above restrictions.

The more common types of factoring are illustrated below.

EXAMPLE 1. Factor $2ax^2 - 4ay^2 + 8a^2x$.

Solution. The polynomial in this problem has $2a$ as a common factor.

$$2ax^2 - 4ay^2 + 8a^2x \equiv 2a(x^2 - 2y^2 + 4ax).$$

---

* For the proof of this statement as well as a general discussion of prime numbers, see R. Courant and H. Robbins, *What Is Mathematics?* New York: Oxford University Press, 1941; and Harriet Griffin, *Elementary Theory of Numbers.* New York: McGraw-Hill Book Company, 1954.

EXAMPLE 2. Factor $x(a + 2b) - 3y(a + 2b)$.

Solution. Each of the two expressions has the common term $(a + 2b)$. Therefore,

$$x(a + 2b) - 3y(a + 2b) \equiv (a + 2b)(x - 3y).$$

EXAMPLE 3. Factor $(4x^2/y^2) - (9a - b)^2$.

Solution. This expression is the difference between two perfect squares.

$$\frac{4x^2}{y^2} - (9a - b)^2 \equiv \left(\frac{2x}{y}\right)^2 - (9a - b)^2$$

$$\equiv \left[\frac{2x}{y} + (9a - b)\right]\left[\frac{2x}{y} - (9a - b)\right]$$

$$\equiv \left(\frac{2x}{y} + 9a - b\right)\left(\frac{2x}{y} - 9a + b\right).$$

EXAMPLE 4. Factor $9x^2 - 30xy + 25y^2$.

Solution. This algebraic expression is a perfect square.

$$9x^2 - 30xy + 25y^2 \equiv (3x - 5y)^2.$$

EXAMPLE 5. Factor $27x^3 + (8/y^3)$.

Solution. The algebraic expression is the sum of two cubes. Accordingly,

$$27x^3 + \frac{8}{y^3} \equiv \left(3x + \frac{2}{y}\right)\left(9x^2 - \frac{6x}{y} + \frac{4}{y^2}\right).$$

EXAMPLE 6. Factor $12x^2 + 7xy - 10y^2$.

Solution. This trinomial in the form of Eq. (1–23) is factored by trial and error. The result will be in the form $(ax + by)(cx + dy)$, where $ac = 12$, $bd = -10$, and $ad + bc = 7$. Here a and c are both positive and b and d are different in sign. The correct combination, we find, is

$$12x^2 + 7xy - 10y^2 \equiv (4x + 5y)(3x - 2y).$$

EXAMPLE 7. Factor $6x^4 + 7x^2y^2 - 3y^4$.

Solution. This is the same type as Example 6.

$$6x^4 + 7x^2y^2 - 3y^4 \equiv (3x^2 - y^2)(2x^2 + 3y^2).$$

Although the first term on the right is the difference of two squares, it cannot be factored further, for such factorization would introduce irrational quantities.

PROBLEMS

Factor the following completely.

1. $4x - 20$

2. $10x + 15yz$

3. $3y^2 - 9y$

4. $4x^3y^2 + 6x^2y^3$

5. $xy^2z^3 - 3x^2yz^2 + 5xy^3z^2$

6. $a^2b^3c^4 - a^3b^4c^5 + 2a^2b^4c^4$

7. $3y(2x + 5) - 4x(2x + 5)$

8. $3y(4 - y) + 6x^2(4 - y)$

9. $2z^2(x + 3y) - 6xz(x + 3y)$

10. $3x(3 - 2y) - 2xy(3 - 2y)$

11. $9 - a^2$

12. $16x^2 - 9y^2$

13. $225a^8 - 64b^2$

14. $(c^6/d^8) - 121$

15. $x^3y^4 - 25xd^6$

16. $0.01x^4 - 196y^8$

17. $(x + 2y)^2 - z^2$

18. $(3x - 2y)^2 - 25z^2$

19. $(a + b)^2 - (c + d)^2$

20. $9(2x - y)^2 - 4(2a + b)^2$

21. $81(4x - 3y)^2 - 25(3z + w)^2$

22. $x^2 + 6x + 9 - (y^2 + 4y + 4)$

23. $x^2 - 8x + 16$

24. $4a^2 - 12ab + 9b^2$

25. $66xy + 9x^2y^2 + 121$

26. $2x^3 - 28x^2 + 98x$

27. $5z^2 - 30wz + 45w^2$

28. $x^{2n} + 2x^ny^n + y^{2n}$

29. $(3 - x)^2 + 8(3 - x) + 16$

30. $25 - 30(2x - 3y) + 9(2x - 3y)^2$

31. $a^3 - 8$

32. $1 + (8/x^9)$

33. $8x^{6n} + 27y^{3m}$

34. $x^3 - (y^3/64)$

35. $27(x - y)^3 - 8(x + y)^3$

36. $5(a - 2b)^3 - 625(a - 2b)^3$

37. $x^2 - 7x + 12$

38. $y^2 - 2y - 8$

39. $a^2b^2 - ab - 20$

40. $2x^2 + 8x + 6$

41. $35x^2 - 24x + 4$

42. $3y^2 - y - 10$

43. $6a^2 + 7a - 20$

44. $2x^2 - 23xy - 39y^2$

45. $(x + y)^2 - 7(x + y) + 10$

46. $(y + z)^2 + (y + z) - 42$

47. $2(2x + y)^2 - (2x + y) - 10$

48. $6(x + y)^2 + 5(x + y)(y + z) - 6(y + z)^2$

49. $12(a + b)^2 - 14(a + b)(c + d) - 10(c + d)^2$

50. $4(x - 2)^2 + 5(x - 2)(y + 4) - 21(y + 4)^2$

There are many algebraic expressions which, by proper grouping, can be put into one of the forms in the previous examples and then factored.

EXAMPLE 8. Factor $ax - ay - bx + by$.

Solution. By grouping the first two terms together, and the last two together, and factoring out the common term, we transform the expression into the form of Example 2.

$$ax - ay - bx + by \equiv a(x - y) - b(x - y)$$
$$\equiv (x - y)(a - b).$$

EXAMPLE 9. Factor $4x^3 - 12x^2 - x + 3$.

Solution. Again we group the first two terms and the last two terms.

$$4x^3 - 12x^2 - x + 3 \equiv 4x^2(x - 3) - (x - 3)$$
$$\equiv (x - 3)(4x^2 - 1)$$
$$\equiv (x - 3)(2x + 1)(2x - 1).$$

In both these examples we could have grouped the first and third, and the second and fourth terms, and obtained the same result.

EXAMPLE 10. Factor $4x^2 - 12xy + 9y^2 + 4x - 6y - 3$.

Solution. If we group the first three terms, the solution becomes clear.

$$4x^2 - 12xy + 9y^2 + 4x - 6y - 3 \equiv (2x - 3y)^2 + 2(2x - 3y) - 3$$
$$\equiv [(2x - 3y) + 3][(2x - 3y) - 1]$$
$$\equiv (2x - 3y + 3)(2x - 3y - 1).$$

EXAMPLE 11. Factor $x^4 + 2x^2y^2 + 9y^4$.

Solution. If the coefficient of the second term were 6, the expression would be a perfect square. Therefore, if we add (and subtract) $4x^2y^2$, our solution becomes evident.

$$x^4 + 2x^2y^2 + 9y^4 \equiv x^4 + 6x^2y^2 + 9y^4 - 4x^2y^2$$
$$\equiv (x^2 + 3y^2)^2 - (2xy)^2$$
$$\equiv (x^2 + 3y^2 + 2xy)(x^2 + 3y^2 - 2xy).$$

PROBLEMS

Factor the following expressions:

1. $ax - ay - by + bx$
2. $ax - 2ay - 6by + 3bx$
3. $x^3 - 2x^2 + 4x - 8$
4. $y^3 - 2y^2 + 5y - 10$
5. $2a - 6 - ab^2 + 3b^2$
6. $x^3 + 3x^2 - 9x - 27$
7. $x^2 - 2x + 1 - y^2$
8. $xy^3 + 2y^2 - xy - 2$
9. $4x^2 - y^2 + 4y - 4$
10. $x^6 - 7x^3 - 8$
11. $x^2 + 2xy + y^2 - z^2 + 2zw - w^2$
12. $4a^2 - x^2 + b^2 - y^2 - 4ab - 2xy$
13. $x^2 + 4xy + 4y^2 - x - 2y - 6$
14. $x^3 - 5x^2 - x + 5$
15. $x^4 - 7x^2y^2 + 9y^4$
16. $y^4 + y^2 + 25$
17. $a^4 + 2a^2b^2 + 9b^4$
18. $x^4 + 4y^4$
19. $a^8 - b^8$
20. $x^6 + 1$
21. $x^2 + 2xy - z^2 - 2yz$
22. $(x^2 + 2x - 3)^2 - 4$
23. $(x - y - 2z)^2 - (2x + y - z)^2$
24. $2(x + 2)^2(x - 3) + 3(x + 2)(x - 3)^2$

CHAPTER 2

FRACTIONS, EXPONENTS, AND RADICALS

In this chapter we shall continue our discussion of fundamental notions and processes. The ideas considered here will appear throughout this book, and they must be thoroughly understood.

2–1 Simplification of fractions. A basic principle for fractions, algebraic as well as arithmetic, states that the value of a fraction is not changed if its numerator and denominator are both multiplied or both divided by the same quantity (not zero). Hence the simplification or reduction of a fraction to lowest terms is always possible. Factor both the numerator and denominator into their prime factors and, using the basic principle, divide the numerator and denominator by all their common factors.

EXAMPLE 1. Reduce $8x^4y^7/12x^6y^3$ to lowest terms.

Solution.
$$\frac{8x^4y^7}{12x^6y^3} \equiv \frac{2^3x^4y^7}{2^2 \cdot 3x^6y^3}.$$

By dividing both numerator and denominator by $2^2x^4y^3$, we have

$$\frac{8x^4y^7}{12x^6y^3} \equiv \frac{2y^4}{3x^2}.$$

EXAMPLE 2. Reduce $(x^2 - 7x + 10)/(2x^2 - x - 6)$ to lowest terms.

Solution. If we factor both numerator and denominator, we have

$$\frac{x^2 - 7x + 10}{2x^2 - x - 6} \equiv \frac{(x - 5)(x - 2)}{(2x + 3)(x - 2)},$$

and dividing both numerator and denominator by $x - 2$, we get

$$\frac{x^2 - 7x + 10}{2x^2 - x - 6} \equiv \frac{x - 5}{2x + 3}.$$

The elimination of a common factor by dividing the numerator and denominator of a fraction by this factor is called *cancellation*. Such a process should be done with care (remember that division by zero is impossible), so that in this case the identity is true for all values of x except $x = 2$, or $x = -3/2$, which are not permissible values.

21

EXAMPLE 3. Reduce $(12x^2 + 30x - 72)/(52x - 8x^2 - 60)$ to lowest terms.

Solution. $\dfrac{12x^2 + 30x - 72}{52x - 8x^2 - 60} \equiv \dfrac{6(2x - 3)(x + 4)}{4(3 - 2x)(x - 5)} \equiv \dfrac{3(x + 4)}{2(5 - x)}.$

This identity follows from the fact that $2x - 3 \equiv -(3 - 2x)$.

PROBLEMS

Reduce to lowest terms:

1. $\frac{28}{63}$

2. $\dfrac{27x^3}{225x^5}$

3. $\dfrac{a^4 x^3 y}{a^2 x y^3}$

4. $\dfrac{a^2 + ab}{3a + 2a^3}$

5. $\dfrac{a^2 x - a^2 y}{ax^2 - ay^2}$

6. $\dfrac{24a^2}{6a^2 - 9a}$

7. $\dfrac{x^2 - 1}{x^2 - x}$

8. $\dfrac{x^2 - 4x + 4}{x^2 - 4}$

9. $\dfrac{x^2 - 16}{x^2 - 8x + 16}$

10. $\dfrac{a^2 - 3a - 4}{a^2 - a - 12}$

11. $\dfrac{y^2 - y - 6}{y^2 + 2y - 15}$

12. $\dfrac{2x^2 + 5x - 12}{4x^2 - 4x - 3}$

13. $\dfrac{6a^2 - 7a - 3}{4a^2 - 8a + 3}$

14. $\dfrac{ax + ay - bx - by}{am - bm - an + bn}$

15. $\dfrac{14x - 24 - 2x^2}{x^2 + x - 20}$

16. $\dfrac{(4x^2 - 9y^2)(18x - 12)}{(2x - 3y)(12x - 8)}$

17. $\dfrac{x^2 - 36}{x^3 - 216}$

18. $\dfrac{2x^2 - 14x + 20}{7x - 2x^2 - 6}$

19. $\dfrac{2(x^2 - y^2)xy + x^4 - y^4}{x^4 - y^4}$

20. $\dfrac{y^6 + 64}{y^4 - 4y^2 + 16}$

2–2 Addition of fractions. The algebraic sum of two or more fractions having the same denominator is a fraction with the common denominator and a numerator which is the algebraic sum of the numerators of the fractions considered.

ILLUSTRATION. $\dfrac{2x^2}{x - 4} - \dfrac{3x}{x - 4} + \dfrac{5}{x - 4} \equiv \dfrac{2x^2 - 3x + 5}{x - 4}.$

To find the algebraic sum of two or more fractions with different denominators, we must replace the fractions with equivalent fractions having the same denominators. It is preferable to use the *least common denominator* (L.C.D.). The L.C.D. of two or more fractions consists of the product of all the unique prime factors in the denominators, each with an exponent equal to the largest exponent with which the factor appears.

EXAMPLE 1. Find the L.C.D. of the fractions

$$\frac{3x}{x^2 - 4x + 4}, \quad \frac{5x^2}{3(x^2 - 4)}, \quad \frac{2}{2x^2 - x - 6}.$$

Solution. Factoring each denominator, we have

$$x^2 - 4x + 4 \equiv (x - 2)^2, \quad 3(x^2 - 4) \equiv 3(x + 2)(x - 2)$$

$$2x^2 - x - 6 \equiv (2x + 3)(x - 2).$$

The L.C.D. is $3(x + 2)(x - 2)^2(2x + 3)$.

After the L.C.D. has been determined, equivalent fractions may be formed. Divide the L.C.D. of a given fraction by the denominator of that fraction, and then multiply both numerator and denominator of the given fraction by the result. The equivalent fractions may now be added, as in Illustration 1.

EXAMPLE 2. Change the following fractions to equivalent ones, with their L.C.D. as denominator, and find their sum:

$$\frac{4}{x + 2}, \quad \frac{x + 3}{x^2 - 4}, \quad \frac{2x + 1}{x - 2}.$$

Solution. The L.C.D. is $(x + 2)(x - 2)$. Therefore,

$$\frac{4}{x + 2} \equiv \frac{4(x - 2)}{(x + 2)(x - 2)}, \quad \frac{x + 3}{x^2 - 4} \equiv \frac{x + 3}{(x + 2)(x - 2)},$$

$$\frac{2x + 1}{x - 2} \equiv \frac{(2x + 1)(x + 2)}{(x + 2)(x - 2)},$$

and

$$\frac{4}{x + 2} + \frac{x + 3}{x^2 - 4} + \frac{2x + 1}{x - 2}$$

$$\equiv \frac{4(x - 2)}{(x + 2)(x - 2)} + \frac{x + 3}{(x + 2)(x - 2)} + \frac{(2x + 1)(x + 2)}{(x + 2)(x - 2)}$$

$$\equiv \frac{(4x - 8) + (x + 3) + (2x^2 + 5x + 2)}{x^2 - 4}$$

$$\equiv \frac{2x^2 + 10x - 3}{x^2 - 4}.$$

Problems

Reduce to a single fraction and simplify:

1. $\frac{2}{3} + \frac{5}{6} - \frac{3}{10}$

2. $5 - \frac{4}{9} - \frac{7}{15}$

3. $\frac{3x}{4y} - \frac{4y}{3x}$

4. $\frac{a^2}{b} - \frac{b^2}{a}$

5. $\frac{2x + 3}{6} - \frac{4x - 7}{9}$

6. $\frac{3x - 1}{5} + \frac{4 - 5x}{6}$

7. $x + y + \frac{x^2}{x - y}$

8. $\frac{x + 1}{x + 2} - \frac{x + 3}{x}$

9. $\frac{3x - 2y}{5x - 3} + \frac{2x - y}{3 - 5x}$

10. $\frac{2}{12x^2 - 3} + \frac{3}{2x - 4x^2}$

11. $\frac{5}{x} - \frac{4}{y} + \frac{3}{z}$

12. $\frac{4}{x^2 - 4x - 5} + \frac{2}{x^2 - 1}$

13. $\frac{2x - 1}{4 - x} + \frac{x + 2}{3x - 12}$

14. $\frac{x + 5}{x^2 + 7x + 10} - \frac{x - 1}{x^2 + 5x + 6}$

15. $\frac{x - 1}{2x^2 - 13x + 15} + \frac{x + 3}{2x^2 - 15x + 18}$

16. $\frac{2x + 3}{3x^2 + x - 2} - \frac{3x - 4}{2x^2 - 3x - 5}$

17. $\frac{3}{a - 3} + \frac{a^2 + 2}{a^3 - 27}$

18. $\frac{2xy}{x^3 + y^3} - \frac{x}{x^2 - xy + y^2}$

19. $\frac{2}{x^2 + 3x + 2} - \frac{3}{x^2 + 5x + 6} - \frac{4}{x^2 + 4x + 3}$

20. $x + 6 + \frac{5x + 1}{12x^2 + 5x - 2} - \frac{x}{3x + 2}$

21. $2y - 3 + \frac{y - 2}{4y^2 - 12y + 9} + \frac{y + 2}{2y^2 - y - 3}$

22. $\frac{1}{(x - y)(y - z)} + \frac{1}{(y - z)(z - x)} + \frac{1}{(z - x)(x - y)}$

23. $\frac{x}{(x - y)(y - z)} + \frac{y}{(y - z)(z - x)} + \frac{z}{(z - x)(x - y)}$

24. $\frac{2x - 1}{2x^2 - x - 6} + \frac{x + 3}{6x^2 + x - 12} - \frac{2x - 3}{3x^2 - 10x + 8}$

2–3 Multiplication and division of fractions.   In algebra, as in arithmetic, *the product of two or more fractions* is a fraction whose numerator is the product of all numerators and whose denominator is the product of the denominators.   In obtaining these products, the process of dividing out factors common to the numerator and denominator may be used. Results should be reduced to their simplest form.

ILLUSTRATION 1. $\dfrac{x-4}{2x+8} \cdot \dfrac{4x+8}{x^2-16} \equiv \dfrac{(x-4)\cdot 2^2 \cdot (x+2)}{2(x+4)(x+4)(x-4)}$

$$\equiv \frac{2(x+2)}{(x+4)^2}.$$

The *reciprocal* of any number is 1 divided by the number.   Specifically, the reciprocal of a $(a \neq 0)$ is $1/a$, and the reciprocal of any fraction b/c is $1/(b/c)$.   If we multiply both numerator and denominator of this fraction by c/b, we obtain

$$\frac{1}{\dfrac{b}{c}} \cdot \dfrac{\dfrac{c}{b}}{\dfrac{c}{b}} \equiv \frac{\dfrac{c}{b}}{1} \equiv \frac{c}{b}.$$

Thus the reciprocal of any fraction may be expressed as the fraction inverted.   We may now state the rule for division of fractions.   The quotient of two fractions is the fraction formed by multiplying the dividend by the reciprocal of the divisor.

ILLUSTRATION 2.

$$\frac{3x-15}{x+3} \div \frac{12x+18}{4x+12} \equiv \frac{3x-15}{x+3} \cdot \frac{4x+12}{12x+18}$$

$$\equiv \frac{3(x-5)}{x+3} \cdot \frac{4(x+3)}{6(2x+3)}$$

$$\equiv \frac{2(x-5)}{2x+3}.$$

PROBLEMS

Find the reciprocal of each of the following:

1. 4   2. $\frac{7}{10}$ 3. $2\frac{3}{7}$ 4. 0.68   5. $a+b$ 6. $\dfrac{x+2}{3x-4}$

Perform the following operations and reduce the result to its simplest form:

7. $\dfrac{3x^3}{4y^2} \cdot \dfrac{5y}{x^2}$ 8. $\dfrac{7a}{12b^3} \cdot \dfrac{20b^5}{35a^3}$

9. $\dfrac{40x^3y^2}{24xy^4} \div \dfrac{27xy}{8x^2y^3}$

10. $\dfrac{xy^3}{yz} \div x^2z$

11. $\dfrac{x^2 - y^2}{x^3 - y^3} \div \dfrac{x+y}{x}$

12. $\dfrac{x^2 - 2x + y^2}{x^3 - y^3} \cdot \dfrac{x^2 + xy + y^2}{x - y}$

13. $\dfrac{x^2 - 6x + 9}{x^2 - 7x + 12} \cdot \dfrac{x^3 - 4x^2 + 9x - 36}{x^4 - 81}$

14. $\dfrac{y^2 - 2y - 15}{y^2 - 9} \div \dfrac{12 - 4y}{y^2 - 6y + 9}$

15. $\dfrac{x^4 - y^4}{(x-y)^2} \cdot \dfrac{y^2}{x^2 + y^2} \cdot \dfrac{x - y}{xy + y^2}$

16. $(a^2 - b^2) \div \left[\dfrac{a^2 + ab}{b^2 + ab} \div \dfrac{a^2 - ab}{b^2 - ab}\right]$

17. $\dfrac{9x^2 + 6x - 8}{6x^2 + 5x - 4} \cdot \dfrac{2x^2 - 7x - 4}{2x^2 - 5x - 12} \cdot \dfrac{4x^2 + 4x - 3}{6x^2 - x - 2}$

18. $\left[\dfrac{y^3 + 4y^2 - 5y}{y^2 - 2y + 1} \div \dfrac{y^2 + y - 2}{y^4 + 8y}\right] \cdot \dfrac{y - 4}{y^2 - 2y + 4}$

19. $\left[\dfrac{2x}{x - 1} + \dfrac{x^2}{x^2 - 1}\right] \div \dfrac{x^3}{1 - x}$

20. $\left[\dfrac{3x}{x - 3} - \dfrac{3x + 2}{x^2 - 6x + 9}\right] \cdot \left[\dfrac{x + 2}{x + 3} - \dfrac{x}{x^2 + 6x + 9}\right]$

Most of the fractions considered have been simple fractions. Any fraction which contains one or more other fractions in either numerator or denominator, or in both, is called a *complex* fraction. It may be simplified by reducing the numerator and denominator to single fractions and then dividing.

EXAMPLE. Simplify $\dfrac{a - \dfrac{1}{a}}{a - \dfrac{1}{a^2}}$.

Solution. $\dfrac{a - \dfrac{1}{a}}{a - \dfrac{1}{a^2}} \equiv \dfrac{a^2 - 1}{a} \div \dfrac{a^3 - 1}{a^2}$

$\equiv \dfrac{(a + 1)(a - 1)}{a} \cdot \dfrac{a^2}{(a - 1)(a^2 + a + 1)}$

$\equiv \dfrac{a(a + 1)}{a^2 + a + 1}$.

PROBLEMS

Reduce each of the following to a single fraction in simplest form.

1. $\dfrac{3 + \dfrac{4}{5}}{\dfrac{2}{3} - 1}$

2. $\dfrac{\dfrac{a}{b} + \dfrac{a}{c}}{ab + ac}$

3. $\dfrac{x - \dfrac{x}{y}}{z - \dfrac{z}{y}}$

4. $\dfrac{\dfrac{4x}{5} + \dfrac{2y}{3}}{\dfrac{3x}{5} - \dfrac{3y}{4}}$

5. $\dfrac{\dfrac{2}{x} + \dfrac{5}{y}}{\dfrac{2}{x} - \dfrac{5}{y}}$

6. $\dfrac{\dfrac{1}{x} + \dfrac{1}{y}}{\dfrac{1}{x^2} - \dfrac{1}{y^2}}$

7. $\dfrac{x^2 - \dfrac{1}{x}}{x + 1 + \dfrac{1}{x}}$

8. $\dfrac{\dfrac{1}{2} - \dfrac{4}{x^3}}{\dfrac{1}{x^2} + \dfrac{1}{4} + \dfrac{1}{2x}}$

9. $\dfrac{9x^2 - 4y^2}{\dfrac{x - y}{y - 2x} - 1}$

10. $\dfrac{\dfrac{x}{y} + \dfrac{y^2}{x^2}}{\dfrac{y}{x^2} - \dfrac{1}{x} + \dfrac{1}{y}}$

2–4 Integral and zero exponents. We discussed the meaning of a^n ($a \neq 0$), where n was any positive integer, in Article 1–5. In order to define a^n where n is any integer, positive, negative, or zero, we may use the theorems on exponents [Eqs. (1–10)–(1–15)]. We recall from Eq. (1–15) that $a^n/a^n \equiv 1$. If Eq. (1–13) were permissible, we would have $a^{n-n} \equiv a^0 \equiv 1$. We can therefore give the following definitions:

DEFINITION 2–1. *For any $a \neq 0$,*

$$a^0 \equiv 1. \qquad (2\text{–}1)$$

DEFINITION 2–2. *For any $a \neq 0$, and any positive integer n,*

$$a^{-n} \equiv \frac{1}{a^n}. \qquad (2\text{–}2)$$

We now have the resulting theorems:

THEOREM 2–1. *For any $a \neq 0$, and any integers (positive, negative, or zero) n and m,*

$$a^n a^m \equiv a^{n+m}, \qquad (2\text{–}3)$$

$$(ab)^n \equiv a^n b^n, \qquad (2\text{–}4)$$

$$(a^n)^m \equiv a^{nm}, \qquad (2\text{–}5)$$

and

$$\frac{a^n}{a^m} \equiv a^{n-m}. \qquad (2\text{–}6)$$

Proof. The proofs follow directly from the previous definitions and are left as exercises.

ILLUSTRATION.

$$5^0 = 1, \qquad 2x^0 \equiv 2 \cdot 1 = 2, \qquad (2x^2y)^0 \equiv 1,$$

$$x^{-2} \equiv 1/x^2, \qquad (x^3)^4 \equiv x^{12}, \qquad x^3/x^5 \equiv x^{-2} \equiv 1/x^2.$$

PROBLEMS

Remove the negative and zero exponents and simplify the following expressions.

1. $8x^0$

2. $(8x)^0$

3. $3x^{-2}y^4$

4. $5y^{-2}x^3z^0$

5. $\dfrac{2x^3y^{-2}}{3x^{-2}y^3}$

6. $\dfrac{4x^{-2}y^4}{6x^{-5}y^{-2}}$

7. $\dfrac{a^{-1} + b^{-1}}{(cd)^{-1}}$

8. $\dfrac{x^{-2} + y^{-2}}{x^{-1} + y^{-1}}$

9. $\dfrac{a^{-1} + b^{-1}}{(a+b)^{-1}}$

10. $(a^{-1} + b^{-1})^{-1}$

11. $(x^ny^2)^m$

12. $(-1)^n(-1)^m(-1)^1$

2–5 Rational exponents. In the previous article we extended our definitions to zero and negative exponents, and now we shall extend the definitions to rational exponents. Any number a whose nth power (n, any positive integer) is equal to b and which satisfies the equation $a^n = b$, is called *an nth root of b*. We recall, for example, that either 2 or -2 are square roots of 4, since $2^2 = 4$ and $(-2)^2 = 4$. Similarly, since $(-2)^3 = -8$, -2 is a cube root of -8. In general, every number except zero has exactly n distinct nth roots, although most or all of them may be imaginary numbers.* In many cases it is convenient to have a *principal nth root* defined. The principal nth root of a positive number is the positive root. The principal nth root of a negative number is the negative root if n is odd. If n is even and the number is negative, no principal nth root is defined, for no real value exists. (Consider, for example, the equation $x^2 = -4$.) The symbol $\sqrt[n]{b}$ means the principal nth root; n is called the *index* and b the *radicand* of the *radical*.

ILLUSTRATION 1. $\sqrt{9} = 3$, $\sqrt[3]{-8} = -2$, $\sqrt[4]{81} = 3$ are the principal square root, cube root, and fourth root of 9, -8, and 81, respectively.

We are now able to extend the laws of exponents to rational values p/q, where p and q are any two relatively prime positive integers. If $n = 1/q$ where q is any positive integer, and we wish to have our result

* See Chapter 17.

consistent with Eq. (1–10), that is, we wish to have

$$\underbrace{b^{1/q} \cdot b^{1/q} \cdot b^{1/q} \cdots b^{1/q}}_{q \text{ factors } b^{1/q}} \equiv b^{q/q} \equiv b, \qquad (2\text{–}7)$$

we must define $b^{1/q}$ as a qth root of b. In fact, the symbol $b^{1/q}$ is defined as the principal qth root. Likewise, if Eq. (1–11) is to be satisfied, we must define

$$(b^{1/q})^p \equiv b^{p/q}. \qquad (2\text{–}8)$$

This identity states that $b^{1/q}$ is a pth root of $b^{p/q}$ and that $b^{p/q}$ is the pth power of the principal qth root of b. Also we can now show, by using Eq. (2–8), that

$$\underbrace{b^{p/q} \cdot b^{p/q} \cdot b^{p/q} \cdots b^{p/q}}_{q \text{ factors } b^{p/q}} \equiv b^p, \qquad (2\text{–}9)$$

and thus $b^{p/q}$ is also the principal qth root of b^p. Therefore we have, from (2–8), (2–9), and the previous notation,

$$\boxed{b^{p/q} \equiv (b^p)^{1/q} \equiv \sqrt[q]{b^p},*} \qquad (2\text{–}10)$$

and also

$$\boxed{b^{p/q} \equiv (b^{1/q})^p = (\sqrt[q]{b})^p.} \qquad (2\text{–}11)$$

It can now be shown that the five theorems on exponents, Eqs. (2–2) through (2–6), hold for all rational exponents, as well as integers.

ILLUSTRATION 2. $8^{2/3} = \sqrt[3]{8^2} = \sqrt[3]{64} = 4$, or

$$= (\sqrt[3]{8})^2 = 2^2 = 4.$$

ILLUSTRATION 3. $81^{-3/4} = \dfrac{1}{(\sqrt[4]{81})^3} = \dfrac{1}{3^3} = \dfrac{1}{27}.$

ILLUSTRATION 4. $x^{1/4} \cdot x^{2/3} \equiv x^{1/4+2/3} \equiv x^{11/12} \equiv \sqrt[12]{x^{11}}.$

ILLUSTRATION 5. $x^{1/4} \div x^{2/3} \equiv x^{1/4-2/3} \equiv x^{-5/12} \equiv \dfrac{1}{\sqrt[12]{x^5}}.$

ILLUSTRATION 6. $(x^{-4})^{-3/4} \equiv x^3.$

---

* We must exclude the case where b is negative and q is even, as we did in our definition of principal value.

PROBLEMS

Find the numerical value of the following.

1. $25^{1/2}$ 2. $81^{3/4}$ 3. $(\frac{16}{49})^{1/2}$

4. $(\frac{8}{125})^{-1/3}$ 5. $(\frac{64}{27})^{2/3}$ 6. $32^{-4/5}$

7. $(2^{10})^{-3/5}$ 8. $(2^{-6})^{2/3}$ 9. $3^{7/2} \cdot 3^{1/2}$

Remove the negative exponents, simplify, and express the result in radical form.

10. $x^{1/4} \cdot x^{1/5}$ 11. $x^{1/4} \div x^{1/5}$ 12. $(x^{1/4})^{1/5}$

13. $x^{1/4} \cdot x^{-1/5}$ 14. $(x^{1/4})^{-1/5}$ 15. $(x^{-1/4})^{-1/5}$

Remove the negative and zero exponents and simplify:

16. $(9x^{-4}y^2)^{1/2}$ 17. $(2x^{1/6}y^{5/6})^{-6}$

18. $(2x^{-3}y^4)^3$ 19. $\left(\frac{125x^4y^3}{27x^{-2}y^6}\right)^{1/3}$

20. $\left(\frac{5^0x^4y^3z}{16x^{-6}yz^5}\right)^{-1/2}$ 21. $(a^{1/2} + b^{1/2})^2$

22. $(a^{1/2} + b^{1/2})(a^{1/2} - b^{1/2})$ 23. $(x^{1/3} + y^{1/3})(x^{2/3} - x^{1/3}y^{1/3} + y^{2/3})$

24. $(x + y)^{-2}(x^{-2} - y^{-2})$ 25. $(x + y^{-1})^2$

2–6 Radicals. In many cases it is more advantageous to express a quantity in terms of radicals than in terms of rational exponents. The laws of radicals follow directly from the previous definitions and theorems on exponents. If m and n are positive integers and a and b are positive where m or n are even,

$$(\sqrt[n]{a})^n \equiv a, \tag{2–12}$$

$$\sqrt[n]{ab} \equiv (ab)^{1/n} \equiv a^{1/n} \cdot b^{1/n} \equiv \sqrt[n]{a} \cdot \sqrt[n]{b}, \tag{2–13}$$

$$\sqrt[n]{\frac{a}{b}} \equiv \left(\frac{a}{b}\right)^{1/n} \equiv \frac{a^{1/n}}{b^{1/n}} \equiv \frac{\sqrt[n]{a}}{\sqrt[n]{b}}, \tag{2–14}$$

$$\sqrt[m]{\sqrt[n]{a}} \equiv (a^{1/n})^{1/m} \equiv a^{1/nm} \equiv \sqrt[nm]{a}. \tag{2–15}$$

ILLUSTRATION 1. $\sqrt{50} = \sqrt{25 \cdot 2} = \sqrt{25} \cdot \sqrt{2} = 5\sqrt{2}.$

ILLUSTRATION 2. $\sqrt[3]{\frac{4}{27}} = \frac{\sqrt[3]{4}}{\sqrt[3]{27}} = \frac{\sqrt[3]{4}}{3}.$

ILLUSTRATION 3. $\sqrt[6]{27} = \sqrt{\sqrt[3]{27}} = \sqrt{3}.$

A complete simplification of radicals by the use of these laws will yield:

(1) No factors which are perfect nth powers under a radical whose index is n.
(2) No fractions under the radical sign.
(3) The smallest possible index of the radical.

Any radical that satisfies these conditions is said to be in *simplest form*. In addition to the three illustrations above, which are in simplest form, we give the following examples.

EXAMPLE 1. Simplify $\sqrt[3]{81x^5y^7}$.

Solution. In this expression it will be necessary to remove from the radicand all factors that are perfect cubes.

$$\sqrt[3]{81x^5y^7} \equiv \sqrt[3]{27x^3y^6 \cdot 3x^2y} \equiv \sqrt[3]{27x^3y^6} \cdot \sqrt[3]{3x^2y} \equiv 3xy^2\sqrt[3]{3x^2y}.$$

EXAMPLE 2. Simplify $\sqrt{\frac{3}{2}}$.

Solution. For computational reasons, it is important to eliminate any fraction which appears as a radicand. Then the radical may be approximated by only one root extraction and a simple division, rather than by two root extractions and a more complicated division. By introducing a perfect square in the denominator, we may remove it from under the radical.

$$\sqrt{\frac{3}{2}} = \sqrt{\frac{3 \cdot 2}{2 \cdot 2}} = \frac{\sqrt{6}}{2}.$$

EXAMPLE 3. Simplify $\sqrt[4]{64x^2y^4/z^2}$.

Solution. Problems of this type are usually more easily grasped if rational exponents are introduced. We also must eliminate the denominator under the radical.

$$\sqrt[4]{\frac{64x^2y^4}{z^2}} \equiv \left(\frac{2^6x^2y^4}{z^2}\right)^{1/4} \equiv \frac{2^{3/2}x^{1/2}y}{z^{1/2}} \cdot \frac{z^{1/2}}{z^{1/2}} = \frac{2y}{z}\sqrt{2xz}.$$

PROBLEMS

Simplify each of the following:

1. $\sqrt{8}$ 2. $\sqrt{98}$ 3. $\sqrt{\frac{75}{12}}$

4. $\sqrt[3]{40}$ 5. $\sqrt[3]{-625}$ 6. $\sqrt[4]{32}$

7. $\sqrt{27x^3y^5}$

8. $\sqrt{192a^3b^7}$

9. $\sqrt[3]{81z^4x^6y^5}$

10. $\sqrt{\frac{3}{5}}$

11. $\sqrt{\frac{125}{63}}$

12. $\sqrt{\frac{1}{4}+\frac{1}{9}}$

13. $\sqrt{a^2b^2+b^2c^2}$

14. $\sqrt{a^{-2}+b^{-2}}$

15. $\sqrt{\frac{3x}{y^3}}$

16. $\sqrt[3]{\frac{x^4y}{z^2}}$

17. $\sqrt[4]{\frac{x^7y^6}{243}}$

18. $\sqrt{x-2+\frac{1}{x}}$

19. $\sqrt[4]{25}$

20. $\sqrt[6]{49x^4}$

21. $\sqrt[3]{\frac{5}{3x^2}}$

22. $\sqrt[6]{\frac{9}{16}}$

23. $\sqrt{\frac{169x^6z^2}{y^4}}$

24. $\sqrt[4]{1-\frac{4}{x}+\frac{4}{x^2}}$

2–7 Addition and subtraction of radicals. In addition or subtraction of radicals, all similar radicals (that is, those which result in the same index and radicand) are combined into single terms. Consider the example.

EXAMPLE. Simplify by combining similar terms,

$$4\sqrt{12}+5\sqrt{8}-\sqrt{50}-7\sqrt{48}.$$

Solution.

$$4\sqrt{12}+5\sqrt{8}-\sqrt{50}-7\sqrt{48}$$
$$=4\sqrt{4\cdot3}+5\sqrt{4\cdot2}-\sqrt{25\cdot2}-7\sqrt{16\cdot3}$$
$$=8\sqrt{3}-28\sqrt{3}+10\sqrt{2}-5\sqrt{2}$$
$$=5\sqrt{2}-20\sqrt{3}.$$

PROBLEMS

Simplify by combining similar terms:

1. $4\sqrt{3}-5\sqrt{12}+2\sqrt{75}$

2. $\sqrt[3]{2}+\sqrt[3]{16}-\sqrt[3]{54}$

3. $5\sqrt{2}-\sqrt[4]{64}+2\sqrt{32}$

4. $\sqrt{x^3}+\sqrt{25x^3}+\sqrt{9x}$

5. $\sqrt{4(x+y)}-2\sqrt{9(x+y)}+3\sqrt{x+y}$

6. $3\sqrt{18}-3\sqrt{32}+3\sqrt{12}-3\sqrt{3}$

7. $\sqrt{a^3bc^5}+\sqrt{ab^7c^3}+\sqrt{a^9b^5c}$

8. $\sqrt{\dfrac{a-b}{a+b}} - \sqrt{\dfrac{a+b}{a-b}} + \sqrt{\dfrac{a^2}{a^2-b^2}}$

9. $8\sqrt{\frac{1}{3}} + \frac{3}{2}\sqrt{108} - \sqrt[4]{9}$

10. $\sqrt{\left(\dfrac{x}{y} - \dfrac{y}{x}\right)\dfrac{1}{xy}} - \sqrt{\dfrac{x+y}{x-y}}$

11. $\dfrac{7 \pm \sqrt{49 - 4 \cdot 10}}{2}$

12. $\dfrac{4 \pm \sqrt{16 - 4 \cdot 2}}{2}$

2–8 Multiplication and division of radicals. The multiplication of two or more radicals is accomplished by using the rule established in Eq. (2–13). If the radicals have the same index, the result follows immediately. If, however, the radicals are of different indices, they must be converted to radicals with the same index before the multiplication takes place. This is always possible, and may be carried out with the aid of equivalent expressions having rational exponents.

EXAMPLE 1. Find the product of $\sqrt{15ax^3}$ and $\sqrt{45a^2xy^3}$ and simplify.

Solution. Since both radicals have the index 2, we use Eq. (2–13) immediately:

$$\sqrt{15ax^3} \cdot \sqrt{45a^2xy^3} \equiv \sqrt{15^2 \cdot 3a^3x^4y^3}$$
$$\equiv 15ax^2y\sqrt{3ay}.$$

EXAMPLE 2. Multiply $\sqrt{6x^3}$ by $\sqrt[3]{4x^4y^2}$ and simplify.

Solution. By converting the radicals to rational exponents, we have

$$\sqrt{6x^3} \cdot \sqrt[3]{4x^4y^2} \equiv (3 \cdot 2x^3)^{1/2} \cdot (2^2x^4y^2)^{1/3}$$
$$\equiv (3 \cdot 2x^3)^{3/6} \cdot (2^2x^4y^2)^{2/6}$$
$$\equiv (3^3 \cdot 2^3 \cdot x^9 \cdot 2^4x^8y^4)^{1/6}$$
$$\equiv \sqrt[6]{3^3 \cdot 2 \cdot 2^6x^{12} \cdot x^5y^4}$$
$$\equiv 2x^2\sqrt[6]{54x^5y^4}.$$

Division of two radicals is handled in a similar manner, by using Eq. (2–14). Again, if the radicals are of different indices, they must be converted to the same index.

EXAMPLE 3. Divide $6\sqrt[3]{5}$ by $2\sqrt{3}$ and simplify.

Solution. Since $\sqrt[3]{5} = \sqrt[6]{25}$ and $\sqrt{3} = \sqrt[6]{27}$, we have

$$\frac{6\sqrt[3]{5}}{2\sqrt{3}} = 3\sqrt[6]{\frac{25}{27}}.$$

Recalling that a radical in simplest form has a denominator free of radicals, we must multiply the numerator and denominator by $\sqrt[6]{27}$. Thus

$$\frac{6\sqrt[3]{5}}{2\sqrt{3}} \equiv 3\sqrt[6]{\frac{25\cdot 27}{27\cdot 27}} \equiv 3\sqrt[6]{\frac{25\cdot 27}{3^6}} \equiv \frac{3}{3}\sqrt[6]{25\cdot 27} = \sqrt[6]{675}.$$

The process of eliminating radicals from the denominator, illustrated in Example 3, and Example 2, Article 2–6, is called *rationalizing the denominator*. The problem of eliminating all radicals in a denominator may be more complicated.

EXAMPLE 4. Rationalize the denominator of $(2 + \sqrt{3})/(\sqrt{5} - \sqrt{3})$.

Solution. Since we wish to eliminate both radicals in the denominator, we must find an expression (*rationalizing factor*) which, when multiplied by $\sqrt{5} - \sqrt{3}$, will give a result free of radicals. Since

$$(\sqrt{5} - \sqrt{3})(\sqrt{5} + \sqrt{3}) = 5 - 3,$$

we multiply both numerator and denominator by $\sqrt{5} + \sqrt{3}$.

$$\frac{2 + \sqrt{3}}{\sqrt{5} - \sqrt{3}} \cdot \frac{\sqrt{5} + \sqrt{3}}{\sqrt{5} + \sqrt{3}} = \frac{2\sqrt{5} + \sqrt{15} + 2\sqrt{3} + 3}{5 - 3}$$
$$= \frac{2\sqrt{5} + \sqrt{15} + 2\sqrt{3} + 3}{2}.$$

PROBLEMS

Perform the following multiplications, expressing the result in simplest form.

1. $\sqrt{5} \cdot \sqrt{13}$
2. $\sqrt{14} \cdot \sqrt{21}$
3. $\sqrt[3]{4} \cdot \sqrt[3]{26}$
4. $\sqrt[3]{3x^2} \cdot \sqrt{2x}$
5. $\sqrt{x^2 - y^2} \cdot \sqrt{x - y}$
6. $\sqrt{3x^2y^3} \cdot \sqrt{12x^5y}$
7. $\sqrt{x^3 + y^3} \cdot \sqrt{x + y}$
8. $\sqrt[3]{9x} \cdot \sqrt[6]{27x^4}$
9. $\sqrt{2} \cdot \sqrt[3]{3} \cdot \sqrt[4]{4}$
10. $\sqrt{a} \cdot \sqrt[3]{a} \cdot \sqrt[4]{a}$
11. $\sqrt{2}(\sqrt{6} + \sqrt{14})$
12. $(2 + \sqrt{3})(2 - \sqrt{3})$
13. $(\sqrt{3} + \sqrt{5})(\sqrt{3} - \sqrt{5})$
14. $(2\sqrt{3} - 3\sqrt{2})^2$
15. $(\sqrt{5} + 2\sqrt{3})(\sqrt{5} - 3\sqrt{3})$
16. $\sqrt{3 + 2\sqrt{2}} \cdot \sqrt{3 - 2\sqrt{2}}$
17. $\left(\frac{\sqrt{5} - 1}{2}\right)^2$
18. $\left(\frac{\sqrt{6} - \sqrt{2}}{4}\right)^2$

Perform the following divisions, expressing the result in simplest form.

19. $4\sqrt{28} \div 3\sqrt{7}$

20. $\sqrt[3]{\frac{4}{5}} \div \sqrt[3]{\frac{108}{25}}$

21. $\sqrt[6]{12} \div \sqrt{3}\sqrt[3]{2}$

22. $(2\sqrt{6} + 3\sqrt{14}) \div \sqrt{2}$

23. $\sqrt[4]{24a^3b} \div \sqrt[4]{8ab^3}$

24. $\sqrt{xy^2} \div \sqrt[3]{x^2y}$

Rationalize the denominator of each of the following.

25. $\dfrac{2\sqrt{3}}{4\sqrt{5}}$

26. $\dfrac{2\sqrt[3]{3}}{4\sqrt[3]{5}}$

27. $\dfrac{4}{\sqrt[3]{16}}$

28. $\dfrac{3}{2 + \sqrt{3}}$

29. $\dfrac{5}{\sqrt{7} - \sqrt{3}}$

30. $\dfrac{\sqrt{2} + \sqrt{3}}{\sqrt{2} - \sqrt{3}}$

31. $\dfrac{x}{x + \sqrt{y}}$

32. $\dfrac{y}{\sqrt{x} - \sqrt{y}}$

33. $\dfrac{2\sqrt{7} + \sqrt{3}}{3\sqrt{7} - 5\sqrt{3}}$

34. $\dfrac{1}{\sqrt[3]{a} + \sqrt[3]{b}}$ [Hint: $x^3 + y^3 \equiv (x + y)(x^2 - xy + y^2)$.]

35. $\dfrac{2}{2 - \sqrt[3]{3}}$

36. $\dfrac{1}{\sqrt[3]{9} + \sqrt[3]{6} + \sqrt[3]{4}}$

37. $\dfrac{1}{\sqrt{2} + \sqrt{3} + \sqrt{5}}$ [Hint: Multiply both numerator and denominator by $(\sqrt{2} + \sqrt{3}) - \sqrt{5}$.]

CHAPTER 3

COORDINATE SYSTEMS, FUNCTIONS, AND
GRAPHICAL REPRESENTATION

There are further notions and concepts which are important in any systematic study of algebra, trigonometry, and analytic geometry. In this chapter we shall introduce and briefly discuss several of these basic ideas.

3–1 A one-dimensional coordinate system. The method of associating numbers with points on a line is of considerable help in mathematics and has resulted in great progress in the application of mathematics to science. Any scale which measures quantities, such as a yardstick or thermometer, makes use of an association of this kind. To each numerical value assumed by the physical quantity there corresponds a position on the scale, and to each position on the scale there corresponds a number. Such a correspondence establishes a coordinate system. The simplest and most useful coordinate system in one dimension employs a one-to-one correspondence between real numbers and the points on a straight line. Let us consider such a system.

On a fixed straight line of reference of unlimited length, we choose any point O, called the *origin*, and lay off equal divisions* of arbitrary length in both directions from O (see Fig. 3–1). We now associate zero with the origin, the positive integers with the successive points on one side, and the negative integers with the successive points on the other. The usual convention on such a horizontal line is to consider the integers to the right as positive and those to the left as negative.

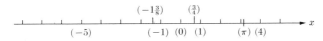

FIGURE 3–1

The point associated with any rational number can be determined by the simple geometric construction used to divide any line segment into b equal parts. Thus the number $\frac{3}{4}$ is represented by a point three-fourths of the way from 0 to the point identified with 1. Also, $-1\frac{3}{8}$ is represented by a point at a distance $1\frac{3}{8}$ units to the left of 0.

The points associated with some irrational numbers may also be found by geometric construction. For example, the point associated with $\sqrt{2}$

---

* There are systems where the subdivisions are not equal. Consider the slide rule scale.

may be located, because $\sqrt{2}$ is the hypotenuse of an isosceles right triangle with each leg one unit in length. Although geometric construction is not possible for all real numbers, we shall assume that the correspondence can be extended to all real numbers. This is done by associating every line segment with a real number which represents its length. Thus with each real number we have associated one point on the line and, conversely, with each point on the line there is associated one real number.

The *coordinate* of a point is defined to be the number associated with that point. It is written (x), and will be referred to as "the point x."

The coordinate system gives us a graphic interpretation of the relative magnitude of numbers. Thus $5 > 3$ (read 5 is greater than 3)* corresponds to the fact that (5) lies to the right of (3), while $-5 < -3$ (read -5 is less than -3) corresponds to the fact that (-5) is to the left of (-3). The notation $x < y < z$ indicates that y is greater than x but less than z.

To express the distance between any two points in this system, we need only subtract the coordinate of the left-hand point from the coordinate of the right-hand point. Thus, if $x_1 < x_2$, where the subscripts 1 and 2 merely denote two distinct values of x, the distance between (x_1) and (x_2) is $x_2 - x_1$, but if $x_2 < x_1$, the distance must be $x_1 - x_2$, since we wish to have the distance always positive. We can avoid the inconvenience of having to distinguish between the two points by employing the notion of absolute value.

The absolute value of x, denoted by $|x|$, indicates its size or magnitude without regard to its sign. For example, $|3| = 3$, and $|-3| = 3$. Specifically, the *absolute value* of a number x is defined as

$$|x| \equiv \begin{cases} x \text{ if } x > 0, \\ -x \text{ if } x < 0, \\ 0 \text{ if } x = 0. \end{cases} \tag{3-1}$$

Here we should recall the definition of the square root sign, $\sqrt{}$. For any positive number a, $\sqrt{a}$ denotes the positive square root of a; that is, for any real number x, x^2 is positive (or zero if $x = 0$) and

$$\sqrt{x^2} \equiv \begin{cases} x \text{ if } x > 0, \\ -x \text{ if } x < 0, \\ 0 \text{ if } x = 0. \end{cases} \tag{3-2}$$

---

* If x and y are any two real numbers, by definition,

$x > y$ is equivalent to the fact that $x - y$ is positive,

$x < y$ is equivalent to the fact that $x - y$ is negative.

Thus $\sqrt{7^2} = 7$, and $\sqrt{(-7)^2} = -(-7) = 7$. Since (3–1) and (3–2) define the same values, either expression can be used to indicate absolute value.

Since two basic properties of absolute value will be used later in work with inequalities, we shall mention them now.

THEOREM 3–1. *If a and b are any two real numbers, the absolute value of their product (or quotient) is equal to the product (or quotient) of their absolute values:*

$$|ab| \equiv |a| \cdot |b|, \tag{3–3}$$

$$\left|\frac{a}{b}\right| \equiv \frac{|a|}{|b|}. \tag{3–4}$$

THEOREM 3–2. *If a and b are any two real numbers, the absolute value of their sum is less than or equal to the sum of their absolute values:*

$$|a + b| \leqq |a| + |b|, \tag{3–5}$$

$$|a - b| \leqq |a| + |b|. \tag{3–6}$$

Proof. Consider the case where a and b have similar signs and where a and b have opposite signs. Also consider the case where either or both a and b are zero.

We are now able to give the general expression for the distance between any two points P_1 and P_2:

THEOREM 3–3. *The distance between any two points P_1 and P_2 with coordinates (x_1) and (x_2) may be expressed*

$$\boxed{d = P_1P_2 = |x_1 - x_2| \equiv \sqrt{(x_1 - x_2)^2}.} \tag{3–7}$$

For example, the distance between the two points (5) and (-3) is given either by the expression $d = \sqrt{[5 - (-3)]^2} = 8$, or the expression $d = \sqrt{(-3 - 5)^2} = 8$.

PROBLEMS

1. Arrange the following numbers in ascending order of magnitude and plot them on a linear coordinate system such as that of Fig. 3–1: 2.3, 0.333, 2^3, 4, $\frac{1}{3}$, -5, -1, 0, -6.5.

2. Choose two negative numbers, a and b, such that $a > b$. Show that $a - b$ is a positive number.

3. State in words the geometrical interpretation of the following:

(a) $a < b$,

(b) $a < 2$,

(c) $a > b$,

(d) $a > b > c$,

(e) $a - b = 1$,

(f) $3.14 < \pi < 3.15$,

(g) $1.41 < \sqrt{2} < 1.42$,

(h) $|5 - 2| > |1 - 3|$,

(i) $|a - b| > 0$,

(j) $|x - 2| < 3$,

(k) $|x - 1| > 4$,

(l) $-1 < x < 1$.

4. If the coordinates of two points, P_1 and P_2, on a line are (2) and (8) respectively, show that the coordinate of the mid-point of the segment P_1P_2 is (5).

5. Find the coordinate of the mid-point of the line joining (4) and (-4), (3) and (-5), (-1.7) and (3.7), $(\sqrt{2})$ and $(\sqrt{3})$, (x_1) and (x_2).

6. Solve the following equations for x:

(a) $x = |10|$,

(b) $x = |2 - 5|$,

(c) $x = \sqrt{3^2}$,

(d) $x = \sqrt{(-4)^2}$,

(e) $x = |-\frac{3}{2}|$,

(f) $x = \sqrt{(-1)^2}$,

(g) $x = |\frac{1}{3} - \frac{5}{3}|$,

(h) $x = |\frac{1}{3}| + |-\frac{5}{3}|$.

7. Solve the following equations for all possible values of x:

(a) $|x| = 2$,

(b) $|x| = \sqrt{5}$,

(c) $\sqrt{x^2} = 3$,

(d) $\sqrt{x^2} = \frac{1}{4}$,

(e) $|x - 2| = 5$,

(f) $|x - 4| = 0$,

(g) $|3 - x| = 6$,

(h) $\sqrt{(x - 1)^2} = 5$,

(i) $\sqrt{(2 - x)^2} = 4$,

(j) $|x - 2| = -3$,

(k) $\sqrt{(x - 4)^2} = -1$,

(l) $\sqrt{(x - 5)^2} = 3$.

8. Recall from plane geometry that a circle is the locus (totality) of points at a given distance from a given point, where the distance is called the radius and the given point is called the center. In this geometry of one dimension, how many points are at a given distance from a fixed point? Of how many points would a "circle" consist?

9. If (1) is a given point, and 2 a given distance, explain how $|x - 1| = 2$ would be the condition that any point (x) must be 2 units distant from (1). This is the condition that the point (x) lies on the "circle" with center (1) and radius 2, and is called the equation of the "circle."

10. In terms of "circles in one dimension," give the geometric significance of each of the equations in Problem 7.

11. Give the equation of a "circle in one dimension" with its center at the point (a) and with radius r.

12. Prove Theorems 3–1 and 3–2.

3–2 A two-dimensional coordinate system. In the preceding article we observed a coordinate system that not only enabled us to view the relative magnitudes of numbers in a graphic way, but also allowed us to represent the distance between two points by the magnitude of their differences.

But the usefulness of a one-dimensional coordinate system is limited. One of the more important concepts in mathematics is the relation or dependence of two sets of numbers. The corresponding values of two such related sets can be regarded as pairs of numbers; hence a system which produces an association between a point and a pair of numbers would be most advantageous in studying such a relationship. A two-dimensional system provides the association.

The most frequently used system that sets up an association between each point in a plane and a pair of real numbers is the rectangular cartesian system of coordinates. In 1637 René Descartes, a French mathematician and philosopher, used this method of associating points with numbers, and by so doing, associated a curve with its equation. Great progress in mathematics and the application of mathematics in science resulted from this unification of algebra and geometry.

Let us construct two perpendicular straight lines and, for convenience, let one of them be horizontal. We shall call these *coordinate axes*. Using the point of intersection as the *origin O*, set up on each line a one-dimensional system. Ordinarily, the same unit of length is used on both lines, although in some cases it is convenient to do otherwise. We now denote by the expression $(x, 0)$ the point on the horizontal line corresponding to the number x in its one-dimensional system. Similarly, we denote the point on the vertical line corresponding to the number y in its one-dimensional system by the symbol $(0, y)$. The horizontal line is called the x-axis, or axis of *abscissas*, while the vertical line is referred to as the y-axis or axis of *ordinates*. As is customary, the point on the y-axis $(0, y)$ is above the x-axis when y is positive.

In the reference system of axes shown in Fig. 3–2, consider any specific pair of values of x and y, x_1 and y_1. To find the point corresponding to this pair of values, we draw lines parallel to the axes through the point $(x_1, 0)$ on the x-axis and the point $(0, y_1)$ on the y-axis. These lines intersect at a point P, a distance x_1 from the y-axis (to the right or left, depending upon whether x_1 is positive or negative) and a distance y_1 from the x-axis (above or below, depending upon whether y_1 is positive or negative). These distances can be called *directed distances*. The point P, determined by the pair of values x_1 and y_1, is denoted by the expression (x_1, y_1), where x_1 and y_1 are called the *coordinates* of P. As might be expected, the x-value is called the *abscissa* of P and the y-value is called its *ordinate*. Clearly, there is only one point determined by any pair of values (x, y). Con-

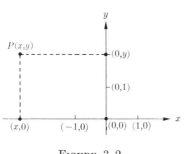

FIGURE 3–2

versely, for each point there is only one pair of values (x, y), since the point has unique directed distances from the axes. Thus a one-to-one correspondence is established between all the points in the plane and the set of all number pairs (x, y).

The two coordinate axes divide the plane into four parts, called the *first, second, third,* and *fourth quadrants.* It is helpful to verify that the coordinates of points located in the different quadrants have the signs shown in the table:

Quadrants	Abscissa	Ordinate
I	+	+
II	−	+
III	−	−
IV	+	−

In Fig. 3–3 the plotting of several points is shown.

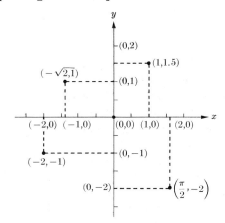

FIGURE 3–3

PROBLEMS

1. Plot the following points:
(a) with abscissa 4 and ordinate 3,
(b) $(4, -3)$,
(c) with $x = -4$ and $y = 3$.

2. Plot the following points:
(a) $(2, 6)$, $(-1, 4)$, $(3, -2)$, $(-1, -3)$;
(b) $(4, 0)$, $(-4, 0)$, $(0, 4)$, $(0, -4)$, $(0, 0)$.

3. What are the coordinates of a point (a) three units to the right of the y-axis, and two above the x-axis? (b) four units to the left of the y-axis, and six above the x-axis? (c) five units to the right of the y-axis, on the x-axis?

4. (a) What is the abscissa of any point on the y-axis? (b) What is the ordinate of any point on the x-axis?

5. Without plotting, indicate the quadrant in which each of the following points lies: $(-1, 2)$, $(2, -4)$, $(-3, -7)$, $(4, 6)$, $(-5, 2)$, $(28, -2)$.

6. (a) Give the coordinates of four points which are the vertices of a rectangle. (b) Give the coordinates of three points which are the vertices of a right triangle. (c) Give the coordinates of four points on a circle with its center at $(2, 3)$ and with radius 4.

7. In each of the following, three vertices of a parallelogram are given. Give the three possible sets of coordinates for the fourth vertex:

(a) $(0, 0)$, $(2, 4)$, and $(6, 0)$;

(b) $(-2, 1)$, $(1, 2)$, and $(0, -3)$.

8. Three vertices of a parallelogram are (a, b), $(0, 0)$, and $(c, 0)$. What are the possible coordinates of the fourth vertex?

9. Indicate in a rectangular coordinate system the location of the set of all the points (x, y) which satisfy the following conditions:

(a) $x = 2$;   (b) $y = -3$;   (c) $x > 2$;

(d) $y > 4$;   (e) $x < -1$;   (f) $x = y$;

(g) $x > 2$,   (h) $x > y$,   (i) $x < y$,
$\quad\ y = 3$;

(j) $x > 2$,   (k) $x = 2$,   (l) $x = 2$,
$\quad\ y < 4$; $\quad\ y < -1$; $\quad\ y = 3$.

10. If in Fig. 3–4, $P(x, y)$ is the mid-point of the line segment joining $P_1(x_1, y_1)$ and $P_2(x_2, y_2)$, and the line PR is drawn parallel to the y-axis, the coordinates of R will be (x, y_1). Since $RP_1 = QR$, $x - x_1 = x_2 - x$. Using this fact, and a similar construction, show that the coordinates of the mid-point of the line joining P_1 and P_2 are

$$x = \frac{x_1 + x_2}{2}, \qquad y = \frac{y_1 + y_2}{2}. \qquad (3\text{–}8)$$

11. Find the coordinates of the mid-point of the line joining (a) $(1, 2)$ and $(-3, 5)$; (b) $(6, -2)$ and $(5, -7)$; (c) $(-4, 3)$ and $(2, -3)$.

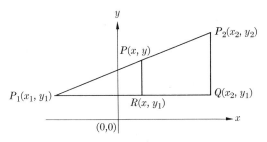

FIGURE 3–4

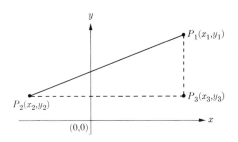

FIGURE 3–5

3–3 The distance formula. We are now prepared to obtain a formula which has many applications in the mathematics dealt with in this book. To obtain an expression for the distance d between any two points $P_1(x_1, y_1)$ and $P_2(x_2, y_2)$, where the same unit lengths are used on both axes, we make use of the famous theorem of Pythagoras. Considering $P_1(x_1, y_1)$ and $P_2(x_2, y_2)$ any two points in the plane, construct a right triangle, as in Fig. 3–5, with P_1P_2 the hypotenuse, and the two legs parallel to the axes. Call their point of intersection, where the right angle is formed, $P_3(x_3, y_3)$. Since $x_3 = x_1$ and $y_3 = y_2$, the distance between P_2 and P_3 is

$$P_2P_3 = \sqrt{(x_1 - x_2)^2}$$

and the distance between P_1 and P_3 is

$$P_1P_3 = \sqrt{(y_1 - y_2)^2}.$$

Recalling the theorem of Pythagoras, which states that

$$\overline{P_1P_2}^2 = \overline{P_2P_3}^2 + \overline{P_1P_3}^2,$$

we obtain

$$\overline{P_1P_2}^2 = (x_1 - x_2)^2 + (y_1 - y_2)^2.$$

This results in the following theorem.

THEOREM 3–4. *The distance between any two points $P_1(x_1, y_1)$ and $P_2(x_2, y_2)$ is given by*

$$\boxed{d = P_1P_2 = \sqrt{(x_1 - x_2)^2 + (y_1 - y_2)^2}.} \qquad (3\text{–}9)$$

EXAMPLE 1. The distance between the points $P_1(-4, 2)$ and $P_2(3, -1)$ is

$$P_1P_2 = \sqrt{[3 - (-4)]^2 + (-1 - 2)^2}$$
$$= \sqrt{58}.$$

EXAMPLE 2. The distance between the origin $(0, 0)$ and any point (x, y) is

$$d = \sqrt{(x - 0)^2 + (y - 0)^2} = \sqrt{x^2 + y^2}.$$

EXAMPLE 3.   The triangle with the points $P_1(-5, -1)$, $P_2(2, 3)$, and $P_3(3, -2)$ as vertices is isosceles.

$$P_1P_2 = \sqrt{(-5 - 2)^2 + (-1 - 3)^2} = \sqrt{49 + 16} = \sqrt{65}.$$

$$P_1P_3 = \sqrt{(-5 - 3)^2 + (-1 + 2)^2} = \sqrt{64 + 1} = \sqrt{65}.$$

PROBLEMS

Starred problems, such as Problem 14, are essential to the continuity of the discussion and should always be assigned.

In each of the following exercises draw the figure on coordinate paper.

1. Find the distance between the given points:

(a) $(3, 2)$ and $(6, 7)$,   (b) $(-4, 3)$ and $(5, -2)$,
(c) $(\frac{5}{2}, -\frac{3}{4})$ and $(\frac{7}{4}, -\frac{3}{2})$,   (d) $(0, 0)$ and $(5, -12)$,
(e) $(-3, 7)$ and $(5, 7)$,   (f) $(-1, 3)$ and (x, y).

2. By proving that two sides of the triangle are equal, show that the triangle whose vertices are $(2, 1)$, $(5, 5)$, and $(-2, 4)$ is an isosceles triangle.

3. Show that the points $(8, 1)$, $(-6, -7)$, and $(2, 7)$ are the vertices of an isosceles triangle.

4. Show that the points $(6, 1)$, $(5, 6)$, $(-4, 3)$, and $(-3, -2)$ are the vertices of a parallelogram.

5. Prove that the points $(2, 3)$, $(-4, -3)$, and $(6, -1)$ are the vertices of a right triangle. Note that we must use the converse of the theorem of Pythagoras to prove this.

6. Show that the points $(12, 9)$, $(20, -6)$, $(5, -14)$, and $(-3, 1)$ are the vertices of a square. What is the length of a diagonal?

7. Test algebraically to see whether or not the following triples of points are collinear (lie on the same line): $(6, 2)$, $(1, 1)$, $(-4, 0)$; $(-6, 5)$, $(3, -10)$, $(-2, -2)$.

8. Find the point on the y-axis which is equidistant from the points $(-4, 4)$ and $(4, 10)$.

9. If two vertices of an equilateral triangle are $(-4, -3)$ and $(4, 1)$, find the remaining vertex.

10. Find those points whose ordinates are -5 and whose distance from the origin is 13.

11. Draw the square whose diagonals lie along the coordinate axes and the length of whose side is a. What are the coordinates of the four vertices?

12. If a circle had its center at the point $(2, 3)$ and passed through $(8, -5)$, what would be its radius? Would it pass through $(-6, 9)$?

13. Consider the circle with its center at the origin and with a radius of 1. Through which of the following points does it pass: (1, 0), (0, −1), (1, 1), $(1/\sqrt{2}, 1/\sqrt{2})$, $(\frac{1}{2}, \frac{1}{2})$, $(-\frac{1}{2}, \sqrt{3}/2)$?

*14. By giving the expression for the distance between the origin and the point (x, y), and equating this distance to 1, we have stated the algebraic condition on x and y which must be satisfied by the coordinates of any point (x, y) lying on the circle whose center is (0, 0) and whose radius is 1. Show that this condition, when simplified, becomes $x^2 + y^2 = 1$. This is called the equation of the unit circle in the plane.

15. If a point lies on a curve, its coordinates must satisfy the equation representing that curve. Check the results of Problem 13 by determining whether the coordinates of the points satisfy the equation of the unit circle obtained in Problem 14, namely, $x^2 + y^2 = 1$.

3–4 The circle and arc length. In any rectangular coordinate system a geometric figure, locus, or curve, such as a circle, may be considered a set of points. The coordinates of each point in this set satisfy some stated condition involving these coordinates. Conversely, if the coordinates of any point satisfy this condition, the point must be in this set. We therefore have the following definition.

DEFINITION 3–1. *An equation of any curve is a statement of the condition which the coordinates of each of the points of that curve, and only these points, must satisfy.*

Equations of several different curves will be considered in later sections. In this section we are concerned with the circle.

We recall the definition of a circle as the locus (totality) of points in the plane that are at a constant distance from a fixed point. Using the distance formula, it is now possible to obtain a general equation of a circle.

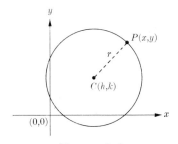

FIGURE 3–6

With $C(h, k)$ as the center and r as the radius (Fig. 3–6), the condition that any point $P(x, y)$ lying on the circle must satisfy is

$$CP = r,$$

which is the same as having the coordinates of P satisfy the condition

$$\sqrt{(x - h)^2 + (y - k)^2} = r$$

from Eq. (3–9). Conversely, if $CP = r$, then P is on the circle. We therefore have

$$(x - h)^2 + (y - k)^2 = r^2, \qquad\qquad (3\text{--}10)$$

which is a general equation of the circle with center (h, k) and with radius r.

EXAMPLE 1. An equation of the circle with its center at $(2, -3)$ and radius 4 is

$$(x - 2)^2 + (y + 3)^2 = 16.$$

EXAMPLE 2. An equation of the circle with its center at the origin and a radius of 1 is

$$(x - 0)^2 + (y - 0)^2 = 1,$$

or

$$x^2 + y^2 = 1.$$

This is called an equation of the *unit circle*, an important special case in our study. Recall Problem 14 of the last section.

We are interested not only in the equation of a circle but also in the notion of length of portions of its circumference. The length of a circular arc is very useful in discussing and measuring angles.

By considering a circular arc $\overarc{AB}$, as in Fig. 3–7, it is possible to assign to this arc $\overarc{AB}$ a length s, although it is impossible to measure the length as though it were a straight line. By denoting several points on $\overarc{AB}$ by C, D, and so on, the length of the polygonal line joining these points is the sum of the lengths of the appropriate chords, obtained by using Eq. (3–9).

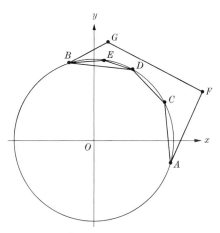

FIGURE 3–7

If we now consider other points on the arc $\overset{\frown}{AB}$, such as E, the new polygonal line $ACDEB$ has a greater length than $ACDB$, since

$$BD < DE + EB.$$

Continuing this process of inserting points, we shall obtain polygonal lines whose lengths are greater than the preceding ones. However, the length of our polygonal line cannot become infinite, for it can be shown that the length of any line obtained in this way is always less than the length of any polygonal line which joins A and B outside the circle, such as $AFGB$. Therefore we have a number of polygonal lines, each with a length greater than the last, and yet smaller than a fixed number. If the number of chords is increased and their lengths become arbitrarily close to zero, it can be shown that the length of the polygonal line will approach a definite value. This definite value, s, is called the arc length of $\overset{\frown}{AB}$.

EXAMPLE. Recall the definition of the real number π, approximately equal to 3.14. The number π is defined as the ratio of the circumference of any circle to its diameter. The circumference or arc length of the entire circle with radius r is therefore equal to $2\pi r$, or approximately 6.28 times the radius. Compare this with the two regular geometric figures shown in Fig. 3–8. Since the inscribed hexagon has a perimeter of $6r$ and the circumscribed square has a perimeter of $8r$, the inequality $6r < 2\pi r < 8r$ would be expected.

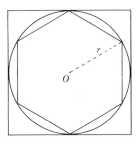

FIGURE 3–8

PROBLEMS

1. Write an equation of the following circles:

(a) center at (3, 1) and radius 5,
(b) center at (4, −2) and radius 3,
(c) center at (−1, 3) tangent to the x-axis,
(d) center at (2, −4) and passing through (5, −8).

2. Write an equation of the circle with its center at the origin and radius r.

3. Describe the set of points (x, y) which satisfies:

(a) $(x - 1)^2 + (y - 1)^2 \leq 1$,
(b) $(x - 2)^2 + (y + 3)^2 \geq 4$,
(c) $(x - 3)^2 + (y + 1)^2 = 0$.

4. What is the length of the perimeter of the square inscribed in a circle of radius r?

5. Determine the length of the perimeter of the regular hexagon circumscribed about a circle of radius r.

*6. Expressing your answer in terms of π, what is the length of the circumference of the unit circle (a circle with a radius of 1)? What is the length of an arc one-fourth the distance around the circle? What is the length of an arc one-sixth the distance around the circle?

3–5 Angles. In plane geometry an angle is usually defined as the configuration consisting of two half-lines (rays) radiating from a point. However, in trigonometry we add to this definition by stating that an angle thus defined by two half-lines has a measure which corresponds to the amount of rotation required to move a ray from the position of one of these lines to the other. Consider Fig. 3–9, with the two lines m and n intersecting at O and lying in a plane perpendicular to our line of vision. If we regard m as the *initial side* and n as the *terminal side* of the angle with O as its vertex, there are two possible directions of rotation of the initial side m. The angle is said to be positive if the rotation is counterclockwise, but negative if clockwise. A curved arrow will indicate the direction of rotation.

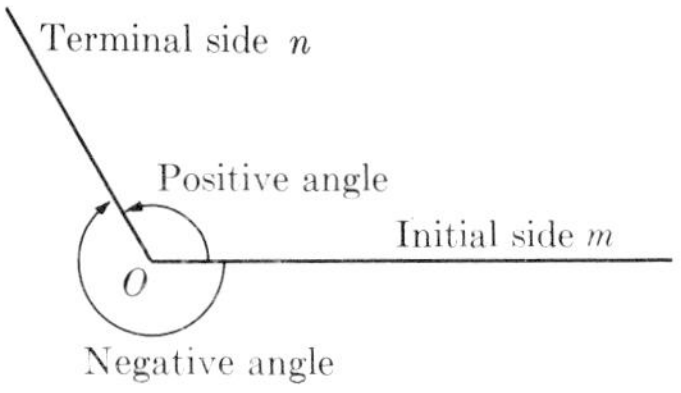

FIGURE 3–9

Let us now consider a ray m which issues from the origin of a rectangular coordinate system and coincides with the positive x-axis (Fig. 3–10). As this ray rotates, any point P on m will trace out part or all of the circumference of a circle of radius OP. In fact, the circumference may be traced several times. After the rotation, OP will be in some position OP', where the circular arc $\overset{\frown}{PP'}$, denoted by s, may be used to measure the angle POP'. An angle such as POP' is said to be in *standard position*, and to be in the quadrant in which its terminal side OP' is located.

The most logical units for measuring the magnitude of an angle would seem to be the number of revolutions resulting from the rotation from the initial to the terminal side of the angle. Since the number of revolutions of any angle is determined by the ratio of the intercepted circular arc length s to the circumference of the circle, we define the magnitude of an angle in revolutions as

$$\text{Angle\dagger in revolutions} = \frac{s}{2\pi r}. \qquad (3\text{–}11)$$

---

† Since we so frequently consider the magnitude of an angle rather than the angle itself, we shall use the word "angle" in place of "measure of the angle."

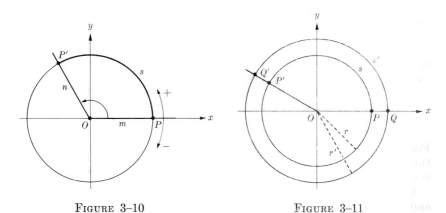

FIGURE 3–10   FIGURE 3–11

For example, if P traces out an arc one-half the circumference, the corresponding angle is measured as one-half a revolution. Likewise, if the arc is twice the circumference, the angle measure is two revolutions.

Consider the two concentric circles at O, in Fig. 3–11, with $\overset{\frown}{PP'}$ an arc of length s on the circle of radius r, and $\overset{\frown}{QQ'}$ an arc of length s' on the circle of radius r'. It should be intuitively clear that each arc length is the same portion of the corresponding circumference, so that

$$\frac{s'}{2\pi r'} = \frac{s}{2\pi r}.$$

This may be proved by using the theorem that similar triangles have proportional sides. If we recall the definition of arc length from Article 3–4, $s'/r' = s/r$, and our result follows. The magnitude of any angle is thus independent of the length of its initial or terminal side.

Although the use of revolutions is the most natural method for measuring angles, there are other more convenient systems.

The system most commonly used in practical work such as surveying and navigation is the *sexagesimal system*, in which the degree* is the fundamental unit. In this system one revolution = 360°, 1° = 60′ (minutes), and 1′ = 60″ (seconds). Thus:

> Angle in degrees = (number of revolutions)(360°).   (3–12)

For example, one-half a revolution is 180°, or an angle of two revolutions is 720°.

---

* The origin of the use of the degree for measurement is discussed by O. Neugebauer in *Studies of the History of Science*. Philadelphia: University of Pennsylvania Press, 1941. Bicentennial Conference. Chapter on "Ancient Astronomy," p. 16.

The system used in calculus and other more advanced mathematics is the *radian system*. Recalling that the circumference of the unit circle is 2π, we define one revolution to be 2π radians and have

$$\text{Angle in radians} = (\text{number of revolutions})(2\pi). \qquad (3\text{-}13)$$

For example, one-half a revolution is π radians, or an angle of two revolutions is 4π radians. When no unit of measure is designated, radian measure is understood.

We have two immediate results from these definitions. Solving (3–12) and (3–13) for number of revolutions and equating, we find the relationship between an angle expressed in degrees and radians to be

$$\frac{\text{Angle in degrees}}{360°} = \frac{\text{Angle in radians}}{2\pi}. \qquad (3\text{-}14)$$

EXAMPLE 1. An angle of 45° is equal to

$$\frac{45°}{360°} 2\pi = \frac{\pi}{4} \text{ radians.}$$

EXAMPLE 2. An angle of $5\pi/6$ radians is equal to

$$\frac{5\pi/6}{2\pi} 360° = 150°.$$

EXAMPLE 3. To express an angle of one radian in degrees, the same method is used:

$$1 \text{ radian} = \frac{1}{2\pi} 360° = \frac{360°}{2\pi} = 57°18' \text{ (approximately).} \qquad (3\text{-}15)$$

Similarly, for an angle of one degree,

$$1° = 2\pi\left(\frac{1°}{360°}\right) = 0.01745 \text{ radian (approximately).} \qquad (3\text{-}16)$$

EXAMPLE 4. Transform an angle of 194°23' to radian measure.

Solution. In Table I in the Appendix, the angles are given in both degrees and radians. We may use this table to change from one system to the other. Since

$$194°23' = 180° + 14°23',$$

we work with 14°23'.

$$14°20' = 0.2502 \text{ radian,}$$

and

$$14°30' = 0.2531 \text{ radian.}$$

Since 23′ is 0.3 of the difference between 30′ and 20′, the radian measure of the required angle is greater than 0.2502 by 0.3 of the difference between 0.2531 and 0.2502, or

$$14°23' = 0.2511 \text{ radian.}$$

Therefore,

$$194°23' = (\pi + 0.2511) \text{ radians}$$
$$= 3.3927 \text{ radians (approximately).}$$

The second result shows the advantage of the radian system in measuring angles.

We are able to express the length of a circular arc in terms of its radius and the subtending central angle measured in radians. Writing (3–13) with the substitution from (3–11), we have

$$\text{Angle in radians} = \frac{s}{2\pi r}(2\pi) = \frac{s}{r}.$$

Therefore the length of the circular arc s cut by a central angle θ (measured in radians) in a circle of radius r is given by

$$\boxed{s = r\theta.} \qquad (3\text{–}17)$$

EXAMPLE 5. A circle has a radius of 40 inches. (a) How long is the arc subtended by a central angle of 36°? (b) How large is the central angle that subtends an arc of 15 inches?

Solution. (a) Since the number of radians corresponding to 36° is $\pi/5$,

$$s = 40\left(\frac{\pi}{5}\right) = 8\pi \text{ inches.}$$

If we use an approximation for π, this answer can be written to any desired degree of accuracy. (b) Again using $s = r\theta$, we have $15 = 40\theta$ or $\theta = \frac{3}{8}$ radian. If the result is desired in degrees, we merely change $\frac{3}{8}$ radian into degrees, obtaining 21°30′.

PROBLEMS

1. In a rectangular coordinate system, locate the following angles in standard position, showing the initial and terminal sides. Use a curved arrow to indicate the direction in which the angle is measured.

(a) $\frac{1}{4}$ rev,   (b) $-\frac{3}{4}$ rev,   (c) 3 rev,   (d) $\frac{3}{8}$ rev,
(e) $-\frac{1}{6}$ rev,   (f) $-\frac{5}{4}$ rev,   (g) $\frac{5}{6}$ rev,   (h) $-\frac{5}{3}$ rev.

2. Repeat Problem 1 for the following angles expressed in degrees:

(a) 45°,   (b) 135°,   (c) −225°,   (d) −300°,
(e) 240°,   (f) 450°,   (g) 720°,   (h) −120°.

3. Repeat Problem 1 for the following angles expressed in radians:

(a) $\pi/6$,   (b) $2\pi/3$,   (c) $\pi/4$,   (d) $4\pi/9$,

(e) $-3\pi/2$,   (f) $-5\pi/6$,   (g) $5\pi/12$,   (h) -5π.

4. Express the angles given in Problems 1 and 2 in radian measure, leaving the answer in terms of π.

5. Express the angles given in Problems 2 and 3 in revolutions.

6. Express the angles given in Problems 1 and 3 in degrees.

7. Transform the following angles to radians, using Table I if needed, and giving the answer to four decimal places.

(a) $27°$,   (b) $156°20'$,   (c) $47°$,

(d) $189°32'$,   (e) $253°10'$,   (f) $-378°49'$.

8. Transform the following angles to degrees and minutes, using Table I if needed, and giving the answer to the nearest minute.

(a) $\pi/8$,   (b) $-2\pi/13$,   (c) 0.2443,   (d) -1.3730,

(e) 1.8600,   (f) $\frac{9}{4}$,   (g) -1.2900,   (h) 5.7200.

9. Express each of the following as a single angle in degrees and minutes from $0'$ to $59'$.

(a) $15°27' + 32°14'$,   (b) $18°41' + 15°12'$,

(c) $13°32' + 37°28'$,   (d) $142°5' + 8°55'$,

(e) $29°43' + 51°38'$,   (f) $61°19' + 23°58'$,

(g) $180° - 15°13'$,   (h) $90° - 47°38'$,

(i) $360° - 147°23'$,   (j) $270° - 63°48'$,

(k) $\frac{1}{2}(18°47' + 56°29')$,   (l) $\frac{1}{2}(56°28' - 47°36')$.

10. If an arc 20 feet long subtends an angle of 2 radians at the center of a circle, find its radius.

11. If a wheel of radius 2 feet rolls 3 feet, how many radians has it turned? How many degrees has it turned?

12. In a circle of radius 14 inches, how long an arc does a central angle of $82°$ intersect?

13. How many degrees are there between the minute and hour hands of a clock at 4:00 o'clock? At 1:00? At 9:15? At 5:47?

14. Assuming that the earth's radius is 3960 miles, find the distance on the surface of the earth from Columbus, Ohio, to the equator. The latitude of Columbus is $40°$.

15. If a point on the circumference of a wheel whose diameter is 20 inches travels 3000 feet per minute, through how many radians does the wheel turn in one second?

16. For small angles, the intercepted arc and chord are approximately the same length. Assuming that the earth moves around the sun in a circle of radius 93,000,000 miles, find the sun's diameter if it subtends an angle of $32'$ at the earth.

*17. In the unit circle ($r = 1$), Eq. (3–17) becomes $s = \theta$. Explain the meaning of this extremely important formula. What would be the length of the arc of the unit circle intercepted by a central angle of 5 radians? 1 radian? θ radians?

3–6 Functions. In mathematics, the concept of *function* is most important and useful. In considering the unit circle, discussed in Example 2, Article 3–4, we found its equation to be $x^2 + y^2 = 1$. By subtracting x^2 from both members of this equality, and taking the positive square root, we have

$$y = \sqrt{1 - x^2}, \tag{3–18}*$$

the equation of the "top" half of the circle (Fig. 3–12).

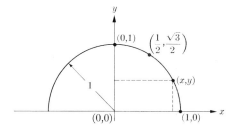

FIGURE 3–12

From the figure of this half-circle, we see that for a particular point to be on the curve, its y-coordinate is determined uniquely if its x-coordinate is given. Similarly, from the equation (3–18) there must be a certain value of y which corresponds to any specific value of x between -1 and 1. For example, if $x = 0$, y must be 1; if $x = 1$, y must be 0; or if $x = \frac{1}{2}$, y must be $\sqrt{3}/2$. The equation (3–18) defines a pairing of numbers in the sense that for each value of x between -1 and 1 there is a specified value of y. The x and y are called *variables*. The x is called the *independent variable*, since it represents any number substituted in the equation, and y is called the *dependent variable*, since it results from the original choice of the substituted value of x. We express this relationship between the variables x and y by calling y a *function* of x.

Let us define this basic concept in general.

DEFINITION 3–2. *If two variables x and y are so related that whenever a value is assigned to x, one and only one value of y is determined by some rule, then y is said to be a* function *of x.*

In this book the rule for determining the value of y will usually be expressed by an equation, a table of values, or a graph. The customary method for designating y as a function of x is to write $y = f(x)$, read "y is a function of x" or "y equals f of x." The symbol $f(a)$ will denote the value of the function when a is substituted for x. Thus for $y = f(x) = \sqrt{1 - x^2}$, $f(0) = 1$, $f(1) = 0$, and $f(\frac{1}{2}) = \sqrt{3}/2$.

---

* The identity symbol, $\equiv$, will not be used in equations defining functions.

The set of values of x for which the function is defined is called the *domain of the function*, while the corresponding values of y form a set of values called the *range of the function*. In the case of the function $y = \sqrt{1 - x^2}$, the domain is the set of all real values of x where x satisfies $-1 \leq x \leq 1$, while the range of the function is $0 \leq y \leq 1$. Unless otherwise stated, both the domain and range of any function will be the largest possible set of suitable real numbers.

When it is necessary to refer to more than one function in some discussion, expressions such as $g(x)$, $F(x)$, $P(x)$ may also be used.

Let us summarize the concept of function. There are three important parts: the domain or set of x-values, the range or set of y-values, and the rule, relationship, or correspondence which associates these two sets.

ILLUSTRATION 1. The equation $y = f(x) = 2x - 6$ expresses y as a first degree function of x. The values of x may be any real numbers, as may the values of y. Specifically, $f(0) = -6$, $f(1) = -4$, $f(3) = 0$, $f(4) = 2$, and so on.

ILLUSTRATION 2. The area A of a circle of radius r is given by the expression $A = \pi r^2$. Since π is a quantity which remains fixed in value (called a *constant*),

$$A = f(r) = \pi r^2, \quad \text{for} \quad r \geq 0.$$

For example, $f(0) = 0$, $f(1) = \pi$, $f(2) = 4\pi$, and so on. This function has for its domain and range all positive values.

ILLUSTRATION 3. Let $y = f(x)$ be defined

$$f(x) = \begin{cases} x \text{ for } x \geq 0, \\ -x \text{ for } x < 0. \end{cases}$$

This function, defined by different expressions over different parts of the domain, may be written $y = |x|$. [Recall Eq. (3–1).]

ILLUSTRATION 4. Let $f(\theta)$ be defined for any real number θ as the ordinate of the point reached by starting at $(1, 0)$ and measuring an arc of length $|\theta|$ along the unit circle $x^2 + y^2 = 1$, in the counterclockwise direction if $\theta > 0$, but in the clockwise direction if $\theta < 0$. This function is defined by a rule, and is not expressible by an algebraic equation. Verify that

$$f(0) = 0, \qquad f(\pi/2) = 1,$$
$$f(\pi) = 0, \qquad f(3\pi/2) = -1.$$

This is a very important function and will be discussed in detail in Chapter 4.

In the definition of a function $y = f(x)$, the value of the variable y is unique, corresponding to any specific value of x. Other possibilities do exist, however, so that for a given value of x, there may exist two, three, or even an infinite number of corresponding values of y. For example, if we solve the equation of the unit circle, $x^2 + y^2 = 1$, for y, we have

$$y = \pm\sqrt{1 - x^2}.$$

In this case there are two values of y which correspond to any value of x between -1 and 1. Although this might be called a double-valued (and in general, multiple-valued) function, we prefer to call such a correspondence a *relation*, and not a function of any kind.

DEFINITION 3–3. *If two variables x and y are so related that whenever a value is assigned to x, at least one value of y is determined by some rule, then this correspondence is called a* relation.

As in the case of a function, a relation has a domain and range. Although relations will be mentioned in this book, we shall restrict our discussion to functions whenever possible.

PROBLEMS

1. If $f(x) = 2x - 5$, find $f(0)$, $f(1)$, $f(3)$, $f(-1)$.

2. If $f(x) = x^2 - 7x + 10$, find $f(2)$, $f(5)$, $f(3)$, $f(0)$.

3. If $f(x) = 1/(x - 3)$, find $f(4)$, $f(2)$, $f(-1)$. What can be said about $f(3)$?

4. If $f(x) = 2^x$, find $f(0)$, $f(1)$, $f(5)$, $f(-1)$, $f(-5)$.

5. If $f(x) = x^{1/2}$, find $f(0)$, $f(2)$, $f(4)$. What domain must this function have in order to have real values of $f(x)$?

6. Define $f(x)$ so that $10^{f(x)} = x$. Find $f(1)$, $f(10)$, $f(100)$, $f(\frac{1}{10})$, $f(\frac{1}{100})$.

7. If $y = f(x) = |x - 2|$, find $f(0)$, $f(2)$, $f(4)$, $f(-2)$. Give the domain and the range of $f(x)$.

8. If x is the length of one side of a square, express the perimeter P as a function of x. Express the area A as a function of x.

9. If x is the length of one side of an equilateral triangle, express the perimeter P as a function of x. Express the area A as a function of x. [*Hint:* In a 30°-60° triangle, the hypotenuse is double the shorter leg.] Use the Pythagorean Theorem to find the altitude, and recall that $A = \frac{1}{2}$ (base) · (altitude).

10. With s measured in feet and t in seconds, the function $s = f(t) = -16t^2 + 32t$ expresses the height of a ball above the ground after t seconds if it were thrown upward with a velocity of 32 ft/sec. Find $f(0)$, $f(\frac{1}{2})$, $f(1)$, $f(\frac{3}{2})$, $f(2)$, and explain the result.

11. Verify the values of the function given in Illustration 4.

*12. For the same θ as that described in Illustration 4, define $g(\theta)$ as the abscissa of the point on the unit circle, rather than the ordinate. Find $g(0)$, $g(\pi/2)$, $g(\pi)$, $g(3\pi/2)$, $g(2\pi)$.

*13. If $f(x) = x^2$, show that $f(-x) \equiv f(x)$. Any function satisfying the condition $f(-x) \equiv f(x)$ is called an *even function*. Give another example of such a function.

*14. If $f(x) = x^3$, show that $f(-x) \equiv -f(x)$. Any function satisfying this condition is called an *odd function*. Give another example of an odd function.

3–7 Graphical representation of functions.

Through the use of the rectangular coordinate system discussed in Article 3–2, we are able to exhibit the relationship between x and y (or any two variables) in the case of any particular function. Although all the points (x, y) whose coordinates satisfy a given relation $y = f(x)$ cannot be plotted, usually a sufficient number may be, so that a good approximation to a picture of the function may be obtained. The aggregate of all such points forms *the graph of the function* or the *curve* which represents the function. (Recall Definition 3–1.)

EXAMPLE 1. Draw the graph of the function $y = f(x) = 3x - 4$.

Solution. By assigning arbitrary values for x, and computing the corresponding y-values, we can obtain any number of points (x, y) whose coordinates satisfy the equation $y = 3x - 4$. The points, arranged in the table below, are then plotted, and joined by a smooth curve. This function is represented by a straight line (Fig. 3–13).

x	0	1	2	3	4
y	-4	-1	2	5	8

EXAMPLE 2. Draw the graph of the function $y = f(x) = x^2 - x - 6$.

Solution. Again, assign values to x, compute the corresponding y-values, and arrange the results in a table.

x	0	1	2	3	4	-1	-2	-3
y	-6	-6	-4	0	6	-4	0	6

If we draw a smooth curve through these points (x, y), starting with the point whose abscissa is -3, then $-2, -1$, and so on, we obtain the result shown in Fig. 3–14. This curve, called a *parabola*, is the required graph. Often, to complete the graph correctly, additional points [e.g. $(\frac{1}{2}, -6\frac{1}{4})$] whose coordinates satisfy the relation must be found.

We have noticed in both Examples 1 and 2 that the graph of the function crosses the x-axis. At any such point, the y-coordinate is zero. The x-value

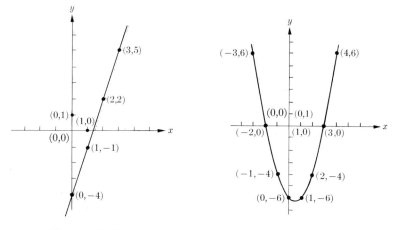

FIGURE 3–13   FIGURE 3–14

at such points is called a *zero* of the function. In Example 1, the zero of
the function is $x = \frac{4}{3}$; in Example 2, there are two zeros of the function,
−2 and 3. In general, a *zero of a function* is the abscissa of a point where
the graph of the function crosses or touches the x-axis.

EXAMPLE 3. Draw the graph of the function $y = f(x) = |x - 2|$.

Solution. We construct the table,

x	0	1	2	3	4	5	−1
y	2		0	1	2	3	3

plot the points, and draw the graph. (See Fig. 3–15.) Note that $x = 2$ is
the zero of this function, although the curve does not cross the x-axis.

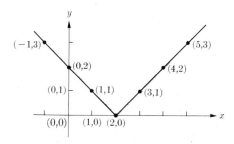

FIGURE 3–15

PROBLEMS

Draw the graph of each of the following functions on ruled paper, showing the scales on both axes and giving the zeros of the function in each case:

1. $y = 2x + 5$ 2. $y = 6 - 3x$

3. $y = x^2$ 4. $y = -4x^2$

5. $y = x^2 - 7x + 10$ 6. $y = -x^2 - x + 30$

7. $y = |x - 1|$ 8. $y = |2x - 3|$

9. $y = \sqrt{x - 1}$ [*Hint:* y is never negative.]

10. $y = x^3$ 11. $y = x^3 - x$

12. $y = \sqrt{x(2 - x)}$. What is the domain and the range of this function?

3–8 Graphical representation of empirical data. Certain functional relations are expressed most clearly by a table of statistics or scientific data. Often such material cannot be expressed by even a mathematical formula, but an adaptation of the method of graphing may be used. Consider the example showing how our population has grown. The table shows the total population at intervals of twenty years since 1790, when the first census was taken.

Year (t)	1790	1810	1830	1850	1870	1890	1910	1930	1950
Population (y) (in millions)	3.9	7.2	12.9	23.2	39.8	62.9	92.0	122.8	150.7

This functional relationship differs from those previously considered, for its domain is a finite set of integers, but we can use an adaptation of our method of graphing to obtain a clear representation of the data. With the t-axis chosen as horizontal, the points are plotted and a smooth curve is drawn through these points to indicate the general trend. The graph is shown in Fig. 3–16.

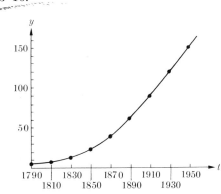

FIGURE 3–16

PROBLEMS

Construct a graph representing the data given in each of the following problems. Indicate the scales clearly in each case.

1. This table lists the percentage of the population of the United States which is foreign-born, at ten-year intervals since 1890.

Year (t)	1890	1900	1910	1920	1930	1940	1950
Percentage (y)	14.7	13.6	14.7	13.2	11.6	8.7	6.7

2. This table lists the total horsepower hours of energy (in billions) used from mineral fuel and water power in the United States since 1860.

Year (t)	1860	1880	1900	1920	1940	1950
Energy (y)	25	40	78	190	280	410

3. This table lists the buying power of per capita yearly income for certain years since 1839 in the United States. The figures are adjusted to represent modern purchasing power.

(t)	1839	1859	1879	1899	1919	1929	1933	1941
(y)	198	296	309	482	620	681	495	792

4. This table lists the public school attendance (in millions) of students in the United States, since 1880.

(t)	1880	1890	1900	1910	1920	1930	1940	1950
(y)	6.1	8.2	10.6	12.8	16.2	21.3	22.0	21.7

5. This table lists the number of teachers (in units of 10,000) in the United States, since 1880.

(t)	1880	1890	1900	1910	1920	1930	1940	1950
(n)	28.7	36.4	42.3	52.3	67.9	85.4	87.5	85.9

CHAPTER 4

THE CIRCULAR FUNCTIONS

4–1 Trigonometry. In about 1600 A.D., Bartholomaus Pitiscus, a professor of mathematics at Heidelberg, wrote the first textbook to bear the title *Trigonometry*. He had in mind exactly what the name implies: triangle measurement. Actually, however, trigonometry had its origin in early historical times. It was a part of the attempt to study the celestial sphere in which the sun, moon, and stars were supposed to move, and to calculate the positions of the heavenly bodies by means of angles. The most famous men interested in this development were two Greek astronomers, Hipparchus of Nicaea (2nd century B.C.) and Claudius Ptolemy (2nd century A.D.). As a consequence, one often gains the impression that the principal if not the sole application of trigonometry is the solving of triangles, and thus that the application of trigonometry lies in the fields of astronomy, navigation, and surveying. This may have been true 2000 or even 400 years ago, but it is certainly not the case today.

With the development of trigonometry, the general study of the circular functions has progressed. In fact, we now define trigonometry as that branch of mathematics which is concerned with the properties and applications of the circular or trigonometric functions.

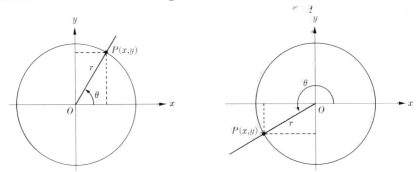

FIGURE 4–1

4–2 Definitions of the circular functions. Consider an angle θ, in standard position, which has been generated by the portion of the rotating ray of length r (Fig. 4–1). Let (x, y) be the coordinates of P, the point on the terminal side of the angle, a distance r from the origin. We define the *sine, cosine,* and *tangent functions of θ* in terms of these coordinates and of r, the radius of the generated circle. Although x and y may be positive or negative depending upon the position of P, r is always considered positive. Using the usual abbreviations, we have:

DEFINITION 4–1.

$$\sin \theta = \frac{y}{r}, \tag{4-1}$$

$$\cos \theta = \frac{x}{r}, \tag{4-2}$$

and

$$\tan \theta = \frac{y}{x} \quad (x \neq 0). \tag{4-3}$$

These functions are uniquely determined for any specific value of θ except in (4–3). In this case, for certain values of θ, $\tan \theta$ is not defined, because $x = 0$ and in no way depends upon the distance of P from the origin. To clarify this statement, consider the two concentric circles with r and r' as radii and $P(x, y)$ and $P'(x', y')$ lying on the terminal side of angle θ, as in Fig. 4–2. Since the right triangles formed with the lengths of the coordinates x, y, x', and y' as legs are similar, the corresponding ratios which define these functions are equal.

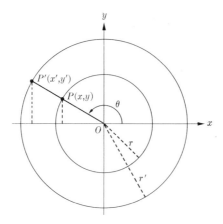

FIGURE 4–2

Note the relationship between these functions. Since $\tan \theta = y/x \equiv (y/r)/(x/r)$, we have

$$\tan \theta \equiv \frac{\sin \theta}{\cos \theta}, \tag{4-4}$$

which is defined for all values of θ except where $\cos \theta = 0$. In this case $\tan \theta$ is undefined (see Article 1–1).

From Article 3–2 we recall the signs of the coordinates of points in the different quadrants. By noting the signs of x or y, we determine in which quadrants the circular functions are positive or negative. Since $r = \sqrt{x^2 + y^2} > 0$ in every quadrant, we have the following table, which the reader should verify.

Quadrant	$\sin \theta = y/r$	$\cos \theta = x/r$	$\tan \theta = y/x$
I	$+$	$+$	$+$
II	$+$	$-$	$-$
III	$-$	$-$	$+$
IV	$-$	$+$	$-$

EXAMPLE 1. Let θ be an angle in standard position with its terminal side passing through $(-3, 4)$. Find $\sin \theta$, $\cos \theta$, and $\tan \theta$.

Solution. Since $x = -3$ and $y = 4$, $r = \sqrt{(-3)^2 + 4^2} = \sqrt{9 + 16} = \sqrt{25} = 5$. Thus, $\sin \theta = \frac{4}{5}$, $\cos \theta = -\frac{3}{5}$, and $\tan \theta = -\frac{4}{3}$.

EXAMPLE 2. Find the value of $\cos \theta$ and $\tan \theta$ if $\sin \theta = -\frac{5}{13}$ and $\tan \theta > 0$.

Solution. Since $\sin \theta < 0$ and $\tan \theta > 0$, θ terminates in the third quadrant. Moreover, with $\sin \theta = -\frac{5}{13}$, we may assume that the terminal side of θ passes through $(-12, -5)$. (Why?) Therefore $\cos \theta = -\frac{12}{13}$ and $\tan \theta = \frac{5}{12}$.

EXAMPLE 3. Let θ be an angle in standard position with its terminal side passing through $(4, -3)$. Find the sine, cosine, and tangent of $\theta + \pi/2$ and $\theta + \pi$.

Solution. By similar right triangles, the terminal side of $\theta + \pi/2$, in standard position, passes through $(3, 4)$, while that of $\theta + \pi$ passes through $(-4, 3)$. Since $r = 5$ in all cases, we have

$$\sin (\theta + \pi/2) = \tfrac{4}{5}, \qquad \sin (\theta + \pi) = \tfrac{3}{5},$$
$$\cos (\theta + \pi/2) = \tfrac{3}{5}, \qquad \cos (\theta + \pi) = -\tfrac{4}{5},$$
$$\tan (\theta + \pi/2) = \tfrac{4}{3}, \qquad \tan (\theta + \pi) = -\tfrac{3}{4}.$$

If θ were increased or decreased by an integral multiple of 2π (or $360°$), the terminal side of the new angle would coincide with the original terminal side, so that P would have the same coordinates. Therefore we have:

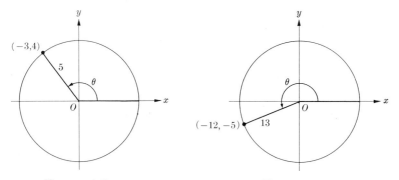

FIGURE 4–3　　　　　　　　　　FIGURE 4–4

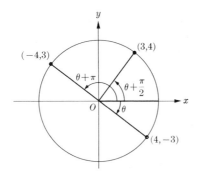

FIGURE 4–5

THEOREM 4–1. *For any angle θ and any integer k,*

$$\sin [\theta + k(2\pi)] \equiv \sin \theta, \qquad (4\text{–}5)$$

and

$$\cos [\theta + k(2\pi)] \equiv \cos \theta. \qquad (4\text{–}6)$$

Hence, if we know the values of $\sin \theta$ and $\cos \theta$ in the range $0 \leq \theta \leq 2\pi$, we know their values of all θ. The sine and cosine functions are called *periodic functions*, with a period 2π.*

The tangent function differs from the sine and cosine functions in regard to its period. Since $\tan \theta = y/x = -y/-x$, and the point $P'(-x, -y)$ lies on the terminal side of the angle $\theta + \pi$, we have:

---

* In general, any function of θ is said to be *periodic*, with period p, provided the function of $\theta + p$ is equal to the function of θ. Note that $k = 1$ in Eq. (4–5) gives the smallest value for p, 2π, for which this is true.

THEOREM 4–2. *For any angle θ, and any integer k,*

$$\tan (\theta + k\pi) \equiv \tan \theta. \tag{4–7}$$

The tangent function is periodic, with a period π.

There are three other circular functions; they are less important than those already defined. The *cosecant, secant,* and *cotangent functions* are defined in terms of the coordinates of $P(x, y)$ as follows:

DEFINITION 4–2.

$$\csc \theta = \frac{r}{y} \qquad (y \neq 0), \tag{4–8}$$

$$\sec \theta = \frac{r}{x} \qquad (x \neq 0), \tag{4–9}$$

and

$$\cot \theta = \frac{x}{y} \qquad (y \neq 0). \tag{4–10}$$

It will be noticed immediately, by using Eqs. (4–1), (4–2), and (4–3), that

$$\sin \theta \csc \theta \equiv 1, \tag{4–11}$$

$$\cos \theta \sec \theta \equiv 1, \tag{4–12}$$

and

$$\tan \theta \cot \theta \equiv 1. \tag{4–13}$$

Because of Eqs. (4–11)–(4–13), the three functions defined in Definition 4–2 are called the *reciprocal functions.* Recall the definition of the reciprocal of a number, given in Article 2–3. If $\sin \theta$, $\cos \theta$, and $\tan \theta$ are known, any of the other three functions can be found immediately. For this reason we shall not discuss them further.

PROBLEMS

Which of the following expressions are positive? Which are negative?

1. $\sin 164°$	2. $\cos 158°$	3. $\tan 195°$
4. $\cos 327°$	5. $\tan 227°$	6. $\sin 264°$
7. $\sin (-38°)$	8. $\cot (-125°)$	9. $\tan (-213°)$
10. $\cos 2\pi/3$	11. $\tan 5\pi/4$	12. $\sin (-11\pi/6)$
13. $\cot 9\pi/7$	14. $\sec (-7\pi/8)$	15. $\csc (-\pi/8)$

Assuming that θ is in standard position, determine the quadrants in which θ may lie under the following conditions:

16. $\sin \theta > 0$ 17. $\cos \theta > 0$

18. $\tan \theta > 0$ 19. $\sin \theta < 0$

20. $\cos \theta < 0$ 21. $\sec \theta > 0$

22. $\sin \theta > 0$ and $\cos \theta > 0$ 23. $\cos \theta > 0$ and $\sin \theta < 0$

24. $\tan \theta > 0$ and $\sin \theta < 0$ 25. $\sin \theta > 0$ and $\cos \theta < 0$

26. $\sin \theta < 0$ and $\cos \theta < 0$

In each of the following, the terminal side of the angle, in standard position, passes through the indicated point. Sketch and find the circular functions of each angle.

27. $(3, 4)$ 28. $(-5, 12)$ 29. $(-4, 3)$

30. $(24, -7)$ 31. $(-8, -15)$ 32. $(10, -8)$

33. $(0, -2)$ 34. $(-1, 7)$ 35. $(6, 0)$

Find the values of $\sin \theta$, $\cos \theta$, and $\tan \theta$ under the following conditions:

36. $\sin \theta = \frac{5}{13}$, θ in the first quadrant.

37. $\cos \theta = -\frac{4}{5}$, θ in the third quadrant.

38. $\tan \theta = -\frac{1}{3}$, θ in the second quadrant.

39. $\sin \theta = \frac{2}{3}$, θ not in the first quadrant.

40. $\cot \theta = \frac{4}{3}$, θ not in the first quadrant.

41. $\cos \theta = \frac{5}{6}$, θ not in the first quadrant.

42. $\tan \theta = \frac{1}{2}$, and $\sin \theta$ is positive.

43. $\sin \theta = -\frac{3}{5}$ and $\tan \theta$ is positive.

44. $\cos \theta = -\frac{7}{9}$, and $\tan \theta$ is negative.

45. $\tan \theta = \frac{2}{3}$.

46. $\sec \theta = -\frac{5}{3}$.

47. $\csc \theta = \frac{12}{7}$.

In Problems 48 through 52, the terminal side of the angle θ, in standard position, passes through $(8, 15)$.

48. Sketch and find the circular functions of $\theta + \pi/2$.

49. Sketch and find the circular functions of $\theta + 180°$.

50. Sketch and find the circular functions of $\theta + 270°$.

51. Sketch and find the circular functions of $\theta - \pi$.

52. Sketch and find the circular functions of $\theta - 90°$.

*53. For any angle θ in standard position with its terminal side intersecting the circle of radius r at P, show that P has coordinates $(r \cos \theta, r \sin \theta)$. This is a most important concept.

4–3 The unit circle. We have mentioned *the unit circle*, with its center at the origin and a radius of one. Since the circular functions are independent of the radius of the circle, many general properties can be obtained through the use of this circle.

Consider the angle θ, in standard position (Fig. 4–6), with its terminal side intersecting the unit circle at $P(x, y)$. Since $r = 1$, we have $\sin \theta = y$

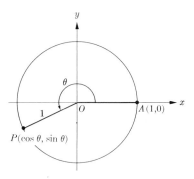

FIGURE 4–6

and $\cos \theta = x$. In other words, P is the point with coordinates ($\cos \theta$, $\sin \theta$). The values of the circular functions for certain angles are immediately apparent. The terminal side of the angle $0°$ or of 0 radians coincides with the initial side, so that the coordinates of P are $(1, 0)$. Hence,

$$\sin 0 = 0, \qquad \tan 0 = \tfrac{0}{1} = 0,$$
$$\cos 0 = 1, \qquad \sec 0 = \tfrac{1}{1} = 1,$$

while $\cot 0$ and $\csc 0$ (i.e., $1/0$) are undefined.

In the angle $90° = \pi/2$ the terminal side intersects the unit circle at the point $(0, 1)$. If we use this fact, the values of circular functions of $90°$ are easily found. The functional values of the other *quadrantal angles* (any angle which is a multiple of $90°$) are also obtained by noting the coordinates of the point where the terminal side of the angle intersects the unit circle.

It is now clear how the values of these functions change as θ increases from 0 to 2π. Verify the following table:

Quadrant	θ varies from	Value of $\sin \theta$ varies from	Value of $\cos \theta$ varies from
I	0 to 90° (0 to $\pi/2$)	0 to 1	1 to 0
II	90° to 180° ($\pi/2$ to π)	1 to 0	0 to -1
III	180° to 270° (π to $3\pi/2$)	0 to -1	-1 to 0
IV	270° to 360° ($3\pi/2$ to 2π)	-1 to 0	0 to 1

The fact that the values of the sine and cosine function are never larger than one is apparent from the table. That this must be so is clear, since

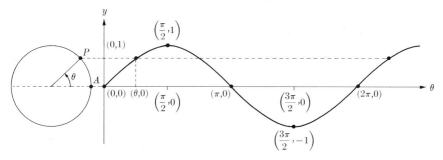

FIGURE 4–7

these values are the coordinates of some point on the unit circle. The tangent, however, can have any positive or negative real number for its value.

We have observed the changes in both sin θ and cos θ as the point $P(\cos \theta, \sin \theta)$ moves around the unit circle. If we wish to consider the behavior of sin θ alone, we can conveniently study the graph of $y = \sin \theta$, with values of θ plotted on the horizontal axis and values of y on the vertical axis. Such a graph may be obtained directly from the unit circle.

Consider a rectangular coordinate system with lengths $\pi/2$ laid off along the θ-axis, as in Fig. 4–7. A unit circle is drawn with its center on the θ-axis. To obtain the graph of $y = \sin \theta$, the ordinate of P is carried over to the point whose abscissa is θ. As many points as may be desired on the graph are obtained by bisecting the area in each of the four quadrants, then bisecting the resulting area, and so on. By drawing a smooth curve through the points located in this way, we have a graph of $y = \sin \theta$.* The curve continues indefinitely to the right and left, but need only be drawn from 0 to 2π. (Why?)

With the use of radian measure and the unit circle, the value of θ corresponds exactly to the length of its subtended arc. Thus, in Fig. 4–7, the length of the arc $\overset{\frown}{AP}$ is equal to the distance from 0 to θ on the θ-axis. Note how clearly the following properties are shown by the graph of $y = \sin \theta$.

1. This function is periodic with period 2π. [Recall Eq. (4–5).]

2. In the first quadrant this function is an *increasing function*.† (In what other quadrant is this the case?)

3. The values of sin θ are positive for θ in the first and second quadrants, and negative in the third and fourth quadrants.

---

* Such a graph may also be plotted using points whose coordinates are obtained from Table I in the Appendix. A further discussion of the graphing of circular functions appears in Chapter 16.

† If $\theta_1 > \theta_2$, then sin $\theta_1 >$ sin θ_2.

4. The values of sin θ lie between -1 and $+1$.

5. The zeros of sin θ are at multiples of π,

$$\sin k\pi = 0, \qquad k = 0, \pm 1, \pm 2, \ldots$$

6. This function has the property that $f(\theta) \equiv -f(-\theta)$, specifically $\sin \theta \equiv -\sin (-\theta)$ [see Eq.(4-27)]. Thus the sine function is odd. Recall Problem 14, Article 3-6.

In Fig. 4-8 the graph of $y = \cos \theta$ is shown. It may be constructed by a procedure similar to the one just described. The use of this graph makes it possible to list properties of the cosine function similar to those given above for the sine function.

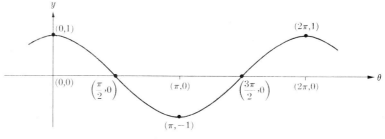

FIGURE 4-8

We have already noticed certain relations between the various functions, such as (4-4), (4-11), (4-12), (4-13). Others can also be derived. Since $\cot \theta \equiv 1/\tan \theta$ [see (4-13)] and $\tan \theta \equiv \sin \theta/\cos \theta$ [see (4-4)],

$$\cot \theta \equiv \frac{\cos \theta}{\sin \theta}. \tag{4-14}$$

More important, however, are the following results. Since the coordinates of any point on the unit circle are $(\cos \theta, \sin \theta)$, and these coordinates must satisfy the equation of the unit circle, $x^2 + y^2 = 1$, we have

$$\sin^2 \theta + \cos^2 \theta \equiv 1 \tag{4-15}$$

for any value of θ, where $\sin^2 \theta$ is the usual notation for $(\sin \theta)^2$, and so on. By dividing each term of (4-15) by $\cos^2 \theta$, we get

$$\frac{\sin^2 \theta}{\cos^2 \theta} + 1 \equiv \frac{1}{\cos^2 \theta},$$

or

$$\boxed{\tan^2 \theta + 1 \equiv \sec^2 \theta.} \qquad (4\text{--}16)$$

By dividing each term of (4–15) by $\sin^2 \theta$, we obtain

$$1 + \frac{\cos^2 \theta}{\sin^2 \theta} \equiv \frac{1}{\sin^2 \theta},$$

or

$$\boxed{1 + \cot^2 \theta \equiv \csc^2 \theta.} \qquad (4\text{--}17)$$

EXAMPLE. Find all six functions of θ if $\cos \theta = \frac{3}{5}$.

Solution. This example is similar to Example 2, Article 4–2. We can now solve it by a second method. Using (4–12), we have $\sec \theta = \frac{5}{3}$. From (4–15),

$$\sin \theta \equiv \pm \sqrt{1 - \cos^2 \theta} = \pm \sqrt{1 - \tfrac{9}{25}} = \pm \sqrt{\tfrac{16}{25}} = \pm \tfrac{4}{5}.$$

The sign depends on the quadrant of θ. Since $\cos \theta > 0$, we know θ is in the first or fourth quadrant. If it were in the first, the plus sign would appear before the $\frac{4}{5}$; if it were in the fourth, the minus sign would be chosen. From (4–4), $\tan \theta = \sin \theta / \cos \theta = \pm \frac{4}{5} / \frac{3}{5} = \pm \frac{4}{3}$. Using (4–11), we have $\cot \theta = \pm \frac{3}{4}$, and (4–8) gives us $\csc \theta = \pm \frac{5}{4}$.

PROBLEMS

1. What are the values of the six circular functions of θ when $\theta = \pi$?

2. What are the values of the six circular functions of $\theta = 270°$?

3. What are the values of the six circular functions of 2π? How do these values compare with those for $\theta = 0$?

4. What are the values of the six circular functions of $-\pi/2$?

5. What are the values of the six circular functions of the following angles?

(a) 3π,   (b) $7\pi/2$,   (c) $9\pi/2$,
(d) 16π,   (e) 15π,   (f) 100π,
(g) $450°$,   (h) $720°$,   (i) $900°$.

6. What are the values of the six circular functions of the following angles?

(a) -5π,   (b) $-\pi/2$,   (c) $-3\pi/2$,
(d) -6π,   (e) $-11\pi/2$,   (f) -40π,
(g) $-180°$,   (h) $-630°$,   (i) $-450°$.

7. (a) Verify the table in this article for the variation of $\sin \theta$ and $\cos \theta$. (b) Make a similar table for the other four functions.

8. Do Problems 36 through 47 of Article 4–2 by the method outlined in the example of this article.

9. Show that sin $(k\pi) = 0$ and cos $(k\pi) = (-1)^k$ for any integer k (positive, negative, or zero).

*10. Construct a graph of $y = \cos \theta$, as in Fig. 4–8, indicating the procedure used. From the graph list properties for cos θ, similar to those listed for sin θ.

11. In the same rectangular coordinate system sketch both the curve $y = \sin \theta$ and $y = \cos \theta$, one curve superimposed on the other. Although the following facts will be proved later in this chapter, could they be deduced from the figure?

(a) $\sin (\pi/2 + \theta) \equiv \sin (\pi/2 - \theta)$,   (b) $\sin (-\theta) \equiv -\sin \theta$,
(c) $\cos (\pi/2 - \theta) \equiv -\cos (\pi/2 + \theta)$,   (d) $\cos (-\theta) \equiv \cos \theta$,
(e) $\cos \theta \equiv \sin (\pi/2 - \theta)$,   (f) $\sin \theta \equiv \cos (\pi/2 - \theta)$.

*12. Obtain an expression in terms of θ for the length of any chord (in a unit circle) whose corresponding arc is subtended by the central angle θ. [*Hint:* In Fig. 4–6 the coordinates of A are $(1, 0)$ and of P are $(\cos \theta, \sin \theta)$. If we use the distance formula (3–9), we have

$$AP = \sqrt{(1 - \cos \theta)^2 + \sin^2 \theta}$$
$$= \sqrt{1 - 2\cos \theta + \cos^2 \theta + \sin^2 \theta},$$

or

$$\text{Length of chord} = \sqrt{2 - 2\cos \theta}.] \qquad (4\text{--}18)$$

13. Find the length of the chord in a unit circle if the subtending angle is (a) $\pi/2$, (b) π.

14. In Fig. 4–9 the terminal side of angle θ intersects the unit circle at P. Draw the tangent to the circle at A and extend the terminal side from the origin O through P. The point at which these lines intersect can be called R. Labeling the point $(0, 1)$ on the circle B, draw the tangent to the circle through this point. This tangent line will intersect the line from O through P and the tangent line to the circle at A. Call these points S and T respectively. (a) Verify for this figure that tan θ is equal in magnitude to the length of the line segment

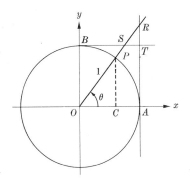

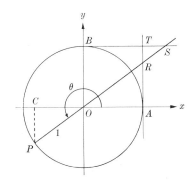

FIGURE 4–9   FIGURE 4–10

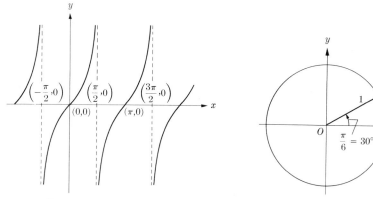

FIGURE 4-11   FIGURE 4-12

AR. Draw a line from P perpendicular to the x-axis. Call the foot of this perpendicular C. Then triangle OPC is similar to ORA. Use the ratio of similar sides of these triangles to obtain the result. (b) Verify that $\cot \theta$ is equal in magnitude to the length of the line segment BS.

15. Figure 4-10 has been drawn in the same manner as Fig. 4-9, except that P is in the third quadrant. In a similar manner, construct two other figures, one where θ is in the second quadrant and one where θ is in the fourth quadrant.

16. Using the figures from Problem 15, Fig. 4-9 and Fig. 4-10, and the results of Problem 14, verify that the following definitions are equivalent to the original definitions: (a) $\tan \theta$ is the y-coordinate of the point R, (b) $\cot \theta$ is the x-coordinate of the point S.

*17. By using the unit circle and the definition for $\tan \theta$ given in Problem 16, construct a graph of $y = \tan \theta$ (see Fig. 4-11).

18. From the graph of $y = \tan \theta$ given in Fig. 4-11, list properties for this function similar to those listed for the sine function.

4-4 Values of the circular functions of special angles. The circular functions of certain angles other than the quadrantal angles can also be found exactly. Consider the angle $\pi/6 = 30°$, located in standard position with the unit circle in Fig. 4-12. In plane geometry it is shown that in a right triangle with an angle of 30°, the hypotenuse is twice as long as the side opposite this angle. Since the point P' lies on the unit circle and has $\frac{1}{2}$ for its y-coordinate, substituting in $x^2 + y^2 = 1$, the equation of the circle, we have $x^2 + (\frac{1}{2})^2 = 1$ or $x^2 = \frac{3}{4}$. Thus, in the first quadrant, $x = \pm\sqrt{3}/2$, and

$$\sin 30° = \tfrac{1}{2}, \qquad \cot 30° = \sqrt{3},$$
$$\cos 30° = \sqrt{3}/2, \qquad \sec 30° = 2/\sqrt{3},$$
$$\tan 30° = 1/\sqrt{3}, \qquad \csc 30° = 2.$$

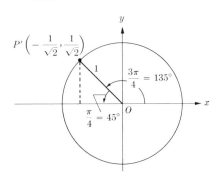

FIGURE 4–13

By properly placing a 30°-60° triangle in the unit circle, with one end of its hypotenuse at the center, the coordinates of a point on the terminal side of any nonquadrantal angle of size $k \cdot 30°$, with k an integer, can be found. From these coordinates, the values of the circular functions of any such angle result.

Again consider $\theta = 3\pi/4 = 135°$. Since $135° = 90° + 45°$ in Fig. 4–13, the right triangle, with OP' as hypotenuse and also as the terminal side of the angle 135°, is isosceles. Since P' lies on the unit circle and has x- and y-coordinates equal in size, with $y = -x$, on substituting, we have $x^2 + x^2 = 2x^2 = 1$, or $x = \pm 1/\sqrt{2}$. Since an angle of 135° terminates in the second quadrant, we choose the minus sign, so that $x = -1/\sqrt{2}$. Hence,

$$\sin 135° = 1/\sqrt{2}, \qquad \cot 135° = -1,$$
$$\cos 135° = -1/\sqrt{2}, \qquad \sec 135° = -\sqrt{2},$$
$$\tan 135° = -1, \qquad \csc 135° = \sqrt{2}.$$

The values of the circular functions of any other odd multiple of 45° can be obtained by similar methods.

PROBLEMS

Draw a figure showing each angle in the unit circle and verify the following by finding the exact values.

1. (a) $\sin \pi/3 = \cos \pi/6$,   (b) $\sin 30° = \cos 60°$.
2. (a) $\sin \pi/6 = \sin 5\pi/6$,   (b) $\cos 150° = -\cos 30°$.
3. (a) $\tan 45° = \tan 225°$,   (b) $\cot 135° = \cot 315°$.
4. (a) $\sec 11\pi/6 = \sec \pi/6$,   (b) $\csc 2\pi/3 = -\csc 4\pi/3$.
5. (a) $\sin 120° = \sin(-240°)$,   (b) $\cos 7\pi/6 = \cos(-5\pi/6)$.
6. (a) $\sin 60° = 2 \sin 30° \cos 30°$,   (b) $\sin \pi/2 = 2 \sin \pi/4 \cos \pi/4$.

7. (a) $\sin \dfrac{\pi}{6} = \sqrt{\dfrac{1 - \cos \pi/3}{2}}$,   (b) $\cos \dfrac{\pi}{6} = \sqrt{\dfrac{1 + \cos \pi/3}{2}}$.

8. $\tan 30° = \dfrac{1 - \cos 60°}{\sin 60°} = \dfrac{\sin 60°}{1 + \cos 60°}$.

9. $\cos 60° = \cos^2 30° - \sin^2 30° = 2 \cos^2 30° - 1$.

Find the exact numerical values of the following:

10. (a) $\sin^2 \pi/6 + \cos^2 \pi/6$,   (b) $\sin^2 0 + \cos^2 0$.
11. (a) $\sec^2 \pi/3 - \tan^2 \pi/3$,   (b) $\sec^2 5\pi/4 - \tan^2 5\pi/4$.
12. (a) $\csc^2 315° - \cot^2 315°$,   (b) $\csc^2 135° - \cot^2 135°$.
13. $\sin 2\pi/3 + \cos 7\pi/6 + \tan 5\pi/3$.
14. $\tan 5\pi/4 + \cot 7\pi/4 - \sec 5\pi/6$.
15. $\csc 150° - \cos 240° + \tan 120°$.
16. $\sin 120° \cos 150° + \cos 120° \sin 150°$.
17. $\cos 3\pi/4 \cos \pi/4 - \sin 3\pi/4 \sin \pi/4$.
18. $\sin 330° \cos 120° \tan 135°$.
19. $(\cos 11\pi/6 + \sin \pi/3)(\tan \pi/6 + \cot 4\pi/3)$.
20. $(\tan 5\pi/4 + \sin 3\pi/2) \cos 5\pi/6$.

Find all the angles between 0° and 360° that satisfy each of the following equations, and express your answers in degrees and in radians:

21. $\sin \theta = \frac{1}{2}$ 22. $\cos \theta = -\frac{1}{2}$
23. $\tan \theta = 1/\sqrt{3}$ 24. $\sin \theta = -\sqrt{3}/2$
25. $\tan \theta = -1$ 26. $\cos \theta = -\sqrt{2}/2$
27. $\sin \theta = \sqrt{2}/2$ 28. $\sec \theta = 2$
29. $\cot \theta = -\sqrt{3}$ 30. $\csc \theta = 2/\sqrt{3}$

31. By drawing a figure for each of the following angles in the unit circle, make a table giving the angle in both degrees and radians and the six circular functions of each: 0°, 30°, 45°, 60°, 90°, 120°, 135°, 150°, 180°, 210°, 225°, 240°, 270°, 300°, 315°, 330°, 360°.

32. Using formula (4–18), find the length of the chord in a unit circle if the subtending angle is (a) $\pi/6$, (b) $\pi/3$, (c) $2\pi/3$.

4–5 Exact values of the circular functions for $\theta = \pi/5$. There is one other special value of an angle which is of interest. Although a slightly more complicated construction is required for 36° or $\pi/5$, we are able to find exact values for the circular functions of this angle, and thus in all have exact values for the functions of π, $\pi/2$, $\pi/3$, $\pi/4$, $\pi/5$, and $\pi/6$.

Consider the unit circle with center O and radius OP (see Fig. 4–14). Locate the point E on the radius OP so that

$$\frac{\text{Length } OP}{\text{Length } OE} = \frac{\text{Length } OE}{\text{Length } EP}.$$

* This location is possible with the use of ruler and compass, and is essentially the same as that used for constructing a regular pentagon.

By letting t denote the length of OE, we have the relationship

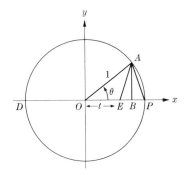

$$\frac{1}{t} = \frac{t}{1-t}. \qquad (4\text{-}19)^*$$

FIGURE 4-14

Solving this quadratic equation† for the positive value of t, we find $t = (\sqrt{5} - 1)/2$.

Locate A so that the length of the chord AP is equal to t. Then the triangles OPA and AEP are similar, and thus triangle AEP is isosceles, so that the length of AE is $AE = t$, and triangle OEA is also isosceles. From this it follows directly that $\angle OPA$ is twice $\angle AOP$ (see Problems 3, 4, and 5). Since $\angle OPA$ is measured by $\frac{1}{2}\widehat{AD}$,‡ $\angle AOP$ is measured by $\frac{1}{4}\widehat{AD}$. Also $\angle AOP$ is measured by $\widehat{AP}$. Thus $\widehat{AD} = 4\widehat{AP}$. But $\widehat{AD} + \widehat{AP} = \pi$. As a direct result, $\widehat{AP} = \pi/5$ and $\theta = \pi/5 = 36°$.

By considering AB perpendicular to OP at B, we easily find the exact lengths of OB and AB, that is, the cosine and sine of $\pi/5$. The length of EP is

$$EP = 1 - t = 1 - \frac{\sqrt{5} - 1}{2} = \frac{3 - \sqrt{5}}{2};$$

thus the length of EB is $(3 - \sqrt{5})/4$. Therefore the length of OB is

$$OB = \frac{\sqrt{5} - 1}{2} + \frac{3 - \sqrt{5}}{4} = \frac{\sqrt{5} + 1}{4}.$$

---

* The ratio defined by Eq. (4-19) has been considered since the time of the Greek mathematicians, and is called the *golden section*. Much has been written on this subject that would be of interest to the student. For example:

1. H. V. Baravalle, "The Geometry of the Pentagon and the Golden Section," *Mathematics Teacher*, Jan. 1948.

2. W. W. Rouse Ball, *Mathematical Recreations and Essays*, rev. by H. S. M. Coxeter, 11th Ed. London: Macmillan and Company, Limited, 1940.

3. R. Courant and H. Robbins, *What is Mathematics?* New York: Oxford University Press, 1941.

4. Jay Hambridge, *The Elements of Dynamic Symmetry*. New York: Brentano's, 1926.

† The solution of quadratic equations is discussed in Article 6-2. See Problem 3 (second list).

‡ Use is made of the theorem in plane geometry which states that an angle inscribed in a circle is measured by one-half the intercepted arc.

Also, in the right triangle OAB,

$$(\text{length of } AB)^2 = 1 - \left(\frac{\sqrt{5}+1}{4}\right)^2 = \frac{5-\sqrt{5}}{8}.$$

Thus

$$\sin\frac{\pi}{5} = \sqrt{\frac{5-\sqrt{5}}{8}}, \qquad \cos\frac{\pi}{5} = \frac{\sqrt{5}+1}{4}. \qquad (4\text{–}20)$$

Should the numerical values of the other functions be desired, they can now be found.

PROBLEMS

Referring to Fig. 4–14, prove the following in detail:

1. Triangle AEP is isosceles.
2. Triangle OEA is isosceles.
3. Angles AOP, OAE, and EAP are equal.
4. $\angle OAP = \angle OPA$.
5. $\angle APO = $ twice $\angle AOP$.

6. Using formula (4–18), find the length of the chord in a unit circle which is subtended by the angle $\pi/5$. How does this value compare with the value of t?

4–6 The fundamental circular function identities.   In the last few articles we have considered some of the useful relations between the different circular functions. There are eight of these, known as *the fundamental circular function identities*, and from these, other simple identities may be proved. They consist of the three reciprocal relations, Eqs. (4–11), (4–12), (4–13), the tangent and cotangent relations, Eqs. (4–4) and (4–14), and the Pythagorean relations, Eqs. (4–15), (4–16), (4–17).

With the use of these relations, all the circular functions may be expressed in terms of any one circular function. Consider the following example.

EXAMPLE 1. Express the six circular functions of θ in terms of $\sin\theta$.

Solution. Of course $\sin\theta = \sin\theta$. By Eq. (4–15),

$$\cos^2\theta \equiv 1 - \sin^2\theta,$$

and therefore

$$\cos\theta \equiv \pm\sqrt{1-\sin^2\theta},$$

where the choice of the sign will depend on the quadrant of θ. From this and Eq. (4–4),

$$\tan\theta \equiv \pm\frac{\sin\theta}{\sqrt{1-\sin^2\theta}}.$$

The reciprocal relations, Eqs. (4–11) through (4–13), are used for the other three functions:

$$\csc \theta \equiv \frac{1}{\sin \theta},$$

$$\sec \theta \equiv \pm \frac{1}{\sqrt{1 - \sin^2 \theta}},$$

$$\cot \theta \equiv \pm \frac{\sqrt{1 - \sin^2 \theta}}{\sin \theta}.$$

Another example will illustrate the method of proving any circular function identity with the aid of the fundamental identities. Supply the reason for each step.

EXAMPLE 2. By transforming the left member to the form of the right, prove that

$$\frac{1}{\sin \theta} - \sin \theta \equiv \cot \theta \cos \theta.$$

Solution.

$$\frac{1}{\sin \theta} - \sin \theta \equiv \frac{1 - \sin^2 \theta}{\sin \theta} \equiv \frac{\cos^2 \theta}{\sin \theta} \equiv \frac{\cos \theta}{\sin \theta} \cos \theta \equiv \cot \theta \cos \theta.$$

Unfortunately, there is no uniform procedure to be followed in proving identities. Factoring and the addition of fractions or other algebraic simplifications are often advantageous, but the introduction of radicals should be avoided whenever possible. If in doubt, it may be helpful to express all the functions in terms of sines and cosines and simplify. The establishing of an identity is accomplished by transforming (1) the left member into the exact form of the right, (2) the right into the exact form of the left, or (3) each side separately into the same form. In the following examples, give the reason for each step.

EXAMPLE 3. By transforming each side separately to the same form, prove that $\tan \theta \sin \theta \equiv \sec \theta - \cos \theta$.

Solution.

$$\tan \theta \sin \theta \qquad \sec \theta - \cos \theta$$

$$\frac{\sin \theta}{\cos \theta} \sin \theta \qquad \frac{1}{\cos \theta} - \cos \theta$$

$$\frac{\sin^2 \theta}{\cos \theta} \qquad \frac{1 - \cos^2 \theta}{\cos \theta}$$

$$\frac{\sin^2 \theta}{\cos \theta} \equiv \frac{\sin^2 \theta}{\cos \theta}.$$

EXAMPLE 4. Prove the identity $\dfrac{1 - \sin \theta}{\cos \theta} \equiv \dfrac{\cos \theta}{1 + \sin \theta}$.

Solution.
$$\frac{1 - \sin \theta}{\cos \theta} \equiv \frac{(1 - \sin \theta)(1 + \sin \theta)}{\cos \theta(1 + \sin \theta)}$$
$$\equiv \frac{1 - \sin^2 \theta}{\cos \theta(1 + \sin \theta)}$$
$$\equiv \frac{\cos^2 \theta}{\cos \theta(1 + \sin \theta)}$$
$$\equiv \frac{\cos \theta}{1 + \sin \theta}.$$

There are three different reasons for learning to prove identities such as those in the following set of problems. By working with and proving such relationships, one more easily masters the formulas and definitions of the circular functions. One also matures mathematically through the acquisition or review of certain algebraic manipulations. Most important, however, many such identities are often used in more advanced mathematics and in practical applications.

PROBLEMS

By means of the fundamental identities, express each of the following in terms of $\sin \theta$ only:

1. $\csc \theta$ 2. $\cos^2 \theta$ 3. $\cos \theta$
4. $\sec \theta$ 5. $\tan \theta$ 6. $\cot \theta$

By means of the fundamental identities, express each of the following in terms of $\cos \theta$ only:

7. $\sec \theta$ 8. $\sin^2 \theta$ 9. $\sin \theta$
10. $\csc \theta$ 11. $\tan \theta$ 12. $\cot \theta$

13. Express all six functions of θ in terms of $\tan \theta$. [*Hint:* Use the identity $\sec^2 \theta \equiv 1 + \tan^2 \theta$.]

14. Express $(\sin \theta + \tan \theta)/(\sec \theta + 1)$ in terms of $\sin \theta$ only.

15. Express $(\tan \theta + \cot \theta)/(\sec \theta \sin \theta)$ in terms of $\cos \theta$ only.

Prove the following identities:

16. $\tan \theta + \cot \theta \equiv \sec \theta \csc \theta$ 17. $1 - 2 \sin^2 \theta \equiv 2 \cos^2 \theta - 1$

18. $\sin \theta \cos \theta \sec \theta \csc \theta \equiv 1$ 19. $\dfrac{1}{1 + \sin \theta} + \dfrac{1}{1 - \sin \theta} \equiv 2 \sec^2 \theta$

20. $\cos \theta + \tan \theta \sin \theta \equiv \sec \theta$ 21. $\cos^4 \theta - \sin^4 \theta \equiv \cos^2 \theta - \sin^2 \theta$

22. $\dfrac{\tan \theta - \cot \theta}{\tan \theta + \cot \theta} \equiv 2 \sin^2 \theta - 1$ 23. $\dfrac{\sin \theta}{1 + \cos \theta} + \dfrac{1 + \cos \theta}{\sin \theta} \equiv 2 \csc \theta$

24. $\dfrac{1 - \cos \theta}{\sin \theta} \equiv \dfrac{\sin \theta}{1 + \cos \theta}$

25. $\cos^2 \theta - \sin^2 \theta \equiv \dfrac{1 - \tan^2 \theta}{1 + \tan^2 \theta}$

26. $\cot \theta + \tan \theta \equiv \cot \theta \sec^2 \theta$

27. $\dfrac{1 + \tan^2 \theta}{\tan^2 \theta} \equiv \csc^2 \theta$

28. $(\csc \theta - \cot \theta)^2 \equiv \dfrac{1 - \cos \theta}{1 + \cos \theta}$

29. $(\sec \theta - \tan \theta)^2 \equiv \dfrac{1 - \sin \theta}{1 + \sin \theta}$

30. $(\cos \theta - \sin \theta)^2 + 2 \sin \theta \cos \theta \equiv 1$

31. $\dfrac{\cot^2 \theta - 1}{1 + \cot^2 \theta} \equiv 2 \cos^2 \theta - 1$

32. $\dfrac{1 + \csc \theta}{\csc \theta - 1} \equiv \dfrac{1 + \sin \theta}{1 - \sin \theta}$

33. $\dfrac{\tan \theta}{1 - \cot \theta} + \dfrac{\cot \theta}{1 - \tan \theta} \equiv 1 + \tan \theta + \cot \theta$

34. $\dfrac{1 - \tan^2 \theta}{1 + \tan^2 \theta} \equiv 1 - 2 \sin^2 \theta$

35. $\dfrac{2 \sin^2 \theta - 1}{\sin \theta \cos \theta} \equiv \tan \theta - \cot \theta$

36. $\sec \theta \csc \theta - 2 \cos \theta \csc \theta \equiv \tan \theta - \cot \theta$

37. $\dfrac{\cos \theta - \sin \theta}{\cos \theta + \sin \theta} \equiv \dfrac{\cot \theta - 1}{\cot \theta + 1}$

38. $\dfrac{\sin \theta}{\csc \theta - \cot \theta} \equiv 1 + \cos \theta$

39. $\dfrac{(\cos^2 \theta - \sin^2 \theta)^2}{\cos^4 \theta - \sin^4 \theta} \equiv 1 - 2 \sin^2 \theta$

40. $\dfrac{\sec^2 \theta}{1 + \sin \theta} \equiv \dfrac{\sec^2 \theta - \sec \theta \tan \theta}{\cos^2 \theta}$

41. $1 + \cot \theta \equiv \dfrac{(1 - \cot^2 \theta) \sin \theta}{\sin \theta - \cos \theta}$

42. $\dfrac{\sec \theta + \tan \theta}{\cos \theta - \tan \theta - \sec \theta} \equiv -\csc \theta$

43. $\sin \theta + \cos \theta + \dfrac{\sin \theta}{\cot \theta} \equiv \sec \theta + \csc \theta - \dfrac{\cos \theta}{\tan \theta}$

44. $\dfrac{\sin \theta \cos \theta + \cos \theta \sin \theta}{\cos \theta \cos \theta - \sin \theta \sin \theta} \equiv \dfrac{\tan \theta + \tan \theta}{1 - \tan \theta \tan \theta}$

4–7 Proof of the formula for cos ($\alpha - \beta$). We are now in a position to deal with two additional general types of circular function relations. They differ from those studied thus far in that they contain functions of more than one angle. The problem of expressing a circular function of θ plus some multiple of $\pi/2$ as a function of only θ (as in Example 3, Article 4–2) is by no means the only situation frequently encountered; often we wish to consider circular functions of two angles in general. Such functions, we shall see, can be expressed in terms of functions of each angle separately. More specifically, we know that sin ($\pi/4 + \pi/3$) is not equal to sin $\pi/4$ + sin $\pi/3$, since the latter is equal to $1/\sqrt{2} + \sqrt{3}/2$ (a value greater than one), an impossible value for the sine function. However, sin ($\pi/4 + \pi/3$) can be expressed in terms of functions of $\pi/4$ and $\pi/3$ and its value readily

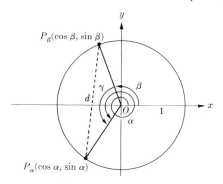

$P_\beta(\cos\beta, \sin\beta)$

$P_\alpha(\cos\alpha, \sin\alpha)$

FIGURE 4–15

obtained. We find it convenient to develop first a formula for cos $(\alpha - \beta)$, one of the truly basic formulas of trigonometry.

THEOREM 4–3. *For any two angles α and β,*

$$\cos(\alpha - \beta) \equiv \cos\alpha\cos\beta + \sin\alpha\sin\beta. \qquad (4\text{–}21)$$

Proof. As in Fig. 4–15, let α and β be any two angles in standard position in the unit circle. Denote by P_α and P_β the points where the terminal sides of the angles intersect the unit circle. Since the coordinates of P_α are $(\cos\alpha, \sin\alpha)$ and of P_β are $(\cos\beta, \sin\beta)$, the distance d between these two points, Eqs. (3–9), is given by

$$d = \sqrt{(\cos\alpha - \cos\beta)^2 + (\sin\alpha - \sin\beta)^2}$$
$$= \sqrt{\cos^2\alpha - 2\cos\alpha\cos\beta + \cos^2\beta + \sin^2\alpha - 2\sin\alpha\sin\beta + \sin^2\beta}$$
$$= \sqrt{2 - 2(\cos\alpha\cos\beta + \sin\alpha\sin\beta)}.$$

By recalling (4–18), the expression for the length of any chord whose subtending angle is θ in the unit circle, we have another expression for d. Since d represents the length of the chord whose subtending angle is γ, where $\gamma = (\alpha - \beta) \pm$ (some integral multiple of 360°),

$$d = \sqrt{2 - 2\cos\gamma}$$
$$= \sqrt{2 - 2\cos(\alpha - \beta)}.$$

Upon equating these two expressions for d and simplifying, we see that

$$\cos(\alpha - \beta) \equiv \cos\alpha\cos\beta + \sin\alpha\sin\beta, \qquad (4\text{–}21)$$

which was to be proved. It should be emphasized that this formula expresses the cosine of $\alpha - \beta$ in terms of the functions of α and β themselves, and *holds for any value of α or β*. It is in this respect that the formula becomes important, as will be evident in the remaining articles in this chapter.

4–8 Special reduction formulas. As is probably somewhat evident by this time, any circular function of any angle can be expressed as a function of an angle between zero and $\pi/4$. This is shown by using certain reduction formulas derived from (4–21) with special values for α or β.

If we replace α by $90°$ in (4–21), we obtain

$$\cos (90° - \beta) \equiv \cos 90° \cos \beta + \sin 90° \sin \beta.$$

Since $\cos 90° = 0$ and $\sin 90° = 1$, we have

$$\boxed{\cos (90° - \beta) \equiv \sin \beta.} \qquad (4\text{–}22)$$

It should again be emphasized that relations such as (4–22) hold for all angles α or β, and the reader should observe this as the formulas are derived. If in (4–22) we replace β by $90° - \beta$, the relation

$$\cos [90° - (90° - \beta)] \equiv \sin (90° - \beta)$$

holds for all β. Simplifying, we find

$$\boxed{\sin (90° - \beta) \equiv \cos \beta.} \qquad (4\text{–}23)$$

From (4–22) and (4–23), we immediately see that

$$\boxed{\tan (90° - \beta) \equiv \cot \beta,} \qquad (4\text{–}24)$$

and

$$\boxed{\cot (90° - \beta) \equiv \tan \beta.} \qquad (4\text{–}25)$$

Although true for all values, these four results are especially useful in the computation of functions for acute angles. For example,

$$\sin 56° = \cos 34°, \qquad \tan 81° = \cot 9°, \qquad \text{or} \quad \cos 72° = \sin 18°.$$

We have noticed that circular functions have names which can be paired. In each pair, one function is the cofunction of the other. The sine is the cofunction of the cosine, and the cosine is the cofunction of the sine, and so on. The four relations above can be stated: *The cofunction of any angle equals the function of the complementary angle.*

The relationship between the function of any angle and its negative is very useful, and also follows from (4–21). Letting $\alpha = 0°$,

$$\cos (0° - \beta) \equiv \cos 0° \cos \beta + \sin 0° \sin \beta.$$

Since $\cos 0° = 1$ and $\sin 0° = 0$,

$$\boxed{\cos (-\beta) \equiv \cos \beta.} \qquad (4\text{–}26)$$

Also, if we replace β by $-\beta$ in (4–22),

$$\cos (90° + \beta) \equiv \sin (-\beta).$$

Since $90° + \beta = \beta - (-90°)$,

$$\begin{aligned} \sin (-\beta) &\equiv \cos [\beta - (-90°)] \\ &\equiv \cos \beta \cos (-90°) + \sin \beta \sin (-90°) \\ &\equiv (\cos \beta)(0) + (\sin \beta)(-1), \end{aligned}$$

or

$$\boxed{\sin (-\beta) \equiv -\sin \beta.} \qquad (4\text{–}27)$$

It follows directly from (4–26) and (4–27) that

$$\tan (-\beta) \equiv -\tan \beta. \qquad (4\text{–}28)$$

Example: $\sin (-15°) = -\sin 15°$, and $\tan (-176°) = -\tan 176°$, but $\cos (-279°) = \cos 279°$. Note the significance of (4–26) and (4–27) in Fig. 4–16.

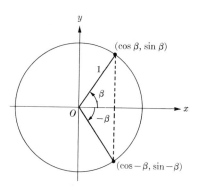

FIGURE 4–16

4-9 General addition formulas. We shall now derive the general formulas for the sine, cosine, and tangent of the sum or difference of two angles. Since

$$\begin{aligned} \cos (\alpha + \beta) &\equiv \cos [\alpha - (-\beta)] \\ &\equiv \cos \alpha \cos (-\beta) + \sin \alpha \sin (-\beta), \end{aligned}$$

we have

$$\cos{(\alpha + \beta)} \equiv \cos{\alpha} \cos{\beta} - \sin{\alpha} \sin{\beta}. \qquad (4\text{--}29)$$

Also,

$$\sin{(\alpha + \beta)} \equiv \cos{[90° - (\alpha + \beta)]}$$
$$\equiv \cos{[(90° - \alpha) - \beta]}$$
$$\equiv \cos{(90° - \alpha)} \cos{\beta} + \sin{(90° - \alpha)} \sin{\beta},$$

and we have

$$\sin{(\alpha + \beta)} \equiv \sin{\alpha} \cos{\beta} + \cos{\alpha} \sin{\beta}. \qquad (4\text{--}30)$$

Replacing β by $-\beta$ in (4–30), we immediately find

$$\sin{(\alpha - \beta)} \equiv \sin{\alpha} \cos{\beta} - \cos{\alpha} \sin{\beta}. \qquad (4\text{--}31)$$

The tangent formulas,

$$\tan{(\alpha + \beta)} \equiv \frac{\tan{\alpha} + \tan{\beta}}{1 - \tan{\alpha} \tan{\beta}} \qquad (4\text{--}32)$$

and

$$\tan{(\alpha - \beta)} \equiv \frac{\tan{\alpha} - \tan{\beta}}{1 + \tan{\alpha} \tan{\beta}}, \qquad (4\text{--}33)$$

result from the fact that $\tan{\theta} \equiv \sin{\theta}/\cos{\theta}$.

By using (4–29) and (4–30), we have

$$\tan{(\alpha + \beta)} \equiv \frac{\sin{(\alpha + \beta)}}{\cos{(\alpha + \beta)}}$$

$$\equiv \frac{\sin{\alpha} \cos{\beta} + \cos{\alpha} \sin{\beta}}{\cos{\alpha} \cos{\beta} - \sin{\alpha} \sin{\beta}}$$

$$\equiv \frac{\dfrac{\sin{\alpha} \cos{\beta}}{\cos{\alpha} \cos{\beta}} + \dfrac{\cos{\alpha} \sin{\beta}}{\cos{\alpha} \cos{\beta}}}{\dfrac{\cos{\alpha} \cos{\beta}}{\cos{\alpha} \cos{\beta}} - \dfrac{\sin{\alpha} \sin{\beta}}{\cos{\alpha} \cos{\beta}}}$$

$$\equiv \frac{\tan{\alpha} + \tan{\beta}}{1 - \tan{\alpha} \tan{\beta}}.$$

Formula (4–33) may be derived in a similar way, or by using (4–28).

EXAMPLE 1. Compute $\sin 7\pi/12$ from the functions of $\pi/3$ and $\pi/4$.

Solution. $\sin 7\pi/12 = \sin (\pi/3 + \pi/4)$

$$= \sin \pi/3 \cos \pi/4 + \cos \pi/3 \sin \pi/4$$
$$= \sqrt{3}/2 \cdot \sqrt{2}/2 + \tfrac{1}{2} \cdot \sqrt{2}/2$$
$$= \sqrt{6}/4 + \sqrt{2}/4 = (\sqrt{6} + \sqrt{2})/4.$$

EXAMPLE 2. Compute $\cos 15°$.

Solution. $\cos 15° = \cos (60° - 45°)$

$$= \cos 60° \cos 45° + \sin 60° \sin 45°$$
$$= \tfrac{1}{2} \cdot \sqrt{2}/2 + \sqrt{3}/2 \cdot \sqrt{2}/2$$
$$= \sqrt{2}/4 + \sqrt{6}/4 = (\sqrt{2} + \sqrt{6})/4.$$

EXAMPLE 3. Consider $\sin \alpha = \tfrac{12}{13}$, with α in the first quadrant, and $\cos \beta = \tfrac{3}{5}$, with β in the first quadrant. In what quadrant does $\alpha + \beta$ lie?

Solution. Since α and β are both in the first quadrant, $\alpha + \beta$ is either in the first or second quadrant. Since the cosine is positive in the first and negative in the second, it will suffice to find $\cos (\alpha + \beta)$. We are able to find $\cos \alpha$ and $\sin \beta$ as in Article 4–2: $\cos \alpha = \tfrac{5}{13}$ and $\sin \beta = \tfrac{4}{5}$. Thus,

$$\cos (\alpha + \beta) = \cos \alpha \cos \beta - \sin \alpha \sin \beta$$
$$= \tfrac{5}{13} \cdot \tfrac{3}{5} - \tfrac{12}{13} \cdot \tfrac{4}{5}$$
$$= \tfrac{15}{65} - \tfrac{48}{65} = -\tfrac{33}{65}.$$

Since $\cos (\alpha + \beta)$ is negative, it follows that $\alpha + \beta$ is in the second quadrant.

EXAMPLE 4. Show that $\sin (270° - \theta) \equiv -\cos \theta$.

Solution. In (4–31) let $\alpha = 270°$ and $\beta = \theta$. Therefore,

$$\sin (270° - \theta) \equiv \sin 270° \cos \theta - \cos 270° \sin \theta$$
$$\equiv (-1) \cos \theta - (0) \sin \theta$$
$$\equiv -\cos \theta.$$

EXAMPLE 5. Express $3 \sin \theta + 4 \cos \theta$ in the form $k \sin (\theta + \theta_1)$, where θ_1 is in the first quadrant.

Solution. By multiplying and dividing the expression by $\sqrt{3^2 + 4^2} = 5$, we have

$$5(\tfrac{3}{5} \sin \theta + \tfrac{4}{5} \cos \theta) \equiv 5(\sin \theta \cdot \tfrac{3}{5} + \cos \theta \cdot \tfrac{4}{5}).$$

Letting $\cos \theta_1 = \frac{3}{5}$, we find that $\sin \theta_1 = \frac{4}{5}$; thus the above expression becomes

$$5(\tfrac{3}{5} \sin \theta + \tfrac{4}{5} \cos \theta) \equiv 5 \sin (\theta + \theta_1),$$

where θ_1 has its sine equal to $\frac{4}{5}$ and its cosine equal to $\frac{3}{5}$.

PROBLEMS

1. Find the exact value of the sine, cosine, and tangent of $5\pi/12 = 75°$ by setting $\alpha = 45°$ and $\beta = 30°$ in one of the formulas previously derived.

2. Find the exact value of $\sin 15°$ and $\tan 15°$ by taking $15° = 60° - 45°$.

3. Find the exact value of $\cos 7\pi/12$ and $\tan 7\pi/12$, as done in Example 1.

4. Find the exact values of the sine, cosine, and tangent of $11\pi/12 = 165°$ by setting $\alpha = 3\pi/4$ and $\beta = \pi/6$.

It is interesting to note that with the results of Problems 1–4 and previously known results, the exact values of the circular functions of any integral multiple of $\pi/12$ have been or can be readily found.

5. If $\sin \alpha = \frac{4}{5}$, $\sin \beta = \frac{12}{13}$, and both α and β are in the first quadrant, find

(a) $\sin (\alpha + \beta)$,   (b) $\cos (\alpha + \beta)$,   (c) $\tan (\alpha + \beta)$,
(d) $\sin (\alpha - \beta)$,   (e) $\cos (\alpha - \beta)$,   (f) $\tan (\alpha - \beta)$.

6. If $\cos \alpha = -\frac{24}{25}$, $\tan \beta = \frac{9}{40}$, α is in the second quadrant, and β is in the third quadrant, find

(a) $\sin (\alpha + \beta)$,   (b) $\cos (\alpha + \beta)$,   (c) $\tan (\alpha + \beta)$,
(d) $\sin (\alpha - \beta)$,   (e) $\cos (\alpha - \beta)$,   (f) $\tan (\alpha - \beta)$.

7. (a) In what quadrant is $\alpha + \beta$ in Problem 5? (b) In what quadrant is $\alpha - \beta$ in Problem 6?

Find $\sin (\alpha + \beta)$ and $\cos (\alpha + \beta)$, given that:

8. $\tan \alpha = \frac{3}{4}$, $\sec \beta = \frac{13}{5}$, and neither α nor β is in the first quadrant.

9. $\tan \alpha = -\frac{15}{8}$, $\sin \beta = -\frac{7}{25}$, and neither α nor β is in the fourth quadrant.

Express each of the following in terms of functions of θ only:

10. $\cos (\pi/4 + \theta)$ 11. $\tan (\theta + \pi/6)$ 12. $\sec (\theta - 45°)$
13. $\cot (\pi/4 + \theta)$ 14. $\sin (\theta + 60°)$ 15. $\csc (\theta - 30°)$
16. $\cos (\pi/6 - \theta)$ 17. $\sin (\theta - 45°)$

Show that the following statements are true:

18. $\tan (\theta + \pi/4) - \tan (\theta - 3\pi/4) \equiv 0$.

19. $\sin (\theta - \pi/6) + \cos (\theta - \pi/3) \equiv \sqrt{3} \sin \theta$.

20. $\cot (\alpha + \beta) \equiv \dfrac{\cot \alpha \cot \beta - 1}{\cot \alpha + \cot \beta}$.

21. $\tan (\theta + \pi/4) \equiv (1 + \tan \theta)/(1 - \tan \theta)$.

22. $\sin (\alpha + \beta)/\cos \alpha \cos \beta \equiv \tan \alpha + \tan \beta$.

*23. (a) $\sin (\alpha + \beta) + \sin (\alpha - \beta) \equiv 2 \sin \alpha \cos \beta$,
     (b) $\sin (\alpha + \beta) - \sin (\alpha - \beta) \equiv 2 \cos \alpha \sin \beta$.

24. (a) $\cos (\alpha + \beta) + \cos (\alpha - \beta) \equiv 2 \cos \alpha \cos \beta$,

    (b) $\cos (\alpha + \beta) - \cos (\alpha - \beta) \equiv -2 \sin \alpha \sin \beta$.

*25. By letting $\alpha + \beta = x$, $\alpha - \beta = y$, and dividing the respective members of Problems 23(a) and (b), prove

$$\frac{\sin x - \sin y}{\sin x + \sin y} \equiv \frac{\tan \frac{1}{2} (x - y)}{\tan \frac{1}{2} (x + y)}.$$

Show that the following relations are true.

26. (a) $\sin (\alpha + \beta) \sin (\alpha - \beta) \equiv \sin^2 \alpha - \sin^2 \beta$,

    (b) $\cos (\alpha + \beta) \cos (\alpha - \beta) \equiv \cos^2 \alpha - \sin^2 \beta$.

27. $\cos (\alpha + \beta) \cos \beta + \sin (\alpha + \beta) \sin \beta \equiv \cos \alpha$.

28. $\sin (\alpha - \beta) \cos \beta + \cos (\alpha - \beta) \sin \beta \equiv \sin \alpha$.

Express the following in the form $k \sin (\theta + \theta_1)$, where θ_1 is between $-\pi/2$ and $\pi/2$.

29. $5 \sin \theta + 12 \cos \theta$ 30. $15 \sin \theta + 8 \cos \theta$

31. $4 \sin \theta - 3 \cos \theta$ 32. $24 \sin \theta + 7 \cos \theta$

33. $\sin \theta + \cos \theta$ 34. $2 \sin \theta - 5 \cos \theta$

4–10 General reduction formulas. It is often necessary to express the circular functions of a given angle in terms of functions of an acute angle. We are able to do this by using reduction formulas obtained from (4–21). If we wish to reduce an angle by multiples of 90°, in order to work with the acute angle, we can recall (Problem 9, Article 4–3) that

$$\sin (2k \cdot 90°) = 0 \quad \text{and} \quad \cos (2k \cdot 90°) = (-1)^k$$

for any integer k (positive, negative, or zero). Since

$$\sin (2k \cdot 90° + \beta) \equiv \sin (2k \cdot 90°) \cos \beta + \cos (2k \cdot 90°) \sin \beta,$$

we have

$$\sin (2k \cdot 90° + \beta) \equiv (-1)^k \sin \beta, \qquad (4\text{–}34)$$

and similarly,

$$\cos (2k \cdot 90° + \beta) \equiv (-1)^k \cos \beta. \qquad (4\text{–}35)$$

These two relationships are for β increased or decreased by even multiples of 90°. The function is not changed, although the sign may be. For odd multiples of 90°, the function is changed to its cofunction, and again the sign may also change, for

$$\sin [(2k + 1) 90° + \beta]$$
$$\equiv \sin [90° + (2k \cdot 90° + \beta)]$$
$$\equiv \sin 90° \cos (2k \cdot 90° + \beta) + \cos 90° \sin (2k \cdot 90° + \beta)$$
$$\equiv \cos (2k \cdot 90° + \beta),$$

and therefore, by (4–35),

$$\sin [(2k + 1)\, 90° + \beta] \equiv (-1)^k \cos \beta. \qquad (4\text{–}36)$$

Moreover,

$$\cos [(2k + 1)\, 90° + \beta]$$
$$\equiv \cos [90° + (2k \cdot 90° + \beta)]$$
$$\equiv \cos 90° \cos (2k \cdot 90° + \beta) - \sin 90° \sin (2k \cdot 90° + \beta)$$
$$\equiv -\,(-1)^k \sin \beta,$$

and thus,

$$\cos [(2k + 1)\, 90° + \beta] \equiv (-1)^{k+1} \sin \beta. \qquad (4\text{–}37)$$

The special case of (4–34) and (4–35), where k has the value 2, is important, since

$$\sin (\beta + 2\pi) \equiv \sin \beta \qquad (4\text{–}38)$$

and

$$\cos (\beta + 2\pi) \equiv \cos \beta. \qquad (4\text{–}39)$$

It was for this reason that these functions were called *periodic functions*, with periods of 2π. Recall Eqs. (4–5) and (4–6).

EXAMPLE 1. Express $\sin 624°$ as a function of a positive acute angle less than 45°.

Solution. Since $624° = 6 \cdot 90° + 84°$, by using (4–34) we have $\sin 624° = -\sin 84°$. From (4–22), $-\sin 84° = -\cos 6°$, and we have $\sin 624° = -\cos 6°$.

EXAMPLE 2. Express $\cos 1243°$ as a function of a positive acute angle less than 45°.

Solution. Again $1243° = 13 \cdot 90° + 73°$. Thus, using (4–37), $\cos 1243° = -\sin 73°$, and by (4–22), we have $\cos 1243° = -\cos 17°$.

EXAMPLE 3. Repeat Examples 1 and 2 for $\cos (-497°)$.

Solution. Since $-497° = -5 \cdot 90° - 47°$, we have $\cos (-497°) = -\sin 47° = -\cos 43°$.

Now that the procedure is familiar to us, we should be able to write the answer without the use of formulas (4–34) through (4–37). Draw a figure, choose the sign of the function value to be simplified, depending upon the quadrant, and with this sign write the corresponding acute angle. In considering Example 1, since $624°$ is in the third quadrant, $\sin 624°$ is negative, and the corresponding acute angle is 84°. Thus $\sin 624° = -\sin 84°$.

Problems

Express each of the following as a function of a positive acute angle less than 45°:

1. sin 196°
2. cos 147°
3. sin 319°
4. cos 254°
5. tan 294°
6. cos 728°
7. sin (−625°)
8. cos (−435°)
9. tan 1004°
10. sin 248°25′
11. cos 106°18′
12. tan 163°17′
13. cos 204°46′
14. tan 136°34′
15. sin 156°39′

By using (4–21), or (4–29) through (4–33), show that each of the following statements is true. Check those involving sines or cosines by (4–34) through (4–37).

16. $\sin (180° + \theta) \equiv -\sin \theta$
17. $\cos (180° + \theta) \equiv -\cos \theta$
18. $\sin (180° - \theta) \equiv \sin \theta$
19. $\cos (180° - \theta) \equiv -\cos \theta$
20. $\tan (270° - \theta) \equiv \cot \theta$
21. $\cos (\theta - 180°) \equiv -\cos \theta$
22. $\cos (270° + \theta) \equiv \sin \theta$
23. $\sin (\theta + 270°) \equiv -\cos \theta$
24. $\tan (180° + \theta) \equiv \tan \theta$
25. $\cos (360° - \theta) \equiv \cos \theta$
26. $\sin (360° - \theta) \equiv -\sin \theta$

27. In Problem 24 we showed that $\tan (\theta + \pi) \equiv \tan \theta$. This was proved as a special case of (4–7), with $k = 1$. What is the period of $\tan \theta$?

28. What are the periods of the cotangent, secant, and cosecant functions?

4–11 General identities. We have emphasized throughout that the general identities

$$\sin (\alpha \pm \beta) \equiv \sin \alpha \cos \beta \pm \cos \alpha \sin \beta, \qquad (4\text{–}40)$$

$$\cos (\alpha \pm \beta) \equiv \cos \alpha \cos \beta \mp \sin \alpha \sin \beta, \qquad (4\text{–}41)$$

$$\tan (\alpha \pm \beta) \equiv \frac{\tan \alpha \pm \tan \beta}{1 \mp \tan \alpha \tan \beta} \qquad (4\text{–}42)$$

were proved for all angles. As the fundamental identities were used to prove the simple identities (Article 4–6), so these can be used to prove other identities, several of which appear in the next list of problems. Also, they are used to obtain the important double- and half-angle identities. Since Eqs. (4–40) through (4–42) are true for any α and β, letting $\alpha = \beta$, we immediately have

$$\sin 2\alpha \equiv \sin (\alpha + \alpha)$$
$$\equiv \sin \alpha \cos \alpha + \cos \alpha \sin \alpha,$$

or

$$\boxed{\sin 2\alpha \equiv 2 \sin \alpha \cos \alpha.} \qquad (4\text{–}43)$$

Also,
$$\cos (\alpha + \alpha) \equiv \cos \alpha \cos \alpha - \sin \alpha \sin \alpha,$$
or

$$\cos 2\alpha \equiv \cos^2 \alpha - \sin^2 \alpha \qquad (4\text{--}44)$$
$$\equiv 1 - 2 \sin^2 \alpha \qquad (\text{Why?}) \qquad (4\text{--}45)$$
$$\equiv 2 \cos^2 \alpha - 1. \qquad (\text{Why?}) \qquad (4\text{--}46)$$

Moreover,
$$\tan (\alpha + \alpha) \equiv \frac{\tan \alpha + \tan \alpha}{1 - \tan \alpha \tan \alpha},$$
or

$$\tan 2\alpha \equiv \frac{2 \tan \alpha}{1 - \tan^2 \alpha}. \qquad (4\text{--}47)$$

The half-angle identities are also readily established. If we use (4–45) with $2\alpha = \theta$, or $\alpha = \theta/2$,

$$\cos \theta \equiv 1 - 2 \sin^2 \frac{\theta}{2}.$$

Solving for $\sin \theta/2$, we have

$$2 \sin^2 \frac{\theta}{2} \equiv 1 - \cos \theta, \qquad (4\text{--}48)$$

so that

$$\sin \frac{\theta}{2} \equiv \pm \sqrt{\frac{1 - \cos \theta}{2}}, \qquad (4\text{--}49)$$

where the choice of the sign before the radical is determined by the quadrant in which $\theta/2$ lies. Similarly, if we use (4–46) with the same substitution $\alpha = \theta/2$,

$$\cos \theta \equiv 2 \cos^2 \frac{\theta}{2} - 1,$$

and solving for $\cos \theta/2$, we get

$$2 \cos^2 \frac{\theta}{2} \equiv 1 + \cos \theta, \qquad (4\text{--}50)$$

or

$$\cos \frac{\theta}{2} \equiv \pm \sqrt{\frac{1 + \cos \theta}{2}}, \qquad (4\text{--}51)$$

with the choice of the sign again depending on the location of $\theta/2$.

There are two identities for tan $\theta/2$, and these can be obtained by using (4–48) and (4–50). In the identity

$$\tan\frac{\theta}{2} \equiv \frac{\sin\theta/2}{\cos\theta/2},$$

by multiplying the numerator and denominator of the right member by $2\sin\theta/2$, we have

$$\tan\frac{\theta}{2} \equiv \frac{2\sin^2\theta/2}{2\sin\theta/2\cos\theta/2},$$

or

$$\tan\frac{\theta}{2} \equiv \frac{1-\cos\theta}{\sin\theta}. \qquad (4\text{--}52)$$

In the same expression, multiplying by $2\cos\theta/2$, we have

$$\tan\frac{\theta}{2} \equiv \frac{2\sin\theta/2\cos\theta/2}{2\cos^2\theta/2},$$

or

$$\tan\frac{\theta}{2} \equiv \frac{\sin\theta}{1+\cos\theta}. \qquad (4\text{--}53)$$

Some of the uses of the identities of this article will be more clearly understood by considering the following examples.

EXAMPLE 1. Compute the value of $\sin\pi/12$ and $\cos\pi/12$ from the functions of $\pi/6$.

Solution. We use (4–49) and obtain

$$\sin\frac{\pi}{12} = \sin\frac{1}{2}\cdot\frac{\pi}{6} = \sqrt{\frac{1-\cos\pi/6}{2}} = \sqrt{\frac{1-\sqrt{3}/2}{2}} = \frac{\sqrt{2-\sqrt{3}}}{2}.$$

Also, by (4–51),

$$\cos\frac{\pi}{12} = \cos\frac{1}{2}\cdot\frac{\pi}{6} = \sqrt{\frac{1+\cos\pi/6}{2}} = \sqrt{\frac{1+\sqrt{3}/2}{2}} = \frac{\sqrt{2+\sqrt{3}}}{2}.$$

Explain the difference between this result and that in Example 2, Article 4–9.

EXAMPLE 2. Express $\sin 2\theta$, $\cos 2\theta$, and $\tan 2\theta$ in terms of x if $x = \tan\theta$.

Solution. First let us find $\sin\theta$ and $\cos\theta$ in terms of x. Since

$$\sec\theta \equiv \pm\sqrt{1+\tan^2\theta} \equiv \pm\sqrt{1+x^2},$$

$$\cos\theta \equiv \pm\frac{1}{\sqrt{1+x^2}}.$$

Also,

$$\sin \theta \equiv \tan \theta \cos \theta \equiv \pm \frac{x}{\sqrt{1 + x^2}} \cdot$$

Therefore,

$$\sin 2\theta \equiv 2 \sin \theta \cos \theta \equiv \frac{2x}{1 + x^2} \cdot$$

A complete analysis, considering θ in the first, second, third, and fourth quadrants, is necessary to show that the sign in the above example is correct. In addition, we have

$$\cos 2\theta \equiv \cos^2 \theta - \sin^2 \theta \equiv \frac{1 - x^2}{1 + x^2}$$

and

$$\tan 2\theta \equiv \frac{2 \tan \theta}{1 - \tan^2 \theta} \equiv \frac{2x}{1 - x^2} \cdot$$

EXAMPLE 3. Reduce $\sin^4 \theta$ to an expression involving only functions of θ raised to the first power.

Solution. By (4–48), we have

$$\sin^2 \theta \equiv \frac{1 - \cos 2\theta}{2} \cdot$$

Thus we notice that by doubling the angle we have changed the exponent of the circular function from 2 to 1. Hence

$$\sin^4 \theta \equiv (\sin^2 \theta)^2 \equiv \frac{(1 - \cos 2\theta)^2}{4} \equiv \frac{1 - 2 \cos 2\theta + \cos^2 2\theta}{4},$$

and replacing

$$\cos^2 2\theta \text{ by } \frac{1 + \cos 4\theta}{2}$$

(why is this possible?), we obtain

$$\sin^4 \theta \equiv \frac{3 - 4 \cos 2\theta + \cos 4\theta}{8} \cdot$$

This type of transformation is extremely useful in calculus.

PROBLEMS

1. Verify the identities for $\sin 2\theta$ and $\tan 2\theta$ for the value $\theta = \pi/3$.
2. Use the double-angle identities to compute $\sin 4\pi/3$, $\cos 4\pi/3$, and $\tan 4\pi/3$ from the functions of $2\pi/3$.
3. Compute $\sin 7\pi/12$, $\cos 7\pi/12$, and $\tan 7\pi/12$ from the values of the functions of $7\pi/6$.

4. If $\sin\theta = \frac{3}{5}$ and θ is in the first quadrant, find the exact value of

(a) $\sin 2\theta$, (b) $\cos 2\theta$, (c) $\tan 2\theta$,
(d) $\sin\theta/2$, (e) $\cos\theta/2$, (f) $\tan\theta/2$.

5. If $\cos\theta = -\frac{5}{13}$ and θ is in the second quadrant, find the exact value of

(a) $\sin 2\theta$, (b) $\cos 2\theta$, (c) $\tan 2\theta$,
(d) $\sin\theta/2$, (e) $\cos\theta/2$, (f) $\tan\theta/2$.

6. Reduce $\sin^2\theta$ to an expression involving only circular functions of θ, raised to the first power.

7. Reduce $\cos^4\theta$ to an expression involving only circular functions of θ which are raised to the first power.

8. Derive identity (4–53) by using the identity $\sin\omega/2 \equiv \sin(\omega - \omega/2)$. [*Hint:* $\sin\omega/2 \equiv \sin\omega\cos\omega/2 - \cos\omega\sin\omega/2$ or $(1 + \cos\omega)\sin\omega/2 \equiv \sin\omega\cos\omega/2$.]

9. Derive identity (4–52) by using the identity

$$\cos\frac{\omega}{2} \equiv \cos\left(\omega - \frac{\omega}{2}\right).$$

10. Derive the identity

$$\tan\frac{\omega}{2} \equiv \pm\sqrt{\frac{1 - \cos\omega}{1 + \cos\omega}}.$$

11. Derive the identity $\tan\omega/2 \equiv \csc\omega - \cot\omega$.

Prove the following identities:

12. $\sin 3\theta \equiv 3\sin\theta - 4\sin^3\theta$

13. $\cos 3\theta \equiv 4\cos^3\theta - 3\cos\theta$

14. $\sin\frac{\theta}{2}\cos\frac{\theta}{2} \equiv \frac{\sin\theta}{2}$

15. $\frac{1 - \cos 2\theta}{\sin 2\theta} \equiv \tan\theta$

16. $\left(\cos\frac{\theta}{2} - \sin\frac{\theta}{2}\right)^2 \equiv 1 - \sin\theta$

17. $\csc 2\theta - \cot 2\theta \equiv \tan\theta$

18. $\csc 2\theta + \cot 2\theta \equiv \cot\theta$

19. $\tan 3\theta \equiv \frac{3\tan\theta - \tan^3\theta}{1 - 3\tan^2\theta}$

20. $\frac{\tan\theta/2 + \cot\theta/2}{\cot\theta/2 - \tan\theta/2} \equiv \sec\theta$

21. $\frac{\sin 2\theta}{\sin\theta} - \frac{\cos 2\theta}{\cos\theta} \equiv \sec\theta$

22. $\frac{\sin 3\theta}{\sin\theta} - \frac{\cos 3\theta}{\cos\theta} \equiv 2$

23. $\frac{\sin 3\theta}{\cos\theta} + \frac{\cos 3\theta}{\sin\theta} \equiv 2\cot 2\theta$

24. $\frac{2\tan\theta}{1 + \tan^2\theta} \equiv \sin 2\theta$

25. $\frac{\cot^2\theta - 1}{\csc^2\theta} \equiv \cos 2\theta$

26. In Fig. 4–17, A is the mid-point of an arc of the unit circle subtended by a central angle θ. Using this figure, where $\theta < \pi$, and (4–18), show that

$$\sin\frac{\theta}{2} \equiv \sqrt{\frac{1 - \cos\theta}{2}}.$$

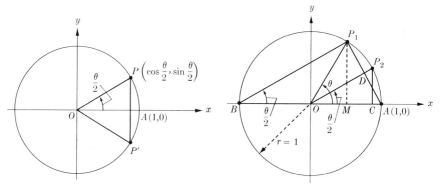

FIGURE 4–17   FIGURE 4–18

27. In the unit circle in Fig. 4–18, P_2 is the mid-point of the arc $\widehat{AP_1}$, cut by the central angle θ. BP_1 is drawn parallel to OP_2, so that $\angle P_1BA = \angle P_2OA = \theta/2$. (Why?)

(a) Verify that $BP_1 \equiv 2 \cos \theta/2$ and $P_1A = 2 \sin \theta/2$. [*Hint: $CP_2 = AD = P_1A/2$, and $OC = OD = BP_1/2$.*]

(b) Verify from the figure that $\sin \theta = 2 \sin \theta/2 \cos \theta/2$.

(c) Verify from the figure that

$$\sin \frac{\theta}{2} = \sqrt{\frac{1 - \cos \theta}{2}}.$$

(d) Verify from the figure that

$$\cos \frac{\theta}{2} = \sqrt{\frac{1 + \cos \theta}{2}}.$$

4–12 Conversions of sums and products. It is quite often necessary to convert a product of two circular functions into a sum of two functions, and vice versa. This can be done by using the identities (4–40) and (4–41). (The following identities are not as important as the previous ones in this chapter.) By adding the members of the two identities given by (4–40), we get

$$\sin (\alpha + \beta) + \sin (\alpha - \beta) \equiv 2 \sin \alpha \cos \beta,$$

or

$$\sin \alpha \cos \beta \equiv \tfrac{1}{2} [\sin (\alpha + \beta) + \sin (\alpha - \beta)]. \tag{4–54}$$

By subtracting the members of the two identities given in (4–40), we obtain

$$\cos \alpha \sin \beta \equiv \tfrac{1}{2} [\sin (\alpha + \beta) - \sin (\alpha - \beta)]. \tag{4–55}$$

Similarly, using (4–41), by adding and then subtracting, we obtain

$$\cos \alpha \cos \beta \equiv \tfrac{1}{2} [\cos (\alpha + \beta) + \cos (\alpha - \beta)], \tag{4–56}$$

$$\sin \alpha \sin \beta \equiv \tfrac{1}{2} [\cos (\alpha - \beta) - \cos (\alpha + \beta)]. \tag{4–57}$$

As an example, the product $\cos 6\theta \cos 3\theta$ may be represented as a sum. Using (4–56) with $\alpha = 6\theta$ and $\beta = 3\theta$, we have

$$\cos 6\theta \cos 3\theta \equiv \tfrac{1}{2}\,(\cos 9\theta + \cos 3\theta).$$

The same four identities can also be used for transforming a sum into a product. Such a transformation is useful when logarithms are to be used, for products are more readily calculated by logarithms than are sums. For convenience, we change the notation by letting $\alpha + \beta = \theta$ and $\alpha - \beta = \omega$. Solving these equations for α and β, we obtain $\alpha = (\theta + \omega)/2$, and $\beta = (\theta - \omega)/2$. Substituting these values in the above identities and simplifying, we obtain

$$\sin \theta + \sin \omega \equiv 2 \sin \frac{\theta + \omega}{2} \cos \frac{\theta - \omega}{2}, \qquad (4\text{–}58)$$

$$\sin \theta - \sin \omega \equiv 2 \cos \frac{\theta + \omega}{2} \sin \frac{\theta - \omega}{2}, \qquad (4\text{–}59)$$

$$\cos \theta + \cos \omega \equiv 2 \cos \frac{\theta + \omega}{2} \cos \frac{\theta - \omega}{2}, \qquad (4\text{–}60)$$

$$\cos \theta - \cos \omega \equiv -2 \sin \frac{\theta + \omega}{2} \sin \frac{\theta - \omega}{2}. \qquad (4\text{–}61)$$

EXAMPLE. Express $\sin \theta + \sin 3\theta + \sin 5\theta + \sin 7\theta$ as a product.

Solution. By grouping the first two and the last two terms and using (4–58), we get

$$\sin \theta + \sin 3\theta + \sin 5\theta + \sin 7\theta$$
$$\equiv 2 \sin \frac{\theta + 3\theta}{2} \cos \frac{\theta - 3\theta}{2} + 2 \sin \frac{5\theta + 7\theta}{2} \cos \frac{5\theta - 7\theta}{2}$$
$$\equiv 2 \sin 2\theta \cos (-\theta) + 2 \sin 6\theta \cos (-\theta)$$
$$\equiv 2 \cos \theta\,(\sin 2\theta + \sin 6\theta) \qquad \text{(Why?)}$$
$$\equiv 2 \cos \theta\,(2 \sin 4\theta \cos 2\theta) \qquad \text{(Why?)}$$
$$\equiv 4 \cos \theta \cos 2\theta \sin 4\theta.$$

PROBLEMS

Express each of the following products as a sum.

1. $\sin 3\theta \cos 5\theta$
2. $4 \cos \pi/3 \cos \pi/6$
3. $\cos 7\theta \sin 5\theta$
4. $6 \sin 2\pi/3 \sin \pi/3$
5. $\sin 5\theta \cos 2\theta$
6. $\cos 2\theta \cos 6\theta$
7. $\cos \theta \sin \theta/2$
8. $2 \sin 7\theta \sin 2\theta$

Express each of the following sums as products.

9. $\sin \pi/9 + \sin 2\pi/9$

10. $\cos 2\theta - \cos \theta$

11. $\cos 7\pi/9 + \cos 2\pi/9$

12. $\sin \pi/4 - \sin \pi/5$

13. $\sin 8\theta + \sin 4\theta$

14. $\cos 4\theta - \cos 8\theta$

15. $\sin 5\theta/3 - \sin 5\theta/6$

16. $\cos 6\theta + \cos 7\theta$

Prove the following identities:

17. $\dfrac{\sin 5\theta - \sin 3\theta}{\cos 5\theta + \cos 3\theta} \equiv \tan \theta$

18. $\dfrac{\cos 6\theta + \cos 4\theta}{\sin 6\theta - \sin 4\theta} \equiv \cot \theta$

19. $\dfrac{\sin 8\theta + \sin 2\theta}{\cos 8\theta + \cos 2\theta} \equiv \tan 5\theta$

20. $\dfrac{\sin 3\theta - \sin \theta}{\cos^2 \theta - \sin^2 \theta} \equiv 2 \sin \theta$

21. $\dfrac{\sin \alpha - \sin \beta}{\cos \alpha + \cos \beta} \equiv \tan \dfrac{\alpha - \beta}{2}$

22. $\dfrac{\sin \alpha - \sin \beta}{\sin \alpha + \sin \beta} \equiv \dfrac{\tan \frac{1}{2}(\alpha - \beta)}{\tan \frac{1}{2}(\alpha + \beta)}$

23. $\dfrac{\sin \theta + \sin 3\theta + \sin 5\theta}{\cos \theta + \cos 3\theta + \cos 5\theta} \equiv \tan 3\theta$

24. $\sin \left(\dfrac{\pi}{4} - \theta \right) \sin \left(\dfrac{\pi}{4} + \theta \right) \equiv \frac{1}{2} \cos 2\theta$

4–13 Function values of any angle. In several of the previous articles of this chapter we computed the values of the circular functions for certain angles. Considering $60° = \pi/3$ radians, we found $\cos 60° = 0.5000$, an exact decimal value, while $\sin 60° = \sqrt{3}/2$ and $\tan 60° = \sqrt{3}$ could be approximated as decimal values to whatever accuracy we wished. Such approximations to exact values, expressed in radicals, can be obtained only in special cases.

To find the values of the functions for any given angle, we might draw the angle in standard position with the use of a protractor. By measuring the x- and y-coordinates of the point p, where the terminal side of the angle intersects the unit circle, we could find approximate values for the sine and cosine functions. Because of inaccuracies in drawing and measuring, such a method has definite limitations. The usual method for finding the values of the functions to a good degree of accuracy is based on calculus and is beyond the scope of this book.

We are able to find exact values of the functions for angles of any integral multiple of 3°, however, by a completely elementary process. Although this method is *not* an efficient way of obtaining the values for a table, it has sufficient mathematical interest to warrant this brief discussion. By combining the exact values of the functions for $\theta = 30°, 36°, 45°, 60°,$ and $90°$ (which we have already found) and using some of the relations of Article 4–9, we obtain our results.

Let us find exact values for $\sin 3°$ and $\cos 3°$. By applying the values found for $\cos 36°$ (Article 4–5) to Eqs. (4–49) and (4–50), we have

$$\sin 18° = \sqrt{\frac{1 - \cos 36°}{2}} = \sqrt{\frac{3 - \sqrt{5}}{8}} ,$$

and

$$\cos 18° = \sqrt{\frac{1 + \cos 36°}{2}} = \sqrt{\frac{5 + \sqrt{5}}{8}} .$$

Also, from Example 2 and Problem 2, Article 4–9, we have

$$\sin 15° = \frac{\sqrt{6} - \sqrt{2}}{4} ,$$

and

$$\cos 15° = \frac{\sqrt{6} + \sqrt{2}}{4} .$$

Since $18° - 15° = 3°$, we have, by using (4–31),

$$\begin{aligned}
\sin 3° &= \sin (18° - 15°) \\
&= \sin 18° \cos 15° - \cos 18° \sin 15° \\
&= \sqrt{\frac{3 - \sqrt{5}}{8}} \frac{\sqrt{6} + \sqrt{2}}{4} - \sqrt{\frac{5 + \sqrt{5}}{8}} \frac{\sqrt{6} - \sqrt{2}}{4} \\
&= \sqrt{\frac{(3 - \sqrt{5})(8 + 4\sqrt{3})}{128}} - \sqrt{\frac{(5 + \sqrt{5})(8 - 4\sqrt{3})}{128}} ,
\end{aligned}$$

so that

$$\sin 3° = \frac{\sqrt{12 - 2\sqrt{15} - 4\sqrt{5} + 6\sqrt{3}} - \sqrt{20 - 2\sqrt{15} + 4\sqrt{5} - 10\sqrt{3}}}{8} .$$

$$(4\text{--}62)$$

In a similar way, using (4–21), we obtain

$$\cos 3° = \frac{\sqrt{20 + 2\sqrt{15} + 4\sqrt{5} + 10\sqrt{3}} + \sqrt{12 + 2\sqrt{15} - 4\sqrt{5} - 6\sqrt{3}}}{8} .$$

$$(4\text{--}63)$$

The values of the other functions can be found from these exact values. Of course, approximated decimal values can also be obtained to any degree of accuracy desired, but the actual computation is long.

The functions of other angles could be handled similarly. For example, $6° = 36° - 30°$, $9° = 45° - 36°$, $12° = 30° - 18°$, and so on. The purpose of this discussion has been to demonstrate how a workable table *could be* constructed by a completely elementary process.

It is also interesting to note, although the proof will not be given, that the same angles, the angles of n degrees, with n an integral multiple of 3, are exactly those which are constructible with ruler and compass.

The more common angles are included in tables of trigonometric functions, which we can use either to find the approximate value of the functions of a given angle or to find the angle when the value of some function of that angle is given. Table I, at the back of the book, lists the values, approximated to four decimal places, of the sine, cosine, tangent, and cotangent of angles at 10′ intervals in the first quadrant. From the values of the functions for these angles, given in both degree and radian measure, it is possible to find the functions of angles of any size.

Since the circular function of any angle is the same as the cofunction of the complementary angle, Table I is constructed so that angles of 0° to 45° are at the left, while angles from 45° to 90° are at the right. Moreover, the circular functions listed at the top go with the angles at the left, while those at the bottom go with the angles at the right.

For example, opposite 24°10′ and in the column under sine, we find 0.4094, which is sin 24°10′. The value for sin 68°20′ is 0.9293, which we find in the column above sine, since 68°20′ is given at the right.

By assuming that the graph of the circular functions approximates a straight line, we may use the method of *linear interpolation* to find the circular functions of other angles. (This method is discussed generally in Chapter 11.) If x and $x + 10$ are consecutive angles in the table, measured in minutes, and if r is an integer between 0 and 10, we may approximate sin $(x + r)$ by interpolating by proportion:

$$\sin (x + r) = \sin x + \frac{r}{10} [\sin (x + 10) - \sin x]. \qquad (4\text{--}64)$$

The other functions are found by similar formulas.

EXAMPLE 1. Find sin 24°16′.

Solution. Since the angle 24°16′ lies between 24°10′ and 24°20′,

$$\begin{aligned}
\sin 24°16′ &= \sin 24°10′ + \tfrac{6}{10} [\sin 24°20′ - \sin 24°10′] \\
&= 0.4094 + \tfrac{6}{10} (0.4120 - 0.4094) \\
&= 0.4094 + 0.0016 \\
&= 0.4110.
\end{aligned}$$

EXAMPLE 2. Find cos 57°42′.

Solution. With 57°42′ between 57°40′ and 57°50′, we have

$$\begin{aligned}
\cos 57°42′ &= \cos 57°40′ + \tfrac{2}{10} [\cos 57°50′ - \cos 57°40′] \\
&= 0.5348 + \tfrac{2}{10} (0.5324 - 0.5348) \\
&= 0.5348 - 0.0005 \\
&= 0.5343.
\end{aligned}$$

Table I may also be used to find the angle between 0° and 90° if the value of a circular function is given. For example, if tan $\theta = 0.9435$, by looking in the tangent column we find the entry 0.9435 opposite 43°20′, and thus $\theta = 43°20′$.

The table may also be interpolated to find an angle, approximated to the nearest minute, when the value of a function of this angle lies between two entries in the table. If sin θ is given, we find two consecutive entries in the sine column between which the given value lies. Thus, letting $\theta = x + r$, where r is some integer between 0 and 10, and x and $x + 10$ are the consecutive entries in the table, we find r by using the approximation

$$\frac{r}{10} = \frac{\sin (x + r) - \sin x}{\sin (x + 10) - \sin x}. \qquad (4\text{--}65)$$

Other functions follow the same pattern.

EXAMPLE 3. Find the angle θ between 0° and 90° if sin $\theta = 0.6231$.

Solution. We locate 0.6231 in the sine column between sin 38°30′ = 0.6225 and sin 38°40′ = 0.6248. Thus,

$$\frac{r}{10} = \frac{0.6231 - 0.6225}{0.6248 - 0.6225},$$

or

$$r = 10 \left(\frac{0.0006}{0.0023}\right) = 3,$$

so that $\theta = 38°33′$, approximated to the nearest minute.

EXAMPLE 4. Find the angle θ if cos $\theta = 0.5741$.

Solution. We find cos 54°50′ = 0.5760, and cos 55° = 0.5736. Therefore,

$$\frac{r}{10} = \frac{0.5741 - 0.5760}{0.5736 - 0.5760},$$

so that

$$r = 10 \left(\frac{0.0019}{0.0024}\right) = 8,$$

and our result is $\theta = 54°58′$.

If the angle is larger than 90°, the reduction formulas of Article 4–10 must be used. Moreover, it should be clear that other angles greater than 90° satisfy the conditions of Examples 3 and 4. The finding of such angles is discussed in Chapters 5 and 13.

PROBLEMS

1. Establish (4–63) of this section.

2. Express 21°, 24°, and 27° by using combinations similar to those above that might be used to find the sines or cosines of such values.

3. Do the same for 33°, 39°, and 42°.

4. If you have access to a computing machine, find the decimal approximation for sin 3° and cos 3°, using (4–62) and (4–63). Check your results with the values given in Table I.

5. Find the value of each of the following by using Table I:

(a) sin 14°20′,   (b) tan 52°40′,
(c) cos 28°50′,   (d) sin 63°30′,
(e) tan 21°10′,   (f) cos 72°20′,
(g) sin 115°30′,   (h) cos 161°10′.

6. Find the approximate value of each of the following by using Table I and interpolation:

(a) sin 72°43′,   (b) cos 28°46′,
(c) tan 51°29′,   (d) cos 63°23′,
(e) tan 39°18′,   (f) sin 128°36′,
(g) cos 153°17′,   (h) sin 8°9′.

7. Find the angle θ between 0° and 90° using Table I if:

(a) sin θ = 0.4253,   (b) tan θ = 1.1237,
(c) cos θ = 0.8857,   (d) sin θ = 0.8450,
(e) tan θ = 0.2156,   (f) cos θ = 0.2447,
(g) sin θ = 0.3475,   (h) cos θ = 0.7844.

8. Find the approximate value between 0° and 90° of θ to the nearest minute, by using Table I and interpolation, if:

(a) tan θ = 0.8172,   (b) sin θ = 0.5331,
(c) cos θ = 0.2717,   (d) cos θ = 0.9392,
(e) sin θ = 0.7531,   (f) tan θ = 0.8083,
(g) cos θ = 0.5386,   (h) sin θ = 0.9648.

CHAPTER 5

LINEAR FUNCTIONS

5–1 The zero of the linear function. The circular functions considered in Chapter 4 were not defined by algebraic expressions but rather by rule and, in fact, cannot be expressed algebraically. Probably the simplest function defined in mathematics by means of a nontrivial algebraic expression is the function

$$f(x) = mx + b, \qquad (5\text{–}1)$$

where m and b are constants. This function of the first degree in x is called a *linear function*, since the graph of $y = f(x) = mx + b$ is a straight line. Moreover, any straight line other than $x = k$ (a straight line parallel to the y-axis) can be represented by such an equation with the appropriate m and b. These statements will be proved in Article 5–3. Here we shall concern ourselves with the linear function's algebraic properties and its zero, rather than its geometric properties.

We recall (Article 3–7) that a zero of a function is an x-coordinate or x-value for which y, the value of the function, is zero. Hence we let $y = 0$, and we can then find the zero of a linear function by solving the equation $mx + b = 0$ for x. In general, the zeros of a function are the *roots* or *solutions* of the equation $f(x) = 0$. Before considering the solving of such a linear equation specifically, let us consider the problems involved in the solving of any equation.

Various methods can be used in solving equations. Any device that produces an *equivalent equation*, one which has the same roots, and only those roots, is permitted. Some procedures, such as squaring, may introduce new factors, and some, such as dividing, may lose some factors, so that extreme care should be exercised in using such procedures. Furthermore, it is always wise to check any purported solution, for the ultimate test of a number as a root of any equation is not how it is obtained, but whether it satisfies the equation. The following operations are called *permissible*, since they always result in a new equivalent equation.

1. The same number or algebraic expression may be added to or subtracted from both members of an equation.

2. Both members of an equation may be multiplied or divided by any nonzero number not involving the variable.

ILLUSTRATION 1. In the solving of $4x - 5 = x + 7$, 5 is added and x is subtracted from both members, giving $3x = 12$. Then, division by 3 yields $x = 4$.

It should be clear that any permissible operation is reversible.

In addition to the permissible operations mentioned, an operation such as squaring both members of an equation is sometimes used. This device, however, is not reversible. Although no root of the original equation will be lost by the process, certain values may be introduced which are roots of the new equation, but not of the original one. If this type of operation is employed, the roots of the final equation *must* be examined to determine whether they are roots of the original equation.

ILLUSTRATION 2. If in the equation $x - 1 = 3$, which has the root $x = 4$, both members are squared, $(x - 1)^2 = 9$. This process has introduced for x the additional value -2, which does not satisfy the original equation.*

ILLUSTRATION 3. In solving the equation $\sin^2 \theta - \frac{1}{2} \sin \theta = 0$ for values of θ between 0 and $\pi/2$, we find $\sin \theta = 0$ or $\frac{1}{2}$ and $\theta = 0$ or $\pi/6$. If we were to divide both members by $\sin \theta$, however, we would have only the value $\sin \theta = \frac{1}{2}$. The value $\sin \theta = 0$ would have been "lost."†

EXAMPLE 1. Solve the equation $\dfrac{2x + 5}{2} - \dfrac{5x}{x - 1} = x$ for all possible values of x.

Solution. We first clear the equation of fractions by multiplying by the L.C.D., $2(x - 1)$.

$$(2x + 5)(x - 1) - (5x)(2) = (x)(2)(x - 1),$$

or

$$2x^2 + 3x - 5 - 10x = 2x^2 - 2x.$$

Combining similar terms, we have

$$-7x - 5 = -2x.$$

Adding $2x + 5$ to both members,

$$-5x = 5,$$

and dividing by -5, we get

$$x = -1.$$

This result should be verified by substituting $x = -1$ in the original equation.

———————

* An equation which, because of some mathematical process, has acquired an extra root is sometimes called a *redundant equation*.

† An equation which, because of some mathematical process, has fewer roots than its original is sometimes called a *defective equation*.

EXAMPLE 2. Solve the equation $2 \cos \theta + 3 = 2$ for all values of θ between 0 and 2π.

Solution. Although this equation is not algebraic and therefore not linear, it is linear in the circular function of θ, and can be solved for $\cos \theta$ as though it were linear. The values of θ can then be found. Problems 7 and 8 of Article 4–13 were simple examples of this type.

$$2 \cos \theta + 3 = 2,$$
$$2 \cos \theta = -1,$$
$$\cos \theta = -\tfrac{1}{2}.$$

Therefore $\theta = 2\pi/3$ or $4\pi/3$, since θ must be in the second or third quadrant when its cosine is negative.

EXAMPLE 3. Solve the equation $s = \dfrac{a - rl}{1 - r}$ for r.

Solution. This equation, one in which some or all of the known quantities are represented by letters, is called a *literal equation*. Each step in the solution should be verified.

$$s = \frac{a - rl}{1 - r},$$
$$s(1 - r) = a - rl,$$
$$s - rs = a - rl,$$
$$rl - rs = a - s,$$
$$r(l - s) = a - s,$$
$$r = \frac{a - s}{l - s}, \qquad \text{if} \quad l \neq s.$$

PROBLEMS

Find the zeros of the following linear functions:

1. $2x + 4$ 2. $-5x + 10$ 3. $10 - 12x$
4. $6x - 9$ 5. $8x + 24$ 6. $5x - 17$

Solve the following linear equations and check:

7. $4x - 2 = 6x + 12$ 8. $3x + 7 = 5x - 13$
9. $5 + 2(3 - x) = 4 + 2(x - 2) + 5x$
10. $x^2 - 7x + 10 = x^2 + 5x - 6$

11. $\dfrac{3x + 5}{12} - \dfrac{4 - x}{6} = \dfrac{x - 2}{3}$

12. $\dfrac{3x - 6}{5} = \dfrac{2x - 5}{10} + \dfrac{x - 4}{2}$

13. $\dfrac{3x + 2}{x - 1} - \dfrac{6}{5} = 0$

14. $\dfrac{2}{6x - 7} - \dfrac{5}{3x - 4} = 0$

Using Table I if necessary, find the values of θ between 0 and 2π which satisfy each of the following equations:

15. $2\sin\theta - \sqrt{3} = 0$

16. $\dfrac{\cos\theta - 2}{3} = 3 - \dfrac{\cos\theta + 9}{3}$

17. $\dfrac{1 + \tan\theta}{1 - \tan\theta} = 2$

18. $\sin 3\theta = 2 - 3\sin 3\theta$

19. $\dfrac{4\cos\left(2\theta + \dfrac{\pi}{6}\right)}{5} = \dfrac{4 + \cos\left(2\theta + \dfrac{\pi}{6}\right)}{10}$

20. $\dfrac{1}{2\tan(\theta + \pi)} = \dfrac{2}{\tan(\theta + \pi)} + 1$

Solve the following equations for the letters indicated:

21. $ax - bx = c$, for x

22. $ay + by = c + dy$, for y

23. $A = \frac{1}{2}bh$, for b

24. $A = \frac{1}{2}(b_1 + b_2)h$, for b_1

25. $l = a + (n - 1)d$, for d

26. $l = a + (n - 1)d$, for n

27. $S = \dfrac{a - rl}{1 - r}$, for l

28. $S = \dfrac{a - rl}{1 - r}$, for a

29. $S = \dfrac{n}{2}(a + l)$, for l

30. $S = v_0 t + \frac{1}{2}gt^2$, for v_0

31. $\dfrac{y}{\tan\theta_1} = \dfrac{a + y}{\tan\theta_2}$, for y

32. $\tan\theta_1\left(\dfrac{x}{\tan\theta_2} + a\right) = x$, for x

In solving the following problems, *read the problem carefully*, let one of the unknown quantities be x, and express all other unknown quantities as functions of x. Find two expressions or quantities that are equal, equate these, and solve the resulting equation. Check all answers.

33. A man 42 years old has a son 12. In how many years will the father be twice as old as his son?

34. The tens digit of a number is 3 less than the units digit. If the number is divided by the sum of the digits, the quotient is 4 and the remainder 3. What is the original number? [*Hint:* If x equals the units digit, $x - 3$ is the tens digit, and the number may be written $10(x - 3) + x$.]

35. A man left one-half of his estate to his wife, one-sixth to his daughter, and the remainder, an amount of \$15,000, to his son. How large was the entire estate?

36. A starts walking along a road at 3 mi/hr. Two hours later B starts in the same direction at 3.5 mi/hr. How far from the starting point will B overtake A? [*Hint:* Rate · time = distance.]

37. A can do a certain job in 3 hours, while the same job takes B 4 hours. How long will it take both of them working together? [*Hint:* If x = number of hours for both to complete the work, $1/x$ will be the amount of the work done by both in 1 hour.]

38. If the larger of two integers, whose sum is 88, is divided by the smaller, the quotient is 5 and the remainder is 10. What are the two numbers?

5–2 Arithmetic progressions.   Let us consider the linear function $f(x) = 2x - 1$ where the domain of the function consists of the positive integral values of x. In this case the function assumes the values $1, 3, 5, \ldots,$ $2n - 1, \ldots$ Similarly, if the function is $y = 2^x$, where again the domain of the function is the positive integers, the corresponding functional values are $2, 4, 8, \ldots, 2^n, \ldots$ Both of these sets of numbers are examples of sequences. In general, a *sequence* is the range of some function whose domain is either all or a part of the set of positive integers. The functional value of the integer 1 is the first term of the sequence, of 2 the second term, of 3 the third term, and so on. In this way, the first, second, third, etc., values in the sequence are specifically determined. If the entire set of integers is considered, the sequence is *infinite;* but if only the first n positive integers make up the domain of the function, the sequence is *finite.* We are concerned in this article with one specific type of sequence.

DEFINITION 5–1. *An* arithmetic progression *is a sequence in which each term after the first is obtained by adding the same fixed number, called the* common difference, *to the preceding term.*

ALTERNATE DEFINITION 5–2. *An* arithmetic progression *is any sequence for which the "defining function" is linear. (See Problem 33.)*

ILLUSTRATION 1.   The finite sequence 2, 5, 8, 11, 14 is an arithmetic progression with the common difference of 3. The function defining this sequence is $f(x) = 3x - 1$.

ILLUSTRATION 2.   The infinite sequence 7, 2, -3, -8, -13, $\ldots$ is an arithmetic progression with the common difference -5: $f(x) = 12 - 5x$.

Let us use the following general notations for any arithmetic progression:

a, the first term,
d, the common difference,
n, the number of terms,
l, the last or nth term.

Thus, in Illustration 1, $a = 2$, $d = 3$, $n = 5$, and $l = 3n - 1$, while for Illustration 2, $a = 7$, $d = -5$, and $l = 12 - 5n$. Note that the nth term really represents the function which defined the sequence.

In general, the first n terms of an arithmetic progression may be represented by

$$a, a + d, a + 2d, a + 3d, \ldots, a + (n - 1)d.$$

The last value also gives us the expression for the nth term l, in terms of a, n, and d,

$$l = a + (n - 1)d. \tag{5–2}$$

EXAMPLE 1. Find the 25th term of the arithmetic progression $2, 5, 8, 11, \ldots$

Solution. In this progression, since $a = 2$ and $d = 3$, we have

$$l = a + (n - 1)d$$
$$= 2 + (24)3 = 74.$$

EXAMPLE 2. If the 6th term of an arithmetic progression is 27 and the 12th term is 48, find the first term.

Solution. We have the two relations,

$$27 = a + 5d$$

and

$$48 = a + 11d.$$

Subtracting the respective members of the first equation from those of the second, we obtain $21 = 6d$, or

$$d = \tfrac{7}{2}.$$

Substituting this value in the first equation, we have

$$27 = a + 5(\tfrac{7}{2}),$$

and we find

$$a = 9\tfrac{1}{2}.$$

EXAMPLE 3. Find the arithmetic progression of 6 terms if the first is $\tfrac{2}{3}$ and the last is $7\tfrac{1}{3}$.

Solution. Using Eq. (5–2), we have

$$\tfrac{22}{3} = \tfrac{2}{3} + (5)d,$$

and solving,

$$d = \tfrac{4}{3}.$$

Therefore the required progression is

$$\tfrac{2}{3}, 2, \tfrac{10}{3}, \tfrac{14}{3}, 6, \tfrac{22}{3}.$$

We are often interested in the sum of the general finite arithmetic progression. We let

$$S_n = a + (a + d) + (a + 2d) + \cdots + [a + (n - 1)d]. \quad (5\text{–}3)$$

We may also write this expression in reverse order:

$$S_n = [a + (n - 1)d] + [a + (n - 2)d] + \cdots + (a + d) + a.$$

If we add the respective members of these equations and group the corresponding terms,

$$2S_n = [2a + (n-1)d] + [2a + (n-1)d]$$
$$+ [2a + (n-1)d] + \cdots + [2a + (n-1)d].$$

Since there are n terms, $2a + (n-1)d$, on the right side of this equation, we have

$$2S_n = n[2a + (n-1)d],$$

or

$$S_n = \frac{n[2a + (n-1)d]}{2}. \qquad (5\text{-}4)^*$$

Recalling that $l = a + (n-1)d$, we may also write Eq. (5–4) as

$$\boxed{S_n = \frac{n(a+l)}{2}.} \qquad (5\text{-}5)$$

EXAMPLE 4. Find the sum of the first 30 terms of the arithmetic progression $-15, -13, -11, \ldots$

Solution. Since $a = -15$, $d = 2$, and $n = 30$, we have

$$S_{30} = \frac{30[2(-15) + (30-1)2]}{2}$$
$$= \frac{30(-30 + 58)}{2} = 420.$$

EXAMPLE 5. The sum of the first 15 terms of an arithmetic progression is 270. Find the first term and the common difference if the 15th term is 39.

Solution. By using Eq. (5–5), we obtain

$$270 = \frac{15(a + 39)}{2}.$$

Solving for a, we have

$$15a + 585 = 540,$$
$$15a = -45,$$
$$a = -3.$$

Since $l = a + (n-1)d$,

$$39 = -3 + 14d,$$

or

$$d = 3.$$

---

* This relation can also be proved by mathematical induction (see Problem 17, Article 8–1).

Problems

Write the next three terms in each of the following arithmetic progressions, and find l and S_n.

1. 1, 4, 7, . . . to 9 terms. 2. 27, 25, 23, . . . to 30 terms.

3. 10, 7, 4, . . . to 15 terms. 4. $-\frac{5}{4}, -\frac{1}{4}, \frac{3}{4}, \ldots$ to 8 terms.

In Problems 5–11, three of the elements a, l, d, n, and S_n of the arithmetic progression are given. Find the missing elements in each case.

5. $a = 2, d = 4, n = 12$ 6. $a = 3, n = 4, l = 12$

7. $a = -2, n = 14, S_n = 20$ 8. $d = 3, n = 5, l = 14$

9. $d = \frac{1}{2}, n = 14, S_n = 30$ 10. $a = 4, d = 4, S_n = 40$

11. $a = 6, d = 5, l = 36$

12. Find the value of k so that $8k + 4$, $6k - 2$, and $2k - 7$ will form an arithmetic progression.

13. What are the first three terms of an arithmetic progression whose 9th term is 16 and 40th term is 47?

14. The 18th and 52nd terms of an arithmetic progression are 3 and 173, respectively. Find the 25th term.

15. Find the sum of all the even integers from 12 to 864, inclusive.

16. Find the sum of all the odd integers from 27 to 495, inclusive.

*17. The terms between any two terms of an arithmetic progression are called the *arithmetic means* between these two terms. Insert four arithmetic means between −1 and 14.

18. Insert five arithmetic means between 14 and 86.

19. Insert three arithmetic means between −18 and 4.

*20. Insert one arithmetic mean between 24 and 68. Such a number is called the *arithmetic mean* of the two numbers.

21. Find the arithmetic mean of (a) 7 and −15, (b) $\frac{3}{5}$ and $\frac{5}{3}$.

*22. A *harmonic progression* is a sequence of numbers whose reciprocals form an arithmetic progression. Insert two harmonic means between 4 and 8.

23. For any sequence of numbers forming an arithmetic progression, show that the products formed by multiplying each term by any constant also form an arithmetic progression.

24. If a^2, b^2, and c^2 form an arithmetic progression, show that $a + b$, $c + a$, and $b + c$ form a harmonic progression.

25. How many numbers between 10 and 200 are exactly divisible by 7? Find their sum.

26. How many numbers between 25 and 400 are exactly divisible by 11? Find their sum.

27. If a clock strikes the appropriate number of times on each hour, how many times will it strike in one week?

28. A man accepts a position at the rate of $3600 a year with the understanding that he will receive an increase of $250 every six months. What will his salary be after working 15 years? How much will his entire earnings be?

29. The force of gravity causes a body to fall 16.1 feet during the first second, 48.3 the next second, 80.5 the third, and so on. How far will the body fall in 10 seconds?

30. A man bought a house at the beginning of 1945 for $10,000. If it increased $500 in value each year, how much was it worth at the end of 1959?

31. A piece of equipment cost a certain factory $29,000. If it depreciates in value 15% the first year, 13.5% the second, 12% the third, and so on, what will its value be at the end of 10 years, all percentages applying to the original cost?

32. A certain antique originally worth $1600 is evaluated at $5660 after 80 years. Find the value at the end of each ten-year period if the increase in value during each such period was $125 more than during the preceding ten years.

33. By using Eq. (5–2), prove that the two definitions of an arithmetic progression are equivalent.

5–3 Slope of a line. The most logical method of giving the direction of a straight line is to state this direction in terms of an angle with a fixed line. We do this by giving two fundamental definitions.

DEFINITION 5–3. *The inclination of a line is the smallest positive angle measured from the positive x-axis to this line.*

Note that such an angle will always be less than 180°.

DEFINITION 5–4. *The slope of a line is the tangent of its inclination. If the inclination is denoted by θ, and the slope by m, we have*

$$\tan \theta = m. \tag{5–6}$$

Since tan 90° does not exist, the slope of a line parallel to the y-axis does not exist. However, a horizontal line or line parallel to the x-axis has the slope zero.

The slope of any line, if it exists, may be found in terms of the coordinates of any two points on the line. In Fig. 5–1 the lines drawn through P_1 and P_2 parallel to the axes meet at Q, whose coordinates are (x_2, y_1).

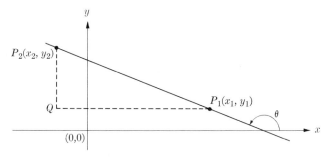

FIGURE 5–1

(Why?) Therefore,

$$m = \tan \theta = \frac{y_2 - y_1}{x_2 - x_1},$$

and we have the result:

THEOREM 5–1. *If* $P_1(x_1, y_1)$ *and* $P_2(x_2, y_2)$ *are any two points on a line with slope* m,

$$m = \frac{y_2 - y_1}{x_2 - x_1}. \tag{5–7}$$

Any two nonvertical lines l_1 and l_2 that are parallel have the same inclination and consequently the same slope. Conversely, if $\tan \theta_1 = \tan \theta_2$, where θ_1 and θ_2 are positive and less than 180°, the inclinations themselves are equal, and the lines are parallel. Thus:

THEOREM 5–2. *Two nonvertical lines are parallel if and only if their slopes are equal.*

We also can easily prove a theorem for perpendicular lines.

THEOREM 5–3. *Two nonvertical lines are perpendicular if and only if their slopes are negative reciprocals of each other.*

Proof. As in Fig. 5–2, for any two nonvertical perpendicular lines, the inclination of one line must be 90° greater than the other. Denoting these by θ_1 and θ_2, we have

$$\theta_2 = \theta_1 + 90°,$$

and thus

$$\tan \theta_2 = \tan (\theta_1 + 90°) = -\frac{1}{\tan \theta_1},$$

or

$$m_2 = -\frac{1}{m_1}. \tag{5–8}$$

Since each angle is less than 180°, these steps are reversible, and the proof is complete.

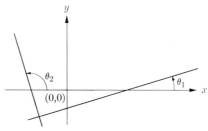

FIGURE 5–2

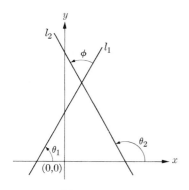

FIGURE 5–3

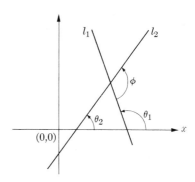

FIGURE 5–4

When the two lines are neither parallel nor perpendicular, we are of course interested in the angle from one line to the other. This angle is defined as the positive angle, less than 180°, measured from the first line to the second. See Figs. 5–3 and 5–4. We can find this angle in terms of the slopes of the lines.

THEOREM 5–4. *The tangent of the angle θ from one nonvertical line l_1 to a second nonvertical line l_2, which is not perpendicular to it, is given by the relation*

$$\tan \phi = \frac{m_2 - m_1}{1 + m_2 m_1}. \tag{5–9}$$

Proof. If $\theta_2 > \theta_1$, as in Fig. 5–3, $\phi = \theta_2 - \theta_1$. If $\theta_1 > \theta_2$, as in Fig. 5–4, $\phi = 180° + (\theta_2 - \theta_1)$. But since

$$\tan (\theta_2 - \theta_1) = \tan [180° + (\theta_2 - \theta_1)],$$

we have, using Eq. (4–33),

$$\tan \phi = \frac{\tan \theta_2 - \tan \theta_1}{1 + \tan \theta_2 \tan \theta_1} = \frac{m_2 - m_1}{1 + m_2 m_1}.$$

It is interesting to note what significance is attached to Eq. (5–9) if the numerator or denominator of the right member is zero.

PROBLEMS

1. Find the slopes of the lines joining the following pairs of points:

(a) $(-2, 3)$ and $(5, -3)$,   (b) $(-3, 4)$ and $(-3, 7)$,

(c) $(6, 2)$ and $(5, -1)$,   (d) $(7, -1)$ and $(2, -1)$.

2. Prove, using slopes, that the points $(6, 1)$, $(5, 6)$, $(-4, 3)$, and $(-3, -2)$ are the vertices of a parallelogram. (Recall Problem 4, Article 3–3.)

3. Prove, using slopes, that the points $(2, 3)$, $(-4, -3)$, and $(6, -1)$ are the vertices of a right triangle. (Recall Problem 5, Article 3–3.)

4. Test algebraically to see whether or not the following triples of points are collinear: $(6, 2)$, $(1, 1)$, and $(-4, 0)$; $(-6, 5)$, $(3, -10)$, and $(-2, -2)$.

5. Find the acute angles of the right triangle given in Problem 3.

6. Find the angles of the parallelogram given in Problem 2.

7. Find the acute angle between the diagonals of the parallelogram given in Problem 2.

8. Find the angles of the triangle whose vertices are the points $(1, 3)$, $(5, 4)$, and $(3, 0)$.

9. Find the angles of the triangle whose vertices are the points $(-1, 2)$, $(3, 3)$, and $(-2, -3)$.

10. Find the slope of any line perpendicular to the line joining the following pairs of points:

(a) $(-4, 6)$ and $(1, -5)$,   (b) $(2, 3)$ and $(6, -1)$,

(c) $(6, -2)$ and $(-3, -2)$,   (d) $(7, 1)$ and $(-4, 3)$.

11. If the four points $A(-3, 2)$, $B(1, 7)$, $C(4, 3)$, $D(3, -2)$ are the vertices of a quadrilateral, find the slopes of each side.

12. Recalling the result of Problem 10, Article 3–2, find the mid-points of the sides of the quadrilateral given in Problem 11.

*13. Show that the mid-points found in Problem 12 are the vertices of a parallelogram.

14. If the angle from the line through $(2, 3)$ and $(-4, 5)$ to the line l is $45°$, find the slope of line l.

15. If the angle from line l to the line joining $(-3, 6)$ and $(2, 4)$ is $135°$, find the slope of line l.

16. Find the value of k so that the line joining $(1, k)$ and $(k, -2)$ has a slope equal to (a) 4, (b) -3, (c) 0.

17. Explain the significance of Eq. (5–9) (a) if the numerator of the right member is zero, (b) if the denominator is zero.

5–4 Equation of a straight line. When we recall from Article 3–4 the definition of an equation of any curve, it is clear that an equation of a straight line is a statement of the condition which the coordinates of each of the points of the line, and only these points, must satisfy.

A specific line can be determined by two distinct points. Moreover, since two distinct points determine the slope of a line, a line can also be determined by its slope (or inclination) and one point on the line. If we denote the slope by m and any specific point on the line by (x_1, y_1), the condition that any other point (x, y) lie on the line, or an equation of this line (if $x \neq x_1$), may be given as

$$m = \frac{y - y_1}{x - x_1},$$

or

$$y - y_1 = m(x - x_1). \qquad (5\text{-}10)$$

It should be noted that the coordinates (x_1, y_1) satisfy (5-10) and more-over, if a point does not lie on this line, (5-10) will not be satisfied. There-fore we have proved the following theorem.

THEOREM 5–5. *An equation of the straight line that has slope m and passes through the point (x_1, y_1) is $y - y_1 = m(x - x_1)$.*

This equation is called the *point-slope form* of an equation of the line.

EXAMPLE 1. Find an equation of the straight line with slope $\frac{1}{2}$, through the point $(5, 2)$.

Solution. Since the slope is $\frac{1}{2}$, we have

$$\frac{1}{2} = \frac{y - 2}{x - 5}.$$

By simplification this becomes

$$x - 5 = 2(y - 2),$$

or

$$x - 2y - 1 = 0.$$

EXAMPLE 2. Find an equation of the straight line through $(2, 3)$ and $(-1, 7)$.

Solution. The slope of this line is given by

$$m = \frac{3 - 7}{2 - (-1)} = -\frac{4}{3}.$$

Considering the point $(2, 3)$ as (x_1, y_1), we have

$$-\frac{4}{3} = \frac{y - 3}{x - 2},$$

or

$$4x + 3y - 17 = 0.$$

By using Eq. (5-10), we can derive two other useful forms of an equation of a straight line. If a straight line is not parallel to either axis, it will intersect each of the axes in one point. If we denote these points by $(a, 0)$ and $(0, b)$, the quantity a is called the *x-intercept* and b the *y-intercept*. The slope of the straight line through these two points is $-b/a$. If Eq. (5-10) is used in this case, we find the result to be the intercept form of the equation of the line, namely,

$$\frac{x}{a} + \frac{y}{b} = 1. \tag{5-11}$$

Note that Eq. (5–11) is not applicable if the line passes through the origin. (Why?)

If the point (x_1, y_1) in Eq. (5–10) is taken as the point $(0, b)$, the equation simplifies to the *slope-intercept form* of the equation of a line,

$$y = mx + b. \tag{5-12}$$

Notice that Eq. (5–12) is not applicable if the line is parallel to the y-axis. (Why?) It should be clear that any straight line can be put either in the form of (5–12) [compare Eq. (5–1)], or in the form $x = k$. Stating this observation as a theorem, we have:

THEOREM 5–6. *Any straight line (vertical or not) has an equation of the first degree in x and y.*

The converse of this theorem is also true.

THEOREM 5–7. *Any equation of the first degree in x and y represents a straight line.*

Proof. Since any such equation may be written

$$Ax + By + C = 0, \tag{5-13}$$

where A, B, and C are constants, we can prove the theorem by showing that this equation represents a straight line. We shall consider the cases where $B = 0$ and where $B \neq 0$.

1. If $B = 0$, A cannot be zero, for the equation would not be of the first degree. Solving for x, we find

$$x = -\frac{C}{A},$$

which is the equation of the line parallel to the y-axis with $-C/A$ for its x-intercept.

2. If $B \neq 0$, we solve for y and obtain

$$y = -\frac{A}{B}x + \frac{-C}{B}.$$

Comparing this to Eq. (5–12), we find it represents a line with slope

$-A/B$ and y-intercept $-C/B$. Thus, in both cases, we have found a straight line for which $Ax + By + C = 0$ is an equation.

In the proof of the theorem we noticed the slope of $Ax + By + C = 0$ to be $-A/B$. This fact is extremely useful. For example, it is then evident that $2x + 3y = 6$ has a slope of $-\frac{2}{3}$.

EXAMPLE. Find the slope and intercepts of the line whose equation is $3x - 4y = 12$.

Solution. We can either solve the equation for y, obtaining $y = \frac{3}{4}x - 3$, and thus find the slope (the coefficient of x) to be $\frac{3}{4}$, or recall that the slope of any linear equation is $-A/B$, for this equation $\frac{3}{4}$.

To find the intercepts, we put the equation in the form of Eq. (5–11) by dividing both members by 12:

$$\frac{x}{4} + \frac{y}{-3} = 1.$$

We immediately see that the x-intercept is 4 and the y-intercept is -3.

PROBLEMS

1. Find an equation of the straight line

(a) through $(1, 5)$, having the slope 3;
(b) through $(-2, 3)$, having the slope -4;
(c) through $(-1, -2)$, having the slope 0;
(d) through $(-3, 5)$, having inclination 45°;
(e) through $(2, 1)$, parallel to y-axis;
(f) through $(1, 3)$, having inclination 135°.

2. Find an equation of the straight line

(a) through the two points $(3, 1)$ and $(-6, 6)$,
(b) through $(2, 3)$, parallel to $2x - 3y = 4$;
(c) through $(2, 3)$, perpendicular to $2x - 3y = 4$;
(d) through $(-1, 3)$, having x-intercept -3;
(e) through $(3, -2)$ having y-intercept 4;
(f) having x-intercept 2, y-intercept -3.

3. Find an equation of the perpendicular bisector of the line segment whose end points are $(0, 5)$ and $(-4, 1)$.

4. Find an equation of the line through $(5, 6)$ parallel to the line joining $(-4, 0)$ and $(1, -6)$.

5. Find an equation of the perpendicular bisector of that part of the line $3x + 4y - 12 = 0$ between the two axes.

*6. Given the triangle whose vertices are $A(-3, 1)$, $B(6, 4)$, and $C(1, -1)$, find an equation (a) for the sides, (b) for the medians, (c) for the perpendicular bisectors of the sides.

7. With reference to the triangle in Problem 6, find an equation of the line through A, parallel to BC.

8. With reference to the triangle in Problem 6, find an equation of the line through the mid-points of AB and BC.

9. With reference to the triangle in Problem 6, find an equation of the altitude from C to AB.

10. Find an equation of the line through $(4, 1)$ which has equal x- and y-intercepts.

11. Find the slope and intercepts of $6x - 3y + 1 = 0$.

12. Find the intercepts of the line which is perpendicular to $6x - 5y = 7$ and passes through $(1, 3)$.

5–5 Solution of two linear equations in two variables. In Article 5–1 we considered the first degree or linear function in one variable. Any function of the first degree in two variables x and y may be written

$$ax + by + c, \qquad (5\text{--}14)$$

where a, b, and c are constants, and is called a *linear function in two variables*. By setting this function equal to zero, we have the general equation of a straight line, Eq. (5–13). Since it is often convenient to write the constant term as the right member of such an equation, we shall consider in this article the equation

$$ax + by = c. \qquad (5\text{--}15)*$$

Since, by definition, a solution of any equation must satisfy that equation, any set of values (x, y) which satisfy Eq. (5–15) is called a solution of $ax + by = c$. There are clearly infinitely many solutions, for there are infinitely many points (x, y) whose coordinates satisfy such an equation. An arbitrary value of x will determine a corresponding value of y, and both values will satisfy the equation. For example, the linear equation $3x - 2y = 5$ has one solution $x = 3$, $y = 2$, another, $x = 1$, $y = -1$, another $x = -1$, $y = -4$, and so on.

We are frequently interested in a solution not of one equation but of a pair of linear equations in x and y, such as

$$a_1x + b_1y = c_1, \qquad a_2x + b_2y = c_2. \qquad (5\text{--}16)$$

Thus we are interested in finding a pair of values (x, y) that satisfies both equations. The graph of each of these equations is a straight line, and hence we must find the coordinates of a point (x, y) which lies on both

---

* The a and b in this equation are not to be confused with the x- and y-intercepts.

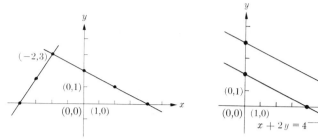

FIGURE 5–5

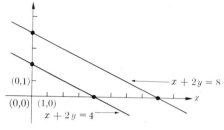

FIGURE 5–6

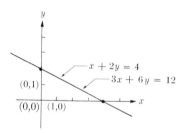

FIGURE 5–7

lines. Since, in general, two straight lines intersect in one point, there is usually a solution. By drawing a graph of each line, we can approximate the coordinates of the point of intersection.

EXAMPLE 1. Solve graphically the pair of equations

$$x + 2y = 4, \qquad 3x - 2y = -12.$$

Solution. The graph of each of these straight lines is shown in Fig. 5–5. It appears that the two lines intersect at the point $(-2, 3)$. This is actually the case, as may be verified by direct substitution, so that the solution is $x = -2$, $y = 3$.

We should remark that two parallel lines such as $x + 2y = 4$ and $x + 2y = 8$, when plotted, will not intersect (Fig. 5–6). The fact that the equations of two such lines have no common solution is of course apparent from the equations, since there can be no pair of numbers such that the first number plus twice the second is equal to 4 and also 8. Two equations of this type are called *inconsistent.*

If two lines such as $x + 2y = 4$ and $3x + 6y = 12$ coincide when their graphs are plotted (Fig. 5–7), any pair of values (x, y) which satisfies one equation will also satisfy the other. Any two equations of this type have an infinite number of solutions, and are said to be *dependent.*

In summary, the two equations (5–16) either

(1) have a unique solution, when their graphs are two straight lines which intersect in one point;
(2) have no solution, when their graphs are two parallel but not co-incident straight lines;
(3) have infinitely many solutions, when their graphs are two straight lines which are parallel and coincide.

Since the graphical method of solution is only approximate, we must also consider some exact method. One of the variables may be eliminated by a proper combination of the two equations (or equations equivalent to them), and the resulting equation may be solved for the other variable. The eliminated variable may then be found by substitution.

EXAMPLE 2. Solve algebraically the two equations of Example 1.

Solution. Since the coefficients of y are equal, but opposite in sign, the members of the first equation may be added to those of the second, and thereby the y is eliminated.

$$
\begin{array}{r}
x + 2y = 4 \\
3x - 2y = -12 \\
\hline
4x = -8
\end{array}
$$

Solving this equation in one variable, we have $x = -2$. When this value is substituted in either of the two original equations, we find $y = 3$. Therefore the required solution is $x = -2$, $y = 3$. We might have found y by multiplying each member of the first equation by -3, adding the members of the resulting equation, $-3x - 6y = -12$, to those of the second equation, $3x - 2y = -12$, and finding $-8y = -24$, or $y = 3$.

EXAMPLE 3. Solve the pair of two general equations (5–16) for x and y in terms of the coefficients.

Solution. If we multiply each member of the first equation by b_2, and of the second by b_1, we have

$$a_1b_2x + b_1b_2y = c_1b_2,$$
$$a_2b_1x + b_1b_2y = c_2b_1.$$

Subtracting the members of the second from those of the first, we obtain

$$a_1b_2x - a_2b_1x = c_1b_2 - c_2b_1.$$

Solving this equation for x, we find

$$(a_1b_2 - a_2b_1)x = c_1b_2 - c_2b_1,$$

$$x = \frac{c_1b_2 - c_2b_1}{a_1b_2 - a_2b_1} \qquad (a_1b_2 - a_2b_1 \neq 0).$$

By multiplying each member of the first equation by a_2, of the second by a_1, and so on, we find

$$y = \frac{a_1c_2 - a_2c_1}{a_1b_2 - a_2b_1} \quad (a_1b_2 - a_2b_1 \neq 0).$$

Although not used in this form, these values for x and y can be considered a *solution by formula*.

PROBLEMS

Solve the following pairs of linear equations algebraically. The graphical method might be used as an approximate check. If an angle is involved, find all possible values between 0 and 2π.

1. $2x - y = 5,$
   $x - 3y = 5.$

2. $3x - 2y = -14,$
   $2x + 3y = 8.$

3. $4x + 3y = 27,$
   $2x - 5y + 19 = 0.$

4. $2x - 5y + 43 = 0,$
   $6x - y + 31 = 0.$

5. $3x + 4 = 4y,$
   $9x + 2y = 9.$

6. $6x + 9y = 7,$
   $3x - 6y + 14 = 0.$

7.† $4 \sin \alpha + \cos \beta = 3,$
   $6 \sin \alpha - 2 \cos \beta = 1.$

8. $\sqrt{3} \sin \alpha - \cos \beta = 1,$
   $\sin \alpha - 3\sqrt{3} \cos \beta = -\sqrt{3}.$

9. $2 \sec \alpha - 4 \tan \beta = 0,$
   $\sec \alpha + \tan \beta = \sqrt{3}.$

10. $\frac{2}{x} + \frac{3}{y} = 2, \quad \frac{4}{x} - \frac{9}{y} + 1 = 0.$

11. $\frac{15}{x} + \frac{4}{y} = 1,$

   $\frac{5}{x} - \frac{12}{y} = 7.$

12. $\frac{15}{2x} - \frac{16}{3y} = \frac{23}{6},$

   $\frac{4}{3x} + \frac{7}{2y} + \frac{31}{72} = 0.$

13. $ax + by = a^2 + 2ab + b^2,$
   $bx - ay = b^2 + 2ab - a^2.$

14. $ax - by = a^2 - b^2,$
   $bx + ay = 2ab.$

*15. $\tan k_1 = \frac{y}{x},$

   $\tan k_2 = \frac{y + a}{x}.$

*16. $\tan k_1 = \frac{a}{y},$

   $\tan k_2 = \frac{a}{y + x}.$

*17. Solve the pair of equations

$$x = x' \cos \alpha - y' \sin \alpha,$$
$$y = x' \sin \alpha + y' \cos \alpha$$

for x' and y' in terms of x and y.

18. The sum of the digits of a two-digit number is 9. If the digits are reversed, the new number is 9 less than the original number. Find the two numbers.

---

† Although Problems 7 through 12 are not linear, they may be solved by the method discussed in this article.

19. A certain fraction has the value $\frac{3}{4}$. If its numerator is decreased by 7 and its denominator increased by 4, the resulting fraction has the value $\frac{1}{2}$. Find the original fraction.

20. The sum of the two nonright angles in a right triangle is, of course, 90°. If twice the first is 40° more than 3 times the second, find the angles.

21. With the wind, an airplane travels 1120 miles in 7 hours. Against the wind, however, it takes 8 hours. Find the rate of the plane in still air and the velocity of the wind.

22. The sum of the reciprocals of two numbers is 9. Twice the reciprocal of the first is 12 less than 4 times the reciprocal of the second. Find the numbers.

23. A and B, working together, can do a job in $6\frac{2}{3}$ hours. A became ill after 3 hours of working with B, and B finished the job, continuing to work alone in $8\frac{1}{4}$ more hours. How long would it take each working alone to do the job?

24. Find α and β, angles between 0 and $\pi/2$, so that

$$2 \sin (\alpha + \beta) = 2 \cos (\alpha - \beta) = \sqrt{3}.$$

25. Find the coordinates of the vertices of the triangle formed by the lines

$$x - y = -3, \qquad 3x + 4y = 5, \qquad 6x + y = 17.$$

26. Check the coordinates found in the equations in Problem 25.

27. Show that the lines

$$2x - y = 4, \qquad x + 3y = 6,$$
$$2x - y = 8, \qquad x + 3y = -1$$

form a parallelogram, and find its vertices.

28. Referring to Problem 6, Article 5–4, show that the three medians meet in a point, and find its coordinates.

29. Referring to Problem 6, Article 5–4, show that the three perpendicular bisectors of the sides meet in a point, and find its coordinates.

30. Find the coordinates of the foot of the perpendicular from $(2, 1)$ to the line $2x - 3y = 6$.

31. Find the distance between the two parallel lines $3x - 4y = 12$ and $3x - 4y + 6 = 0$.

32. Realizing that $y = mx + b$ represents an equation of any straight line (not parallel to the y-axis), and recalling that the coordinates of any point that lies on a line must satisfy its equation, find the values of m and b so that $y = mx + b$ passes through $(-3, 1)$ and $(1, 9)$. [*Note:* This is another method for finding an equation of a straight line through two points.]

33. By the method of Problem 32, find an equation of the straight line that passes through (a) $(2, 3)$ and $(-1, 4)$, (b) $(-4, 2)$ and $(6, -1)$.

5–6 Distance from a point to a line. One of the more useful notions in dealing with points and lines, the relationships between them, and the properties of each, is the (perpendicular) distance from a point to a line. The expression for this distance is given in the following theorem.

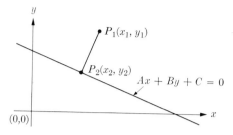

FIGURE 5–8

THEOREM 5–8. *The distance d from any point P_1 (x_1, y_1) to any line whose equation is $Ax + By + C = 0$ is given by the expression*

$$\frac{|Ax_1 + By_1 + C|}{\sqrt{A^2 + B^2}}.$$

(5–17)

Proof.* Let $P_2(x_2, y_2)$ be the foot of the perpendicular drawn from any point P_1 (x_1, y_1) to the line $Ax + By + C = 0$. (See Fig. 5–8.) Since the slope of $Ax + By + C = 0$ is $-A/B$, the slope of line P_1P_2 is B/A. Therefore its equation is

$$\frac{B}{A} = \frac{y - y_1}{x - x_1},$$

or

$$Bx - Ay = Bx_1 - Ay_1.$$

(5–18)

Since we wish to obtain an expression for the distance $d = P_1P_2$, we must find the coordinates of P_2 and then use the formula [Eq. (3–9)] for the distance between the two points. The coordinates of P_2 are obtained by solving $Ax + By + C = 0$ and Eq. (5–18). We find

$$x_2 = \frac{B^2x_1 - ABy_1 - AC}{A^2 + B^2},$$

$$y_2 = \frac{-ABx_1 + A^2y_1 - BC}{A^2 + B^2}.$$

Therefore,

$$x_2 - x_1 = \frac{-A(Ax_1 + By_1 + C)}{A^2 + B^2}$$

and

$$y_2 - y_1 = \frac{-B(Ax_1 + By_1 + C)}{A^2 + B^2},$$

---

* This proof holds only if A and B are not zero. Give a proof if $A = 0$.

from which we have, using Eq. (3–9),

$$d = \sqrt{(x_2 - x_1)^2 + (y_2 - y_1)^2}$$

$$= \sqrt{\frac{A^2(Ax_1 + By_1 + C)^2}{(A^2 + B^2)^2} + \frac{B^2(Ax_1 + By_1 + C)^2}{(A^2 + B^2)^2}}$$

$$= |Ax_1 + By_1 + C| \sqrt{\frac{A^2 + B^2}{(A^2 + B^2)^2}}$$

$$= \frac{|Ax_1 + By_1 + C|}{\sqrt{A^2 + B^2}}.$$

EXAMPLE. Find the distance from the point $(-2, 6)$ to the line

$$3x - 4y = 10.$$

Solution. We must transpose the 10 to the left side of the equation, substitute the coordinates of the given point $(-2, 6)$ into the left member, divide by $\sqrt{3^2 + (-4)^2} = 5$, and simplify. Thus,

$$d = \frac{|3(-2) - 4(6) - 10|}{5} = |-8| = 8.$$

PROBLEMS

1. Find the distance from the point $(2, 3)$ to the line $5x - 12y = 6$.

2. Find the distance from the point $(-2, 5)$ to the line $x - 3y = 7$.

3. In a triangle whose vertices are $A(-1, 2)$, $B(2, 5)$, and $C(3, -1)$, find the length of the altitude from A to BC.

4. Find the area of the triangle mentioned in Problem 3.

5. Find the distance between the parallel lines $2x - 3y = 6$ and $2x - 3y = 9$.

6. Find an equation of the line which is parallel to $3x - 4y = 6$, but 5 units away. [*Hint:* There are two solutions.]

7. Find an equation of the line which is parallel to $5x + 12y - 6 = 0$, but one unit away.

8. A line is parallel to $x - 4y = 7$. Find its equation if it is 3 units away from $(4, 1)$.

9. Find an equation of the line whose points are all equidistant from the two lines $3x - 4y + 6 = 0$ and $12x - 5y - 9 = 0$. What would the line be called?

10. Find an equation of the bisector of the acute angle between the two lines $x - 3y = 6$ and $6x - y = 2$. Construct a graph.

*11. In any triangle whose vertices are $P_1(x_1, y_1)$, $P_2(x_2, y_2)$, and $P_3(x_3, y_3)$, (a) find the length of the altitude from P_2, (b) find the length of the base P_1P_3. (c) Using these results, show that the area of the triangle in terms of the co-ordinates of the vertices is given by

$$K = \tfrac{1}{2}|(y_1 - y_3)x_2 - (x_1 - x_3)y_2 + x_1y_3 - x_3y_1|. \tag{5-19}$$

5–7 Algebraic solution of three linear equations in three variables.
Any equation of the form

$$ax + by + cz = d, \tag{5–20}$$

where a, b, c, and d are constants and a, b, and c are not all equal to zero,
is called a *linear equation in three variables*. A solution of such an equation
is any set of three numbers x, y, and z that satisfies the equation. As was
the case for Eq. (5–15), there are an infinite number of solutions for one
equation of this type.

Although we shall not prove it in this book, the geometric interpretation
of Eq. (5–20) is a plane in a three-dimensional rectangular coordinate
system.* Two nonparallel planes intersect in a straight line, and this
line intersects a third plane, parallel to neither of the first two, in a point.
In general, then, three planes have one point in common. Algebraically,
this may be interpreted by the fact that the system of equations

$$\begin{aligned}
a_1x + b_1y + c_1z &= d_1, \\
a_2x + b_2y + c_2z &= d_2, \\
a_3x + b_3y + c_3z &= d_3
\end{aligned} \tag{5–21}$$

has a single solution for x, y, and z.

To solve such a system, we follow a method which is a generalization
of that used to solve the pair of equations (5–16). We choose a pair from
the three equations and eliminate one of the variables from the pair, obtaining an equation in two variables. Repeating this procedure for another pair of the equations, we obtain a second equation in the same two
variables. We now solve the two resulting equations for the two variables
and, by substitution in any one of the original equations, find the complete
solution. Let us illustrate.

EXAMPLE. Solve the system of equations

$$\begin{aligned}
2x - y + z &= 8, \\
x + 2y + 3z &= 9, \\
4x + y - 2z &= 1.
\end{aligned}$$

Solution. Let us eliminate z by combining the first two equations, and
then by combining the first and third. Multiply each member of the first

---

* A three-dimensional rectangular coordinate system is a generalization of
the one- and two-dimensional systems discussed in Articles 3–1 and 3–2. For
example, each point in the space has three coordinates and is denoted (x, y, z),
and so on.

equation by -3 and add the result, member by member, to the second equation.

$$\begin{array}{rl}
-6x + 3y - 3z &= -24 \\
x + 2y + 3z &= 9 \\
\hline
-5x + 5y \phantom{{}+3z} &= -15
\end{array}$$

or

$$x - y = 3.$$

Multiply each member of the first equation by 2 and add the result, member by member, to the third equation.

$$\begin{array}{rl}
4x - 2y + 2z &= 16 \\
4x + y - 2z &= 1 \\
\hline
8x - y \phantom{{}- 2z} &= 17
\end{array}$$

We now solve the two resulting equations. Give the reasons for each step.

$$\begin{array}{rl}
8x - y &= 17 \\
x - y &= 3 \\
\hline
7x \phantom{{}- y} &= 14
\end{array}$$

Therefore, $x = 2$ and $y = -1$. Substituting these values in the first of the original equations, we have

$$2(2) - (-1) + z = 8,$$
$$z = 3.$$

Therefore the complete solution is $x = 2$, $y = -1$, $z = 3$. All solutions should be checked.

PROBLEMS

Solve each system of equations.

1. $x + 3y - z = 4,$
   $3x - 2y + 4z = 11,$
   $2x + y + 3z = 13.$

2. $3x - y - 2z = -13,$
   $5x + 3y - z = 4,$
   $2x - 7y + 3z = -36.$

3. $2x - y + 3z = 19,$
   $5x - 2y + 4z = 33,$
   $3x + 3y - z = 2.$

4. $6x + 4y - z = 13,$
   $5x - 2y + 7z = 18,$
   $x + y - 8z = -35.$

5. $3x + 5y + 2z = 0,$
   $12x - 15y + 4z = 12,$
   $6x + 25y - 8z = -12.$

6. $7x - 3y + 4z = 18,$
   $13x + 6y + 8z = 30,$
   $11x - 9y - 12z = 16.$

7. $2x + 3y = 28,$
   $3y + 4z = 46,$
   $4z + 5x = 53.$

8. $x - 3y = -11,$
   $2y - 5z = 26,$
   $3z - 7x = 2.$

9. $\dfrac{3}{x} - \dfrac{4}{y} + \dfrac{6}{z} = 1,$

$\dfrac{9}{x} + \dfrac{8}{y} - \dfrac{12}{z} = 3,$

$\dfrac{9}{x} - \dfrac{4}{y} + \dfrac{12}{z} = 4.$

10. $x + y + z = a + b + c,$

$bx - ay + cz = b^2,$

$ax - ay + cz = ab.$

11. The sum of the digits of a three-digit number is 13. If the tens and hundreds digits are interchanged, the new number is 90 less than the original, and if the units and hundreds digits are interchanged, the resulting number is 99 less than the original. Find the original number.

12. Twenty-five coins, whose value is $2.75, are made up of nickels, dimes, and quarters. If the nickels were dimes, the dimes were quarters, and the quarters nickels, the total value would be $3.75. How many coins of each type are there?

13. We recall that the sum of the angles of any triangle is 180°. What are the three angles if the sum of two is equal to the third angle, but the difference of these two is only two-thirds of the third angle?

14. Find the specific quadratic function of the form $f(x) = ax^2 + bx + c$ if its value is 1 when $x = 1$, if its value is 2 when $x = 2$, and if its value is 11 when $x = -1$.

15. If the general equation (3–10) of the circle is expanded, it can be written in the form $x^2 + y^2 + Ax + By + C = 0$. Recalling that the coordinate of any point on the circle must satisfy its equation, find the values of A, B, and C and, thereby, the circle which passes through the points $(1, 1)$, $(-2, 3)$, and $(3, 4)$.

16. If A, B, and C work together on a job, it will take $1\frac{1}{3}$ hours If only A and B work, it would take $1\frac{5}{7}$ hours, but if B and C work, it would take $2\frac{2}{5}$ hours. How long would it take each man, working alone, to complete the job?

5–8 Applications to geometry. With the use of the material from the preceding articles, we can obtain certain geometric results or prove certain geometric theorems. This will be illustrated by two examples. Note that in each case the choice of the coordinate axes simplifies the calculations, and yet the proof is completely general.

EXAMPLE 1. Prove that the diagonals of a parallelogram bisect each other.

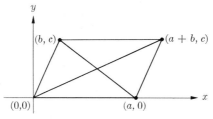

FIGURE 5–9

Solution. Since we may choose the system of axes in any position we wish with respect to the parallelogram, we place the parallelogram with one vertex at $(0, 0)$ and one side along the x-axis. See Fig. 5–9. If c is the altitude of the parallelogram from the side of length a, the other two vertices may be represented by (b, c) and $(b + a, c)$. Why?

To prove that the diagonals bisect each other, we merely need to find the coordinates of the mid-points of each diagonal and notice that they are identical. The mid-point of each is found to be

$$\left(\frac{a + b}{2}, \frac{c}{2}\right),$$

by using Eq. (3–8).

EXAMPLE 2. Prove that the mid-points of the sides of any quadrilateral are the vertices of a parallelogram.

Solution. We again choose one vertex of the quadrilateral as the origin, and one side along the x-axis. These two vertices will have coordinates $(0, 0)$ and $(a, 0)$. The two other vertices are designated by (b, c) and (d, e), as shown in Fig. 5–10. Calling the mid-points of each side P_1, P_2, P_3, and P_4, we find, using Eq. (3–8),

$$P_1 = \left(\frac{b}{2}, \frac{c}{2}\right), \qquad P_2 = \left(\frac{b + d}{2}, \frac{c + e}{2}\right),$$

$$P_3 = \left(\frac{a + d}{2}, \frac{e}{2}\right), \qquad P_4 = \left(\frac{a}{2}, 0\right).$$

Since the slope of P_1P_2, by Eq. (5–3), is

$$\frac{\dfrac{c + e}{2} - \dfrac{c}{2}}{\dfrac{b + d}{2} - \dfrac{b}{2}} = \frac{e}{d},$$

and the slope of P_3P_4 is

$$\frac{\dfrac{e}{2} - 0}{\dfrac{a + d}{2} - \dfrac{a}{2}} = \frac{e}{d},$$

the two lines have the same slope and are parallel. Similarly, the slopes of P_2P_3 and P_1P_4 are both equal to $c/(b - a)$, so that these lines are also parallel.

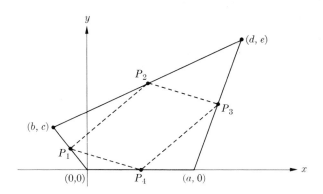

FIGURE 5–10

PROBLEMS

1. Prove that the diagonals of a square are equal and perpendicular.

2. Prove that if the diagonals of a rectangle are perpendicular, then it is a square.

3. State and prove the converse of the theorem stated in Example 1.

4. Prove that the sum of the squares of the lengths of the sides of any parallelogram is equal to the sum of the squares of the lengths of the diagonals.

5. Prove that the line segment joining the mid-points of two sides of a triangle is parallel to the third side and equal in length to one-half of it.

6. Prove that the mid-point of the hypotenuse of any right triangle is equidistant from the three vertices.

7. Prove that the altitudes of a triangle meet in a point.

8. Prove that the medians of a triangle meet in a point.

9. Prove that the perpendicular bisectors of the sides of a triangle meet in a point.

10. Prove that the three points mentioned in Problems 7, 8, and 9 are collinear.

CHAPTER 6

QUADRATIC FUNCTIONS

6–1 The quadratic function. The second type of algebraic function of one variable usually considered is that of the second degree, called the *quadratic function,*

$$f(x) = ax^2 + bx + c, \qquad (6\text{–}1)$$

where a represents the coefficient of the squared term, b the coefficient of the first degree term, and c the constant term. Although either or both b and c may be zero, a is not zero. (Why?) Except for the following brief discussion of the graph of such functions, we shall be concerned in this chapter with their algebraic properties, and a more detailed treatment of the geometric properties will be considered in Chapter 18. The graph of a quadratic function was briefly considered in Article 3–7 (Example 2). Another example seems appropriate.

EXAMPLE 1. Draw the graph of the quadratic function $-2x^2 + 12x - 14$.

Solution. The graph (Fig. 6–1) is drawn by tabulating a sufficient number of points whose coordinates satisfy the equation $y = -2x^2 + 12x - 14$.

x	0	1	2	3	4	5	6
y	-14	-4	2	4	2	-4	-14

In comparing this curve with that in Fig. 3–14, we see that both have the same general shape. The graph of any quadratic function in one variable is of this type and is called a *parabola*. Although we shall not prove it in this chapter (see Chapter 18), when the coefficient of x^2 is positive, the curve opens upward, while the curve opens downward if the coefficient of x^2 is negative. Compare the two examples.

The graph of the general quadratic function may be sketched by the more direct process of expressing the quadratic function in terms of the square of a linear function. Consider

$$y = ax^2 + bx + c. \qquad (6\text{–}2)$$

Factoring out a, and grouping the x^2 and x terms together, we have

$$y = a\left[\left(x^2 + \frac{b}{a}x\right) + \frac{c}{a}\right].$$

126

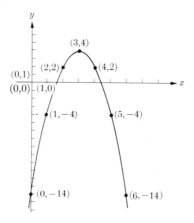

FIGURE 6–1

Recalling Eq. (1–21), we must add $(b/2a)^2$ to $x^2 + (b/a)x$ in order to form a perfect square. Thus, adding and subtracting $b^2/4a^2$ within the brackets,

$$y = a\left[\left(x^2 + \frac{b}{a}x + \frac{b^2}{4a^2}\right) + \frac{c}{a} - \frac{b^2}{4a^2}\right],$$

and simplifying, we have

$$y = a\left[\left(x + \frac{b}{2a}\right)^2 + \frac{4ac - b^2}{4a^2}\right]. \qquad (6\text{–}3)$$

Since the squared quantity $(x + b/2a)^2$ is not less than 0, the expression within the brackets has its least value when $x = -b/2a$. If $a > 0$, the function also has its least value at $x = -b/2a$. This least value of the function, $(4ac - b^2)/4a$, is called its *minimum*. If, however, $a < 0$, when $x = -b/2a$, the function has its greatest value, called its *maximum*, and is also equal to $(4ac - b^2)/4a$. In either case, the point

$$[-b/2a, (4ac - b^2)/4a]$$

is called the *vertex* of the parabola. With this point found, and an additional point or two, the graph can be sketched. It is usually simpler to complete the square in each case than to use the formulas in this discussion.

EXAMPLE 2. Find the vertex of the parabola represented by the equation $y = x^2 - x - 6$. Compare with Example 2, Article 3–7.

Solution. Grouping the first two terms on the right and completing the square, we obtain

$$\begin{aligned}
y &= (x^2 - x) - 6 \\
&= (x^2 - x + \tfrac{1}{4}) - 6 - \tfrac{1}{4} \\
&= (x - \tfrac{1}{2})^2 - \tfrac{25}{4}.
\end{aligned}$$

The vertex is $(\frac{1}{2}, -\frac{25}{4})$. Since $a = 1$, which is positive, the minimum value of the function is $-\frac{25}{4}$, and this occurs when $x = \frac{1}{2}$. The graph of the function appears in Fig. 3–14.

PROBLEMS

For each of the following functions, find the maximum or minimum and draw the graph.

1. $x^2 + 6x + 5$
2. $x^2 + x - 6$
3. $2x^2 + 5x - 12$
4. $-2x^2 + 11x - 15$
5. $6x^2 - 17x + 5$
6. $-2x^2 + 5x + 8$
7. $x^2 + 6x + 11$
8. $-3x^2 + 5x - 4$

9. Find two numbers whose sum is 16 and whose product is a maximum. [*Hint:* If we let x be one number and $16 - x$ the other, the product y can be expressed as a function of x, namely $y = x(16 - x) = 16x - x^2$.]

10. Divide 40 into two parts such that the sum of the squares of these parts is a minimum.

11. A man with 160 feet of fencing wishes to fence off an area in the shape of a rectangle. What should be the dimensions of the area if the enclosed space is to be as large as possible?

12. A man with 160 feet of fencing wishes to fence off an area in the shape of a rectangle. If one side of the area will not require fencing, what should be the dimensions to ensure the largest area possible?

6–2 Solution of the quadratic equation. We are now in a position to find the zeros of any quadratic function. Recalling the definition of the zeros of a function (Article 3–7), we are interested in finding the abscissas of the points where the graph of $y = ax^2 + bx + c$ crosses or meets the x-axis. These may be found graphically by sketching the curve. For example, from Fig. 3–14, the zeros of $x^2 - x - 6$ are -2 and 3. Likewise, from Fig. 6–1, the zeros of $-2x^2 + 12x - 14$ are approximately 1.3 and 4.7. Such values can, of course, be checked by substituting in the original function set equal to zero.

There are, however, more accurate methods for finding the zeros of the function $ax^2 + bx + c$. In finding its zeros or, equivalently, in solving the equation

$$ax^2 + bx + c = 0 \qquad (a \neq 0), \tag{6-4}$$

we may be able to factor the left member. This method, known as the *factoring method*, depends upon the fact that a product is zero when either factor is zero.

EXAMPLE 1. Solve the quadratic equation $x^2 - 7x + 10 = 0$ by factoring.

Solution. Since $x^2 - 7x + 10 \equiv (x - 5)(x - 2)$ (see Article 1-8), the equation may be written

$$(x - 5)(x - 2) = 0.$$

We wish to find a value such that when it is substituted for x in the member on the left, the product will be zero. Such values may be found by solving either of the two linear equations

$$x - 5 = 0 \quad \text{and} \quad x - 2 = 0.$$

For these, we find $x = 5$ or $x = 2$, either of which is a root of the original equation. All answers should be checked.

EXAMPLE 2. Solve the equation $2 \sin^2 \theta + \sin \theta - 1 = 0$ for all possible values of θ between 0 and 2π.

Solution. Like that in Example 2, Article 5-1, this equation is not algebraic, but may be considered a quadratic equation in $\sin \theta$. Factoring the left member, we get

$$2 \sin^2 \theta + \sin \theta - 1 \equiv (2 \sin \theta - 1)(\sin \theta + 1).$$

Thus we have the two equations

$$2 \sin \theta - 1 = 0 \quad \text{and} \quad \sin \theta + 1 = 0$$

to solve for $\sin \theta$, and we obtain

$$\sin \theta = \tfrac{1}{2} \quad \text{or} \quad -1.$$

Since $\sin \theta$ is positive in the first or second quadrant, there are two values of θ between 0 and 2π for which $\sin \theta = \tfrac{1}{2}$. Therefore,

$$\theta = \pi/6, \quad 5\pi/6, \quad \text{or} \quad 3\pi/2.$$

PROBLEMS

1. From the graphs of the functions listed in Problems 1-8 of Article 6-1, give the roots of the corresponding equations. Check these by substituting the results into the original equations.

Solve Problems 2-19 by factoring and check by substitution. In the equations involving circular functions, give all roots between 0 and 2π.

2. $9x^2 - 16 = 0$
3. $2x^2 - 5x - 12 = 0$
4. $4 \sin^2 \theta = 1$
5. $4 \cos^2 \theta = 3$
6. $6x^2 - 5x = 50$
7. $2x^2 - 2 = x - 4x$
8. $1 - \cos^2 \theta = \cos^2 \theta$
9. $\tan \theta (2 \sin \theta - \sqrt{3}) = 0$

10. $3x^2 - x = 10$

11. $4x^2 - 12x + 9 = 0$

12. $2 \cot \theta \cos \theta - \cot \theta = 0$

13. $2 \tan^2 \theta + \tan \theta = 0$

14. $x^2 + 2ax = b^2 - a^2$

15. $8x^2 + 14ax + 3a^2 = 0$

16. $2 \sin^2 \theta - \sin \theta = 1$

17. $2 \cos^2 \theta + 3 \cos \theta + 1 = 0$

18. $\dfrac{x - 2}{x + 3} - 3 = \dfrac{4(x + 3)}{x - 2}$

19. $(x - 2)(x + 3) = 6$

The quadratic expression in an equation may be difficult to factor. Moreover, in many cases factors may not exist. As a result, the most useful method of solving any quadratic equation is *by the quadratic formula.* We obtain this formula by completing the square, as was done in finding the vertex of the parabola.

THEOREM 6–1. *The two roots of any quadratic equation,*

$$ax^2 + bx + c = 0 \qquad (a \neq 0), \tag{6-5}$$

are

$$x = \frac{-b \pm \sqrt{b^2 - 4ac}}{2a}. \tag{6-6}$$

Proof. If we divide by the coefficient of x^2 in (6–5) and transpose the constant term to the right side of the equation, we have

$$x^2 + \frac{b}{a}x = -\frac{c}{a}.$$

We may complete the square of the left member by adding $b^2/4a^2$ to both sides of the equation,

$$x^2 + \frac{b}{a}x + \frac{b^2}{4a^2} = \frac{b^2}{4a^2} - \frac{c}{a},$$

or

$$\left(x + \frac{b}{2a}\right)^2 = \frac{b^2 - 4ac}{4a^2}.$$

If we extract the square root, this becomes

$$x + \frac{b}{2a} = \frac{\pm\sqrt{b^2 - 4ac}}{2a},$$

or

$$x = \frac{-b \pm \sqrt{b^2 - 4ac}}{2a}.$$

The use of the plus and then the minus sign gives the two roots of the quadratic equation $ax^2 + bx + c = 0$, which completes the proof. The reader should verify that each of these roots is actually a solution by substituting them in Eq. (6–5).

Although any quadratic equation can be solved by the *method of completing the square* used to obtain this formula, direct substitution into Eq. (6–6) is more frequently employed because of its efficiency. Consider the following examples.

EXAMPLE 3. Solve the quadratic equation $4x^2 + 5x = 21$.

Solution. Transposing all the members to the left side to put the equation in the form $ax^2 + bx + c = 0$, and comparing the two, we have $a = 4$, $b = 5$, and $c = -21$. Substituting these values into the formula (6–6), we have

$$x = \frac{-5 \pm \sqrt{(5)^2 - 4(4)(-21)}}{2(4)}.$$

Simplification yields

$$x = \frac{-5 \pm \sqrt{25 + 336}}{8} = \frac{-5 \pm \sqrt{361}}{8} = \frac{-5 \pm 19}{8}.$$

Therefore, choosing the plus and then the minus sign, we obtain

$$x = \tfrac{7}{4} \quad \text{or} \quad -3.$$

Both answers should be checked by substituting them in the original equation. The fact that the number under the radical sign is a perfect square guarantees that the roots are rational. Thus the equation could have been solved by the method of factoring. Specifically, $4x^2 + 5x - 21 \equiv (4x - 7)(x + 3)$.

EXAMPLE 4. Solve $\cos^2 \theta + 5 \sin \theta + 2 = 0$ for all values of θ between $0°$ and $360°$.

Solution. Since $\cos^2 \theta$ may be expressed as $1 - \sin^2 \theta$, it is possible to rewrite this equation entirely in terms of $\sin \theta$. Thus,

$$1 - \sin^2 \theta + 5 \sin \theta + 2 = 0,$$

$$\sin^2 \theta - 5 \sin \theta - 3 = 0.$$

Regarding the variable as $\sin \theta$, and using the formula (6–6), we find $a = 1$, $b = -5$, and $c = -3$. Therefore,

$$\sin \theta = \frac{5 \pm \sqrt{25 + 12}}{2} = \frac{5 \pm 6.0828}{2},$$

or

$$\sin \theta = 5.5414 \quad \text{or} \quad -0.5414.$$

Since $|\sin \theta| \leq 1$, we consider only the value -0.5414, which results in an angle in the third quadrant and one in the fourth quadrant. Using Table I, we find that $\sin \alpha = 0.5414$ gives $\alpha = 32°47'$. Therefore,

$$\theta = 180° + 32°47', \quad \text{or} \quad 360° - 32°47'.$$

Thus,

$$\theta = 212°47', \quad \text{or} \quad 327°13'.$$

The values of θ may, of course, be expressed in radian measure. (Recall Example 4, Article 3–5.) Since $32°47' = 0.5721$ radians,

$$\theta = 3.1416 + 0.5721 \quad \text{or} \quad 6.2832 - 0.5721$$
$$= 3.7137 \quad \text{or} \quad 5.711.$$

EXAMPLE 5. Solve $9x^4 - 37x^2 + 4 = 0$.

Solution. Although this is not a quadratic equation, by letting $v = x^2$ and substituting, we have

$$9v^2 - 37v + 4 = 0,$$

an equation that is quadratic in v, which may be written

$$(9v - 1)(v - 4) = 0.$$

Thus,

$$v = x^2 = \tfrac{1}{9} \quad \text{or} \quad 4,$$

and

$$x = \pm\tfrac{1}{3}, \quad \pm 2.$$

EXAMPLE 6. Solve $(x^2 - 5x)^2 + (x^2 - 5x) - 30 = 0$.

Solution. With $v = x^2 - 5x$, we wish to solve

$$v^2 + v - 30 = 0,$$

a quadratic equation in v whose roots are

$$v = 5 \quad \text{or} \quad -6.$$

Hence, we must solve

$$x^2 - 5x - 5 = 0, \quad \text{and} \quad x^2 - 5x + 6 = 0.$$

Our solution is $x = 2, 3$, and $(5 \pm 3\sqrt{5})/2$.

The general procedure in solving any quadratic equation is:

1. Try to solve the equation by the method of factoring.

2. If this method fails, either because the factors are not immediately evident or because they actually do not exist as rational factors, use the quadratic formula.

Problems

Solve the equations of Problems 1–35 by using the quadratic formula. If the equations involve circular functions, find all angles between 0 and 2π. Check all answers.

1. $2x^2 + 5x - 12 = 0$ 2. $4x^2 - 2x = 7$
3. $x^2 + x - 1 = 0$ 4. $2x^2 + x - 12 = 0$
5. $\tan^2 \theta - 3 \sec \theta + 3 = 0$ [*Hint:* $\tan^2 \theta \equiv \sec^2 \theta - 1$.]
6. $2 \cos^2 \theta + 3 \sin \theta = 0$ 7. $x^2 - (a + b)x + ab = 0$
8. $6x^2 + 17x + 12 = 0$
9. $(a - b)x^2 + (b - c)x + (c - a) = 0$
10. $4 \sin^2 \theta - 3 \cos \theta - 2 = 0$ 11. $3 \sec^2 \theta + \tan \theta - 5 = 0$

12. $x^2 - 2x + 1 = 4a^2$ 13. $\dfrac{x-1}{x^2-9} - \dfrac{3x+5}{x+3} = \dfrac{x+3}{x-3}$

14. $\cot 2\theta = 2 + \tan 2\theta$ 15. $4 \sin^2 2\theta + 2 \cos 2\theta = 3$
16. $6ax^2 - 2bx + 3b = 9ax$ 17. $s = v_0 x - gx^2/2$
18. $\tan 2\theta + 5 = 3 \sec^2 2\theta$

19. $\dfrac{1}{x^2 + 3x + 2} - \dfrac{1}{1-x} = \dfrac{2}{x^2-1}$

20. $x^4 - 11x^2 + 28 = 0$ 21. $9x^4 + 5x^2 - 4 = 0$
22. $x^{-4} - 13x^{-2} + 36 = 0$ 23. $x^{-4} - 8x^{-2} + 15 = 0$
24. $x^6 + 7x^3 - 8 = 0$ 25. $8x^{-6} + 7x^{-3} = 1$
26. $x^{2/3} + 2x^{1/3} - 8 = 0$ 27. $x + x^{1/2} = 20$
28. $(x^2 - 7x)^2 + 9(x^2 - 7x) - 10 = 0$
29. $(x^2 + 2x)^2 + (x^2 + 2x) = 12$

30. $\dfrac{2+x}{2-x} + \dfrac{2-x}{2+x} = 2$ 31. $\left(x + \dfrac{1}{x}\right)^2 - 2\left(x + \dfrac{1}{x}\right) + 1 = 0$

32. $3(x + 3) + \sqrt{x + 3} = 2$ 34. $2x^2 - 5x + 10 = 7\sqrt{2x^2 - 5x}$
33. $2x - 9\sqrt{x + 2} + 14 = 0$ 35. $x^2 - x - 4 = \sqrt{x^2 - x - 2}$

36. The product of two consecutive positive integers is 72. Find the integers.
37. The sum of a number and its reciprocal is $\frac{34}{15}$. Find the number.
38. A man completing a 40-mile trip finds that by traveling one more mile per hour, he could have made the journey in 2 hours' less time. At what speed did he actually travel?
39. If $(6 - x)$, $(13 - x)$, and $(14 - x)$ are the lengths of the sides of a right triangle, find the value of x.
40. By how much must a radius of 24 inches be reduced in order to decrease the area of a circle by 49π square inches?
41. A rectangular flower bed 30 yards long by 24 yards wide has a walk of uniform width around it. If the area of the path is one-fourth that of the flower bed, find the width of the path.
42. Working together, two men can do a job in 20 days. Working alone, however, one man would take 9 days longer than the other to complete the job. How long would it take each separately?

43. Using Eq. (5–9), find the slope of the bisector of the angle between $3x - 4y - 6 = 0$ and $12x - 5y - 9 = 0$. (Compare Problem 9, Article 5–6.) Then find the equation of the bisector of this angle.

44. Find the equation of the straight line the product of whose intercepts is 2, and which goes through the point $(4, -1)$.

45. Find the equation of the straight line which passes through the point $(3, -3)$ and forms with the axes a triangle of area 6.

6–3 Inequalities. Since most of the inequalities discussed in this book involve either first or second degree algebraic expressions, it seems appropriate to consider them in this chapter.

We recall the definition from Article 3–1 which stated that for *real numbers*, x is said to be *greater* than y (or y is said to be *less* than x) if the difference $x - y$ is positive. The symbol used to express this condition was $x > y$ (or $y < x$). A statement that one mathematical expression is greater than or less than another is called an *inequality*. As is true for equations (Article 1–2), there are two general types of inequalities in mathematics, the conditional inequality, corresponding to the conditional equation, and the absolute inequality, corresponding to the identity.

DEFINITION 6–1. *An inequality is called an* absolute *inequality if it is true for all permissible values of the variables involved.*

Although frequently an inequality may be true for an entire set of values, if it is not true for every permissible value, the inequality is not absolute.

DEFINITION 6–2. *An inequality is called a* conditional *inequality if it is not true for all permissible values of the variables involved.*

ILLUSTRATION. The inequality $a^2 + b^2 + 1 > 0$ is an absolute inequality. The expression $-4 < 3$ is also of this type. But $2x - 6 > 0$ is a conditional inequality, since it is true only for values of x greater than 3. Also, $\sin \theta < 0$ is conditional, for this is true only for values of θ in the third or fourth quadrants.

As is true in dealing with equations, there are certain important properties to be remembered in working with inequalities. Since the proofs of the theorems below follow directly from the definitions, only the first theorem will be proved.

THEOREM 6–2. *The sense of an inequality is not changed if both members are increased or decreased by the same number.*

Proof. Assume $a > b$. Then $a - b = n$, where n is positive. Therefore,

$$a + c - b - c = (a + c) - (b + c) = n,$$

or

$$(a + c) - (b + c) \text{ is positive.}$$

Thus,

$$a + c > b + c.$$

Similarly, we have

$$a - c > b - c.$$

The usefulness of this property lies in the fact that a term may be transposed from one member of an equality to the other member by changing the sign of the term without changing the sense of the inequality.

THEOREM 6–3. *The sense of an inequality is not changed if both members are multiplied or divided by the same* positive *number.*

THEOREM 6–4. *The sense of an inequality is reversed if both members are multiplied or divided by the same* negative *number.*

Since we wish to confine our discussion to inequalities in one variable, we are interested in those inequalities which may be written $f(x) > 0$ or $f(x) < 0$. First let us consider conditional inequalities. To solve such an inequality, we must find the set of values of x for which the inequality is true. When $f(x)$ is linear or quadratic, this set may be found by either an algebraic or graphical method.

EXAMPLE 1. Solve

$$\frac{x}{3} - 2 < \frac{5x + 9}{2}$$

both algebraically and graphically.

Algebraic solution. Multiplying both members by 6, we have

$$2x - 12 < 15x + 27.$$

Transposing and collecting terms, we obtain

$$-13x < 39.$$

If we divide by -13,

$$x > -3.$$

Graphical solution. If we transpose all terms to the left side of the inequality, we have

$$\frac{x}{3} - 2 - \frac{5x + 9}{2} < 0.$$

Denoting this left member by $f(x)$, we get

$$f(x) \equiv \frac{2x - 12 - 15x - 27}{6} \equiv \frac{-13x - 39}{6}.$$

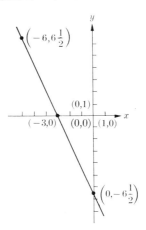

FIGURE 6–2

From the graph of $y = f(x)$ in Fig. 6–2, which can easily be drawn from the table below, it is clear that the inequality is satisfied for $x > -3$. The graphical method is more frequently used for quadratic inequalities.

x	0	-3	-6
y	$-6\frac{1}{2}$	0	$6\frac{1}{2}$

EXAMPLE 2. For what values of x does the inequality $x^2 - x - 6 > 0$ hold?

Solution. If we factor the expression, we have

$$x^2 - x - 6 \equiv (x - 3)(x + 2).$$

Since the product of two terms will be positive only if both are positive or both negative, $x - 3$ and $x + 2$ must both be greater than zero or both less than zero. We see that

$$\left. \begin{cases} x - 3 > 0 \\ \text{and} \\ x + 2 > 0 \end{cases} \right\} \quad \text{or} \quad \left. \begin{cases} x > 3 \\ \text{and} \\ x > -2 \end{cases} \right\} \text{ will both be true if } x > 3,$$

and

$$\left. \begin{cases} x - 3 < 0 \\ \text{and} \\ x + 2 < 0 \end{cases} \right\} \quad \text{or} \quad \left. \begin{cases} x < 3 \\ \text{and} \\ x < -2 \end{cases} \right\} \text{ will both be true if } x < -2.$$

Thus the inequality will be true if $x > 3$ or $x < -2$. This may be checked graphically by Fig. 3–14. It is often helpful to test some value in the set for which the inequality holds. Although this will not guarantee the proper complete solution, it is usually a check of the work.

EXAMPLE 3.   For what values of x does the inequality $-2x^2 + 12x - 14 > 0$ hold?

Solution. Since the left member is not factorable rationally, we use the graphical method. In Fig. 6–1 we have the graph of the function

$$y = f(x) = -2x^2 + 12x - 14,$$

whose zeros we may approximate as 1.6 and 4.4. Thus the inequality holds for values of x where $1.6 < x < 4.4$.

Should we wish to determine the zeros more accurately, we could use the quadratic formula for the equation $-2x^2 + 12x - 14 = 0$, or the equivalent equation $x^2 - 6x + 7 = 0$.

$$x = \frac{6 \pm \sqrt{36 - 28}}{2} = \frac{6 \pm 2\sqrt{2}}{2} = 3 \pm \sqrt{2}.$$

Hence,

$$x = 4.414 \quad \text{or} \quad 1.586,$$

and as a result $1.586 < x < 4.414$.

EXAMPLE 4.   Determine the values of θ, such that $0 \le \theta < 2\pi$, which satisfy the inequality $2 \cos^2 \theta + \sin \theta < 2$.

Solution. Since $\cos^2 \theta \equiv 1 - \sin^2 \theta$, we may express the members of the inequality as functions of $\sin \theta$,

$$2(1 - \sin^2 \theta) + \sin \theta < 2,$$

and simplifying, we have

$$2 - 2 \sin^2 \theta + \sin \theta - 2 < 0,$$

or

$$\sin \theta (1 - 2 \sin \theta) < 0.$$

Since the product of two quantities will be negative if one is negative while the other is positive, we may have

either $\begin{cases} \sin \theta < 0 \\ \text{and} \\ 1 - 2 \sin \theta > 0 \end{cases}$, which gives $\begin{cases} \sin \theta < 0 \\ \text{and} \\ \sin \theta < \frac{1}{2} \end{cases}$,

or $\begin{cases} \sin \theta > 0 \\ \text{and} \\ 1 - 2 \sin \theta < 0 \end{cases}$, which gives $\begin{cases} \sin \theta > 0 \\ \text{and} \\ \sin \theta > \frac{1}{2} \end{cases}$.

The first set is satisfied by $\pi < \theta < 2\pi$, while the second is satisfied by $\pi/6 < \theta < 5\pi/6$.

PROBLEMS

1. Prove that for real numbers a, b, and c, if $a > b$, then $a - c > b - c$.

2. Prove the second property for inequalities of real numbers: if $a > b$ and $c > 0$, then $ac > bc$.

3. Prove the third property for inequalities of real numbers: if $a > b$ and $c < 0$, then $ac < bc$.

Find the values of x for which the following inequalities are satisfied. Use either the algebraic or graphical method.

4. $3x - 27 > 0$ 5. $2x - 12 < 0$

6. $2x + 5 > 4x - 9$ 7. $5x - 3 < 8x - 12$

8. $x^2 + 2x > 99$ 9. $2x^2 + 3x < 14$

10. $6x^2 + x < 1$ 11. $6x^2 - x > 35$

12. $x^2 + 2x > 12$ 13. $x^2 + 2x + 4 > 0$

14. $x^4 + x^2 < 0$ 15. $\dfrac{x - 2}{x - 5} > 0$

16. $\dfrac{1}{x} < \dfrac{1}{5}$ 17. $\dfrac{1}{x - 2} < \dfrac{1}{3}$

18. $|x - 4| < 1$ 19. $|x - 3| > 2$

20. Prove that the sense of an inequality, where both members are positive, is not changed if both members are raised to the same positive integral power or if the same positive root (principal value) of both members is taken.

Find the values of θ for which each of the following inequalities holds. Limit the answers to values of θ, such that $0 \leq \theta < 2\pi$:

21. $2 \sin^2 \theta < 1$ 22. $4 \cos^2 \theta > 1$

23. $\sin^2 \theta > \sin \theta$ 24. $\cos^2 \theta < \cos \theta$

25. $\sin \theta + \sin \dfrac{\theta}{2} < 0$ [*Hint:* Recall Problem 14, Article 4–11.]

26. $\sin \theta + \cos \dfrac{\theta}{2} > 0$ 27. $2 \cos^2 \theta + \sin \theta > 1$

28. $2 \sin^2 \theta + \cos \theta > 2$ 29. $\tan^2 \theta + \sec \theta + 1 \geq 0$

30. $\sqrt{3} \sin^2 \theta + 2\sqrt{3} > 5 \sin \theta$ 31. $\sin \theta > \cos \theta$

Absolute inequalities, of course, will also satisfy the properties mentioned in this section. The usual problem in dealing with absolute inequalities is to establish the validity of the given inequality for all permissible values. Since we must start with a valid inequality in any proof, it is often convenient to assume tentatively the proposition we are proving and reduce it to a simpler inequality which is known to be valid. Then the actual proof will consist of retracing the steps. The method is illustrated below.

EXAMPLE 5. Prove that for all real values of x, $x^2 + 1 \geq 2x$.

Solution. Tentatively assume this to be true. By subtracting $2x$ from both members of

$$x^2 + 1 \geq 2x, \qquad (6\text{--}7)$$

we have

$$x^2 - 2x + 1 \geq 0, \qquad (6\text{--}8)$$

which is known to be true, since $x^2 - 2x + 1 \equiv (x - 1)^2$. Our proof therefore starts with inequality (6–8). Since

$$x^2 - 2x + 1 \geq 0,$$

for all real values of x, by adding $2x$ to both members, we obtain the desired result,

$$x^2 + 1 \geq 2x.$$

EXAMPLE 6. Prove that the sum of any positive number and its reciprocal is greater than or equal to 2.

Solution. If we let x be any positive number, we wish to prove

$$x + \frac{1}{x} \geq 2. \qquad (6\text{--}9)$$

Although this is not an absolute inequality, we shall use one to establish it. If we divide both members of Eq. (6–7) by x, which is positive, we get the required inequality.

We may also be interested in proving that certain absolute inequalities hold when they involve the circular functions.

EXAMPLE 7. Prove the absolute inequality $3 \sin \theta + 4 \cos \theta \leq 5$.

Solution. Recalling Example 5, Article 4–9, we have

$$3 \sin \theta + 4 \cos \theta = 5 \sin (\theta + \theta_1) \leq 5,$$

since $\sin \alpha \leq 1$.

PROBLEMS

Prove each of the following inequalities. The letters in Problems 1–10 represent unequal positive numbers, and θ, α, and β represent any angle. Tell which are conditional and which are absolute inequalities.

1. $a^2 + b^2 > 2ab$

2. $\dfrac{a}{b} + \dfrac{b}{a} > 2$

3. $\dfrac{x + y}{2} > \sqrt{xy}$

4. $\dfrac{a + b}{2} > \dfrac{2ab}{a + b}$

5. $\dfrac{x^2}{y} + \dfrac{y^2}{x} > x + y$ 6. $x^3 + y^3 > x^2 y + xy^2$

7. $x^2 + y^2 + z^2 < (x + y + z)^2$ 8. $a^2 + 2a + 2 > 0$

9. $|a + b| \leq |a| + |b|$ 10. $|a - b| \geq |a| - |b|$

11. $|\sin \theta| + |\csc \theta| \geq 2$ 12. $\cos \theta + \sec \theta \geq 2$

13. $|\cos^4 \theta - \sin^4 \theta| \leq 1$ 14. $|\sin (\alpha + \beta) \cos (\alpha - \beta)| \leq 1$

15. $\sin \theta + \cos \theta \leq \sqrt{2}$ 16. $\sin^2 \theta + \cot^2 \theta \geq 2 \cos \theta$

17. $12 \sin \theta - 5 \cos \theta \leq 13$ 18. $4 \sin \theta + 3 \cos \theta \leq 6$

6–4 Relations between zeros and coefficients of the quadratic function.
In addition to Eq. (6–6), which gives the zeros of the quadratic function
$ax^2 + bx + c$ in terms of the coefficients, there are other relations between
the zeros and the coefficients. By letting r_1 and r_2 be the zeros of $ax^2 + bx + c$, where

$$r_1 = \frac{-b + \sqrt{b^2 - 4ac}}{2a}, \qquad r_2 = \frac{-b - \sqrt{b^2 - 4ac}}{2a}, \qquad (6\text{–}10)$$

we have the sum of the two zeros,

$$\boxed{\; r_1 + r_2 = -\frac{b}{a} \cdot \;} \qquad (6\text{–}11)$$

Likewise, we have the product

$$r_1 \cdot r_2 = \frac{(-b)^2 - (\sqrt{b^2 - 4ac})^2}{4a^2}$$

$$= \frac{b^2 - (b^2 - 4ac)}{4a^2},$$

or

$$\boxed{\; r_1 \cdot r_2 = \frac{c}{a} \cdot \;} \qquad (6\text{–}12)$$

Since the zeros of the function $ax^2 + bx + c$ and the roots of the equation formed by setting this function equal to zero are the same, Eqs. (6–11)
and (6–12) are useful in forming such an equation. The following theorem
will clarify this remark.

THEOREM 6–5.   *If any quadratic equation* $ax^2 + bx + c = 0$ *is written*

$$x^2 + \frac{b}{a} x + \frac{c}{a} = 0, \qquad (6\text{–}13)$$

so that the coefficient of x^2 *is unity,* (1) *the sum of its roots is equal to the
negative of the coefficient of* x, *and* (2) *the product of its roots is equal to
the constant term.*

Proof. We establish this result by comparing the coefficient of x with Eq. (6–11), and the constant term with Eq. (6–12).

EXAMPLE 1. Without obtaining the zeros, find the sum and product of the zeros of $3x^2 - 4x + 8$.

Solution. Since $a = 3$, $b = -4$, and $c = 8$, the sum is $-(-4/3) = \frac{4}{3}$, and the product is $\frac{8}{3}$.

EXAMPLE 2. Write a quadratic equation whose roots are $3 + \sqrt{2}$ and $3 - \sqrt{2}$.

Solution. Since $(3 + \sqrt{2}) + (3 - \sqrt{2}) = 6$, and $(3 + \sqrt{2})(3 - \sqrt{2}) = 9 - 2 = 7$, an equation of this type is

$$x^2 - 6x + 7 = 0.$$

EXAMPLE 3. Without solving, form a quadratic equation whose roots are the squares of the roots of $2x^2 + x - 6 = 0$.

Solution. By letting r_1 and r_2 be the roots of the given equation, we have

$$r_1 + r_2 = -\tfrac{1}{2}, \qquad r_1 r_2 = -3.$$

Since $(r_1 + r_2)^2 \equiv r_1^2 + 2r_1 r_2 + r_2^2$, the sum of the roots for the new equation will be

$$r_1^2 + r_2^2 \equiv (r_1 + r_2)^2 - 2r_1 r_2 = \tfrac{1}{4} + 6 = \tfrac{25}{4},$$

and the product will be

$$(r_1 r_2)^2 = 9.$$

Therefore the required equation is

$$x^2 - \tfrac{25}{4}x + 9 = 0$$

or, clearing fractions,

$$4x^2 - 25x + 36 = 0.$$

The expression $b^2 - 4ac$, under the radical in Eq. (6–10), is another quantity which, in terms of the coefficients, is important in considering the nature of the zeros of the function. If this expression, called the *discriminant*, is negative, no real square root will exist. The zeros will be *imaginary.* Such numbers will be considered in Chapter 17. If $b^2 - 4ac$ is equal to zero, $r_1 = r_2$ and the zeros are equal; while if $b^2 - 4ac$ is positive, the zeros are real and unequal. Since the zeros of the function $ax^2 + bx + c$ and the roots of the equation $ax^2 + bx + c = 0$ are the same, we have immediately the following:

THEOREM 6–6. *Consider the quadratic equation* $ax^2 + bx + c = 0$.

1. *If* $b^2 - 4ac < 0$, *the roots are imaginary.*
2. *If* $b^2 - 4ac = 0$, *the roots are equal.*
3. *If* $b^2 - 4ac > 0$, *the roots are real and unequal.*

If we wished to emphasize the graph of $y = f(x) = ax^2 + bx + c$, rather than the roots of $ax^2 + bx + c = 0$, we could give the following theorem:

THEOREM 6–7. *Consider the quadratic function* $f(x) = ax^2 + bx + c$.

1′. *If* $b^2 - 4ac < 0$, *the graph of the parabola does not touch or cross the x-axis.*
2′. *If* $b^2 - 4ac = 0$, *the graph of the parabola has its vertex on the x-axis.*
3′. *If* $b^2 - 4ac > 0$, *the graph of the parabola intersects the x-axis in two real points.*

EXAMPLE 4. Without solving equations, determine the nature of the zeros of $2x^2 - 9x - 35$.

Solution. Since $a = 2$, $b = -9$, and $c = -35$, $b^2 - 4ac = (-9)^2 - 4(2)(-35) = 81 + 280 = 361$. Since $361 > 0$, the zeros are real and unequal. Moreover, since $b^2 - 4ac = 361$, a perfect square, the zeros will be rational. Is this always true when $b^2 - 4ac$ is a perfect square?

EXAMPLE 5. On the same coordinate axis, sketch graphs of

(a) $y = x^2 - 6x + 5$,
(b) $y = x^2 - 6x + 9$,
(c) $y = x^2 - 6x + 13$.

Check the results by finding $b^2 - 4ac$ in each case.

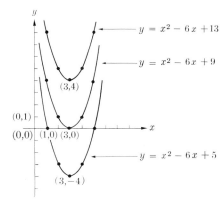

FIGURE 6–3

Solution. The graphs of each are shown in Fig. 6–3. These are consistent with the values for $b^2 - 4ac$, since we have

(a) $b^2 - 4ac = (-6)^2 - 4(1)(5) = 16,$
(b) $b^2 - 4ac = (-6)^2 - 4(1)(9) = 0,$
(c) $b^2 - 4ac = (-6)^2 - 4(1)(13) = -16.$

PROBLEMS

1. Without solving, find the sum and product of the zeros of the functions given in Problems 1 through 8, Article 6–1.

Find quadratic equations with integral coefficients having the following given numbers as roots.

2. $2, -3$

3. $-5, 4$

4. $\frac{2}{3}, -2$

5. $-\frac{3}{4}, \frac{2}{3}$

6. $+\sqrt{3}, -\sqrt{3}$

7. $2 + \sqrt{3}, 2 - \sqrt{3}$

8. $\dfrac{-1 + \sqrt{5}}{2}, \dfrac{-1 - \sqrt{5}}{2}$

9. $\dfrac{-3 + \sqrt{7}}{4}, \dfrac{-3 - \sqrt{7}}{4}$

10. Find a quadratic equation whose roots are the squares of the roots of $4x^2 + 8x - 5 = 0.$

11. Find a quadratic equation whose roots are the reciprocals of the roots of $4x^2 + 8x - 5 = 0.$

$$\left[Hint: \ \frac{1}{r_1} + \frac{1}{r_2} = \frac{r_1 + r_2}{r_1 r_2}. \right]$$

12. Find a quadratic equation whose roots are the squares of the roots of $3x^2 - 5x - 2 = 0.$

13. Find a quadratic equation whose roots are the reciprocals of the roots of $3x^2 - 5x - 2 = 0.$

14. Find a quadratic equation whose roots are twice the roots of $4x^2 + 8x - 5 = 0.$

15. Find a quadratic equation whose roots are one-third the roots of $4x^2 + 8x - 5 = 0.$

16. Find a quadratic equation whose roots are three times the roots of $3x^2 - 5x - 2 = 0.$

17. Find a quadratic equation whose roots are half the roots of $3x^2 - 5x - 2 = 0.$

Find the value of k so that the equation

18. $4x^2 + kx + 6 = 0$ has one root $= -2$

19. $2x^2 + kx - 15 = 0$ has one root $= 3$

20. $3x^2 + kx - 2 = 0$ has roots whose sum is equal to 6

21. $5x^2 - 8x + k = 0$ has roots whose product is equal to $\frac{1}{5}$

22. $4x^2 + 20x + k = 0$ has equal roots

23. $3x^2 - 7x + k = 0$ has equal roots

24. $2x^2 + (4 - k)x - 17 = 0$ has roots numerically equal but opposite in sign

25. $3x^2 - 5x + 8 = kx$ has roots numerically equal but opposite in sign
26. $3x^2 - 7x + 6 = k$ has one root equal to zero
27. $4x^2 + 20x + k = 0$ has one root equal to zero

Find the range of values of k so that the equation

28. $3x^2 - 4kx + k = 0$ will have real roots
29. $2x^2 + 3kx - 9 = 0$ will have real roots
30. $x^2 + (k - 2)x + 4 = 0$ will have real roots
31. $2x^2 - kx + 8 = 0$ will have imaginary roots
32. $kx^2 + 4\sqrt{3}\,x + k = 1$ will have imaginary roots

Find the range of values (or value) of k so that the graph of the function

33. $3x^2 - 9x + k$ will touch (have its vertex on) the x-axis
34. $x^2 + 2kx + \frac{3}{4} - k$ will not intersect the x-axis
35. $4x^2 + 4\sqrt{2}\,kx + k + 3$ will intersect the x-axis in two real points
36. Show that there are no real values of x and y such that

$$\frac{1}{x} + \frac{1}{y} = \frac{1}{x + y}.$$

6–5 Equations involving radicals. The equations in Problems 32–35 of Article 6–2 contain radicals. Fortunately, they are of a special form, and it is possible to solve them by the method prescribed. Many equations involving radicals are not solvable by this method, and the radical or radicals first be eliminated. Then the usual methods may be used. Extreme care must be taken, however, to substitute all possible roots in the original equation, since the method of eliminating radicals involves raising both members of an equality to some power. This process (recall Illustration 2, Article 5–1) may introduce roots of the final equation which are not roots of the original one.

EXAMPLE 1. Solve $\sqrt{2x + 5} = 3$.

Solution. In an equation involving one radical, we must first eliminate the radical by squaring both members of the equation,

$$2x + 5 = 9.$$

Solving, we find

$$x = 2.$$

By substituting, we find that $x = 2$ does satisfy the original equation:

$$\sqrt{2(2) + 5} = \sqrt{9} = 3,$$

so that $x = 2$ is the only root of the original equation.

EXAMPLE 2. Solve $\sqrt{1 - 5x} + \sqrt{1 - x} = 2$.

Solution. With two radicals, it is simpler to transpose one to the opposite side before squaring. Thus,

$$\sqrt{1 - 5x} = 2 - \sqrt{1 - x}.$$

Squaring, we find

$$1 - 5x = 4 - 4\sqrt{1 - x} + 1 - x,$$

and we have

$$-4x - 4 = -4\sqrt{1 - x},$$

or

$$1 + x = \sqrt{1 - x}.$$

Squaring again, we obtain

$$1 + 2x + x^2 = 1 - x,$$
$$x^2 = -3x,$$
$$x = 0, -3.$$

Therefore, no numbers other than 0 or -3 are roots of the original equation. By substitution, we find that 0 satisfies the original equation, but -3 does not. Therefore $x = 0$ is the only solution.

EXAMPLE 3.   Solve $3 \sin \theta + 4 \cos \theta = 5$ for all values of θ between 0° and 360°.

Solution. Although this is not an algebraic equation, it may be solved by the method discussed in this article. In order to express $\cos \theta$ in terms of $\sin \theta$, we recall that $\cos \theta \equiv \pm\sqrt{1 - \sin^2 \theta}$. Thus,

$$\pm 4\sqrt{1 - \sin^2 \theta} = 5 - 3 \sin \theta.$$

Squaring and solving for $\sin \theta$, we have

$$16 - 16 \sin^2 \theta = 25 - 30 \sin \theta + 9 \sin^2 \theta,$$
$$25 \sin^2 \theta - 30 \sin \theta + 9 = 0,$$
$$(5 \sin \theta - 3)^2 = 0,$$
$$\sin \theta = \tfrac{3}{5}.$$

Therefore $\theta = 36°52'$ or $143°8'$. By substituting our results in the original equation, we find $\theta = 36°52'$ is the only solution. This may also be written in radian measure, $\theta = 0.6464$ radians.

PROBLEMS

Solve and check:

1. $\sqrt{2x + 5} = 4$ 2. $\sqrt{6x - 3} = 7$
3. $\sqrt{8x - 7} - x = 0$ 4. $\sqrt{3x + 1} + 1 = x$

5. $\sqrt{3x+1} = \sqrt{x}+3$ 6. $2\sqrt{4x+5} = \sqrt{8-x}-1$

7. $\sqrt{11-x} - \sqrt{x+6} = 3$ 8. $\sqrt{3-x} - \sqrt{2+x} = 3$

9. $\sqrt{2x+\sqrt{2x+4}} = 4$ 10. $\sqrt{2x+\sqrt{7+x}} = 3$

Find and check the values of θ between 0 and 2π which satisfy the following:

11. $4\sin\theta + 3\cos\theta = 2$ 12. $\cos\theta - 2 = \sqrt{3}\sin\theta$

13. $\sin\theta + \cos\theta = 1$ 14. $12\cos\theta - 5\sin\theta = 13$

15. $5\tan\theta - \sqrt{2}\sec\theta + 3 = 0$ 16. $\tan\theta + \sec\theta = 1$

6–6 Variation. Many applications in physical and social science make use of a functional dependence known as *proportion* or *variation*. Often the relations are linear or quadratic (although this is by no means always the case). For example, Ohm's law for an electrical circuit states that the current *varies directly* as the electromotive force, and *varies inversely* as the resistance. Thus the current is a function of both the electromotive force and the resistance. We may write this functional relationship

$$I = k \cdot \frac{E}{R},$$

where k is called the *proportionality constant*. Let us define the three different common types of variation.

DEFINITION 6–3. *If the two variables x and y are so related (no matter how their values change) that the quotient of y divided by x, called the ratio of y to x, is constant, then y is said to* vary directly *as x. This relationship may be written $y/x = k$, or*

$$\boxed{y = kx.} \tag{6-14}$$

DEFINITION 6–4. *If the two variables, x and y, are so related (no matter how their values change) that the product of y and x is constant, then y is said to* vary inversely *as x. This relationship may be written $yx = k$, or*

$$\boxed{y = \frac{k}{x}.} \tag{6-15}$$

DEFINITION 6–5. *If the variable z varies directly as x when y is held constant, and varies directly as y when x is held constant, then z is said to* vary jointly *as x and y, and is written*

$$\boxed{z = kxy.} \tag{6-16}$$

EXAMPLE 1. Express z as a specific function of x and y if z varies directly as x and inversely as the square of y, and $z = 18$ when $x = 3$ and $y = 2$.

Solution. The given proportion may be written

$$z = k\frac{x}{y^2}.$$

Substituting the values for x, y, and z, we have $18 = k(\frac{3}{4})$, and $k = 24$. Therefore the function may be written

$$z = \frac{24x}{y^2}.$$

EXAMPLE 2. At constant temperature, the resistance of a wire varies directly as its length and inversely as the square of its diameter. If a piece of wire 0.1 inch in diameter and 50 feet long has a resistance of 0.1 ohm, what is the resistance of a piece of wire of the same material, 2000 feet long, 0.2 inch in diameter?

Solution. Letting R, L, and d represent the resistance, the length, and the diameter, respectively, of the wire, we have $R = kL/d^2$. By substitution, $0.1 = k(50)/(0.1)^2$, or $k = (0.1)^3/50$. Thus,

$$R = \frac{(0.1)^3}{50} \cdot \frac{L}{d^2}.$$

Therefore,

$$R = \frac{(0.1)^3}{50} \cdot \frac{(2000)}{(0.2)^2} = \frac{(0.001)(2000)}{50(0.04)} = 1 \text{ ohm}.$$

Note that all the measurements need not be expressed in the same unit, although we must be consistent for each variable.

EXAMPLE 3. If y varies inversely as the square of x, how is y affected if x is increased 25%?

Solution. We have $y = k/x^2$. If $x = x_1$, then $y = k/x_1^2$. But $x = 5x_1/4$. Thus,

$$y = \frac{k}{(5x_1/4)^2} = \frac{16}{25} \cdot \frac{k}{x_1^2} = 0.64\frac{k}{x_1^2}.$$

Therefore y is 0.64 of its original value.

PROBLEMS

In Problems 1–8, express the functional relationship as a single algebraic equation, giving the specific value of k if possible.

1. The variable z varies directly as x and inversely as y.
2. The variable z varies directly as x and inversely as the square of y.

3. The variable z varies jointly as x and y, and $z = 72$ when $x = 4$ and $y = 3$.

4. The variable z varies inversely as x, and $z = 8$ when $x = 16$.

5. The circumference of a circle varies directly as the diameter.

6. The area of any triangle varies jointly as the product of the base and altitude.

7. The area of an equilateral triangle varies directly as the square of one side. (Compare Problem 9, Article 3–6.)

8. The distance a falling body travels (neglecting air resistance) varies as the square of the time traveled, and a body starting from rest falls 64 feet in 2 seconds.

9. Since for any specific angle θ, sin θ is a definite value and is defined as y/r (Article 4–2), we may say that for any constant angle, y varies directly as r. What is the proportionality constant for an angle of 30°, 60°, 38°?

10. For the tangent function, y varies directly as x. What is the proportionality constant for this function if θ is 45°, 60°?

11. If z varies jointly as x^2 and y, and $z = 24$ when $x = 2$ and $y = 3$, find the value of z when $x = 3$ and $y = 5$.

12. If z varies directly as x and inversely as y, and if $z = 5$ when $x = 2$ and $y = 3$, find z when $x = 4$ and $y = 2$.

13. The surface area of a sphere varies directly as the square of the radius. If the surface is 36π in^2 when the radius is 3 in., what is the surface area when the radius is 12 in.?

14. With the information in Problem 8, (a) find the distance the body has fallen in 5 seconds, (b) find the distance the body fell during the fifth second.

15. The kinetic energy K varies jointly as the mass m and the square of the velocity v. If K is 36 ergs when m is 8 gm and v is 3 cm/sec, find K if $m = 4$ gm and $v = 6$ cm/sec.

16. The vibrating frequency, or pitch, of a vibrating string varies directly as the square root of the tension of the string. If a string vibrates 216 times/sec due to a tension of 3 pounds, find its rate of vibration caused by a tension of 12 pounds.

17. The intensity of light varies inversely as the square of the distance from its source. How much farther from the light must an object be moved to receive one-fourth the amount of light it now receives if it is now 2 feet from the light?

18. If z varies directly as the square of x and inversely as y, what effect on z does doubling x and tripling y have?

19. The gravitational attraction F between two bodies varies jointly as their masses m_1 and m_2 and inversely as the square of the distance d between them. What is the effect on the gravitational attraction between two bodies if the masses are each doubled and the distance between them is halved?

20. The stiffness of a beam varies jointly as its breadth and depth and inversely as the square of the length. (a) Find the change in stiffness if each of the three dimensions is increased 10%. (b) Find the change in the length that is necessary to increase the stiffness 20% if the breadth and depth are unaltered.

21. Draw the graph of $y = kx$ for $k > 0$. Note that on the graph y increases as x increases. [*Hint:* Use units of k length on the y-axis.]

22. Draw $y = k/x$ for $k > 0$. Note that y decreases as x increases.

6-7 Solution of one linear and one quadratic equation. In Articles 5–5 and 5–7 we discussed systems of linear equations. These systems may be generalized either by considering more variables than two or three, or by considering functions of higher degree than the linear ones. The solutions of such systems, if they exist, are often difficult to obtain. We shall consider one simple but useful generalization in two variables, namely, the case in which one equation is linear and one is of the second degree, or quadratic. Such a system, in general, might be written

$$ax^2 + bxy + cy^2 + dx + ey + f = 0,$$
$$gx + hy + k = 0, \tag{6-17}$$

where a, b, c, d, e, f, g, h, and k are constants, a, b, and c not all zero, and g and h not both zero.

It is possible to solve such a system either graphically or algebraically, as in the case of two linear equations. The graph of the quadratic equation may best be plotted by solving for one variable in terms of the others, before the table of values is obtained. The points of intersection of the graphs of the quadratic equation and the linear equation may be approximated and their coordinates taken as solutions, since the points lie on both curves.

The simplest algebraic method is carried out by eliminating one of the variables. More specifically, we solve the linear equation for one variable in terms of the other, substitute this value in the quadratic equation, and solve the resulting quadratic equation in one variable. With these results substituted in the original linear equation, we obtain our complete solution.

Since this system reduces to the problem of solving one quadratic equation, we shall have either two real, distinct solutions, one real solution, or no real solution (recall Article 6–4).

EXAMPLE 1. Solve the system of equations

$$x^2 - 5x - y + 4 = 0,$$
$$x - 4y = 1.$$

Algebraic solution. Although we are able to eliminate x or y, we choose to solve the linear equation for y in terms of x, and substitute this value in the quadratic, since this approach appears to be simpler.

$$4y = x - 1$$

or

$$y = \frac{x - 1}{4}.$$

Therefore,

$$x^2 - 5x - \left(\frac{x-1}{4}\right) + 4 = 0,$$

$$4x^2 - 20x - x + 1 + 16 = 0,$$

$$4x^2 - 21x + 17 = 0,$$

$$(4x - 17)(x - 1) = 0.$$

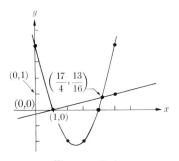

FIGURE 6–4

Thus $x = 1$ or $\frac{17}{4}$. Substitution of these values in the linear equation gives the corresponding values $y = 0, \frac{13}{16}$. The two solutions are $x = 1$, $y = 0$, and $x = \frac{17}{4}$, $y = \frac{13}{16}$.

Graphical solution. The given equations represent the parabola and straight line whose graphs are shown in Fig. 6–4. The intersections of the two curves show the solutions found by the algebraic method.

EXAMPLE 2. Solve the system of equations

$$x^2 - 2y^2 + 3x - 4y + 20 = 0,$$

$$2x - y = 1.$$

*Solution.** Although we are able to eliminate x or y, we choose to solve the linear equation for y and thus work with x, since the work appears to be simpler. Substituting $y = 2x - 1$ in the first equation, we have

$$x^2 - 2(2x - 1)^2 + 3x - 4(2x - 1) + 20 = 0.$$

Simplifying, we obtain

$$x^2 - 8x^2 + 8x - 2 + 3x - 8x + 4 + 20 = 0,$$

$$-7x^2 + 3x + 22 = 0,$$

$$7x^2 - 3x - 22 = 0,$$

$$(7x + 11)(x - 2) = 0.$$

Therefore,

$$x = 2, \qquad -\tfrac{11}{7}.$$

Substitution of these values in the linear equation yields the corresponding values $y = 3, -\frac{29}{7}$. The two solutions are then $x = 2$, $y = 3$, and $x = -\frac{11}{7}$, $y = -\frac{29}{7}$.

---

* A graphical solution involves the plotting of $x^2 - 2y^2 + 3x - 4y + 20 = 0$. Problems of this kind will be discussed in Article 12–1 and Chapter 18.

PROBLEMS

Solve each of the systems in Problems 1 through 6 both graphically and algebraically.

1. $y = 4x^2,$
   $y = 8x.$

2. $x - 2y = 10,$
   $y = x^2 + 2x - 15.$

3. $y^2 = 4x,$
   $x - y = -4.$

4. $(x - 2)^2 + (y - 3)^2 = 4,$
   $x + y + 3 = 0.$

5. $(x - 2)^2 + (y - 3)^2 = 4,$
   $x + y = 4.$
   [*Hint:* Recall Article 3–4 for the graph of this quadratic equation.]

6. $xy = 1,$
   $x + y = 2.$

Solve for x and y:

7. $y^2 + 2xy - 3x^2 + 7 = 0,$
   $x - 3y + 1 = 0.$

8. $x^2 + y^2 - 2x = 1,$
   $2x + y - 5 = 0.$

9. $3xy + 6x = 4y,$
   $2y - 3x - 4 = 0.$

10. $4x^2 + 3xy - 2y^2 - x - y + 1 = 0,$
    $x - 2y + 3 = 0.$

11. The circle $x^2 + y^2 = a^2$ and the straight line $y = mx + b$ will intersect in two points, be tangent, or not intersect, depending upon whether the solutions of this system of equations are real and distinct, real and equal, or imaginary. Find the value of b in terms of a and m so that the straight line will be tangent to the circle.

12. Find the dimensions of a rectangle if its diagonal is 17 inches and its perimeter is 46 inches.

13. The product of a two-digit number and the number obtained by reversing its digits is 736. If the difference of the two numbers is 9, find the numbers.

14. A and B, working together, can complete a certain job in $7\frac{1}{2}$ hours. Working alone, A would take 8 hours longer than B to do the job. How long would it take each working alone?

15. The sum of two numbers is 11, while the sum of their reciprocals is $\frac{11}{28}$. Find the numbers.

CHAPTER 7

DETERMINANTS

In mathematics it is frequently convenient to consider square or rectangular arrays of numbers such as

$$\left\| \begin{array}{ccc} a_1 & b_1 & c_1 \\ a_2 & b_2 & c_2 \end{array} \right\| \tag{7-1}$$

This rectangular array of numbers is called a *matrix*. The numbers $a_1, b_1, \ldots, c_2$ are called the *elements* of the matrix. The horizontal lines of numbers are called *rows*, while the vertical lines of numbers are called *columns*. In general, if a rectangular array has m rows and n columns, we call it an m by n matrix. We shall be interested only in square matrices ($m = n$), since any further study is beyond the scope of this book. Such an n by n matrix is said to be of *order n*.

7-1 Determinants of orders two and three. With each square matrix we associate a number called the *determinant* of the matrix. For a matrix of order 2, this number or determinant is defined to be the product of the elements in the upper left and lower right corners minus the product of the lower left and upper right elements. This determinant is symbolized as

$$D = \left| \begin{array}{cc} a_1 & b_1 \\ a_2 & b_2 \end{array} \right| = a_1 b_2 - a_2 b_1. \tag{7-2}$$

ILLUSTRATION.

(a) $\quad D = \left| \begin{array}{cc} 3 & 2 \\ 5 & 4 \end{array} \right| = (12) - (10) = 2,$

(b) $\quad D = \left| \begin{array}{cc} -1 & -4 \\ 2 & -3 \end{array} \right| = (-1)(-3) - 2(-4) = 11.$

PROBLEMS

Evaluate the determinants in Problems 1 through 6.

1. $\left| \begin{array}{cc} 3 & 4 \\ 5 & 6 \end{array} \right|$
2. $\left| \begin{array}{cc} 6 & -1 \\ 3 & -2 \end{array} \right|$
3. $\left| \begin{array}{cc} -2 & 3 \\ -5 & 6 \end{array} \right|$

4. $\begin{vmatrix} 8 & 0 \\ 1 & 2 \end{vmatrix}$ 5. $\begin{vmatrix} \sin\theta & \cos\theta \\ -\cos\theta & \sin\theta \end{vmatrix}$ 6. $\begin{vmatrix} \sec\theta & \tan\theta \\ \tan\theta & \sec\theta \end{vmatrix}$

*7. From Example 3, Article 5–5, show that the solution of the system of equations

$$a_1 x + b_1 y = c_1, \qquad a_2 x + b_2 y = c_2$$

may be written in terms of determinants as

$$x = \frac{\begin{vmatrix} c_1 & b_1 \\ c_2 & b_2 \end{vmatrix}}{\begin{vmatrix} a_1 & b_1 \\ a_2 & b_2 \end{vmatrix}}, \qquad y = \frac{\begin{vmatrix} a_1 & c_1 \\ a_2 & c_2 \end{vmatrix}}{\begin{vmatrix} a_1 & b_1 \\ a_2 & b_2 \end{vmatrix}}. \tag{7–3}$$

8. Using Eq. (7–3), solve Problems 1, 3, 5 of Article 5–5.

9. Using Eq. (7–3), solve Problems 2, 4, 6 of Article 5–5.

10. Solve for x: $\begin{vmatrix} 3 & 2 \\ x & 4 \end{vmatrix} = 0.$

11. Solve for x: $\begin{vmatrix} 2x & 3 \\ -5 & -4 \end{vmatrix} = 7x.$

12. Prove the identity $\begin{vmatrix} x-2 & 3 \\ x-2 & 5 \end{vmatrix} \equiv 2(x-2).$

13. Prove the identity $\begin{vmatrix} a-b & 0 \\ 1 & c-d \end{vmatrix} \equiv (a-b)(c-d).$

14. For what values of x is $\begin{vmatrix} x & 5 \\ 125 & x \end{vmatrix} > 0?$

15. What can be said about the nature of the roots of

$$ax^2 + bx + c = 0$$

if

$$\begin{vmatrix} b & 4a \\ c & b \end{vmatrix} > 0, \qquad = 0, \qquad < 0?$$

Let us now consider the square matrix of order three,

$$M = \begin{Vmatrix} a_1 & b_1 & c_1 \\ a_2 & b_2 & c_2 \\ a_3 & b_3 & c_3 \end{Vmatrix}. \tag{7–4}$$

For each element in such a matrix there exists a matrix of order 2, obtained by deleting the row and column in which the element lies. The second order determinant associated with the matrix obtained in this way is called the *minor* of the element under consideration. For example, denoting the minor of any element by the corresponding capital letter, we have

$$A_1 = \begin{vmatrix} b_2 & c_2 \\ b_3 & c_3 \end{vmatrix} \qquad B_3 = \begin{vmatrix} a_1 & c_1 \\ a_2 & c_2 \end{vmatrix} \qquad C_2 = \begin{vmatrix} a_1 & b_1 \\ a_3 & b_3 \end{vmatrix}$$

We now define the determinant of the third order matrix in (7–4) by

$$D = \begin{vmatrix} a_1 & b_1 & c_1 \\ a_2 & b_2 & c_2 \\ a_3 & b_3 & c_3 \end{vmatrix} = a_1 A_1 - b_1 B_1 + c_1 C_1. \tag{7-5}$$

EXAMPLE 1. Find the determinant of the matrix

$$\begin{Vmatrix} 2 & -1 & 3 \\ 3 & -2 & 1 \\ 4 & -3 & 2 \end{Vmatrix}$$

Solution.

$$\begin{vmatrix} 2 & -1 & 3 \\ 3 & -2 & 1 \\ 4 & -3 & 2 \end{vmatrix} = 2 \begin{vmatrix} -2 & 1 \\ -3 & 2 \end{vmatrix} - (-1) \begin{vmatrix} 3 & 1 \\ 4 & 2 \end{vmatrix} + 3 \begin{vmatrix} 3 & -2 \\ 4 & -3 \end{vmatrix}$$

$$= 2(-4 + 3) + 1(6 - 4) + 3(-9 + 8)$$

$$= -2 + 2 - 3$$

$$= -3.$$

EXAMPLE 2. Express D, Eq. (7–5), in terms of the elements only.

Solution.

$$D = \begin{vmatrix} a_1 & b_1 & c_1 \\ a_2 & b_2 & c_2 \\ a_3 & b_3 & c_3 \end{vmatrix} = a_1 \begin{vmatrix} b_2 & c_2 \\ b_3 & c_3 \end{vmatrix} - b_1 \begin{vmatrix} a_2 & c_2 \\ a_3 & c_3 \end{vmatrix} + c_1 \begin{vmatrix} a_2 & b_2 \\ a_3 & b_3 \end{vmatrix}$$

$$= a_1(b_2 c_3 - b_3 c_2) - b_1(a_2 c_3 - a_3 c_2) + c_1(a_2 b_3 - a_3 b_2)$$

$$= a_1 b_2 c_3 + a_2 b_3 c_1 + a_3 b_1 c_2 - a_1 b_3 c_2 - a_2 b_1 c_3 - a_3 b_2 c_1. \tag{7-6}$$

PROBLEMS

Evaluate each of the determinants in Problems 1 through 4.

1. $\begin{vmatrix} 1 & 2 & 3 \\ -2 & -1 & -2 \\ 3 & 1 & 4 \end{vmatrix}$

2. $\begin{vmatrix} -1 & 2 & -3 \\ 2 & -1 & -4 \\ 3 & -2 & 1 \end{vmatrix}$

3. $\begin{vmatrix} 2 & 1 & 3 \\ -1 & 4 & 7 \\ 4 & 2 & 6 \end{vmatrix}$

4. $\begin{vmatrix} 1 & -1 & 1 \\ 4 & 2 & 10 \\ 2 & 2 & 6 \end{vmatrix}$

Verify, using the value in Eq. (7–6):

*5. $D = -a_2 A_2 + b_2 B_2 - c_2 C_2$ *6. $D = a_3 A_3 - b_3 B_3 + c_3 C_3$

7. $D = a_1 A_1 - a_2 A_2 + a_3 A_3$ 8. $D = -b_1 B_1 + b_2 B_2 - b_3 B_3$

9. $D = c_1 C_1 - c_2 C_2 + c_3 C_3$

[*Note:* The third order determinant D could have been defined equally well by the equation given in 5, 6, 7, 8, or 9. The definition [Eq. (7–5)] gives the expansion of D by minors according to the elements of the first row. Problems 5 and 6 give the expansion by minors according to the elements of the second and third rows, respectively. Problems 7, 8, and 9 give the expansion by minors according to columns.]

10. Using the results of Problems 5 through 9, and Eq. (7–5), prove the following statement: The determinant of order three may be expressed as the sum of three products formed by multiplying each element of any row (or column) by its minor, where each such product has assigned to it a plus or minus sign, depending upon whether the sum of the number of the row and the number of the column in which each element is located is even or odd.

11. Evaluate Problems 1–4 by expansion by minors according to some row or column other than the first.

*12. Show that

$$\begin{vmatrix} x_1 & y_1 & 1 \\ x_2 & y_2 & 1 \\ x_3 & y_3 & 1 \end{vmatrix} = \begin{vmatrix} x_1 & y_1 \\ x_2 & y_2 \end{vmatrix} - \begin{vmatrix} x_1 & y_1 \\ x_3 & y_3 \end{vmatrix} + \begin{vmatrix} x_2 & y_2 \\ x_3 & y_3 \end{vmatrix}$$

*13. Using Fig. 7–1 and recalling that the area of a trapezoid is $\frac{1}{2}(b_1 + b_2)h$, where b_1 and b_2 are its bases and h its altitude, show that the area K of the triangle ABC in terms of the coordinates of its vertices is

$$K = \text{area of } ADEC + CEFB - ADFB$$

$$= \frac{1}{2} \begin{vmatrix} x_1 & y_1 & 1 \\ x_2 & y_2 & 1 \\ x_3 & y_3 & 1 \end{vmatrix} \qquad [\textit{Hint:} \text{ Use Problem 12.}] \qquad (7\text{–}7)$$

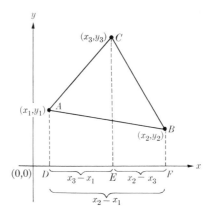

FIGURE 7–1

14. Write Eq. (5–19) in Problem 11, Article 5–6, in terms of three second order determinants, and thus obtain Eq. (7–7) by another process.

15. Find the area of the triangle whose vertices are the points (a) $(2, 3)$, $(5, 4)$, and $(4, 7)$; (b) $(-4, 2)$, $(-2, -3)$, and $(3, -1)$.

16. Find the area of the triangle the coordinates of whose vertices are (x, y), $(2, 3)$, and $(5, -1)$. (See Fig. 7–2.)

*17. The condition that the area of the triangle described in Problem 16 is equal to zero is equivalent to the fact that the point (x, y) lies on the line through $(2, 3)$ and $(5, -1)$. Using this fact, find the equation of the straight line through $(2, 3)$ and $(5, -1)$.

18. Find the equation of the straight line through $(-2, -4)$ and $(3, 5)$, using the method of this section.

19. Do Problem 7, Article 5–6, by the method of this section.

20. Do Problem 8, Article 5–6, by the method of this section.

21. Two nonparallel straight lines in the plane always intersect in one point. The condition that three such lines

$$a_1x + b_1y = c_1,$$

$$a_2x + b_2y = c_2,$$

$$a_3x + b_3y = c_3$$

pass through the same point is that the determinant of the matrix

$$\begin{Vmatrix} a_1 & b_1 & c_1 \\ a_2 & b_2 & c_2 \\ a_3 & b_3 & c_3 \end{Vmatrix}$$

is equal to zero. Assuming that such is the case, show that the three straight lines

$$x - 2y = -3,$$

$$3x - y = 1,$$

$$5x - 2y = 1$$

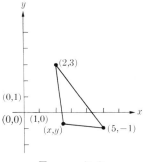

pass through the same point.

22. Show that the system of equations

$$3x - 2y + 11 = 0,$$

$$x - y + 5 = 0,$$

$$2x + y = 2$$

FIGURE 7-2

has a common solution, and find it.

23. By using the condition stated in Problem 21, solve (a) Problem 7, Article 5-8; (b) Problem 8; (c) Problem 9.

24. Find the value of x if

(a) $\begin{vmatrix} 1 & 2 & 5 \\ 1 & x & 5 \\ 3 & -1 & 2 \end{vmatrix} = 0,$

(b) $\begin{vmatrix} 1 & 2 & -3 \\ 1 & x & -3 \\ 1 & 4 & -x \end{vmatrix} = 0.$

7-2 Determinants of order n. As might be expected, there exist determinants of any finite order. To consider them and their general properties, it will be convenient to use a different notation for the elements of the matrix. Let us denote any element by the symbol a_{ij} (read "a sub i-j"), where i denotes the number of the row and j the number of the column in which the particular element appears. The notation for determinants used here was introduced by the English mathematician A. Cayley (1821–1895). According to this notation, Eq. (7–6) is written

$$D = \begin{vmatrix} a_{11} & a_{12} & a_{13} \\ a_{21} & a_{22} & a_{23} \\ a_{31} & a_{32} & a_{33} \end{vmatrix}$$

$$= a_{11}(a_{22}a_{33} - a_{23}a_{32}) - a_{12}(a_{21}a_{33} - a_{23}a_{31})$$
$$+ a_{13}(a_{21}a_{32} - a_{22}a_{31})$$

$$= a_{11}a_{22}a_{33} + a_{12}a_{23}a_{31} + a_{13}a_{21}a_{32} - a_{11}a_{23}a_{32}$$
$$- a_{12}a_{21}a_{33} - a_{13}a_{22}a_{31}. \quad (7–8)$$

It should be clear from this expression that each of the six products consists of one and only one element from each row and each column. Each of these products has been ordered by placing the first subscripts in natural numerical order. With the exception of the first term, the second subscripts are not in natural order. Let us consider the number of *inversions* of the second subscripts, that is, the number of times a greater integer precedes a smaller one.

	Second subscripts			*Number of inversions*
	1	2	3	0
Positive products	2	3	1	2
	3	1	2	2
	1	3	2	1
Negative products	2	1	3	1
	3	2	1	3

From this table, we see that the positive products have an even number of inversions, while the negative products have an odd number. Thus the correct sign for any term can be expressed $(-1)^k$, where k is the number of inversions. It is by means of a direct generalization of this study that we define the nth order determinant of the n square matrix. The expression

$$D = \begin{vmatrix} a_{11} & a_{12} & a_{13} \ldots a_{1n} \\ a_{21} & a_{22} & a_{23} \ldots a_{2n} \\ a_{31} & a_{32} & a_{33} \ldots a_{3n} \\ \vdots & & \vdots \\ a_{n1} & a_{n2} & a_{n3} \ldots a_{nn} \end{vmatrix} \tag{7-9}$$

is the *nth order determinant* associated with an n by n matrix. It is equal to the algebraic sum of all possible products formed by taking one and only one element from each row and each column. The sign of each product is chosen as $(-1)^k$, where k is the number of inversions of the second subscripts when the factors are so arranged that their first subscripts are in natural numerical order.

In any possible product of n elements with the first subscripts in natural order, the second subscript in the first element may be any one of n numbers, the subscript for the second element any one of the remaining $n-1$ numbers, and so on, so that there are $n!^* = n(n-1)(n-2) \cdots 2 \cdot 1$ terms in the expansion of D. For example, we recall that there are $3! = 6$ terms in the expansion of the third order determinant. There are $4! = 24$ in the fourth, and $5! = 120$ terms in the expansion of the fifth order determinant. Because of the large number of terms in the expansion of a

---

* The symbol $n!$ (read "factorial n") denotes the product of the positive integers from 1 to n. Specifically, $1! = 1$, $2! = 2$, $3! = 6$, and so on. This symbol will be used in later chapters.

determinant, our definition is clearly not a convenient way to find the value of the determinant. Before we consider a practical method of evaluation, we shall prove some of the elementary properties of determinants.

THEOREM 7–1. *If the corresponding rows and columns of a matrix are interchanged, its determinant remains unchanged.*

For example,

$$\begin{vmatrix} a_{11} & a_{12} & a_{13} \\ a_{21} & a_{22} & a_{23} \\ a_{31} & a_{32} & a_{33} \end{vmatrix} = \begin{vmatrix} a_{11} & a_{21} & a_{31} \\ a_{12} & a_{22} & a_{32} \\ a_{13} & a_{23} & a_{33} \end{vmatrix}$$

Proof. We recall that for each element our notation indicated the row by the first subscript, and the column by the second subscript. If we now consider the determinant associated with a new matrix M' whose rows and columns are respectively the corresponding columns and rows of M, every term of D' (the determinant associated with M') will again have one element from each row and each column. If the second subscripts are placed in their numerical natural order, the number of inversions of the first subscripts will determine the sign of any particular term. Thus the interchange of rows and columns serves only to change the notation, and the result for each term is the same. Consequently, D' is identical to D.

As a direct result of Theorem 7–1, in any further property of determinants the words "row" and "column" may be interchanged throughout.

THEOREM 7–2. *If any two columns (rows) of a determinant are interchanged, the sign of the determinant is changed.*

Proof. Let us first consider the interchange of two adjacent columns. In the expansion of the new determinant, the first subscripts will remain the same, but the second subscripts—those representing the columns—will be interchanged, and as a result the number of inversions in each term will be increased or decreased by one. Thus the sign of every term, and consequently the value of the determinants, will be changed.

Now suppose we wish to interchange the j and k columns (where for convenience $j < k$) and there are m columns between them. This may be done by moving the jth column to the position just to the left of the kth column (m interchanges), interchanging these two adjacent columns (1 interchange), and moving the kth column back to the original position of the jth column (m interchanges). Since the total number of interchanges, $2m + 1$, is odd, and each requires a change in sign, we again have our required result.

THEOREM 7–3. *If two columns (rows) of a matrix are identical, its determinant is zero.*

Proof. If D is the value of the determinant, with the two identical columns interchanged, the value becomes $-D$, by Theorem 7–2. But since the two columns were identical, the determinant has not changed. Thus, $D = -D$, that is $D = 0$.

THEOREM 7–4. *If each element of a column (row) in a determinant is multiplied by the same number m, the value of the determinant is multiplied by m.*

For example,

$$\begin{vmatrix} a_{11} & ma_{12} & a_{13} \\ a_{21} & ma_{22} & a_{23} \\ a_{31} & ma_{32} & a_{33} \end{vmatrix} = m \begin{vmatrix} a_{11} & a_{12} & a_{13} \\ a_{21} & a_{22} & a_{23} \\ a_{31} & a_{32} & a_{33} \end{vmatrix}$$

Proof. This property follows directly from the definition. If each element of a column is multiplied by m, each term in the expansion of the determinant will have m as a factor.

As a direct result of Theorem 7–4, we have the following corollary:

COROLLARY 7–4. *Any quantity that is a factor of each element in a column (row) is actually a factor of the expansion of the determinant.*

THEOREM 7–5. *If three matrices M_1, M_2, and M_3 have corresponding elements equal except for one column (row) in which the elements of M_1 are the sums of the corresponding elements of M_2 and M_3, then $D_1 = D_2 + D_3$, where D_i is the determinant associated with M_i.*

For example,

$$\begin{vmatrix} a_{11} + a'_{11} & a_{12} & a_{13} \\ a_{21} + a'_{21} & a_{22} & a_{23} \\ a_{31} + a'_{31} & a_{32} & a_{33} \end{vmatrix} = \begin{vmatrix} a_{11} & a_{12} & a_{13} \\ a_{21} & a_{22} & a_{23} \\ a_{31} & a_{32} & a_{33} \end{vmatrix} + \begin{vmatrix} a'_{11} & a_{12} & a_{13} \\ a'_{21} & a_{22} & a_{23} \\ a'_{31} & a_{32} & a_{33} \end{vmatrix}$$

Proof. Every term in the expansion of D_1 contains one and only one of these sums, each of which may be expressed as two terms. The expansions of D_2 and D_3 are the direct result.

THEOREM 7–6. *If each element of any column (row) of a matrix is multiplied by the same number m and added to the corresponding element of another column, the associated determinant remains unchanged.*

For example,

$$\begin{vmatrix} a_{11} & a_{12} & a_{13} \\ a_{21} & a_{22} & a_{23} \\ a_{31} & a_{32} & a_{33} \end{vmatrix} = \begin{vmatrix} a_{11} + ma_{13} & a_{12} & a_{13} \\ a_{21} + ma_{23} & a_{22} & a_{23} \\ a_{31} + ma_{33} & a_{32} & a_{33} \end{vmatrix}$$

Proof. This follows directly by using Theorems 7–5, 7–4, and 7–3 in considering the determinant on the right.

Many of these properties will be useful in the evaluation of the nth order determinant. Methods for such evaluation will be given in the next article.

PROBLEMS

1. Explain why the following two determinants are equal. Verify this fact by actual evaluation.

$$\begin{vmatrix} 2 & 4 & 1 \\ 3 & 2 & -1 \\ -1 & 3 & 2 \end{vmatrix} \qquad \begin{vmatrix} 2 & 3 & -1 \\ 4 & 2 & 3 \\ 1 & -1 & 2 \end{vmatrix}$$

2. Show by actual expansion that the sign of the determinant

$$\begin{vmatrix} 3 & -1 & 2 \\ 2 & 4 & 5 \\ -1 & 3 & 2 \end{vmatrix}$$

is changed if the first and third row are interchanged.

Without evaluating, state why each of the determinants in Problems 3 and 4 is zero. Check by evaluating.

3. $\begin{vmatrix} 2 & -3 & 2 \\ 1 & 2 & 1 \\ 6 & 4 & 6 \end{vmatrix}$
4. $\begin{vmatrix} 3 & 1 & -2 \\ 2 & 7 & 3 \\ 6 & 2 & -4 \end{vmatrix}$

5. Evaluate the following determinant by factoring out the common terms from any row or column and then expanding. Check by expanding directly.

$$\begin{vmatrix} 3 & 3 & 5 \\ 6 & 16 & 8 \\ -12 & 6 & 10 \end{vmatrix}$$

6. Use Theorem 7–5 to express the sum of the two determinants as a single determinant. Check the work by evaluating all three.

$$\begin{vmatrix} 3 & 1 & -2 \\ 2 & 3 & 5 \\ -1 & 4 & 3 \end{vmatrix} + \begin{vmatrix} -2 & 1 & -2 \\ -1 & 3 & 5 \\ 2 & 4 & 3 \end{vmatrix}$$

7. In the following determinant multiply each of the elements in the second row by 3, and form a new determinant by adding these results to the corresponding elements of the first row. Show by direct expansion that the value of the original determinant is unchanged.

$$\begin{vmatrix} 2 & 5 & -6 \\ -1 & 2 & 4 \\ 3 & 1 & 5 \end{vmatrix}$$

8. In the determinant of Problem 7, multiply each of the elements in the third column by 2 and subtract the products from the corresponding elements in the first column, forming a new determinant. Show by direct evaluation that the value of the original determinant is unchanged.

9. Determine the roots of the equation

$$\begin{vmatrix} 1 & 1 & 1 \\ x & a & b \\ x^2 & a^2 & b^2 \end{vmatrix} = 0.$$

[*Hint:* If $x = a$, the first two columns are equal.]

10. Determine the roots of the equation

$$\begin{vmatrix} 1 & a & a^2 & a^3 \\ 1 & b & b^2 & b^3 \\ 1 & c & c^2 & c^3 \\ 1 & x & x^2 & x^3 \end{vmatrix} = 0.$$

11. Find the roots of the equation

$$\begin{vmatrix} 3 & 1 & 9 \\ 2x & 2 & 6 \\ x^2 & 3 & 3 \end{vmatrix} = 0$$

by using Theorems 7–3 and 7–4, and check by expanding the determinant.

12. Prove that

$$2 \begin{vmatrix} a_1 & b_1 & c_1 \\ a_2 & b_2 & c_2 \\ a_3 & b_3 & c_3 \end{vmatrix} = \begin{vmatrix} b_1 + c_1 & c_1 + a_1 & a_1 + b_1 \\ b_2 + c_2 & c_2 + a_2 & a_2 + b_2 \\ b_3 + c_3 & c_3 + a_3 & a_3 + b_3 \end{vmatrix}$$

7–3 Expansion of a determinant by minors. The statement in Problem 10 of the second set of problems in Article 7–1 may be considered the method for the expansion of a third order determinant by minors. The method holds true in general. The *minor* of an element of a square matrix of order n is the $(n - 1)$st order determinant obtained by deleting the row and column in which this element lies. The minor of a_{ij} will be denoted by A_{ij}. We wish to prove the following theorem for the nth order determinant given in (7–9).

THEOREM 7–7. *The determinant is the algebraic sum of the products obtained by multiplying each element of a column (row) by its minor. The sign of each such product is* $(-1)^{i+j}$, *where the element is in the ith row and jth column.*

For example,

$$
\begin{vmatrix} a_{11} & a_{12} & a_{13} & a_{14} \\ a_{21} & a_{22} & a_{23} & a_{24} \\ a_{31} & a_{32} & a_{33} & a_{34} \\ a_{41} & a_{42} & a_{43} & a_{44} \end{vmatrix} = -a_{12}\begin{vmatrix} a_{21} & a_{23} & a_{24} \\ a_{31} & a_{33} & a_{34} \\ a_{41} & a_{43} & a_{44} \end{vmatrix} + a_{22}\begin{vmatrix} a_{11} & a_{13} & a_{14} \\ a_{31} & a_{33} & a_{34} \\ a_{41} & a_{43} & a_{44} \end{vmatrix}
$$

$$
-a_{32}\begin{vmatrix} a_{11} & a_{13} & a_{14} \\ a_{21} & a_{23} & a_{24} \\ a_{41} & a_{43} & a_{44} \end{vmatrix} + a_{42}\begin{vmatrix} a_{11} & a_{13} & a_{14} \\ a_{21} & a_{23} & a_{24} \\ a_{31} & a_{33} & a_{34} \end{vmatrix}
$$

is the expansion of the fourth order determinant by the second column.

Proof. The theorem is proved by noting two facts. Consider first the product $a_{11}A_{11}$. In this product, consisting of all the terms with a_{11} as a factor, all the signs of each term are correct, since the number of inversions in A_{11} is not changed by prefixing a_{11}.

Now consider any element a_{ij}. It may be moved to the original position of a_{11} by first moving the ith row to the first row, requiring $i - 1$ interchanges of rows, and then moving the jth column to the position of the first column, requiring an additional $j - 1$ interchange of columns. This process will produce $i - 1 + j - 1 = i + j - 2$ changes in sign. If D' is the new determinant, its relation to D is expressed by

$$ D' = (-1)^{i+j-2}D = (-1)^{i+j}D. $$

Thus the terms of the expansion with a_{ij} as a factor are

$$ (-1)^{i+j}a_{ij}A_{ij}, $$

where A_{ij} is the original minor of a_{ij} in D. Thus D may be expanded by means of any column (row) as indicated in the theorem.

We are now prepared to evaluate any determinant. In the following examples, note the use of the foregoing theorems.

EXAMPLE 1. Find the value of the determinant

$$D = \begin{vmatrix} -4 & 2 & 5 & 6 \\ 2 & 1 & 0 & 3 \\ 7 & 2 & -3 & 2 \\ 4 & -1 & 7 & 5 \end{vmatrix}$$

Solution. Since $a_{23} = 0$, it will simplify the work to expand by either the second row or third column. Since the elements in the third column are larger than the second row, we shall choose the second row. Thus,

$$D = -2 \begin{vmatrix} 2 & 5 & 6 \\ 2 & -3 & 2 \\ -1 & 7 & 5 \end{vmatrix} + 1 \begin{vmatrix} -4 & 5 & 6 \\ 7 & -3 & 2 \\ 4 & 7 & 5 \end{vmatrix} + 3 \begin{vmatrix} -4 & 2 & 5 \\ 7 & 2 & -3 \\ 4 & -1 & 7 \end{vmatrix}$$

Expanding each of the third order determinants, we get

$$\begin{vmatrix} 2 & 5 & 6 \\ 2 & -3 & 2 \\ -1 & 7 & 5 \end{vmatrix} = 2(-15 - 14) - 5(10 + 2) + 6(14 - 3)$$
$$= -58 - 60 + 66 = -52.$$

$$\begin{vmatrix} -4 & 5 & 6 \\ 7 & -3 & 2 \\ 4 & 7 & 5 \end{vmatrix} = -4(-15 - 14) - 5(35 - 8) + 6(49 + 12)$$
$$= 116 - 135 + 366 = 347.$$

$$\begin{vmatrix} -4 & 2 & 5 \\ 7 & 2 & -3 \\ 4 & -1 & 7 \end{vmatrix} = -4(14 - 3) - 2(49 + 12) + 5(-7 - 8)$$
$$= -44 - 122 - 75 = -241.$$

Using these values, we have

$$D = -2(-52) + 347 + 3(-241) = -272.$$

We notice in this example that the work was shortened by the fact that one of the elements was zero. By making use of Theorem 7–6, we may introduce other zeros and shorten the work still further. Let us consider another example.

EXAMPLE 2. Find the value of the determinant

$$D = \begin{vmatrix} 3 & -2 & -1 & 2 \\ 4 & 1 & 2 & -3 \\ -9 & -5 & 7 & -8 \\ 1 & 5 & 3 & -2 \end{vmatrix}$$

Solution. We look for an element equal to 1 or −1, and work with the row or column containing the ±1. Let us select the −1 in the first row. By using Theorem 7–6, we are able to introduce zeros in the first row. In turn we (1) multiply the elements of the third column by 3 and add the products to the corresponding elements of the first column, (2) multiply the elements of the third column by −2 and add the products to the corresponding elements of the second column, and (3) multiply the elements of the third column by 2 and add the products to the corresponding elements of the fourth column. Therefore,

$$D = \begin{vmatrix} 0 & 0 & -1 & 0 \\ 10 & -3 & 2 & 1 \\ 12 & -19 & 7 & 6 \\ 10 & -1 & 3 & 4 \end{vmatrix}$$

Now, expanding by the first row as in Example 1, we have

$$D = -1 \begin{vmatrix} 10 & -3 & 1 \\ 12 & -19 & 6 \\ 10 & -1 & 4 \end{vmatrix}$$

We may again introduce zeros to simplify the work. In this third order determinant, (1) multiply the elements of the first row by −6 and add the products to the corresponding elements of the second row, (2) multiply the elements of the first row by −4 and add the products to the corresponding elements of the third row. This results in

$$D = -1 \begin{vmatrix} 10 & -3 & 1 \\ -48 & -1 & 0 \\ -30 & 11 & 0 \end{vmatrix}$$

which, expanded by the last column, gives

$$D = -1\{1[(-48)(11) - (-30)(-1)]\}$$
$$= -1(-528 - 30) = 558.$$

If there is no element equal to 1 or -1 in any column or row, we are usually able to introduce such an element by using Theorem 7–6 and continuing as above. Although the introduction of a 1 is not necessary, the process eliminates the possibilities of fractions, if there were none initially.

PROBLEMS

Evaluate each of the following determinants:

1.
$$\begin{vmatrix} 1 & -2 & 2 & -3 \\ 0 & 5 & 0 & -2 \\ 2 & 4 & -6 & 2 \\ 3 & -4 & 1 & -2 \end{vmatrix}$$

2.
$$\begin{vmatrix} 2 & 4 & 3 & -5 \\ 3 & 0 & 2 & -1 \\ -2 & 3 & 1 & 6 \\ 1 & -4 & 2 & 8 \end{vmatrix}$$

3.
$$\begin{vmatrix} 4 & 2 & 4 & 8 \\ 7 & 5 & 2 & 4 \\ -7 & 2 & 3 & -8 \\ 6 & 4 & 5 & 6 \end{vmatrix}$$

4.
$$\begin{vmatrix} 3 & 2 & -1 & 4 \\ 4 & -3 & 5 & -2 \\ 6 & -1 & 4 & 7 \\ 5 & -2 & 8 & 3 \end{vmatrix}$$

5.
$$\begin{vmatrix} 3 & -1 & 2 & 6 \\ 2 & 3 & 5 & 4 \\ 4 & -2 & 2 & 7 \\ -3 & 2 & -1 & -3 \end{vmatrix}$$

6.
$$\begin{vmatrix} 1 & 1 & 1 & 1 \\ 1 & 2 & 3 & 4 \\ 1 & 3 & 6 & 10 \\ 1 & 4 & 10 & 20 \end{vmatrix}$$

7–4 Solution of a system of linear equations by determinants. In Articles 5–5 and 5–7 we discussed the solution of systems of linear equations in two and three unknowns. Systems of linear equations involving any number of unknowns, with the proper number of equations, may be expressed in terms of determinants. In considering the general case with n linear equations in n unknowns,

$$\begin{aligned}
a_{11}x_1 + a_{12}x_2 + \cdots + a_{1n}x_n &= k_1, \\
a_{21}x_1 + a_{22}x_2 + \cdots + a_{2n}x_n &= k_2, \\
&\vdots \\
a_{n1}x_1 + a_{n2}x_2 + \cdots + a_{nn}x_n &= k_n,
\end{aligned} \tag{7-10}$$

we are able to prove a theorem which is known as Cramer's Rule, in honor of the Swiss mathematician Gabriel Cramer (1704–1752).

THEOREM 7–8. *If D is the determinant of the coefficients of the unknowns, the product of D and any one of the unknowns is equal to the determinant D_i, obtained from D by substituting the constant terms in place of the coefficients of that unknown and leaving the other elements unchanged.*

Proof. Since

$$D = \begin{vmatrix} a_{11} & a_{12} \ldots a_{1n} \\ a_{21} & a_{22} \ldots a_{2n} \\ \vdots \\ a_{n1} & a_{n2} \ldots a_{nn} \end{vmatrix},$$

by Theorem 7–4,

$$Dx_1 = \begin{vmatrix} a_{11}x_1 & a_{12} \ldots a_{1n} \\ a_{21}x_1 & a_{22} \ldots a_{2n} \\ \vdots \\ a_{n1}x_1 & a_{n2} \ldots a_{nn} \end{vmatrix}.$$

If we now multiply each element of the second column by x_2, of the third by x_3, and so on, and add all these products to the corresponding elements in the first column, we have, by Theorem 7–6,

$$Dx_1 = \begin{vmatrix} a_{11}x_1 + a_{12}x_2 + \cdots + a_{1n}x_n & a_{12} \ldots a_{1n} \\ a_{21}x_1 + a_{22}x_2 + \cdots + a_{2n}x_n & a_{22} \ldots a_{2n} \\ \vdots \\ a_{n1}x_1 + a_{n2}x_2 + \cdots + a_{nn}x_n & a_{n2} \cdots a_{nn} \end{vmatrix}$$

$$= \begin{vmatrix} k_1 & a_{12} \ldots a_{1n} \\ k_2 & a_{22} \ldots a_{2n} \\ \vdots \\ k_n & a_{n2} \ldots a_{nn} \end{vmatrix} = D_1.$$

In this way, we find

$$Dx_1 = D_1, \qquad Dx_2 = D_2, \qquad \ldots, \qquad Dx_n = D_n, \qquad (7\text{--}11)$$

where D_i is obtained from D by substituting $k_1, k_2, \ldots, k_n$ for the elements $a_{1i}, a_{2i}, \ldots, a_{ni}$ of the ith column of D.

If $D \neq 0$,* the unique solution of (7–10) is obtained from (7–11)

---

* If $D = 0$, solutions may or may not exist. A complete discussion is beyond the scope of this book.

by division:

$$x_1 = \frac{D_1}{D}, \qquad x_2 = \frac{D_2}{D}, \qquad \cdots, \qquad x_n = \frac{D_n}{D}. \qquad (7\text{--}12)$$

It is clear that this set of values satisfies the system given in (7–10), and therefore is a solution. For example, the first equation is satisfied, since

$$k_1 D - a_{11}D_1 - a_{12}D_2 - \cdots - a_{1n}D_n$$

is the expansion of

$$\begin{vmatrix} k_1 & a_{11} & a_{12} \cdots a_{1n} \\ k_1 & a_{11} & a_{12} \ldots a_{1n} \\ k_2 & a_{21} & a_{22} \cdots a_{2n} \\ \vdots & & \\ k_n & a_{n1} & a_{n2} \ldots a_{nn} \end{vmatrix} \qquad (7\text{--}13)$$

by the first row. But this determinant is zero, since the first two rows are identical. The other equations are similarly satisfied.

PROBLEMS

1. Solve the systems of equations given in Problems 1, 3, 5, and 7 of Article 5–7 by the method of this article.

2. Solve the systems of equations given in Problems 2, 4, 6, and 8 of Article 5–7 by the method of this article.

Solve by determinants the following systems of equations:

3. $x + y + z + w = -4,$
   $x + 2y + 3z + 4w = 0,$
   $x + 3y + 6z + 10w = 9,$
   $x + 4y + 10z + 20w = 24.$

4. $x + 2y - z = 8,$
   $y + 3z - w = 3,$
   $z + 4w - x = -20,$
   $w + 5x - y = 9.$

CHAPTER 8

MATHEMATICAL INDUCTION AND THE BINOMIAL THEOREM

8-1 Mathematical induction. One of the most important methods of proof in mathematics is that of mathematical induction. The name is unfortunate, for we are likely to associate the word induction with inductive reasoning, by which a conclusion is drawn from a large number of special cases. No certain conclusion can be reached by the inductive logical process. Actually, mathematical induction is deductive in nature, for it leads to a firm conclusion. Since it will be a convenient method of proof for several important results that appear in our work, we shall consider the method in some detail. It is usually employed in proving the validity of a statement involving all positive integral values of n.

Let us illustrate this method of proof. Assume that we have an ordinary ladder with an indefinite number of steps and that we wish to prove that we can climb to any designated step. We can do this if we know two things:

(a) we can climb to the first step;

(b) if we are on any step, we can climb to the next higher step.

Because of (a) we know that we can get on the first step. With this knowledge and the fact stated in (b), we know we can get on the second step. Again, with this knowledge and the general fact stated in (b), we know we can get on the third step, etc.

One of the methods of finding a square root on an ordinary computing or adding machine is based on the fact that the sum of n odd integers is equal to n^2. Specifically,

$$1 = 1 = 1^2,$$
$$1 + 3 = 4 = 2^2,$$
$$1 + 3 + 5 = 9 = 3^2,$$
$$1 + 3 + 5 + 7 = 16 = 4^2.$$

This property is true for all integers, and is not difficult to prove.

EXAMPLE 1. Prove by mathematical induction that for all positive integral values,

$$1 + 3 + 5 + \cdots + (2n - 1) \equiv n^2.$$

Solution. Part (a): *Verification for a specific value.* We have done this for $n = 1, 2, 3,$ and 4, although such verification is necessary only for one value.

169

Part (b): *Induction property.* If the statement is true for $n = k$, where k denotes any value of n, then we wish to prove that it is true for $n = k + 1$. Thus we assume we know this fact for $n = k$, namely,

$$1 + 3 + 5 + \cdots + (2k - 1) \equiv k^2.$$

Adding $2k + 1$ to both members, we have

$$1 + 3 + 5 + \cdots + (2k - 1) + (2k + 1) \equiv k^2 + (2k + 1)$$
$$\equiv (k + 1)^2.$$

This is precisely the equation $1 + 3 + 5 + \cdots + (2n - 1) \equiv n^2$ stated for $n = k + 1$. Thus the proof of Part (b) is complete.

Part (c): *Conclusion.* We know that the equation is true for $n = 1, 2, 3$, and 4. Since it is true for $n = 4$, and since we have proved the statement in Part (b), we know the original equation is true for $n = 4 + 1 = 5$; since it is true for $n = 5$, it is also true for $n = 6$. We may reason in this manner for all positive integral values of n.

We observe that a proof by mathematical induction consists of three parts.

Part (a). *Verification* of the validity of the statement or theorem for the smallest integral value of n for which the theorem is to hold. (This is analogous to being able to climb to the first step of the ladder.)

Part (b). *Proof of the inductive property.* If the statement or theorem is valid for $n = k$, where k denotes any value of n, then it is valid for $n = k + 1$. (This is analogous to being able to climb from any step of the ladder to the next higher step.)

Part (c). *Conclusion.* The statement or theorem is valid for all integral values of n equal to or greater than that for which it was verified in Part (a).

We know that $x - y$ is a factor of $x - y$, $x^2 - y^2$, and $x^3 - y^3$. Is it a factor of $x^n - y^n$ for any positive integer n?

EXAMPLE 2. Prove by mathematical induction that $x^n - y^n$ is divisible by $x - y$ for all positive integral values of n.

Solution. Part (a): When $n = 1$, $x^n - y^n$ becomes $x - y$, which is clearly divisible by $x - y$. When $n = 2$, $x^2 - y^2 \equiv (x + y)(x - y)$, which again is divisible by $x - y$.

Part (b): We assume that $x^k - y^k$ is divisible by $x - y$. With this assumption, we must show that $x^{k+1} - y^{k+1}$ is also divisible by $x - y$. If we add and subtract xy^k to $x^{k+1} - y^{k+1}$, we have

$$x^{k+1} - y^{k+1} \equiv x^{k+1} - xy^k + xy^k - y^{k+1}$$
$$\equiv x(x^k - y^k) + y^k(x - y).$$

Since each term of the right member of this identity is divisible by $x - y$, the right and therefore the left member is divisible by $x - y$. This completes Part (b).

Part (c): We know that the theorem is true for $n = 1$ and 2. Since it is true for $n = 2$, by Part (b) it is true for $n = 2 + 1 = 3$. Similar reasoning applies for all positive integral values of n.

The fact that both Parts (a) and (b) are necessary for complete proof must be stressed. Consider the following examples.

EXAMPLE 3. In Article 1–8 we considered prime numbers. Does the expression $n^2 - n + 11$ represent a prime number for all positive values of n? For $n = 1, 2, 3, 4$, and 5, we have the prime numbers 11, 13, 17, 23, and 31. Certainly Part (a) is satisfied for our statement. To show that the statement is not valid, however, let $n = 11$, and we have $11^2 - 11 + 11 = 11^2$, which is not a prime number.

EXAMPLE 4. For even integers, let us assume the nonvalid statement that

$$2 + 4 + 6 + \cdots + 2n = n^2 + n + 1$$

is true when $n = k$. We can then prove the statement's validity, given this basic assumption, for $n = k + 1$. We have

$$2 + 4 + 6 + \cdots + 2k = k^2 + k + 1.$$

Adding $2k + 2$ to both members of the equality, we obtain

$$2 + 4 + 6 + \cdots + 2k + 2k + 2 = k^2 + k + 1 + 2k + 2$$
$$= k^2 + 2k + 1 + k + 1 + 1$$
$$= (k + 1)^2 + (k + 1) + 1.$$

Thus, if the statement is valid for $n = k$, it is also valid for $n = k + 1$, and Part (b) has been proved. It is clear, however, that Part (a) and thus the statement itself is not valid, for consider the case where $n = 1, 2$, or 3. We would have $2 = 3, 6 = 7$, or $12 = 13$, respectively.

Another example of a proof particularly suited to the method of mathematical induction is the common proof of a well-known generalization of material in the previous chapter. In Article 7–4 a system of n linear equations in n unknowns was considered. If the constant terms were each zero, this system of n *linear homogeneous equations* in n unknowns would have only the trivial solutions $x_i = 0$ for all i. Although a detailed proof will not be given because of the complex notation involved, we do have the following theorem and its outline of proof.

THEOREM 8–1. *A system of linear equations always has a nontrivial solution (values other than all zeros) if the number of unknowns exceeds the number of equations.*

Outline of proof. Part (a). If no equations in $n > 0$ variables are prescribed, our unknowns may be any values. Let each $x_i = 1$ and the "set of equations" will be "satisfied."

Part (b). Here the proof is based on the successive elimination process used in Article 5–5. After some variable x_j is eliminated, the solutions of the new set of equations in one less variable will also be solutions of the original set. If this process is used, the induction property is not difficult to establish. This should be clear from the elimination process used in Article 5–7.

PROBLEMS

By the method of mathematical induction, prove that the following are valid for all positive integral values of n:

1. $1 + 2 + 3 + \cdots + n = \dfrac{n(n+1)}{2}$

2. $2 + 4 + 6 + \cdots + 2n = n(n+1)$

3. $4 + 8 + 12 + \cdots + 4n = 2n(n+1)$

4. $1 + 4 + 7 + \cdots + (3n-2) = \dfrac{n(3n-1)}{2}$

5. $1 + 3 + 6 + \cdots \dfrac{n(n+1)}{2} = \dfrac{n(n+1)(n+2)}{6}$

6. $1^2 + 2^2 + 3^2 + \cdots + n^2 = \dfrac{n(n+1)(2n+1)}{6}$

7. $1^2 + 3^2 + 5^2 + \cdots + (2n-1)^2 = \dfrac{n(2n-1)(2n+1)}{3}$

8. $\dfrac{1}{2} + \dfrac{1}{2^2} + \dfrac{1}{2^3} + \cdots + \dfrac{1}{2^n} = 1 - \dfrac{1}{2^n}$

9. $2 + 2^2 + 2^3 + \cdots + 2^n = 2^{n+1} - 2$

10. $1^3 + 2^3 + 3^3 + \cdots + n^3 = \dfrac{n^2(n+1)^2}{4}$

11. $1^3 + 3^3 + 5^3 + \cdots + (2n-1)^3 = n^2(2n^2-1)$

12. $\dfrac{1}{1\cdot2} + \dfrac{1}{2\cdot3} + \dfrac{1}{3\cdot4} + \cdots + \dfrac{1}{n(n+1)} = \dfrac{n}{n+1}$

13. $1\cdot2 + 2\cdot3 + 3\cdot4 + \cdots + n(n+1) = \dfrac{n(n+1)(n+2)}{3}$

14. $1\cdot2 + 3\cdot4 + 5\cdot6 + \cdots + (2n-1)(2n) = \dfrac{n(n+1)(4n-1)}{3}$

15. $1 \cdot 2 \cdot 3 + 2 \cdot 3 \cdot 4 + 3 \cdot 4 \cdot 5 + \cdots + n(n + 1)(n + 2)$
$$= \frac{n(n + 1)(n + 2)(n + 3)}{4}$$

*16. $a + ar + ar^2 + \cdots + ar^{n-1} = \dfrac{a - ar^n}{1 - r}$

*17. $a + (a + d) + (a + 2d) + \cdots + a + (n - 1)d = \dfrac{n[2a + (n - 1)d]}{2}$

18. $x^{2n} - y^{2n}$ is divisible by $x - y$

19. $x^{2n-1} + y^{2n-1}$ is divisible by $x + y$

20. $n^3 + 2n$ is divisible by 3

21. If $a > -1$, $(a + 1)^n \geq 1 + na$

22. $\sin (\theta + n\pi) = (-1)^n \sin \theta$

23. $\cos (\theta + n\pi) = (-1)^n \cos \theta$

24. If n is a positive odd integer, $n(n^2 - 1)$ is divisible by 24.

25. $10^n + 3 \cdot 4^{n+2} + 5$ is divisible by 9

*26. Prove by mathematical induction the generalization of Eq. (3–5), namely, that for an algebraic sum of any fixed number of terms

$$|a_1 + a_2 + \cdots + a_n| \leq |a_1| + |a_2| + \cdots + |a_n|.$$

Prove the following by the method of mathematical induction:

27. $\sin \theta + \sin 2\theta + \cdots + \sin n\theta \equiv \dfrac{\sin \frac{1}{2}(n + 1)\theta \sin \frac{1}{2}n\theta}{\sin \theta/2}$

28. $\cos \theta + \cos 2\theta + \cdots + \cos n\theta \equiv \dfrac{\cos \frac{1}{2}(n + 1)\theta \sin \frac{1}{2}n\theta}{\sin \theta/2}$

29. $\sin \theta + \sin 3\theta + \cdots + \sin (2n - 1)\theta \equiv \dfrac{\sin^2 n\theta}{\sin \theta}$

30. $\cos \theta + \cos 3\theta + \cdots + \cos (2n - 1)\theta \equiv \dfrac{\sin 2n\theta}{2 \sin \theta}$

8–2 The binomial theorem. One of the more important theorems proved by mathematical induction is known as the *binomial theorem*. We are interested in obtaining a general expansion of the binomial $(a + b)^n$ for any positive integral value of n. By actual multiplication,

$$(a + b)^1 \equiv a + b,$$
$$(a + b)^2 \equiv a^2 + 2ab + b^2,$$
$$(a + b)^3 \equiv a^3 + 3a^2b + 3ab^2 + b^3,$$
$$(a + b)^4 \equiv a^4 + 4a^3b + 6a^2b^2 + 4ab^3 + b^4,$$
$$(a + b)^5 \equiv a^5 + 5a^4b + 10a^3b^2 + 10a^2b^3 + 5ab^4 + b^5.$$

With n denoting the exponent, we note the following properties for the above identities:

1. The number of terms in any identity is $n + 1$.

2. The first term a^n is the first term of the binomial $a + b$, raised to the nth power.

3. The exponents of a in each term decrease by 1 and those of b increase by 1, so that the sum of the exponents of a and b in any term is n.

4. If the coefficient in any term is multiplied by the exponent of a and divided by the exponent of b increased by 1, the result is the coefficient of the next term.

5. For the first and last, the second and next to the last, the third and third from last, etc., terms of the identity, the coefficients are the same.

If we assume that these are general properties of the expansion for $(a + b)^n$, we have the following theorem.

THEOREM 8–2. *For any positive integer n,*

$$(a + b)^n \equiv a^n + \frac{n}{1} a^{n-1}b + \frac{n(n-1)}{1 \cdot 2} a^{n-2}b^2$$
$$+ \frac{n(n-1)(n-2)}{1 \cdot 2 \cdot 3} a^{n-3}b^3 + \cdots + b^n. \qquad (8\text{–}1)$$

Proof. We must have the expression for the general or rth term. By examining Eq. (8–1), we see that the rth term contains b^{r-1}, and therefore, by Property 3, $a^{n-(r-1)} = a^{n-r+1}$. Also, the fractional coefficient of the rth term has for its denominator the product of the first $r - 1$ integers, $1 \cdot 2 \cdot 3 \cdots (r - 1)$, or factorial $(r - 1)$, $(r - 1)!$ (see footnote in Article 7–2), while its numerator contains $r - 1$ factors, the first being n and each succeeding factor being one less than the preceding, so that the last factor is $n - r + 2$. The rth term, therefore, is

$$\frac{n(n-1)(n-2) \cdots (n-r+2)}{(r-1)!} a^{n-r+1}b^{r-1}. \qquad (8\text{–}2)$$

We are now prepared to prove that Eq. (8–1) holds for all positive integral values of n. Since we have verified it for $n = 1, 2, 3, 4$, and 5, we need only to assume that it is valid for $n = k$, that is,

$$(a + b)^k \equiv a^k + ka^{k-1}b + \frac{k(k-1)}{2!} a^{k-2}b^2 + \cdots$$
$$+ \frac{k(k-1)(k-2) \cdots (k-r+2)}{(r-1)!} a^{k-r+1}b^{r-1} + \cdots + b^k, \qquad (8\text{–}3)$$

and prove from this that it is valid for $n = k + 1$, or

$$(a + b)^{k+1} \equiv a^{k+1} + (k + 1)a^k b + \frac{(k + 1)k}{2!} a^{k-1}b^2 + \cdots$$

$$+ \frac{(k + 1)(k)(k - 1) \cdots (k - r + 3)}{(r - 1)!} a^{k-r+2}b^{r-1} + \cdots + b^{k+1}.$$

$$(8\text{--}4)$$

If we multiply each member of the identity (8–3) by $(a + b)$, we have

$$(a + b)^{k+1} \equiv a^{k+1} + ka^k b + \cdots \frac{k(k - 1) \cdots (k - r + 2)}{(r - 1)!} a^{k-r+2}b^{r-1}$$

$$+ \cdots + ab^k + a^k b + \cdots$$

$$+ \frac{k(k - 1) \cdots (k - r + 3)}{(r - 2)!} a^{k-r+2}b^{r-1} + \cdots + kab^k + b^{k+1}.$$

The terms through ab^k represent the right member of (8–3) multiplied by a, and the remaining terms represent the right member multiplied by b. To obtain the rth term in the result, we have written the rth term in the first half of the right member and the $(r - 1)$st term in the second, thus both contain $a^{k-r+2}b^{r-1}$. If we simplify the whole right member, the total coefficient of $a^{k-r+2}b^{r-1}$ will be

$$\frac{k(k - 1) \cdots (k - r + 2)}{(r - 1)!} + \frac{k(k - 1) \cdots (k - r + 3)}{(r - 2)!}$$

$$= \frac{k(k - 1) \cdots (k - r + 3)}{(r - 1)!} (k - r + 2)$$

$$+ \frac{k(k - 1) \cdots (k - r + 3)}{(r - 1)(r - 2)!} (r - 1)$$

$$= \frac{k(k - 1) \cdots (k - r + 3)}{(r - 1)!} [(k - r + 2) + (r - 1)]$$

$$= \frac{(k + 1)k(k - 1) \cdots (k - r + 3)}{(r - 1)!}.$$

Thus the total right side is exactly that of Eq. (8–4). The conclusion, Part (c), should be clear, and the proof is complete.

EXAMPLE 1. Expand $(a + 2b)^6$ by the binomial theorem and simplify the result.

Solution. With a the first term and $2b$ the second in the binomial to be expanded, we have

$$(a + 2b)^6 \equiv a^6 + 6a^5(2b) + \frac{6 \cdot 5}{2!} a^4(2b)^2 + \frac{6 \cdot 5 \cdot 4}{3!} a^3(2b)^3$$

$$+ \frac{6 \cdot 5 \cdot 4 \cdot 3}{4!} a^2(2b)^4 + 6a(2b)^5 + (2b)^6$$

$$\equiv a^6 + 12a^5 b + 60a^4 b^2 + 160a^3 b^3$$

$$+ 240a^2 b^4 + 192ab^5 + 64b^6.$$

EXAMPLE 2. Find the first four terms of the expansion of $(x^3 - 3y^2)^{12}$.

Solution. Here $a = x^3$ and $b = -3y^2$. Thus,

$$(x^3 - 3y^2)^{12} \equiv (x^3)^{12} + 12(x^3)^{11}(-3y^2) + \frac{12 \cdot 11}{2!} (x^3)^{10}(-3y^2)^2$$

$$+ \frac{12 \cdot 11 \cdot 10}{3!} (x^3)^9(-3y^2)^3 + \cdots$$

$$\equiv x^{36} - 36x^{33}y^2 + 594x^{30}y^4 - 5940x^{27}y^6 + \cdots$$

Note from the method of this example that when the first term of the binomial is plus and the second minus, the signs in the expansion alternate.

The general term [Eq. (8-2)] is of use in many problems involving a specific term.

EXAMPLE 3. Find the sixth term in the expansion of $[(1/2a) - 3]^{16}$.

Solution. In this example the first term is $1/2a$, and the second is -3, $n = 16$, and $r = 6$. If we substitute in (8-2), the sixth term is

$$\frac{16 \cdot 15 \cdot 14 \cdot 13 \cdot 12}{2 \cdot 3 \cdot 4 \cdot 5} \left(\frac{1}{2a} \right)^{11} (-3)^5 = -\frac{66339}{128a^{11}}.$$

PROBLEMS

Expand each of the following by the binomial theorem, and simplify if necessary.

1. $(a + b)^7$

2. $(xy - 2)^4$

3. $(2x + y^2)^5$

4. $\left(a^2 - \frac{x}{2} \right)^6$

5. $(5x - y^2)^4$

6. $(x^{-1} + 2y^{-2})^6$

7. $(x^{1/3} + y^{1/3})^6$

8. $(x^{2/3} - y^{2/3})^5$

9. $(x^{2/5} - 3y^{-2})^5$

10. $(ax^{1/2} - by^{1/3})^6$

Write and simplify the first four terms of the expansions for the following:

11. $\left(\dfrac{x^2}{2} + \dfrac{2}{y^2}\right)^{12}$

12. $(x^{1/3} - y^{1/3})^9$

13. $(x^{1/3} - y^{-1/3})^{11}$

14. $(x^{-2/3} + 2y^{2/3})^8$

15. $(1 + x)^k$

*16. $(1 + k)^{1/k}$

[*Note:* Assume that the binomial theorem holds for $n = 1/k$.]

Write and simplify the indicated term in the expansions of the following:

17. Seventh term of $(2x - y)^{12}$

18. Ninth term of $\left(2 + \dfrac{x}{4}\right)^{15}$

19. Middle term of $(y^2 - \tfrac{1}{2})^8$

20. Middle term of $\left(2 + \dfrac{3}{x}\right)^{10}$

21. Term involving x^7 of $(2x - 3)^{10}$

22. Term involving x^3 of $(5 - 2x)^6$

23. Term involving x^5 of $\left(x + \dfrac{1}{2x}\right)^7$

24. Term involving $\dfrac{x^2}{y^2}$ of $\left(\dfrac{x}{y} - \dfrac{y^2}{2x^2}\right)^8$

25. Prove that the $(r + 1)$st term of Eq. (8–1) is

$$\frac{n(n - 1)(n - 2) \cdots (n - r + 1)}{r!} a^{n-r} b^r.$$

*26. The coefficients in the binomial expansion are called binomial coefficients. The coefficient of the $(r + 1)$st term given in Problem 25 is a function of n and r. If this function is denoted by $C(n, r)$, where

$$C(n, r) = \frac{n(n - 1)(n - 2) \cdots (n - r + 1)}{r!}, \qquad (8\text{–}5)\dagger$$

prove that

$$C(n, r) = \frac{n!}{r!(n - r)!}. \qquad (8\text{–}6)$$

[*Hint:* Multiply numerator and denominator of the right member of (8–5) by $(n - r)!$.]

27. Prove that $C(n, r) = C(n, n - r)$, and thus establish Property 5 of the binomial expansion.

28. Solve $C(n, 4) = 35$ for the positive integer n.

*29. Prove that

$$2^n = (1 + 1)^n = 1 + C(n, 1) + C(n, 2) + C(n, 3) + \cdots + C(n, n).$$

30. Check the statement in Problem 29 for $n = 5$.

---

† This function, $C(n, r)$, also represents the combination of n things taken r at a time, and is well known in the study of permutations and combinations (see Chapter 20).

8–3 The expansion of $(1 + x)^n$. Applying the binomial theorem to $(1 + x)^n$, we have

$$(1 + x)^n \equiv 1 + nx + \frac{n(n - 1)}{2!} x^2$$

$$+ \frac{n(n - 1)(n - 2)}{3!} x^3 + \cdots$$

$$+ \frac{n(n - 1) \cdots (n - r + 2)}{(r - 1)!} x^{r-1} + \cdots, \qquad (8\text{–}7)$$

which contains $n + 1$ terms and is valid for all positive integers n. If n were any real number other than a positive integer, the expansion in (8–7) would not terminate. Under what conditions would this relation still be valid?

Although the proof is beyond the scope of this book, it can be shown that a finite number of terms of the right member of (8–7) approximates $(1 + x)^n$, for any value of n which is not a positive integer if $|x| < 1$. It should be clear that the more terms that are considered, the closer the approximation will be, since the size of each term will be less in magnitude than the preceding one.

EXAMPLE 1. Find the value of $(1.02)^{-4}$ correct to four significant figures.

Solution. We expand $(1.02)^{-4}$ by the relationship of (8–7).

$$(1.02)^{-4} = (1 + 0.02)^{-4}$$

$$= 1^{-4} + (-4) \cdot 1^{-5}(0.02) + \frac{(-4)(-5)}{2!} \cdot 1^{-6}(0.02)^2$$

$$+ \frac{(-4)(-5)(-6)}{3!} \cdot 1^{-7}(0.02)^3$$

$$+ \frac{(-4)(-5)(-6)(-7)}{4!} \cdot 1^{-8}(0.02)^4 + \cdots$$

$$= 1 - 0.08 + 0.004 - 0.00016 + 0.0000056 + \cdots$$

$$= 0.9238456.$$

We must consider a sufficient number of terms to guarantee the required accuracy. Since the last term above has a zero in the fifth decimal place, no additional terms will affect our result, that is,

$$(1.02)^{-4} = 0.9238, \text{ correct to four significant figures.}$$

EXAMPLE 2. Find the value of $\sqrt{15}$ correct to four significant figures.

Solution. Again we use the relationship of (8–7).

$$\sqrt{15} = \sqrt{16 - 1} = (16 - 1)^{1/2} = [16(1 - \tfrac{1}{16})]^{1/2} = 4(1 - \tfrac{1}{16})^{1/2}$$

$$= 4\Big[1 + \tfrac{1}{2} \cdot 1^{-1/2}(-\tfrac{1}{16}) + \frac{\tfrac{1}{2}(-\tfrac{1}{2})}{2!} 1^{-3/2}(-\tfrac{1}{16})^2$$

$$+ \frac{\tfrac{1}{2}(-\tfrac{1}{2})(-\tfrac{3}{2})}{3!} 1^{-5/2}(-\tfrac{1}{16})^3 + \cdots\Big]$$

$$= 4[1 - \tfrac{1}{32} - \tfrac{1}{2048} - \tfrac{1}{65536} \cdots]$$

$$= 4[1 - 0.03125 - 0.000488 - 0.000015\ldots]$$

$$= 3.8730, \text{ correct to four significant figures.}$$

PROBLEMS

Write out the first four terms of each of the expansions for the following expressions:

1. $\dfrac{1}{1 + x} = (1 + x)^{-1}$ 2. $\sqrt{1 + x}$

3. $\dfrac{1}{\sqrt{1 - x}}$ *4. $(1 + x)^{1/x}$

Compute each of the following to four significant figures:

5. $(1.01)^{-2}$ 6. $(1.03)^{-5}$ 7. $\sqrt[4]{1.02}$ 8. $\sqrt{1.05}$

9. $\sqrt{33}$ 10. $\sqrt[4]{17}$ 11. $\sqrt[3]{120}$ 12. $(1.01)^{10}$

CHAPTER 9

FUNCTIONS, LIMITS, AND CONTINUITY

9–1 Additional functions. Combinations of functions. In Article 3–6 we defined the notion of function and considered several simple examples of functions which are "well behaved." In Chapter 4 we dealt with the circular functions, and in Chapters 5 and 6 we discussed the linear and quadratic functions in some detail. There are other more complicated functions in mathematics. Let us clarify some of the common types.

DEFINITION 9–1. *If $f(x)$ can be expressed in the form*

$$f(x) = a_0 x^n + a_1 x^{n-1} + a_2 x^{n-2} + \cdots + a_{n-1} x + a_n, \qquad (9\text{–}1)$$

where $a_0 \neq 0$, n is a positive integer or zero, and a_i ($i = 0, 1, 2, \ldots, n$) are constants, we say that $f(x)$ is a rational integral function *or a* polynomial function *of x.*

This function, considered in detail in Chapter 11, gets its name from the polynomial defined in Article 1–6.

ILLUSTRATION 1. The following are examples of polynomial functions:

$$f(x) = 3x^3 - 7x + 1,$$
$$g(x) = \sqrt{5}x^5 - 8x^3 + 2x^2 - \pi/2,$$
$$F(y) = ay^2 + by + c.$$

The classification of functions follows the pattern suggested in Article 1–1 for numbers. As the polynomial functions correspond to integers, the rational functions correspond to the rational numbers.

DEFINITION 9–2. *If $f(x)$ can be expressed as the quotient of two polynomials in x, that is*

$$f(x) = \frac{P(x)}{Q(x)},$$

where $P(x)$ and $Q(x)$ are polynomial functions of x, $f(x)$ is called a rational function *of x.*

ILLUSTRATION 2. The following are rational functions:

$$f(x) = \frac{5x^2 + 6x - 2}{8x + 1}, \qquad g(y) = \frac{y^2 - 2}{3y^3 - \sqrt{7}y + 1}.$$

Clearly, any polynomial function is also a rational function, for it can be expressed as a fraction with the denominator 1.

DEFINITION 9–3.   *If a function consists of sums, products, quotients, or roots of polynomials in x, it is called an* algebraic function *of x.*

ILLUSTRATION 3.   The following is an example of an algebraic function:

$$f(x) = \frac{\sqrt{x + 5} - \sqrt[3]{x^2 + 1/x}}{6x + 5}.$$

Any rational function is also an algebraic function.

DEFINITION 9–4.   *Any function which is not an algebraic function is called a* transcendental function.

The circular functions are of this type.   Other transcendental functions such as the inverse circular functions and the exponential and logarithmic functions will be considered in Chapters 13 and 14.

We can represent the different types of real functions as follows:

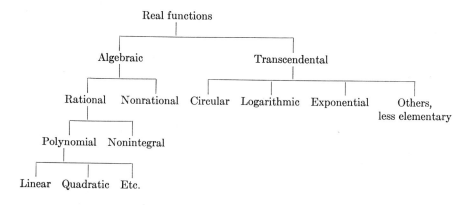

It is also possible to define a function by different expressions (either algebraic or transcendental) for different values of its domain.   To illustrate this method, let us consider several examples of functions.

EXAMPLE 1.   Let $f(x)$ be defined for all real x as the largest integer less than or equal to x.   This is frequently written $f(x) = [x]$.   Plot the function.

Solution.   Since for any x such that $0 \le x < 1, f(x) = 0$, and for any x such that $1 \le x < 2, f(x) = 1$, and so on, the function has only integral values for its range.   Its graph is shown in Fig. 9–1, and the function described by this graph might be termed a *step function*.

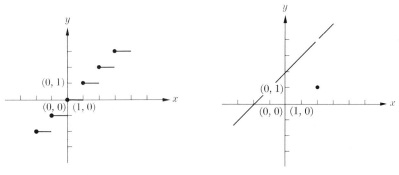

FIGURE 9–1   FIGURE 9–2

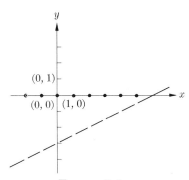

FIGURE 9–3

EXAMPLE 2. Plot the function defined as follows:

$$f(x) = \frac{x^2 - 4}{x - 2} \qquad (x \neq 2),$$

$$= 1 \qquad (x = 2).$$

Solution. Since $(x^2 - 4)/(x - 2) \equiv x + 2$ if x is not equal to 2, the graph of the function is the straight line $y = x + 2$, except at $x = 2$. At $x = 2$ the function has the value 1. (See Fig. 9–2.)

EXAMPLE 3. Plot the function defined as follows:

$$f(x) = \begin{cases} \tfrac{1}{2}x - 3, \text{ for } x \text{ not an integer,} \\ 0, \text{ for } x \text{ an integer.} \end{cases}$$

Solution. Since $f(-1) = 0, f(0) = 0, f(1) = 0$, and so on, the function is represented by the line $y = \tfrac{1}{2}x - 3$ for all x except integral values. In Fig. 9–3 the graph is shown.

The functions described in these three examples are typical of functions that might be termed "not too well behaved." To describe such behavior more accurately, we must consider certain basic combinations of functions. In dealing with combinations, the domains of the functions involved must be taken into consideration at all times, so that the combinations will be clearly defined.

The more important combinations of functions are defined as follows:

DEFINITION 9–5.   *The sum function of two functions $f(x)$ and $g(x)$ is defined as the function $S(x)$, where*

$$S(x) = f(x) + g(x). \tag{9-2}$$

DEFINITION 9–6.   *The product function of two functions $f(x)$ and $g(x)$ is defined as the function $P(x)$, where*

$$P(x) = f(x) \cdot g(x). \tag{9-3}$$

DEFINITION 9–7.   *The quotient function of two functions $f(x)$ by $g(x)$ is defined as the function $Q(f, g; x)$, where*

$$Q(f, g; x) = \frac{f(x)}{g(x)} . \tag{9-4}$$

DEFINITION 9–8.   *The composite function of two functions $f(x)$ by $g(x)$ is defined as the function $C(f, g; x)$, where*

$$C(f, g; x) = f(g(x)). \tag{9-5}$$

Because of Definition 9–7, the quotient function of $g(x)$ by $f(x)$ is $Q(g, f; x) = g(x)/f(x)$. Similarly, by Definition 9–8, the composite function of $g(x)$ by $f(x)$ is $C(g, f; x) = g(f(x))$.

The domain of $S(x)$, $P(x)$, and $Q(f, g; x)$ is the set of all real numbers contained in the domains of both $f(x)$ and $g(x)$, except in the case of the quotient, which is not defined for any x where $g(x) = 0$. The domain of $f(g(x))$ consists of the set of x's for which $g(x)$ is contained in the domain of f. Unless the function is defined for all real values, its domain should be clearly stated.

ILLUSTRATION 4.   If $f(x) = 2x - 1$ and $g(x) = 6 - x - x^2$ for all values of x, the sum function of $f(x)$ and $g(x)$ is

$$S(x) = (2x - 1) + (6 - x - x^2) = 5 + x - x^2,$$

the product function of $f(x)$ and $g(x)$ is

$$P(x) = (2x - 1)(6 - x - x^2) = -2x^3 - x^2 + 13x - 6,$$

the quotient function of $f(x)$ by $g(x)$ is

$$Q(f, g; x) = \frac{2x - 1}{6 - x - x^2}, \qquad (x \neq 2 \quad \text{or} \quad -3),$$

the composite function of $f(x)$ by $g(x)$ is

$$C(f, g; x) = f(g(x)) = 2(6 - x - x^2) - 1 = 11 - 2x - 2x^2,$$

and the composite function of $g(x)$ by $f(x)$ is

$$C(g, f; x) = g(f(x)) = 6 - (2x - 1) - (2x - 1)^2$$
$$= 2(3 + x - 2x^2).$$

PROBLEMS

Plot the graphs of the following functions.

1. $f(x) = \begin{cases} 1, & 0 < x \\ -1, & x < 0 \end{cases}$. How does this compare with $f(x) = |x|/x$?

2. $f(x) = \begin{cases} x, & 0 < x \le 1 \\ 3 - x, & 1 < x \le 2 \end{cases}$ 3. $f(x) = [|2x|], -3 \le x \le 3$

4. $f(x) = [\frac{3}{2} x] + 2$ 5. $f(x) = 3[2x] - 3$

6. $f(x) = \begin{cases} \dfrac{x - 2}{x^2 - 4} & \text{for } x \ne 2 \\ 1 & \text{for } x = 2 \end{cases}$

7. $f(x) = \begin{cases} 0 \text{ for } 0 \le x < 2 \\ 1 \text{ for } 2 \le x < 4 \\ 2 \text{ for } 4 \le x < 6 \end{cases}$. Can this be written in terms of the greatest integer function [ ]?

8. Find an expression for $[f(x) - f(a)]/(x - a)$, $(x \ne a)$, if
   (a) $f(x) = a$,   (b) $f(x) = x$,   (c) $f(x) = 3x$.

9. Simplify the expression for $[f(x) - f(a)]/(x - a)$, $(x \ne a)$, if
   (a) $f(x) = 1/x$,   (b) $f(x) = x^2$,   (c) $f(x) = \sqrt{x}$.

10. Find $S(x)$, $P(x)$, $f(x)/g(x)$, $f(g(x))$, and $g(f(x))$, and give the domain for each combination if
   (a) $f(x) = 2x - 3$, $g(x) = 3x + 2$,
   (b) $f(x) = x^2 - x$, $g(x) = x + 4$,
   (c) $f(x) = 4 - 3x$, $g(x) = 2x - 3x^2$,
   (d) $f(x) = 2/x$, $g(x) = x - 3$,
   (e) $f(x) = \sqrt{x}$, $g(x) = x^3$.

11. If $f(g(x)) = 1 - x^2$ and $g(x) = 1 - x^2$, find $f(x)$.
12. If $f(g(x)) = 1 - x^2$ and $g(x) = x$, find $f(x)$.
13. If $f(g(x)) = x^2 + 2x + 1$ and $f(x) = x^2$, find $g(x)$.
14. If $f(g(x)) = x^2$ and $f(x) = x - 1$, find $g(x)$.
15. If $f(x) = 2x + 1$, find $(f(x))^2$, $f(x^2)$, and $f(f(x))$. Are the three expressions equal?

9–2 Introduction to limits. The most important concept in basic mathematics, aside from the idea of function, is the idea of limit. The introduction of limits permits us to proceed from elementary mathematics consisting of algebra, trigonometry, and the simpler parts of geometry to more advanced mathematics consisting of calculus and its many applications.

The concept of a limit is not a simple notion. Intuitively, the idea may be clear; it has been met in elementary geometry. The area of a circle was defined and evaluated as the common limit of the areas of the sets of regular inscribed and circumscribed polygons as the number of sides increases. Arc length was introduced also through a limit process (recall Article 3–4). However, the notion is actually quite complicated and great effort should be made to gain as thorough an understanding as possible.

For any value of the independent variable x in the domain of the function, $f(x)$ has a corresponding value. In Example 1, Article 3–7, this fact was used to plot the function $f(x) = 3x - 4$. If x is close to 3, the function $3x - 4$ is close to 5. The following table, similar to that in Article 3–7, indicates this relation.

x	2.9	2.99	2.999	3.001	3.01	3.1
$f(x) = 3x - 4$	4.7	4.97	4.997	5.003	5.03	5.3

Since $3x - 4$ is close to 5 if x is close to 3, but not equal to 3, we say that the limit of $3x - 4$ as x approaches 3 is 5. We write this statement

$$\underset{x \to 3}{\text{limit}} \, (3x - 4) = 5.$$

We see that the closeness of $3x - 4$ to 5 *depends* on the nearness of x to 3. If

$$2.9 < x < 3.1,$$

then

$$3(2.9) - 4 < 3x - 4 < 3(3.1) - 4,$$

or

$$4.7 < 3x - 4 < 5.3.$$

Similarly, if

$$2.999 < x < 3.001,$$

then

$$4.997 < 3x - 4 < 5.003.$$

In terms of absolute values, we have the following: if

$$|x - 3| < 0.1, \qquad \text{then} \qquad |(3x - 4) - 5| < 0.3,$$

and if

$$|x - 3| < 0.001, \qquad \text{then} \qquad |(3x - 4) - 5| < 0.003.$$

Thus if x is within 0.1 unit of 3, $3x - 4$ is within 0.3 unit of 5, and if x is within 0.001 unit of 3, $3x - 4$ is within 0.003 unit of 5. This suggests that the values of $3x - 4$ can be made to differ from 5 by as small an amount as we please if we choose x sufficiently close to 3.

Let us consider a somewhat more complicated illustration.

ILLUSTRATION 1. If $f(x) = 5x^2 + x + 2$, $\text{limit}_{x \to 2} f(x) = 24$. In order to show this, we refer to the table of values of x near 2 and the corresponding values of the function:

x	1.9	1.999	2.001	2.1
$f(x)$	21.95	23.979	24.021	26.05

We note that if x is close to 2, $f(x)$ is close to 24. Moreover, if

$$1.9 < x < 2.1,$$

we have

$$21.95 < f(x) < 26.05,$$

that is, if

$$|x - 2| < 0.1, \qquad \text{then} \qquad |f(x) - 24| < 2.05.$$

Similarly, if

$$|x - 2| < 0.001, \qquad \text{then} \qquad |f(x) - 24| < 0.021.$$

It would therefore appear that $f(x) = 5x^2 + x + 2$ can be made to differ from 24 by as small an amount as we wish if we choose x sufficiently close to 2. This is indeed the case, and we therefore say

$$\lim_{x \to 2} (5x^2 + x + 2) = 24.$$

If for values of x close to a fixed value a, the corresponding values of $f(x)$ are close to a fixed value A and, moreover, if the values of $f(x)$ can be made to differ from A by as small an amount as we please if we choose x sufficiently close to a, and if this is true for all such values of x in the domain of the function, except possibly for $x = a$, then we say the limit of $f(x)$ as x approaches a is equal to A, and we write

$$\lim_{x \to a} f(x) = A. \qquad (9\text{-}6)$$

It must be emphasized that we are *not* interested in the value of $f(x)$ at $x = a$. A more analytic and concise definition seems appropriate. It will be used in proofs of the theorems on limits which appear in Article 9–3.

DEFINITION 9–9. *The limit of $f(x)$ as x approaches a is equal to A, that is*

$$\underset{x \to a}{\text{limit}}\, f(x) \;=\; A,$$

if for any positive number ϵ there exists a positive number δ depending on ϵ such that if x is in the domain of the function and

$$0 < |x - a| < \delta, \qquad then \qquad |f(x) - A| < \epsilon.*$$

Although a need not be in the domain of $f(x)$, we assume that all the values of x arbitrarily close to a are in this domain.

Figure 9–4 shows the geometric interpretation of the existence of the limit of a function at a point.

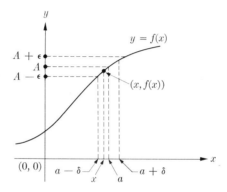

FIGURE 9–4

The definition states exactly what was mentioned in the previous illustration. The value of x at $x = a$ is not considered. Moreover, δ, the choice of the difference between x and a, is dependent on ϵ, the difference between $f(x)$ and A. In the example of the function $f(x) = 3x - 4$, $\delta = 0.1$ for $\epsilon = 0.3$ and $\delta = 0.001$ for $\epsilon = 0.003$. It would appear that $\delta = \epsilon/3$ might always be the relation between ϵ and δ for this function at $x = 3$, and such is the case since

$$|(3x - 4) - 5| = |3x - 9| = 3|x - 3|.$$

If no A exists that satisfies the definition, we say that $\text{limit}_{x \to a}\, f(x)$ does not exist.

Although it is sometimes difficult to find the largest particular δ in terms of ϵ for a particular function at a value a, it should be noticed that if a satisfactory δ is found, any $\delta' < \delta$ will suffice.

---

* The symbol ϵ is the Greek letter epsilon. It is frequently used to denote a (small) positive constant. The symbol δ is the Greek letter delta.

EXAMPLE 1. In Example 2 of Article 9–1, let us determine $\text{limit}_{x \to 2} f(x)$ and find a δ corresponding to an arbitrary ϵ.

Solution. Since

$$f(x) = \frac{x^2 - 4}{x - 2} \equiv x + 2$$

if x is not equal to 2, we see that if x is sufficiently close to 2 (but not equal to 2), $x + 2$ will be close to 4. To prove that $\text{limit}_{x \to 2} f(x) = 4$ according to the definition, for any positive number ϵ we must find another positive number δ, depending on ϵ, such that if

$$0 < |x - 2| < \delta, \qquad \text{then} \qquad \left| \frac{x^2 - 4}{x - 2} - 4 \right| < \epsilon.$$

If we take $\delta = \epsilon$, then

$$\left| \frac{x^2 - 4}{x - 2} - 4 \right| = |x + 2 - 4| = |x - 2| < \epsilon,$$

and the limit is established. Note that the value of the function for the specific value $x = a$ has nothing to do with $\text{limit}_{x \to a} f(x)$. In this example $\text{limit}_{x \to 2} f(x) = 4$, but $f(2) = 1$.

EXAMPLE 2. Find

$$\underset{x \to 1}{\text{limit}} \frac{x - 1}{\sqrt{x + 3} - 2}.$$

Solution. If we substitute $x = 1$ in this expression, we see that the function is not defined. (Why?) However, by rationalizing the denominator, we have

$$\frac{x - 1}{\sqrt{x + 3} - 2} \cdot \frac{\sqrt{x + 3} + 2}{\sqrt{x + 3} + 2} = \frac{(x - 1)(\sqrt{x + 3} + 2)}{x + 3 - 4} = \sqrt{x + 3} + 2,$$

so that if $x \neq 1$,

$$\frac{x - 1}{\sqrt{x + 3} - 2} = \sqrt{x + 3} + 2.$$

Thus, if x is sufficiently close to 1 but distinct from 1, $\sqrt{x + 3} + 2$ is close to $\sqrt{1 + 3} + 2 = 4$. We therefore have

$$\underset{x \to 1}{\text{limit}} \frac{x - 1}{\sqrt{x + 3} - 2} = 4.$$

EXAMPLE 3. Show that $\text{limit}_{x\to2} f(x)$ does not exist, where $f(x) = [x]$.

Solution. If the limit exists and is equal to A, for any preassigned positive number ϵ we must find a δ such that if $0 < |x - 2| < \delta$, then $|[x] - A| < \epsilon$. Let us take $\epsilon = \frac{1}{2}$. Then it is clear that no matter how small a positive δ is chosen, there will be some x's where $|x - 2| < \delta$, such that $[x] = 1$ and others for which $[x] = 2$. Thus there could be no value A such that for all these x's $|[x] - A| < \frac{1}{2}$. Recall Example 1, Article 9–1, and Fig. 9–1.

PROBLEMS

Evaluate each of the limits, if they exist, in Problems 1–16.

1. $\text{limit}_{x\to6} (2x - 5)$

2. $\text{limit}_{x\to0} (3x^2 - 4x + 2)$

3. $\text{limit}_{x\to1} \dfrac{3x + 2}{x}$

4. $\text{limit}_{x\to-1} 4 - \dfrac{3}{x^2}$

5. $\text{limit}_{x\to4} \dfrac{\sqrt{x + 5}}{3}$

6. $\text{limit}_{x\to-6} \dfrac{\sqrt{x + 5}}{2}$

7. $\text{limit}_{x\to1} \dfrac{x}{x - 1}$

8. $\text{limit}_{x\to6} \dfrac{x^2 - 5x - 6}{x - 6}$

9. $\text{limit}_{x\to2} \dfrac{x^2 - 7x + 10}{x - 2}$

10. $\text{limit}_{x\to0} \dfrac{(3 + x)^2 - 9}{x}$

11. $\text{limit}_{x\to0} \dfrac{(16 + x)^{-2} - 16^{-2}}{x}$

12. $\text{limit}_{x\to-1} \dfrac{x + 1}{3 - \sqrt{x + 10}}$

13. $\text{limit}_{x\to2} \dfrac{x - 2}{3 - \sqrt{2x + 5}}$

14. $\text{limit}_{x\to2} \dfrac{3x - 6}{1 - \sqrt{4x - 7}}$

15. $\text{limit}_{h\to0} \dfrac{(x + h)^2 - x^2}{h}$

16. $\text{limit}_{h\to0} \dfrac{\sqrt{x + h} - \sqrt{x}}{h}$

[*Hint:* Rationalize the numerator.]

17. If $f(x) = (x^2 - 5x + 6)/(x^2 - 4)$, find
    (a) $\text{limit}_{x\to1} f(x)$,
    (b) $\text{limit}_{x\to2} f(x)$,
    (c) $\text{limit}_{x\to3} f(x)$,
    (d) $\text{limit}_{x\to-2} f(x)$.

18. If $f(x) = (x^2 - 3x - 10)/(x^2 - 4)$, find
    (a) $\text{limit}_{x\to1} f(x)$,
    (b) $\text{limit}_{x\to2} f(x)$,
    (c) $\text{limit}_{x\to5} f(x)$,
    (d) $\text{limit}_{x\to-2} f(x)$.

19. In Example 3, Article 9–1, explain why the limit of the function exists as x approaches each integral value. Notice that this does not depend on the value of the function at the integral values.

20. What can be said about $\text{limit}_{x \to 0} f(x)$ in Problem 1, Article 9–1?

21. What can be said about $\text{limit}_{x \to 1} f(x)$ in Problem 2, Article 9–1?

22. What can be said about $\text{limit}_{x \to 1/2} f(x)$ in Problem 5, Article 9–1?

23. What can be said about $\text{limit}_{x \to 2} f(x)$ in Problem 7, Article 9–1?

24. What value of δ should be chosen in showing that $\text{limit}_{x \to a} f(x)$ exists if $f(x) = 5$? What is the value of this limit?

25. Prove rigorously (in terms of ϵ and δ) that $\text{limit}_{x \to 3} (4x - 4) = 8$.

There are two important generalizations of the type of limit defined by Definition 9–9.

If we let

$$f(x) = \frac{1}{(x - 3)^2},$$

and set up a table showing corresponding values of this function for values of x close to 3, we note that these functional values are large.

x	2.5	2.9	2.99	3.01	3.1	3.5
$f(x) = \dfrac{1}{(x - 3)^2}$	4	100	10,000	10,000	100	4

Moreover, it seems evident (as is the case) that the value of the function can be made as large as we wish if we choose x sufficiently close to 3. If, for example,

$$2.5 < x < 3.5 \quad \text{or} \quad |x - 3| < 0.5 \quad \text{then} \quad f(x) > 4.$$

Similarly, if

$$|x - 3| < 0.1, \quad \text{then} \quad f(x) > 100.$$

Let us make a general statement, of which the last illustration is a special case. If $f(x)$ is greater than any arbitrarily large positive number for all values of x sufficiently close to the value a, but not equal to a, then $f(x)$ becomes positively infinite as x approaches a. This is written

$$\underset{x \to a}{\text{limit}} \, f(x) = \infty, \tag{9–7}$$

so that for the case where

$$f(x) = \frac{1}{(x - 3)^2},$$

we have

$$\underset{x \to 3}{\text{limit}} \, \frac{1}{(x - 3)^2} = \infty.$$

The symbol ∞ is usually read "infinity." It is *not* a number; its specific meaning is given above. In analytic notation, similar to that for the original definition of the limit of a function, we have the equivalent concise workable definition for (9–7):

DEFINITION 9–10. *The limit of $f(x)$ as x approaches a becomes infinite positively, that is*

$$\lim_{x \to a} f(x) = \infty,$$

if for any large positive number N there exists a sufficiently small positive number δ (depending on N) such that if

$$0 < |x - a| < \delta, \quad \text{then} \quad f(x) > N.$$

ILLUSTRATION 2. If

$$f(x) = \frac{1}{(x - 3)^2},$$

we can choose $\delta = 1/\sqrt{N}$. In this case, when x is such that

$$0 < |x - 3| < \frac{1}{\sqrt{N}},$$

we have

$$|x - 3|^2 < \frac{1}{\sqrt{N^2}}, \quad \text{or} \quad \frac{1}{|x - 3|^2} > N,$$

so that the limit becomes infinite positively. See Fig. 9–5.

If we again consider

$$f(x) = \frac{1}{(x - 3)^2}$$

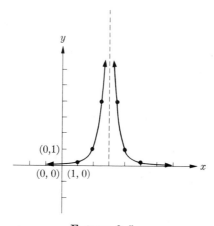

FIGURE 9–5

and the table showing corresponding values of this function for large values of x, it appears that the values of the function can be made to differ from zero by as small an amount as we wish.

x	5	10	100
$f(x) = \dfrac{1}{(x-3)^2}$	0.25	0.02	0.0001

If $x > 5$, then

$$\left| \frac{1}{(x-3)^2} - 0 \right| < 0.25,$$

if $x > 10$, then

$$\left| \frac{1}{(x-3)^2} - 0 \right| < 0.02,$$

and if $x > 100$, then

$$\left| \frac{1}{(x-3)^2} - 0 \right| < 0.0001.$$

Usually, if the difference between $f(x)$ and some fixed value A can be made numerically as small as we please for all x greater than some value N, we say the limit of $f(x)$ as x becomes infinite positively is A, and we write

$$\lim_{x \to +\infty} f(x) = A. \qquad (9\text{--}8)$$

In the last illustration, then,

$$\lim_{x \to +\infty} \frac{1}{(x-3)^2} = 0.$$

More formally, we have the following:

DEFINITION 9–11. *The limit of $f(x)$ as x becomes infinite positively is A, that is*

$$\lim_{x \to +\infty} f(x) = A,$$

if for any arbitrarily small positive number ϵ there exists a sufficiently large positive number N (depending on ϵ) such that if

$$x > N, \qquad then \qquad |f(x) - A| < \epsilon.$$

ILLUSTRATION 3. For the same function mentioned in Illustration 2, $\lim_{x \to +\infty} f(x) = 0$. If N is chosen to be $1/\sqrt{\epsilon}$, for all x such that

$$x - 3 > N = \frac{1}{\sqrt{\epsilon}} \quad \text{or} \quad x > 3 + \frac{1}{\sqrt{\epsilon}},$$

$$\left| \frac{1}{(x-3)^2} - 0 \right| = \left| \frac{1}{(x-3)^2} \right| < \frac{1}{N^2} = \epsilon.$$

EXAMPLE 4. Find

$$\underset{x \to +\infty}{\text{limit}} \frac{2x + 1}{x - 3}.$$

Solution. Although we could probably guess this limit by substituting larger and larger values of x in the expression, that is, $x = 10$, 100, 1000, . . . , the work is simplified by dividing both numerator and denominator by x. We obtain

$$\frac{2x + 1}{x - 3} \equiv \frac{2 + \dfrac{1}{x}}{1 - \dfrac{3}{x}},$$

which is an identity for all values of x except $x = 0$ and $x = 3$. (Why?) It should now be clear that if we take x sufficiently large, this quotient can be made to differ from 2 by as small a value as we please. Therefore,

$$\underset{x \to +\infty}{\text{limit}} \frac{2x + 1}{x - 3} = 2.$$

The graph of the function is shown in Fig. 9–6.

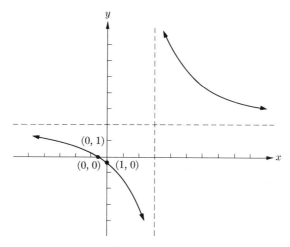

FIGURE 9–6

PROBLEMS

Evaluate each of the limits in Problems 1–6.

1. $\lim_{x \to 0} \dfrac{1}{x^2}$

2. $\lim_{x \to 5} \dfrac{x+3}{(x-5)^2}$

3. $\lim_{x \to 2} \left(3 - \dfrac{1}{(x-2)^2}\right)$

4. $\lim_{x \to -3} \left(\dfrac{6}{(3+x)^4} - 7\right)$

5. $\lim_{x \to 5} \dfrac{x}{\sqrt{x-5}}$

6. $\lim_{x \to 2} \dfrac{3}{\sqrt{2-x}}$

7. Explain why the $\lim_{x \to 5} x/(x-5)$ does not exist and how it differs from $\lim_{x \to 5} x/\sqrt{x-5}$.

8. Explain why $\lim_{x \to 0} 1/x$ doesn't exist according to our definition.

Evaluate each of the limits in Problems 9–20.

9. $\lim_{x \to +\infty} \dfrac{5}{x}$

10. $\lim_{x \to +\infty} \left(\dfrac{7}{x^2} - 3\right)$

11. $\lim_{x \to +\infty} \left(\dfrac{2}{x^2} + \dfrac{4}{x}\right)$

12. $\lim_{x \to +\infty} \left(\dfrac{3}{x} + 6\right)$

13. $\lim_{x \to +\infty} \dfrac{3x-1}{2x+5}$

14. $\lim_{x \to +\infty} \dfrac{2x^2+5x}{x^2-7}$

15. $\lim_{x \to +\infty} \dfrac{2x-1}{3x^2+7}$

16. $\lim_{x \to +\infty} \dfrac{2x+3}{\sqrt{(3x-2)^3}}$

17. $\lim_{x \to +\infty} \dfrac{x^2-7x+10}{2x}$

18. $\lim_{x \to +\infty} \dfrac{2x^3-4x-7}{5x^2+7x}$

19. $\lim_{x \to 0} \dfrac{3x-1}{2x+5}$

20. $\lim_{x \to 0} \dfrac{2x^2+5x}{x^2-7}$

21. Explain what is meant by $\lim_{x \to a} f(x) = -\infty$, and give an equivalent analytic definition.

22. Explain what is meant by $\lim_{x \to -\infty} f(x) = A$, and give an equivalent analytic definition.

9–3 Theorems on limits. In obtaining significant results in calculus or in making use of the limit notions just discussed, we shall be frequently operating with limits. The theorems or properties given below will not all be rigorously proved in this book, for although the proofs are not too difficult, they are long and demand considerable discussion.* We shall

---

* For detailed proofs of the theorems mentioned in this article, see E. G. Begle, *Introductory Calculus*, Henry Holt and Company.

state and prove only the first theorem; the others will be assumed. If the first and third theorems have been proved in the case of two functions, the results may be shown to hold, by mathematical induction, for any finite number of functions.

THEOREM 9–1. *The limit of the sum of two functions is equal to the sum of the limits; that is, if*

$$\operatorname{limit}_{x \to a} f(x) = A \qquad and \qquad \operatorname{limit}_{x \to a} g(x) = B, \qquad (9\text{–}9)$$

then

$$\operatorname{limit}_{x \to a} (f(x) + g(x)) = A + B. \qquad (9\text{–}10)$$

Proof. We must show that for any positive number ϵ there exists a δ which depends on ϵ such that

$$|(f(x) + g(x)) - (A + B)| < \epsilon$$

for all values of x where

$$0 < |x - a| < \delta.$$

We first note, using relation (3–5), that

$$|(f(x) + g(x)) - (A + B)| = |(f(x) - A) + (g(x) - B)|$$
$$\leq |(f(x) - A| + |g(x) - B|. \qquad (9\text{–}11)$$

Since $\operatorname{limit}_{x \to a} f(x) = A$ implies that for any positive number $\epsilon/2$ there exists a δ_1 depending on $\epsilon/2$, and of course on $f(x)$, such that for all x where

$$0 < |x - a| < \delta_1, \qquad |f(x) - A| < \epsilon/2.$$

Similarly, since $\operatorname{limit}_{x \to a} g(x) = B$, for the same $\epsilon/2$ there exists a δ_2 depending on $\epsilon/2$ and $g(x)$ such that for all x where

$$0 < |x - a| < \delta_2, \qquad |g(x) - B| < \epsilon/2.$$

Now, choosing the smaller of δ_1 and δ_2 and calling it δ, we have for all x where $0 < |x - a| < \delta$

$$|f(x) - A| < \epsilon/2 \qquad and \qquad |g(x) - B| < \epsilon/2,$$

or

$$|f(x) - A| + |g(x) - B| < \epsilon,$$

which, by (9–11), gives us the required result.

THEOREM 9–2. *The limit of the difference of two functions is equal to the difference of the limits; that is, if*

$$\lim_{x \to a} f(x) = A \qquad and \qquad \lim_{x \to a} g(x) = B,$$

then

$$\lim_{x \to a} (f(x) - g(x)) = A - B. \tag{9–12}$$

The proof of this theorem is very similar to that for Theorem 9–1.

THEOREM 9–3. *The limit of the product of two functions is equal to the product of the limits; that is, with the same conditions stated in (9–9),*

$$\lim_{x \to a} [f(x)g(x)] = AB. \tag{9–13}$$

THEOREM 9–4. *The limit of the quotient of two functions is equal to the quotient of the limits, provided that the limit of the denominator is not zero; that is, with the same conditions stated in (9–9), and where $B \neq 0$,*

$$\lim_{x \to a} \frac{f(x)}{g(x)} = \frac{A}{B}. \tag{9–14}$$

A much more complicated theorem to understand thoroughly and also to prove is the following.

THEOREM 9–5. *If for two functions $f(x)$ and $g(x)$,*

$$\lim_{x \to a} f(x) = A \qquad and \qquad \lim_{x \to a} g(x) = B,$$

where $A \neq 0$, then

$$\lim_{x \to a} f(x)^{g(x)} = A^B. \tag{9–15}$$

This theorem will be useful in Chapter 14, where we shall consider $f(x)$ raised to a power other than a rational number. By far the most frequent use we will make of the theorem is in the case where $g(x)$ is a constant function and, in fact, where the constant is a rational number.

THEOREM 9–6. *If $f(x) < g(x) < h(x)$ where the functions are all defined for the same domain, and if $\lim_{x \to a} f(x) = \lim_{x \to a} h(x) = A$, then $\lim_{x \to a} g(x) = A$.*

Several examples of this theorem appear in the next article. Its proof is not too difficult if the analytic definition of a limit is used.

To see how the above theorems apply, consider the following illustrations, noting carefully which theorem is used in each step.

ILLUSTRATION 1.

$$\lim_{x \to 3} (2x^3 - 7x^2 + 6) = \lim_{x \to 3} (2x^3) - \lim_{x \to 3} 7x^2 + \lim_{x \to 3} 6$$

$$= \lim_{x \to 3} 2 \, (\lim_{x \to 3} x)^3 - \lim_{x \to 3} 7 \, (\lim_{x \to 3} x)^2 + \lim_{x \to 3} 6$$

$$= 2(3)^3 - 7(3)^2 + 6 = -3.$$

ILLUSTRATION 2.

$$\lim_{x \to 2} ((x^2 - x)\sqrt{3x + 1}) = \lim_{x \to 2} (x^2 - x) \lim_{x \to 2} \sqrt{3x + 1}$$

$$= \left(\lim_{x \to 2} x^2 - \lim_{x \to 2} x \right) \sqrt{\lim_{x \to 2} 3x + \lim_{x \to 2} 1}$$

$$= \left[\left(\lim_{x \to 2} x \right)^2 - \lim_{x \to 2} x \right] \sqrt{\lim_{x \to 2} 3 \lim_{x \to 2} x + \lim_{x \to 2} 1}$$

$$= (2^2 - 2)\sqrt{3 \cdot 2 + 1} = 2\sqrt{7}.$$

PROBLEMS

Evaluate each of the limits in Problems 1–6, indicating which theorems are used.

1. $\lim\limits_{x \to 1} (x^2 + 2x - 5)$

2. $\lim\limits_{x \to 2} \dfrac{x^2 - 3}{x + 1}$

3. $\lim\limits_{x \to 5} \dfrac{\sqrt{x^2 + 7}}{4}$

4. $\lim\limits_{x \to 3} \dfrac{x^3\sqrt{x - 2}}{(x - 3)^2}$

5. $\lim\limits_{x \to 2} \left(5 - \dfrac{x - 2}{x} \right)$

6. $\lim\limits_{x \to 3} \left(x^2 - \dfrac{\sqrt{x - 3}}{x^3} \right)$

7. Give a proof of Theorem 9–2 similar to that for Theorem 9–1.
8. Give a proof of Theorem 9–6.

9–4 Basic circular function limits. We are now ready to evaluate certain limits that are of fundamental importance in connection with the circular functions, and at the same time to use our results to find approximate values of the circular functions for small values of θ. By recalling the definition for $\sin \theta$ and $\tan \theta$, and restricting θ to a small positive value (recall Problem 16, Article 4–3), we would expect the values of $\sin \theta$, $\tan \theta$, and θ to be approximately the same. This is actually the case. In Fig. 9–7, which shows a unit circle with θ in standard position, let A and P be the points where the initial and terminal sides of θ intersect the circle. The line from P is drawn perpendicular to the x-axis, intersecting

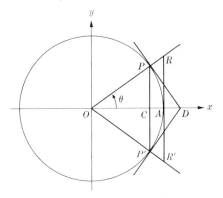

FIGURE 9–7

the circle at P'. The x-axis bisects the vertical chord $P'P$ at C and the arc $\overset{\frown}{P'P}$ at A. The tangent to the circle at A is drawn, intersecting the two lines OP and OP' (extended) at R and R', respectively. The tangents to the circle at P and P' then intersect at D, a point on the x-axis. (Why?) Consider the chord $P'CP$, the arc $\overset{\frown}{P'AP}$, and the segments of the tangents to the circle, $P'D$ and DP. From a proposition in plane geometry,

$$P'CP < \overset{\frown}{P'AP} < P'DP.$$

Dividing these lengths by 2, we have

$$CP < \overset{\frown}{AP} < DP.$$

But $DP = AR$. (Why?) Therefore,

$$CP < \overset{\frown}{AP} < AR,$$

or

$$\sin \theta < \theta < \tan \theta. \qquad (9\text{–}16)$$

It should be pointed out that (9–16) holds where $0 < \theta < \pi/2$, while the inequality is reversed if $-\pi/2 < \theta < 0$. In either case, if we divide each member of the inequality by $\sin \theta$, with the appropriate size of θ, we have

$$1 < \frac{\theta}{\sin \theta} < \sec \theta.$$

Considering the reciprocals, we get

$$\cos \theta < \frac{\sin \theta}{\theta} < 1, \qquad (9\text{–}17)$$

and since $\cos\theta = \sqrt{1 - \sin^2\theta} > \sqrt{1 - \theta^2}$ (why?), we have

$$\sqrt{1 - \theta^2} < \frac{\sin\theta}{\theta} < 1, \qquad (9\text{–}18)$$

which now holds for all values of θ such that $-\pi/2 < \theta < \pi/2$.

Since $\operatorname{limit}_{\theta\to 0} \sqrt{1 - \theta^2} = 1$ and $\operatorname{limit}_{\theta\to 0} 1 = 1$, by using Theorem 9–6, we immediately have one extremely important result.

THEOREM 9–7.

$$\operatorname*{limit}_{\theta\to 0} \frac{\sin\theta}{\theta} = 1. \qquad (9\text{–}19)$$

If each member of (9–16) is divided by $\tan\theta$ where $0 < \theta < \pi/2$, (or the inequality reversed if $-\pi/2 < \theta < 0$), we have for all values of θ where $-\pi/2 < \theta < \pi/2$

$$\cos\theta < \frac{\theta}{\tan\theta} < 1, \qquad (9\text{–}20)$$

or

$$\sqrt{1 - \theta^2} < \frac{\theta}{\tan\theta} < 1,$$

and by use of the reciprocal relation this becomes

$$1 < \frac{\tan\theta}{\theta} < \frac{1}{\sqrt{1 - \theta^2}}. \qquad (9\text{–}21)$$

Again using Theorem 9–6, we have the following:

THEOREM 9–8.

$$\operatorname*{limit}_{\theta\to 0} \frac{\tan\theta}{\theta} = 1. \qquad (9\text{–}22)$$

In order to obtain approximate values of the circular functions for small values of θ, we may use certain of the above relations. Specifically, if we multiply each member of (9–18) by θ, where $\theta > 0$, we have

$$\theta\sqrt{1 - \theta^2} < \sin\theta < \theta. \qquad (9\text{–}23)$$

If we multiply each member of (9–21) by θ, where $\theta > 0$, we obtain

$$\theta < \tan\theta < \frac{\theta}{\sqrt{1 - \theta^2}}. \qquad (9\text{–}24)$$

It is also possible to find the value of $\cos\theta$ for small positive values of θ. Since $\cos\theta \equiv 1 - 2\sin^2\theta/2$, we have

$$\cos\theta > 1 - 2\frac{\theta^2}{4},$$

and thus,

$$1 > \cos \theta > 1 - \frac{\theta^2}{2}. \tag{9-25}$$

Relations (9–23), (9–24), and (9–25) give us bounds for $\sin \theta$, $\tan \theta$, and $\cos \theta$.

EXAMPLE. Find an approximate value of $\sin \pi/60$.

Solution. Substituting in (9–23) for $\theta = \pi/60$, where $\pi = 3.1416$, we find

$$0.05229 < \sin \pi/60 < 0.05236.$$

Thus, correct to four decimal places, $\sin \pi/60 = 0.0523$. Note the value listed in Table I.

PROBLEMS

1. With $\pi = 3.1416$, find the best possible approximation for $\sin \pi/30$, $\cos \pi/30$, and $\tan \pi/30$, using the above inequalities.

2. Find approximations for $\cos \pi/60$ and $\tan \pi/60$. Compare these values with those given in Table I.

*3. Prove:

(a) $\lim\limits_{\theta \to 0} \sin \theta = 0$, [*Hint:* Use Eq. (9–23).]

(b) $\lim\limits_{\theta \to 0} \cos \theta = 1$,   (c) $\lim\limits_{\theta \to 0} \tan \theta = 0$.

4. Using the result of Theorem 9–3, and Eqs. (9–19) and (9–23), prove

$$\lim\limits_{\theta \to 0} \frac{\sin \theta}{\tan \theta} = 1.$$

5. Using the result of Problem 3(b), prove

$$\lim\limits_{\theta \to 0} \frac{\sin \theta}{\tan \theta} = 1.$$

Also prove this relationship by considering products.

6. With the use of (9–17) and (9–25), obtain the bounds for $\sin \theta$:

$$\theta(1 - \tfrac{1}{2}\theta^2) < \sin \theta < \theta.$$

This inequality does not involve a square root, and thus its use is advantageous in certain cases.

7. Recall from plane geometry the expression for the perimeter P of a regular n-gon inscribed in a circle of radius r, $P = 2nr \sin (\pi/n)$, and $\lim\limits_{n \to \infty} P = 2\pi r$ (the limit of the perimeter of a regular n-gon as the number of sides increases indefinitely is the circumference, $2\pi r$). Set up a limit by eliminating P from these two expressions and, by substituting $\theta = \pi/n$, prove $\lim\limits_{\theta \to 0} \sin \theta/\theta = 1$.

9–5 Continuity. In many cases the limit$_{x \to a} f(x) = f(a)$. This very natural value for the limit at a value of x occurs so frequently that we give it a special name.

DEFINITION 9–12. *The function $f(x)$ is* continuous *at the value $x = a$ if a is in the domain of $f(x)$ ($f(a)$ is defined) and if*

$$\lim_{x \to a} f(x) = f(a). \tag{9–26}$$

It should be emphasized that three assertions are made in this definition.

(1) $f(x)$ is defined at $x = a$.

(2) Limit$_{x \to a} f(x)$ exists.

(3) The value of $f(x)$ at $x = a$ is equal to this limit.

If any one or more of these conditions fail to be satisfied, the function is called *discontinuous* (or *not continuous*).

Several of the functions discussed in this chapter are not continuous. The function defined in Example 2, Article 9–1, fails to be continuous at $x = 2$, for although the limit$_{x \to 2} f(x)$ exists, its value, 4, is not equal to 1, the value of the function at $x = 2$ (see Example 1, Article 9–2). It would have been continuous if $f(2)$ had been defined as 4. The function in Example 3 is continuous except where x has integral values. If the values of $f(x)$ had not been defined as zero, but equal to the various limits as x approaches the integral values, the function would have been continuous everywhere. The function discussed in Example 2, Article 9–2, is not continuous at $x = 1$, since $f(1)$ is not defined. If we define $f(1) = 4$, the function is then continuous.

Although these functions are not continuous, the limits at the various questionable values do exist. The function mentioned in Example 3, Article 9–2, however, is not continuous at the integral values of x, since limits at these points do not exist. Nor is the function of Illustration 2 in the same article continuous at $x = 3$, since the limit$_{x \to 3} f(x)$ does not exist. (Why?)

We have observed several functions that are not continuous. We do not intend, however, to give the impression that such is the general situation. Actually, most of the functions with which we deal are continuous functions. With the help of the theorems in Article 9–3, as used in Illustration 1 of that article, we can prove:

THEOREM 9–9.   *Any rational function is continuous except for those values which are zeros of the denominator.*

Proof. See Problem 10.

Moreover, by using Theorem 9–5 where $g(x)$ is a rational constant, as in Illustration 2 of Article 9–3, we can prove the following theorem:

THEOREM 9–10. *A root of a continuous function is continuous for values of x where the function under the radical sign is positive if the root is even, and for all values if the root is odd.*

Proof. See Problem 11.

PROBLEMS

1. At what values (if any) are the functions defined in Problems 1–7, Article 9–1, not continuous?

At what values (if any) are the functions in Problems 2–6 discontinuous? Sketch the graphs of the functions.

2. $f(x) = \dfrac{1}{(x - 7)^2}$

3. $f(x) = \dfrac{1}{x - 7}$

4. $f(x) = \dfrac{1}{(x - 2)(x - 3)}$

5. $f(x) = 2^{1/x}$. [*Hint:* Care should be taken in considering values of $f(x)$ for both positive and negative values of x near zero. Functions of this type will be considered in more detail in Chapter 14.]

6. $f(x) = \dfrac{1}{1 + 2^{1/x}}$

7. Prove that $f(x) = \sin x$ is continuous at $x = 0$. [*Hint:* Use relation (9–23) and Theorem 9–6.]

8. Prove that $f(x) = \tan x$ is continuous at $x = 0$.

9. Prove that $f(x) = \cos x$ is continuous at $x = 0$.

10. Prove Theorem 9–9 by using the necessary theorems of Article 9–3.

11. Prove Theorem 9–10 by using the necessary theorems of Article 9–3.

CHAPTER 10

DERIVATIVES

10–1 Two special limits. Let us look at two particular problems that lead naturally to the concept of a limit.

Consider first a particle moving along a straight line and let s be the distance in feet through which the particle has passed from its original position in t seconds. For example, in the case of the descent of a freely falling body, $s = 16t^2$, approximately, provided the body has fallen from a resting position. In general, the distance s is expressed in terms of t by a function $s = f(t)$, the law of the particular motion. At the end of t seconds the particle will have moved $f(t)$ feet, and if t increases until $t = a$, the particle will have traveled $f(a)$ feet. Since the distance covered in the time interval $a - t$ will be $f(a) - f(t)$, unless the particle reverses the direction of its motion between t and a (a possibility that we will not consider at the moment), we define the average velocity in the logical way.

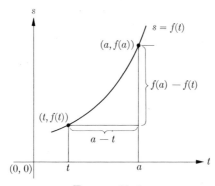

FIGURE 10–1

DEFINITION 10–1. *If $s = f(t)$ expresses distance traveled, the average velocity over the time interval $a - t$ is defined by the expression*

$$Average\ velocity = \frac{f(a) - f(t)}{a - t}\ ft/sec. \tag{10–1}$$

See Fig. 10–1.

ILLUSTRATION. (a) For a body falling from rest, governed by the law $s = 16t^2$, the average velocity over the first second of motion is

$$\frac{16(1)^2 - 16(0)^2}{1 - 0} = 16\ ft/sec.$$

(b) Over the second half-second, the average velocity is

$$\frac{16(1)^2 - 16(\frac{1}{2})^2}{1 - \frac{1}{2}} = \frac{16 - 4}{\frac{1}{2}} = 24 \text{ ft/sec,}$$

and over the interval from $t = \frac{3}{4}$ to $t = 1$, it is

$$\frac{16(1)^2 - 16(\frac{3}{4})^2}{1 - \frac{3}{4}} = \frac{16 - 9}{\frac{1}{4}} = 28 \text{ ft/sec.}$$

We see from this illustration that the velocity is not constant, but differs for different intervals. Moreover, it would seem appropriate to define the velocity at $t = a$ as a limit of the expression given by (10–1) as t approaches a. This we do to define the *instantaneous velocity* at a given time.

DEFINITION 10–2. *The velocity of a particle at a given time $t = a$ is a limit of the average velocity as t approaches a, namely*

$$\underset{t \to a}{\text{limit}} \frac{f(t) - f(a)}{t - a}.\qquad(10\text{--}2)$$

The problem of finding the line which is tangent to a curve at a given point is similar to the one just considered. Recall the definition of the slope of a straight line (Article 5–3). In Fig. 10–2 $y = f(x)$ does not represent a straight-line function. Because of this, the slopes of the straight lines of PQ_1, PQ_2, and PQ_3 are not the same. Thus, if we think of Q as moving and P remaining in a fixed position on the curve, the slope of PQ does not necessarily remain constant. The slopes of the different lines PQ_i can be thought of as average rates of change of $f(x)$ over the corresponding intervals. Let us define the *tangent line to the curve at P* as the limiting position of PQ (if it exists as the point Q approaches P along the curve). Specifically, let the point P on the curve of $y = f(x)$ have coordinates $(a, f(a))$, and Q ($\neq P$), another point on the curve, have coordinates $(x, f(x))$. If the function is continuous at $x = a$, the distance between P and Q approaches 0 as x approaches a; that is, Q approaches P along the curve. Since the slope of the line PQ is a function of the position of Q, that is, a function of x, $m(x)$, we define the limiting position of PQ as Q approaches P

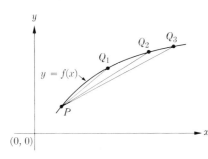

FIGURE 10–2

along the curve as the line through P with slope equal to $\text{limit}_{x \to a} \, m(x)$. Since the slope of the line through P and Q is given by the function

$$m(x) = \frac{f(x) - f(a)}{x - a},$$

we have the following definition:

DEFINITION 10–3. *The tangent line to the curve $f(x)$ at any point P whose coordinates are $(a, f(a))$ is the line through P whose slope is*

$$\boxed{\text{limit}_{x \to a} \frac{f(x) - f(a)}{x - a},} \qquad (10\text{–}3)$$

if the limit exists.

We see that the two problems have been reduced to finding a certain limit involving a function. Both limits are clearly of the same form. This particular form occurs so frequently that in the next article we shall give it a name and discuss it abstractly before interpretations of its use and other examples are given.

PROBLEMS

If $s = f(t)$, where $f(t)$ is given as indicated in Problems 1–4, find the value of the limits and give an interpretation to the answer.

1. $f(t) = 16t^2$; $\text{limit}_{t \to 1} \dfrac{f(t) - f(1)}{t - 1}$

2. $f(t) = 16t^2$; $\text{limit}_{t \to t_1} \dfrac{f(t) - f(t_1)}{t - t_1}$

3. $f(t) = 16t^2 - 8t + 4$; $\text{limit}_{t \to a} \dfrac{f(t) - f(a)}{t - a}$

4. $f(t) = at^2 + bt + c$; $\text{limit}_{t \to t_1} \dfrac{f(t) - f(t_1)}{t - t_1}$

If $y = f(x)$, where $f(x)$ is given as indicated in Problems 5–10, find the value of the following limits and give a geometric interpretation to the answer.

5. $f(x) = x^2$; $\text{limit}_{x \to 2} \dfrac{f(x) - f(2)}{x - 2}$

6. $f(x) = mx + b$; $\text{limit}_{x \to a} \dfrac{f(x) - f(a)}{x - a}$

7. $f(x) = x^2 - 6x + 8$; $\text{limit}_{x \to 1} \dfrac{f(x) - f(1)}{x - 1}$

8. $f(x) = ax^2 + bx + c;\ \underset{x \to x_1}{\text{limit}} \dfrac{f(x) - f(x_1)}{x - x_1}$

9. $f(x) = x^n$, a positive integer; $\underset{x \to x_1}{\text{limit}} \dfrac{f(x) - f(x_1)}{x - x_1}$

  (Recall Example 2, Article 8–1.)

10. $f(x) = 5;\ \underset{x \to a}{\text{limit}} \dfrac{f(x) - f(a)}{x - a}$

*11. Let $P_1(x_1, y_1)$ be a fixed point on the curve $y = f(x)$, and Q be a neighboring point also on the curve such that the coordinates of Q are $(x_1 + h, f(x_1 + h))$, where h denotes the difference between the x-coordinates of P_1 and Q. With this substitution in terms of h and Fig. 10–3, show that (10–3) reduces to the expression

$$\underset{h \to 0}{\text{limit}} \dfrac{f(x_1 + h) - f(x_1)}{h}, \tag{10-4}$$

representing the slope of the line tangent to the curve $y = f(x)$ at the point P_1.

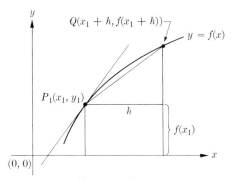

FIGURE 10–3

10–2 Definition of derivative. Let us define, in a general way, the limit formed for the two special problems in the preceding article.

DEFINITION 10–4. *If*

$$\underset{x \to x_1}{\text{limit}} \dfrac{f(x) - f(x_1)}{x - x_1}$$

exists, this limit involving $f(x)$ is called the derivative *of $f(x)$ at $x = x_1$.*

When this limit exists, the function $f(x)$ is said to be *differentiable* for the value $x = x_1$. Hence we can denote the derivative by $f'(x_1)$ (read "f prime of x_1") and write

$$\boxed{f'(x_1) = \underset{x \to x_1}{\text{limit}} \dfrac{f(x) - f(x_1)}{x - x_1}.} \tag{10-5}$$

It is important to note that the limit must exist whether x approaches x_1 through values greater than x_1 or less than x_1. If the derivative exists for an entire set of numbers x_1 where $a \leq x_1 \leq b$, then the derivative is itself a function of x. In addition to the notation $f'(x)$ for the derivative functions, the notations $Df(x)$ and $df(x)/dx$ are also used. If the fact that $y = f(x)$ is emphasized, y', Dy, and dy/dx are also used. The last expression is merely a symbol and should *not* be considered a fraction at this time. It will rarely be used in this book.

EXAMPLE 1. Find $f'(x)$ for any value of x, if $f(x) = 4x^2$.

Solution. We must find the expression for $f'(x)$ for any value of x. Letting x_1 be some value of x, we have

$$\frac{f(x) - f(x_1)}{x - x_1} = \frac{4x^2 - 4x_1^2}{x - x_1} = 4(x + x_1), \qquad \text{where } x \neq x_1.$$

Therefore,

$$\underset{x \to x_1}{\text{limit}} \frac{f(x) - f(x_1)}{x - x_1} = \underset{x \to x_1}{\text{limit}} \, 4(x + x_1) = 8x_1.$$

But since x_1 could have been any value of x,

$$f'(x) = 8x.$$

EXAMPLE 2. Find the derivative of $f(x) = \sqrt{1 - x^2}$. (Recall the example in Article 3–6, and Fig. 3–12.)

Solution. Again, if we let x_1 be some value of x, then for any $x \neq x_1$ and such that $|x| \leq 1$ (why?) we have

$$\frac{f(x) - f(x_1)}{x - x_1} = \frac{\sqrt{1 - x^2} - \sqrt{1 - x_1^2}}{x - x_1}$$

$$= \frac{\sqrt{1 - x^2} - \sqrt{1 - x_1^2}}{x - x_1} \cdot \frac{\sqrt{1 - x^2} + \sqrt{1 - x_1^2}}{\sqrt{1 - x^2} + \sqrt{1 - x_1^2}}$$

$$= \frac{1 - x^2 - (1 - x_1^2)}{(x - x_1)(\sqrt{1 - x^2} + \sqrt{1 - x_1^2})}$$

$$= \frac{x_1^2 - x^2}{(x - x_1)(\sqrt{1 - x^2} + \sqrt{1 - x_1^2})}$$

$$= -\frac{x + x_1}{\sqrt{1 - x^2} + \sqrt{1 - x_1^2}},$$

so that

$$f'(x_1) = \lim_{x \to x_1} -\frac{x + x_1}{\sqrt{1 - x^2} + \sqrt{1 - x_1^2}} = \frac{-2x_1}{2\sqrt{1 - x_1^2}}.$$

Therefore,

$$f'(x) = \frac{-x}{\sqrt{1 - x^2}} \qquad \text{for} \qquad |x| < 1.$$

EXAMPLE 3. Find $Df(x)$ if $f(x) = \sin x$.

Solution. Again we are interested in the expression

$$\frac{f(x) - f(x_1)}{x - x_1} = \frac{\sin x - \sin x_1}{x - x_1} \qquad \text{for} \qquad x \neq x_1.$$

Using Eq. (4–59), we have this expression equal to

$$\frac{2 \cos \frac{x + x_1}{2} \sin \frac{x - x_1}{2}}{x - x_1} = \cos \frac{x + x_1}{2} \cdot \frac{\sin \frac{x - x_1}{2}}{\frac{x - x_1}{2}}.$$

Thus,

$$\lim_{x \to x_1} \frac{f(x) - f(x_1)}{x - x_1} = \lim_{x \to x_1} \cos \frac{x + x_1}{2} \cdot \frac{\sin \frac{x - x_1}{2}}{\frac{x - x_1}{2}}.$$

Since

$$\lim_{x \to x_1} \frac{\sin \frac{x - x_1}{2}}{\frac{x - x_1}{2}} = 1 \qquad \text{(why?)},$$

we get $f'(x) = \cos x$.

It is important to note the difference between a function which is differentiable at a certain value and one which is merely continuous at that value.

THEOREM 10–1. *A function which is differentiable at a value x_1 is continuous at that value.*

Proof. If $f(x)$ is differentiable at x_1, we know

$$\lim_{x \to x_1} \frac{f(x) - f(x_1)}{x - x_1} = f'(x_1).$$

Thus, since $\lim_{x \to x_1} (x - x_1) = 0$, we have

$$\text{limit}_{x \to x_1} [f(x) - f(x_1)] = \text{limit}_{x \to x_1} \left[\frac{f(x) - f(x_1)}{x - x_1} \cdot (x - x_1) \right]$$

$$= \text{limit}_{x \to x_1} \frac{f(x) - f(x_1)}{x - x_1} \text{limit}_{x \to x_1} (x - x_1)$$

$$= f'(x_1) \cdot 0 = 0.$$

That is, $\text{limit}_{x \to x_1} [f(x) - f(x_1)] = 0$, or $\text{limit}_{x \to x_1} f(x) = f(x_1)$, the requirement for $f(x)$ to be continuous at the value x_1.

That the converse is *not* true may be seen by considering the previously mentioned example $f(x) = |x|$ (Illustration 3, Article 3–6, and the appropriate figure similar to Fig. 3–15) at $x = 0$. The function is continuous at $x = 0$, but

$$\text{limit}_{x \to 0} \frac{f(x) - f(0)}{x - 0} = \text{limit}_{x \to 0} \frac{|x|}{x},$$

and since

$$\frac{|x|}{x} = \begin{cases} -1 & \text{if} \quad x < 0, \\ 1 & \text{if} \quad x > 0, \end{cases}$$

this limit does not exist. Thus $f(x) = |x|$ is not differentiable at zero.

Problems

In Problems 1–4 find $f'(x)$ at the values indicated if

1. $f(x) = 2x - 5$ at $x = 1$
2. $f(x) = x^2 - 1$ at $x = -2$
3. $f(x) = x^3$ at $x = a$
4. $f(x) = 1/x$ at $x = 3$

In Problems 5–14 find $Df(x)$ where

5. $f(x) = 2x - 5$
6. $f(x) = x^2 - 1$
7. $f(x) = x^3$
8. $f(x) = 1/x$
9. $f(x) = \sqrt{x}$
10. $f(x) = \sqrt{2x - 3}$
11. $f(x) = 1/\sqrt{x - 2}$
*12. $f(x) = \cos x$

[*Ans.* $Df(x) = -\sin x.$]

13. $f(x) = \sin 2x$
14. $f(x) = \cos 3x$

15. Find $f'(x)$ for all values of x for which the derivative exists if $f(x) = |x|$. [*Hint:* If $x \neq x_1$, consider $[f(x) - f(x_1)]/(x - x_1)$ where $x_1 < 0$ and $x_1 > 0$ separately. Also recall discussion of this function at $x = 0$, in this article.]

16. Find $f'(x)$ for all values of x for which the derivative exists if $f(x) = |x - 2|$. See Fig. 3–14.

10–3 Theorems on derivatives. With the use of several of the theorems on limits in Chapter 9, we are able to differentiate easily most of the ordinary functions without returning to the original definition. It should be kept in mind constantly, however, that when a derivative is found from a formula resulting from one of the following theorems, this derivative is actually a limit, and that limit is the basic concept underlying the notion of the derivative.

THEOREM 10–2. *If $f(x) = c$, any fixed constant, for all values of x, then $f'(x) = 0$.*

Proof. For any $x \neq x_1$,

$$\frac{f(x) - f(x_1)}{x - x_1} = \frac{c - c}{x - x_1} = 0.$$

Thus,

$$\lim_{x \to x_1} \frac{f(x) - f(x_1)}{x - x_1} = 0.$$

THEOREM 10–3. *If $f(x) = x$ for all values of x, then $f'(x) = 1$.*

Proof. Since for any $x \neq x_1$,

$$\frac{f(x) - f(x_1)}{x - x_1} = \frac{x - x_1}{x - x_1} = 1, \quad \lim_{x \to x_1} \frac{f(x) - f(x_1)}{x - x_1} = 1.$$

Before we prove further theorems on particular functions, let us prove several general theorems involving the combinations of functions defined in Chapter 9.

THEOREM 10–4. *If $f(x)$ and $g(x)$ are differentiable at the value x_1, the sum function $S(x)$ is also differentiable at this value, and*

$$DS(x_1) = Df(x_1) + Dg(x_1); \qquad (10\text{–}6)$$

that is, the derivative of the sum of two functions is the sum of the derivatives of the same two functions.

Proof. Since

$$\frac{S(x) - S(x_1)}{x - x_1} = \frac{f(x) + g(x) - f(x_1) - g(x_1)}{x - x_1}$$

$$= \frac{f(x) - f(x_1)}{x - x_1} + \frac{g(x) - g(x_1)}{x - x_1},$$

we need only make use of Theorem 9–1, Article 9–3, to obtain the desired result.

The same type of theorem is of course true of $g(x)$ if regarded as $-h(x)$, and we have the result that the derivative of the difference of two functions is the difference of their derivatives.

For the product function, the result is somewhat different than might be expected.

THEOREM 10–5. *If $f(x)$ and $g(x)$ are differentiable at the value x_1, the derivative of $P(x)$ also exists at x_1 and*

$$\boxed{DP(x_1) = f(x_1)\, Dg(x_1) + g(x_1)\, Df(x_1).} \qquad (10\text{–}7)$$

Proof. We make use of the identity

$$\frac{P(x) - P(x_1)}{x - x_1} = \frac{f(x)\, g(x) - f(x_1)\, g(x_1)}{x - x_1}$$

$$= \frac{f(x)\, g(x) - f(x)\, g(x_1) + f(x)\, g(x_1) - f(x_1)\, g(x_1)}{x - x_1}$$

$$= f(x)\, \frac{g(x) - g(x_1)}{x - x_1} + g(x_1)\, \frac{f(x) - f(x_1)}{x - x_1}.$$

We are given that $f(x)$ and $g(x)$ are both differentiable. Also, because of the differentiability of $f(x)$, $f(x)$ is continuous (Theorem 10–1), that is, $\lim_{x \to x_1} f(x) = f(x_1)$. In addition, $\lim_{x \to x_1} g(x_1) = g(x_1)$. Using these facts and Theorems 9–1 and 9–3, Article 9–3, we have the required result.

The quotient function may be differentiated in much the same way.

THEOREM 10–6. *If $f(x)$ and $g(x)$ are differentiable at the value x_1 and $g(x) \neq 0$, the derivative of the quotient function $f(x)$ by $g(x)$ also exists at x_1, and*

$$\boxed{DQ(x_1) = \frac{g(x_1)\, Df(x_1) - f(x_1)\, Dg(x_1)}{g(x_1)^2}.} \qquad (10\text{–}8)$$

Proof. Again we have the useful identity

$$\frac{Q(x) - Q(x_1)}{x - x_1} = \frac{\dfrac{f(x)}{g(x)} - \dfrac{f(x_1)}{g(x_1)}}{x - x_1}$$

$$= \frac{f(x)\, g(x_1) - f(x_1)\, g(x)}{g(x)\, g(x_1)(x - x_1)}$$

$$= \frac{1}{g(x)\, g(x_1)} \cdot \frac{f(x)\, g(x_1) - f(x_1)\, g(x_1) + f(x_1)\, g(x_1) - f(x_1)\, g(x)}{x - x_1}$$

$$= \frac{1}{g(x)\, g(x_1)} \left[g(x_1)\, \frac{f(x) - f(x_1)}{x - x_1} - f(x_1)\, \frac{g(x) - g(x_1)}{x - x_1} \right].$$

Now by using the appropriate theorems and definitions from this chapter and Chapter 9, we obtain the desired result (the specific reasons and theorems should be noted).

One important special case of Theorem 10–5 is very useful. If one of the functions is a constant for all values of x, we may use this theorem with Theorem 10–2 to establish Theorem 10–7. The proof follows directly.

THEOREM 10–7. *If $f(x)$ is differentiable at $x = x_1$ and c is any constant, then $c f(x)$ is differentiable at this value x_1, and*

$$D(c f(x)) = c Df(x). \tag{10–9}$$

Let us consider the derivative of the especially important function $f(x) = x^n$. Here we can obtain the derivative by mathematical induction for the case in which n is a positive integer.

THEOREM 10–8. *If $f(x) = x^n$, where n is a positive integer, then $f'(x)$ exists for all values of x, and*

$$Df(x) = nx^{n-1}. \tag{10–10}$$

Proof. (a) *Verification.* When $n = 1$, $f(x) = x^1$, so that $f'(x)$ should equal $1x^{1-1} = x^0 = 1$, and this is true by Theorem 10–3.

(b) *Proof of the inductive property.* Assume that the theorem is true when $n = k$, that is, $Dx^k = kx^{k-1}$. We must show, on this assumption, that (10–10) holds for $n = k + 1$. Since $x^{k+1} = x \cdot x^k$, we use Theorem 10–5 with $f(x) = x$ and $g(x) = x^k$. Therefore,

$$Dx^{k+1} = D(x \cdot x^k) = x Dx^k + x^k Dx.$$

Since $Dx^k = kx^{k-1}$ and $Dx = 1$, we have

$$Dx^{k+1} = x \cdot kx^{k-1} + x^k \cdot 1 = kx^k + x^k = (k + 1)x^k,$$

which is the statement of the theorem when $n = k + 1$.

(c) The conclusion follows immediately and the theorem is proved.

It should be clear from these results that the derivative of any rational function of x (recall Article 9–1) may be obtained. Such functions will be illustrated in the following examples. It should be pointed out that Theorem 10–8 was proved only for the case where n was a positive integer. However, the theorem holds for any rational or even irrational exponent (recall Theorem 9–5, Article 9–3), and it will be used although its proof cannot be given at this time.

EXAMPLE 1. Find $f'(x)$ if $f(x) = 3x^4 - 7x^2 + 9$, and give the reasons for each step.

Solution.

$D(3x^4 - 7x^2 + 9) = D(3x^4) - D(7x^2) + D(9)$,   by Theorem 10–4;
$D(3x^4) = 3\,D(x^4) = 3 \cdot 4x^3 = 12x^3$,   by Theorems 10–7 and 10–8;
$D(7x^2) = 7\,D(x^2) = 7 \cdot 2x = 14x$,   by Theorems 10–7 and 10–8;
$D(9) = 0$,   by Theorem 10–2.

Thus, $Df(x) = 12x^3 - 14x$.

EXAMPLE 2. Find $Df(x)$ if $f(x) = (2x^3 + 3)(x^2 + 4x)$.

Solution. By considering $f(x) = 2x^3 + 3$, $g(x) = x^2 + 4x$, and using Theorem 10–5, we have

$$
\begin{aligned}
P'(x) &= (2x^3 + 3)\,D(x^2 + 2x) + (x^2 + 4x)\,D(2x^3 + 3) \\
&= (2x^3 + 3)(2x + 2) + (x^2 + 4x)(6x^2) \\
&= 10x^4 + 28x^3 + 6x + 6.
\end{aligned}
$$

Check the result by obtaining the product before differentiation, and then find the derivative as in Example 1.

EXAMPLE 3. Find $Dh(x)$ if $h(x) = (5x^2 + 6)/(2x + 3)$.

Solution. By considering $f(x) = 5x^2 + 6$, $g(x) = 2x + 3$, and using Theorem 10–6, we have

$$
\begin{aligned}
Dh(x) &= \frac{(2x + 3)\,D(5x^2 + 6) - (5x^2 + 6)\,D(2x + 3)}{(2x + 3)^2} \\
&= \frac{(2x + 3)(10x) - (5x^2 + 6)2}{(2x + 3)^2} = \frac{10x^2 + 30x - 12}{(2x + 3)^2}.
\end{aligned}
$$

EXAMPLE 4. If $f(x) = \tan x$, find $Df(x)$.

Solution. Since $\tan x \equiv \sin x/\cos x$, we may use Theorem 10–6. Recalling the results from Example 3 and Problem 12 of Article 10–2, we have

$$
\begin{aligned}
D(\tan x) &= \frac{\cos x\,D(\sin x) - \sin x\,D(\cos x)}{\cos^2 x} \\
&= \frac{\cos x \cos x - \sin x\,(-\sin x)}{\cos^2 x} \\
&= \frac{\cos^2 x + \sin^2 x}{\cos^2 x} = \frac{1}{\cos^2 x}.
\end{aligned}
$$

Thus,

$$
D(\tan x) = \sec^2 x. \tag{10–11}
$$

Problems

1. Differentiate each of the following functions:

(a) $f(x) = 4x^6$,   (b) $f(x) = 5x^3$,   (c) $f(x) = 18x^2$.

2. Differentiate each of the following functions:

(a) $f(x) = 2x^2 + 5x + 6$,   (b) $f(x) = 5x^2 - 6x$,

(c) $f(x) = x^3 + x^2 + x + 1$.

3. Find the derivative of the function $y = mx + b$, and give a geometric interpretation of your answer.

4. Find $Df(x)$ by using Theorem 10–5, and check by multiplying out before differentiating:

(a) $f(x) = (x^2 + 1)(x + 2)$,   (b) $f(x) = (x^2 - 1)(x^3 + 3)$,

(c) $f(x) = x^3(3x^2 + 4x - 5)$,   (d) $f(x) = (x - 1)(x - 2)(x - 3)$.

5. Differentiate by using Theorem 10–6:

(a) $\dfrac{x^2 + 1}{x + 2}$,   (b) $\dfrac{2x}{x^2 + 1}$,

(c) $\dfrac{1}{x}$,   (d) $x^3 + \dfrac{1}{x^2}$.

6. Differentiate each of the following functions:

(a) $f(y) = \sqrt{y}\left(1 - \dfrac{y^2}{2}\right)$,   (b) $f(s) = \sqrt{s} - \dfrac{1}{\sqrt{s}}$,

(c) $f(t) = (1 + t^2)^2$,   (d) $f(t) = (1 - t)^3$.

7. Find the derivative of each of the following functions:

(a) $f(x) = x^{1/3} - \dfrac{1}{x^{1/3}}$,   (b) $f(x) = \sqrt[3]{x^2}$.

*8. Differentiate each of the functions below:

(a) $f(x) = \cot x$, $\left[\textit{Hint: } \cot x \equiv \dfrac{\cos x}{\sin x}.\right]$

(b) $f(x) = \sec x$;   (c) $f(x) = \csc x$.

9. Find the derivative of each of the functions:

(a) $x \sin x$,   (b) $3x^2 \cos x$,

(c) $\sin \theta \cos \theta$,   (d) $\dfrac{\sin x}{x}$.

10. Find a function $f(x)$ such that

(a) $f'(x) = 3x^2$,   (b) $f'(x) = x^2 + 1$,

(c) $Df(x) = \sqrt{x}$,   (d) $Df(x) = (x - 1)(x + 3)$.

10–4 Tangent and normal lines to a curve. We are now in a position to make use of the notion of differentiation as it applies to the simple geometry of a curve. We recall Definition 10–3: The *tangent line* to the curve whose equation is $y = f(x)$ at $P(x_1, f(x_1))$, a point on the curve, is the straight line through P whose slope is $f'(x_1)$.

Another important geometric concept is that of the *normal line*.

DEFINITION 10–5. *The* normal line *to the curve at* $P(x_1, f(x_1))$, *a point on the curve, is the straight line through* P *perpendicular to the tangent line to the curve at* P.

If we recall the relationship of the slopes of two perpendicular lines (Theorem 5–3, Article 5–3), the slope of the normal line is easily found. From this we can obtain its equations.

DEFINITION 10–6. *The slope of a curve at* $P(x_1, f(x_1))$, *a point on the curve whose equation is* $y = f(x)$, *is* $f'(x_1)$, *the slope of the tangent line at that point.*

EXAMPLE 1. (a) Find the expression for the slope of the curve whose equation is $y = x^3 - 4x + 2$ at that point on the curve whose abscissa is 2. (b) Find an equation of the tangent at this point. (c) Find an equation of the normal at this point.

Solution. (a) Since $f'(x) = 3x^2 - 4$ at any point, $f'(2) = 8$, the slope of the curve at the required point. (b) In order to find an equation of the tangent line, we not only need the slope value, but also both coordinates of the point of tangency. Since $x = 2$ and $y = x^3 - 4x + 2$ for any x, the required y-coordinate is $y = (2)^3 - 4(2) + 2 = 2$. The tangent line therefore is the line through $(2, 2)$ with slope 8.

$$\frac{y - 2}{x - 2} = 8,$$

or

$$8x - y - 14 = 0.$$

(c) Since the normal line is perpendicular to the tangent line whose slope is 8, an equation of the normal line is

$$\frac{y - 2}{x - 2} = -\frac{1}{8},$$

or

$$x + 8y - 18 = 0.$$

Its graph is shown in Fig. 10–4.

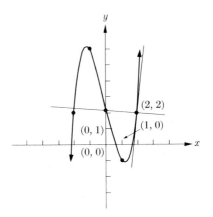

FIGURE 10–4

EXAMPLE 2. Find the coordinates of the point where the tangent to the curve whose equation is $y = x^2 - x - 6$ is horizontal.

Solution. Since $f'(x) = 2x - 1$ at any point (x, y), the tangent will be horizontal when the slope $2x - 1 = 0$. Thus $x = \frac{1}{2}$, and since $y = x^2 - x - 6$, the required y-coordinate is $y = (\frac{1}{2})^2 - \frac{1}{2} - 6 = -\frac{25}{4}$. It should be noted that this curve is a parabola and that we have found the coordinates of its vertex. Recall Example 2, Article 3–7, and Example 2, Article 6–1.

PROBLEMS

Find an equation of the tangent and normal to each of the following curves, Problems 1–8, at the specified point on the curve.

1. $y = x^2 - 4x + 6$ at $x = 3$

2. $y = 4x - 7$ at $x = 2$

3. $y = \dfrac{x}{4 - x}$ at $x = 6$

4. $4x^2 + 9y^2 = 36$ at $\left(\dfrac{3\sqrt{3}}{2}, 1\right)$

5. $y = \sin x$ at $x = \pi/3$

6. $y = \dfrac{5}{x^2 + 1}$ at $(2, 1)$

7. $\sqrt{x} + \sqrt{y} = 5$ at $(9, 4)$

8. $y = \tan x$ at $x = \pi/4$

Find the coordinates of the points on the curves, Problems 9–12, where the tangent line is horizontal.

9. $y = x^2 - 5x + 6$

10. $y = 2x^3 - 6x^2 + 1$

11. $y = \dfrac{x}{1 - x}$

12. $y = \dfrac{x^2}{1 - x}$

13. At what points on the curve $xy = 16$ do the tangents have a slope of -8? Prove that there can be no horizontal tangent to this curve.

14. Find the angle of intersection of the curve $y = x^3 - 3x$ (a) with the x-axis, (b) with the y-axis. [*Hint:* The *angle of intersection of two curves* is defined as the angle between their tangents at the point of intersection.]

15. Find the points of intersection of the following curves, and the angle of intersection at these points:

(a) $y = x^3$ and $y = x$,
(b) $y = x^2$ and $y = \sqrt{x}$,
(c) $x^2 - y^2 = 1$ and $xy = \frac{1}{4}$, [*Hint:* Recall Example 2, Article 10–2.]
(d) $x^2 = 4y$ and $y = \dfrac{8}{4 + x^2}$,
(e) $y = \sin x$ and $y = \cos x$ (between 0 and $\pi/2$),
(f) $y = x/2$ and $y = \dfrac{x}{2} - \sin x$ (between $-\pi/2$ and $\pi/2$).

16. Show that the tangents to the curve $y^2 = 2px$ at the points where $x = p/2$ are perpendicular.

17. Find the points on the curve

$$y = \frac{x^3}{3} - \frac{5x^2}{2} + x + 4,$$

where the tangent is parallel to $5x + y = 6$.

18. Find the points on the curve $y = x^2/(x - 1)$, where the tangent is perpendicular to $x - 4y + 6 = 0$.

19. The normal to the curve $y = 2x/(x - 1)$ at $(2, 4)$ meets this curve in another point. Find its coordinates.

20. Find the points of tangency of the tangents to the curve $y = x^2 - 2x$ through the point $(-1, -6)$ and write an equation of each tangent. [*Hint:* (x_1, y_1), the point of tangency, lies on the curve.]

21. Find the points of tangency of the tangents to the curve $y = -x^2 + 4$ through the point $(-4, -3)$ and write an equation of each tangent.

22. A triangle is formed by the tangent to the curve $xy = 16$ at $(2, 8)$ and the coordinate axes. Find its area. Show that if the point $(2, 8)$ were any point on the curve, the result would be the same.

10–5 Composite functions. In Article 10–3 we proved results for the derivatives of all the combinations of functions discussed in Article 9–1, Eqs. (9–2), (9–3), and (9–4). The composite function, Eq. (9–5), is equally important and was actually considered as a special case in Example 2, Article 10–2. We see that in this example

$$h(x) = \sqrt{1 - x^2}, \qquad |x| \leq 1,$$

we may consider $h(x)$ as $f(g(x))$, where $f(x) = \sqrt{x}$ and $g(x) = 1 - x^2$. If we use the fact that $f'(x) = 1/(2\sqrt{x})$ and $g'(x) = -2x$, the derivative of $h(x)$, which in Example 2 was $-x/\sqrt{1 - x^2}$, may be written in terms of the derivatives of $f(x)$ and $g(x)$.

$$h'(x) = \frac{-x}{\sqrt{1 - x^2}} = \frac{1}{2\sqrt{1 - x^2}} \cdot -2x = \frac{1}{2\sqrt{g(x)}} \cdot g'(x).$$

Therefore,

$$h'(x) = f'(g(x)) \cdot g'(x).$$

This result is true in the general case for composite functions.

THEOREM 10–9. *If* $h(x) = f(g(x))$, *where the range of values of* $g(x)$ *is contained in the domain of* $f(x)$, *and if* $g(x)$ *is differentiable at* x *and* $f(x)$ *is differentiable at* $g(x_1)$, *then* $h'(x)$ *exists and*

$$\boxed{h'(x_1) = f'(g(x_1)) \cdot g'(x_1).} \qquad (10\text{–}12)$$

Proof. Since for any value of $x \neq x_1$,

$$\frac{f(g(x)) - f(g(x_1))}{x - x_1} = \frac{f(g(x)) - f(g(x_1))}{g(x) - g(x_1)} \cdot \frac{g(x) - g(x_1)}{x - x_1},$$

with the limit taken as $x \to x_1$, each quotient will exist as a result of the hypotheses concerning the differentiability of the functions, and since

$$h'(x_1) = \underset{x \to x_1}{\text{limit}} \frac{f(g(v)) - f(g(x_1))}{x - x_1},$$

$$f'(g(x_1)) = \underset{x \to x_1}{\text{limit}} \frac{f(g(x)) - f(g(x_1))}{g(x) - g(x_1)},$$

and

$$g'(x) = \underset{x \to x_1}{\text{limit}} \frac{g(x) - g(x_1)}{x - x_1},$$

we have our result.

Although this proof holds only for functions $g(x)$ where $g(x) - g(x_1)$ will not be zero for any values of x arbitrarily close to x_1, the result nevertheless is true for all functions satisfying the given hypotheses. We will use this result only with functions $g(x)$ for which our proof holds.

ILLUSTRATION 1. Let $h(x) = \sqrt[3]{x^2 + 4}$, so that if $h(x) = f(g(x))$, $g(x) = x^2 + 4$ and $f(x) = \sqrt[3]{x}$ or $f(g(x)) = \sqrt[3]{g(x)}$. Then $f'(g(x)) = \frac{1}{3}(g(x))^{-2/3}$ and $g'(x) = 2x$, so that

$$h'(x) = \frac{1}{3\sqrt[3]{(x^2 + 4)^2}} \cdot 2x = \frac{2x}{3\sqrt[3]{(x^2 + 4)^2}}.$$

ILLUSTRATION 2. If $f(x) = (x^2 + 3x)^3(2x + 1)$, we have

$$f'(x) = (x^2 + 3x)^3 \cdot 2 + (2x + 1) \cdot 3(x^2 + 3x)^2 \cdot (2x + 3),$$

which of course can be simplified. Explain the factor $2x + 3$ in the second term. We notice in this example that we can now differentiate a function such as $(x^2 + 3x)^3$ without first expanding.

ILLUSTRATION 3. If $f(\theta) = \sin^3 4\theta$,

$$f'(\theta) = 3 \sin^2 4\theta \cdot \cos 4\theta \cdot 4.$$

Note that $f(\theta)$ is really "a function of a function of a function." Explain this statement.

The result of Theorem 10–9 considerably broadens the class of functions that can now be differentiated.

PROBLEMS

Find $f'(x)$ in Problems 1–4.

1. $f(x) = (x^2 + 3)^3$

2. $f(x) = \sqrt{3x - 7}$

3. $f(x) = (x^2 - 4x + 6)^2$

4. (a) $f(x) = \sin^2 x$

    (b) $f(x) = -\cos^2 x$

Find $Df(x)$ in Problems 5–10 if

5. $f(x) = (x^2 + x)^3(3x + 2)^4$

6. $f(x) = (x^2 + 1)^2/x^3$

7. $f(x) = (2x + 3)\sqrt{4x - 5}$

8. $f(x) = \sqrt{a^2 - x^2}$

9. $f(x) = \sqrt[3]{x - x^2}$

10. $f(x) = x^3 - x^2\sqrt{x} + 2\sqrt{x^2 - x}$

11. Find the equation of the tangent to the curve

(a) $y = \sqrt{a^2 - x^2}$ at the point on the curve where $x = a/2$,

(b) $y = \dfrac{1}{\sqrt{3 + x^2}}$ at the point on the curve where $x = -1$,

(c) $4x^2 + 9y^2 = 25$ at $(2, -1)$,

(d) $x^{2/3} + y^{2/3} = 1$ at $\left(\dfrac{1}{2\sqrt{2}}, \dfrac{1}{2\sqrt{2}}\right)$.

12. Find the angle of intersection of the curves

$$xy = 2 \quad \text{and} \quad x^2 - y^2 = 3.$$

13. Do the same for

$$x^2 + y^2 = 25 \quad \text{and} \quad xy = 12.$$

14. Do the same for

$$y^2 = 2px \quad \text{and} \quad x^2 = 2py.$$

10–6 Functions defined implicitly by an equation. In our discussion so far, we have considered only functions of one independent variable (recall Article 3–6). We may also define *functions of more than one independent variable*. For example, $x^2 + y^2$, $x + \sin y$, or x/y^2 define functions of two independent variables, and may be represented symbolically as $f(x, y)$, $F(x, y)$, $g(x, y)$, and so on. On many occasions in algebra, trigonometry, and other branches of mathematics, a function of two variables appears as the left member of an equation whose right member is zero. Such was the case in both equations of the system given by Eq. (6–17). One was a first degree function, and the other a second degree function.

By setting such a function $F(x, y)$ equal to zero, a functional relationship is set up between the variables x and y, and one of the variables ceases to be independent. If we solve the equation

$$F(x, y) = 0 \tag{10–13}$$

for y in terms of x, the relationship implied by Eq. (10–13) is expressed explicitly with y a function (or relation, recall Definition 3–3) of x. If we solve for x in terms of y, x is expressed explicitly as a function (or relation) of y, with the latter variable independent. In either of these cases, if $y = f(x)$ or $x = g(y)$, the function is said to be explicitly defined, while the same function in the form of Eq. (10–13) is said to be implicitly defined.

ILLUSTRATIONS.

	$F(x, y) = 0$	$y = f(x)$	$x = g(y)$
(a)	$3x + 4y - 12 = 0$	$y = \dfrac{12 - 3x}{4}$	$x = \dfrac{12 - 4y}{3}$
(b)	$xy - 1 = 0$	$y = \dfrac{1}{x}$	$x = \dfrac{1}{y}$
(c)	$xy - x^2 + 1 = 0$	$y = \dfrac{1 - x^2}{x}$	$x = \dfrac{y \pm \sqrt{y^2 + 4}}{2}$*
(d)	$x^2 + y^2 - 1 = 0$	$y = \pm \sqrt{1 - x^2}$*	$x = \pm \sqrt{1 - y^2}$*

In the present discussion we are primarily concerned with the implicitly defined functions, that is, those in the left column in the illustrations. It is important to realize that some functions, for example that defined by $x - y + \sin y = 0$, cannot readily be solved for both variables. If we can solve for y in terms of x, and the result is one of our familiar functions, we can easily find y'. If this is impossible, as in the expression above, the derivative y' may still be found by the following method. When y is defined as an implicit function of x by an equation $F(x, y) = 0$, the entire expression may be differentiated. If we remember that y is a function of x, and use Eq. (10–12), the differentiated expression may then be solved for $y'(x)$.

EXAMPLE. Find Dy if $x^2 + xy + y^2 - 1 = 0$.

Solution. If we differentiate this expression (recall Theorems 10–4 and 10–5), where y is a function of x, we have

$$2x + x\,Dy + y \cdot 1 + 2y\,Dy - 0 = 0.$$

Solving for Dy, we get

$$x\,Dy + 2y \cdot Dy = -2x - y,$$

---

* There exist two distinct functions, that is, a relation (recall Definition 3–3).

or

$$Dy = -\frac{2x + y}{x + 2y}.$$

It is worth noting that when this type of *"implicit* differentiation" is carried out, the result is usually expressed in terms of both variables, whereas the result from *"explicit* differentiation" is always in terms of the independent variable. In either case, the derivative is actually a function of one variable. (Why?)

Problems

Find Dy in terms of x and y from the expressions in Problems 1–6.

1. $4x^2 + 9y^2 = 36$
2. $xy = 1$
3. $x^2 - y^2 = a^2$
4. $(x - 1)^2 + (y - 2)^2 = 25$
5. $x^{1/2} + y^{1/2} = a^{1/2}$
6. $x - y + \sin y = 0$

7. Find the equations of the tangent lines to the curves at the points indicated:

(a) $x^2 + xy + 4y^2 = 31$ at $(3, 2)$,

(b) $y^2 = 2px$ at $\left(\frac{p}{2}, -p\right)$,

(c) $x^{2/3} + y^{2/3} = a^{2/3}$ at (x_1, y_1).

8. Find equations of the tangent and normal to the curve $4x^2 - 16y^2 = 48$ at $(4, -1)$.

9. Find the angles of intersection of the curves $4x^2 + 9y^2 = 36$ and $9x^2 + 4y^2 = 36$.

10. Prove that the two tangents drawn to the curve $x^2/a^2 + y^2/b^2 = 1$ and to the curve $x^2 + y^2 = a^2$ at points with the same x-coordinate intersect on the x-axis.

11. Find equations of the tangent and normal to the curve $y^2 = x^3$ at $(1, 1)$.

12. Prove that the curve $x^2 + xy - y^2 = 8$ has no horizontal tangent.

10–7 Higher derivatives. We mentioned in Article 10–2 in connection with its definition, Eq. (10–5), that the derivative of $y = f(x)$ is itself a function of x. Therefore it too can have a derivative, denoted by $f''(x)$ or $D^2f(x)$. This function is called the *second derivative of $f(x)$*. Similarly, the derivative of the second derivative, called the *third derivative*, is denoted by $f'''(x)$ or $D^3f(x)$, and so on. The nth derivative of $f(x)$ is denoted by $f^{(n)}(x)$ or $D^nf(x)$. The use and geometric interpretation of higher derivatives will be considered in the next chapter.

EXAMPLE 1. If $f(x) = \sqrt{1 - x^2}$, find $f'(x)$, $f''(x)$, $f'''(x)$.

Solution. As indicated at the beginning of Article 10–5, since $f(x) = (1 - x^2)^{1/2}$,

$$f'(x) = \tfrac{1}{2}(1 - x^2)^{-1/2} \cdot (-2x) = -\frac{x}{(1 - x^2)^{1/2}}.$$

Therefore,

$$f''(x) = - \frac{(1 - x^2)^{1/2} \cdot 1 - x(\frac{1}{2})(1 - x^2)^{-1/2}(-2x)}{[(1 - x^2)^{1/2}]^2}$$

$$= - \frac{(1 - x^2)^{1/2} + \dfrac{x^2}{(1 - x^2)^{1/2}}}{1 - x^2}$$

$$= - \frac{(1 - x^2) + x^2}{(1 - x^2)^{3/2}} = - (1 - x^2)^{-3/2}.$$

Similarly,

$$f'''(x) = - [- \tfrac{3}{2}(1 - x^2)^{-5/2}(-2x)]$$

$$= - 3x(1 - x^2)^{-5/2}.$$

EXAMPLE 2. If $x^2 + y^2 = a^2$, find y''.

Solution. This is a case of considering y an implicitly defined function of x. We have

$$2x + 2yy' = 0 \text{ or } y' = - \frac{x}{y}.$$

Realizing that y' is also a function of x, we are able to differentiate again, using Theorem 10–6.

$$y'' = - \left[\frac{y \cdot 1 - xy'}{y^2} \right] = \frac{xy' - y}{y^2}.$$

Since we ordinarily wish to have the result in terms of x and y, we substitute for the value of y'. Thus,

$$y'' = \frac{x\left(-\dfrac{x}{y}\right) - y}{y^2} = \frac{-x^2 - y^2}{y^3},$$

and since $x^2 + y^2 = a^2$, we may simplify our result.

$$y'' = \frac{-a^2}{y^3}.$$

PROBLEMS

Find D^2y in each of Problems 1–16.

1. $y = x^3 - 5x^2 + 8x - 4$

2. $y = \dfrac{x + 2}{3x}$

3. $y = (2x - 3)(x + 1)^2$

4. $y = \sin 2x$

5. $y = x\sqrt{x - 1}$

6. $y = \dfrac{1}{\sqrt{x}}$

7. $y = \dfrac{x^2}{x+1}$

8. $y = \cos^2 x$

9. $x^2 - y^2 = 25$

10. $xy = 1$

11. $x^2 + xy = 2$

12. $x^2 = y^3$

13. $x^2 = y^2 + 2x$

14. $x = \tan y$

15. $y = 3\sin^2 x \cos x$

16. $\dfrac{x^2}{a^2} + \dfrac{y^2}{b^2} = 1$

Find Dy and D^2y at the values indicated in Problems 17–25.

17. $y = 6x^2 - 7x + 8$ at $x = 1$

18. $y = \dfrac{1}{\sqrt{x^2+5}}$ at $x = 2$

19. $y = \dfrac{x-2}{x^3}$ at $x = -1$

20. $y = ax^2 + bx + c$ at $x = x_1$

21. $y = \dfrac{(x-1)(x-2)}{x}$ at $x = 3$

22. $y = x(x-2)\sqrt{x-3}$ at $x = 3$

23. $y = \sin x \tan x$ at $x = \pi/4$

24. $xy = x + y$ at $x = 5$

25. $x^2 + 9y^2 = 18$ at $(3, 1)$

26. Find the nth derivative of $y = x^n$

27. Find $D^{(n)}f(x)$ if $f(x) = 1/x$

CHAPTER 11

POLYNOMIAL FUNCTIONS

In Chapters 5 and 6 we considered the first and second degree functions in one variable. We wish to generalize this type of function. As was stated in Chapter 9, any function of one variable which can be expressed in the form

$$f(x) = a_0 x^n + a_1 x^{n-1} + a_2 x^{n-2} + \cdots + a_{n-1}x + a_n, \quad (11\text{--}1)$$

where $a_0 \neq 0$, n is a positive integer or zero, and a_i $(i = 0, 1, 2, \ldots n)$ are constants, is called a *rational integral function* or a *polynomial of the nth degree in x*. (Compare the definition in Article 1–6.) Unless otherwise stated, $f(x)$ will denote such a function in this chapter.

11–1 Certain theorems. There are several theorems of considerable importance in the study of the polynomial function which must now be established, not only to facilitate graphing the function but also to help solve polynomial equations.

THEOREM 11–1. (*The Remainder Theorem*) *If a polynomial $f(x)$ is divided by $x - r$, where r is any constant, until a constant remainder independent of x is obtained, this remainder is equal to $f(r)$.*

Proof. Let $q(x)$ denote the quotient when $f(x)$ is divided by $x - r$, and let R denote the constant remainder. Then $f(x)$ may be expressed [recall Eqs. (1–16) and (1–17) of Article 1–6] by the identity

$$f(x) \equiv (x - r) \cdot q(x) + R, \quad (11\text{--}2)$$

where clearly $q(x)$ is of degree $n - 1$, since we assume $f(x)$ is of degree n. Since this identity is true for all values of x, it is true for $x = r$. Therefore,

$$f(r) = (r - r) \cdot q(r) + R = 0 \cdot q(r) + R,$$

or

$$f(r) = R. \quad (11\text{--}3)$$

ILLUSTRATION 1. Let $f(x) = 5x^3 - 14x + 3$, and $r = 2$. Then, as was shown in Example 3, Article 1–6, $R = 15$. By substituting $r = 2$ for x in $f(x)$, we have $f(2) = 5(2)^3 - 14(2) + 3 = 40 - 28 + 3 = 15$, which is in accord with the Remainder Theorem.

224

Because of this theorem, the method of synthetic division described in Article 1–6 is most useful in finding the value of $f(x)$ for different values of x. It has advantages over direct substitution that are especially evident either when n is large or when r is other than a small integer.

THEOREM 11–2. (*The Factor Theorem*) *If* $f(r) = R$ *is zero, that is, r is a zero of* $f(x)$, *then* $(x - r)$ *is a factor of* $f(x)$.

Proof. Since r is a zero of $f(x)$, that is $R = 0$, we have

$$f(x) \equiv (x - r) \cdot q(x) + 0.$$

Thus $(x - r)$ is a factor.

THEOREM 11–3. (*Converse of the Factor Theorem*) *If* $(x - r)$ *is a factor of* $f(x)$, *then* $f(r) = R = 0$, *and r is a zero of the function* $f(x)$.

Proof. Since $x - r$ is a factor of $f(x)$,

$$f(x) \equiv (x - r) \cdot q(x),$$

where $q(x)$ is the quotient of $f(x)/(x - r)$. Therefore,

$$f(r) = (r - r) \cdot q(r) = 0 \cdot q(r) = 0,$$

which states that r is a zero of $f(x)$.

ILLUSTRATION 2. The quantity $x - 3$ is a factor of $f(x) \equiv x^3 - 27$, since $f(3) = (3)^3 - 27 = 0$.

ILLUSTRATION 3. The function $f(x) = x^3 - 6x^2 + 3x + 10$ is exactly divisible by $x - 2$, since $f(2) = 0$. The fact that $f(2) = 0$ is shown by synthetic division.

$$
\begin{array}{rrrr|r}
1 & -6 & 3 & 10 & \underline{2} \\
  & 2 & -8 & -10 & \\
\hline
1 & -4 & -5 & 0 &
\end{array}
$$

PROBLEMS

By using synthetic division, find the remainder, and check by direct substitution, when

1. $3x^2 - 2x - 4$ is divided by $x - 3$
2. $x^3 + 4x - 7$ is divided by $x - 3$
3. $x^3 - 2x^2 + 9$ is divided by $x + 2$
4. $x^4 - 2x^3 - 3x^2 - 4x - 8$ is divided by (a) $x - 2$, (b) $x + 1$
5. $2x^4 - 3x^3 - 20x^2 - 6$ is divided by (a) $x - 4$, (b) $x + 3$
6. $x^3 + 3x^2 - 2x - 5$ is divided by (a) $x + 2$, (b) $x + 3$

By using the Factor Theorem, determine whether the first quantity is a factor of the second in Problems 7–12.

7. $x - 2$, $x^4 + 3x^3 - 5x^2 + 2x - 24$
8. $x + 3$, $x^3 - 4x^2 - 18x + 9$
9. $x - 3$, $x^4 - 5x^3 + 8x^2 + 15x - 2$
10. $x - 5$, $x^3 + 2x^2 - 25x - 50$
11. $2x + 3$, $2x^4 + 5x^3 + 3x^2 + 8x + 12$
12. $3x + 1$, $9x^3 + 6x^2 + 4x + 2$

13. Show that $x - y$ is a factor of $x^5 - y^5$, $x^6 - y^6$, $x^7 - y^7$, and $x^8 - y^8$. By using synthetic division, find the quotient in each case. (Recall Example 2, Article 8–1.)

14. Show that $x + y$ is a factor of $x^5 + y^5$ and $x^7 + y^7$. By using synthetic division, find the quotient in each case.

One of the more important theorems in connection with the zeros of a polynomial function may be expressed in terms of synthetic division.

THEOREM 11–4. *In the synthetic division of*

$$f(x) = a_0 x^n + a_1 x^{n-1} + a_2 x^{n-2} + \cdots + a_{n-1} x + a_n \text{ by } x - r,$$

where $a_0 > 0$,

(1) *if $r > 0$ and all the numbers in the third row are positive, then r is an upper limit for the positive zeros of $f(x)$;*

(2) *if $r < 0$ and the signs of the numbers in the third row alternate in sign, then r is a lower limit for the negative zeros of $f(x)$.*

Proof. Because of the process of synthetic division, in either (1) or (2) a numerical increase in r will numerically increase all the numbers in the third row except the first. Thus, if r were to be increased numerically, the final number in the third row would be numerically increased, so that the remainder would never be zero for any numerical increase in r.

EXAMPLE 1. Find an upper and lower limit to the zeros of $f(x) = x^4 + 3x^3 - 9x^2 + 3x - 10$.

Solution. By using synthetic division, we have

$$
\begin{array}{rrrrr|r}
1 & 3 & -9 & 3 & -10 & \underline{3} \\
  & 3 & 18 & 27 & 90 & \\
\hline
1 & 6 & 9 & 30 & 80 &
\end{array}
$$

Since all the numbers in the third row are positive, 3 is an upper limit to the zeros of $f(x)$.

Again,

$$
\begin{array}{rrrrr|r}
1 & 3 & -9 & 3 & -10 & \underline{-6} \\
 & -6 & 18 & -54 & 306 & \\
\hline
1 & -3 & 9 & -51 & 296 &
\end{array}
$$

Since the signs in the third row alternate, there is no zero less than -6.

The next theorem, unfortunately, has no elementary proof but, because of its importance, will be assumed.

THEOREM 11–5. (*Fundamental Theorem of Algebra*) *Every polynomial function*

$$f(x) = a_0 x^n + a_1 x^{n-1} + a_2 x^{n-2} + \cdots + a_{n-1} x + a_n,$$

$n \geq 1$, $a_0 \neq 0$, *has at least one (real or imaginary)* zero.*

This theorem was first proved by the German mathematician Karl Friedrich Gauss, at the age of 22. It enables us to prove a theorem on the number of zeros of a polynomial function.

THEOREM 11–6. *Every polynomial function,*

$$f(x) = a_0 x^n + a_1 x^{n-1} + a_2 x^{n-2} + \cdots + a_{n-1} x + a_n, \qquad a_0 \neq 0$$

has exactly n zeros.

Proof. Since, by Theorem 11–5, $f(x)$ has at least one zero, r_1, Theorem 11–5 implies that $(x - r_1)$ is a factor of $f(x)$. Thus,

$$f(x) \equiv (x - r_1) \cdot q_1(x), \tag{11-4}$$

where $q_1(x)$ is the quotient of $f(x)$ by $(x - r_1)$. Again, $q_1(x)$ has a zero r_2, so that

$$q_1(x) \equiv (x - r_2) \cdot q_2(x),$$

where $q_2(x)$ is the quotient of $q_1(x)$ by $(x - r_2)$. Therefore we may write

$$f(x) \equiv (x - r_1) \cdot (x - r_2) \cdot q_2(x). \tag{11-5}$$

Since we know that each new quotient is of one degree less than the preceding quotient, we can continue the process until we finally have

$$f(x) \equiv (x - r_1)(x - r_2) \cdots (x - r_n) \cdot q_n(x), \tag{11-6}$$

where, since there are n factors $(x - r_i)$, $q_n(x)$ must be the constant a_0;

---

* Imaginary numbers are discussed in some detail in Chapter 17.

hence
$$f(x) \equiv a_0(x - r_1)(x - r_2) \cdots (x - r_n), \qquad (11\text{–}7)$$

where each r is a zero of $f(x)$.

Let r be any number. Since Eq. (11–7) is an identity, it is true for all values of x. Thus,
$$f(r) \equiv a_0(r - r_1)(r - r_2) \cdots (r - r_n).$$

If $r \neq r_i$ for any i, none of the factors $(r - r_i)$ is zero. Since $a_0 \neq 0$, $f(r) \neq 0$, and r is not a zero of $f(x)$. Therefore there are *exactly* n *zeros*, and the theorem is proved.

ILLUSTRATION 4. The function $(x - 3)^2(x - 1)(x + 2)^3$ is a polynomial of the sixth degree. Its six zeros are 3, 3, 1, -2, -2, -2. Note that any zero which occurs m times is considered as m zeros.

DEFINITION 11–1. *If the polynomial $f(x)$ contains $(x - r)^m$, where m is a positive integer, and no higher power of $x - r$, then $x = r$ is called a zero of order m of $f(x)$. If $m = 1$, $x = r$ is a simple zero, but if $m > 1$, $x = r$ is called a multiple zero of order m.*

In Illustration 4, 3 is a zero of order 2, 1 is a simple zero, and -2 is a zero of order 3. In a problem such as that in Illustration 4 the multiplicity of the zeros is immediately clear. If, however, the polynomial is not factored, the following theorem might be useful.

THEOREM 11–7. *If r is a simple zero of the polynomial $f(x)$, then r is not a zero of $f'(x)$. If r is a multiple zero of order $m > 1$ of $f(x)$, then r is a zero of order $m - 1$ of $f'(x)$.*

Proof. Let r be a multiple zero of order m of $f(x)$. Then
$$f(x) = (x - r)^m Q(x),$$

where $Q(x)$ does not contain $x - r$ as a factor. Differentiating, we have the identity
$$f'(x) \equiv (x - r)^m Q'(x) + Q(x) \cdot m(x - r)^{m-1}$$
$$\equiv (x - r)^{m-1}[mQ(x) + (x - r)Q'(x)].$$

Thus, if $x - r$ occurs as a single factor of $f(x)$, it is not a factor of $f'(x)$, since $m = 1$, and $1 - 1 = 0$. However, if $m > 1$, we see that if $(x - r)$ occurs m times in $f(x)$, it will occur $m - 1$ times in $f'(x)$. (Recall $Q(r) \neq 0$.)

The converse of this theorem is also true.

THEOREM 11–7'. *If r is a zero of $f'(x)$ of order $m - 1$ and is also a zero of the polynomial $f(x)$, then r is a zero of order m of $f(x)$.*

Proof. This follows from the identity established in the proof of Theorem 11–7.

Thus, in order to use Theorems 11–7 and 11–7′, we should find the zeros of $f'(x)$ and substitute them in $f(x)$. Any zero of order k of $f'(x)$ which, when substituted in $f(x)$, results in $f(x) = 0$ will be a zero of order $k + 1$ of $f(x)$.

EXAMPLE 2.   Find all multiple zeros of $f(x) = 2x^3 + 5x^2 - 4x - 12$.

Solution. We find $f'(x) = 6x^2 + 10x - 4 = 2(x + 2)(3x - 1)$. Substituting $x = -2$ and $\frac{1}{3}$ in $f(x)$, we have $f(-2) = 0$, but $f(\frac{1}{3}) \neq 0$. Therefore, since -2 is a simple zero of $f'(x)$ and is a zero of $f(x)$, it is a double zero of $f(x)$.

PROBLEMS

Find by inspection the zeros of each of the following functions, and give the multiplicity of each.

1. $(x - 2)(x - 3)^2(x + 4)^3$
2. $(x + 1)^4(x - 2)^5$
3. $(x + 7)(2x - 3)^3$
4. $(x^2 - 4x + 4)(x^2 + 3x - 10)$
5. $(3x + 5)(x^2 - 6x + 9)^2$

6. By using Theorem 11–7 or 11–7′, check the results of Problems 4 and 5.

Find the multiple zeros of each of the polynomials given in Problems 7–10.

7. $x^3 - 3x^2 + 4$
8. $18x^3 - 39x^2 + 20x - 3$
9. $2x^4 - 5x^3 + 3x^2 + x - 1$
10. $x^4 - 16x^3 + 24x^2 - 3x + 16$

11. Show that $4a^3 = 27b^2$ if the polynomial $x^3 - ax + b$ has a double zero.

Find an upper limit and a lower limit for the zeros of the following functions:

12. $x^3 - 3x^2 - 2x + 15$
13. $x^3 + 2x^2 - 7x - 8$
14. $x^4 - 2x^3 - 7x^2 + 10x + 10$
15. $x^4 - x^3 - x^2 - 2x - 6$
16. $x^4 - 4x^3 + x^2 + 6x + 2$
17. $x^4 - 5x^2 + 6x - 9$
18. $x^3 - 8x + 5$
19. $x^3 + 16x - 29$
20. $x^5 + 5x^2 - 7$
21. $x^5 - 3x^3 + 24$

11–2 Graphing of polynomial functions. One of the methods of finding the real zeros of a function was mentioned in connection with the graphs in Article 3–7. It is quite possible to use this method for any polynomial function. Since, by using synthetic division, we can easily obtain the values of the function for any value of the variable, a table of values can be constructed and the graph may be sketched. Care must be taken in joining the plotted points. We recall that the real zeros of a function $f(x)$ are the abscissas of the points where the graph of $y = f(x)$ crosses or touches the x-axis.

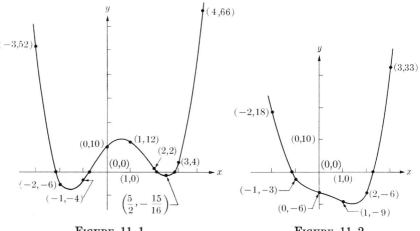

FIGURE 11–1   FIGURE 11–2

EXAMPLE 1. Draw the graph of $y = f(x) = x^4 - 2x^3 - 7x^2 + 10x + 10$, and verify that it has one real zero between -3 and -2, one between -1 and 0, and two between 2 and 3.

Solution. First construct the table of values shown below. For any arbitrary x, the corresponding value of the function is found by synthetic division. Usually it is wise to use all integral values of x between an upper and lower limit. (Why?) In addition, fractional values may be necessary to ascertain the shape of the curve. The values from the table have been plotted as points and the graph drawn in Fig. 11–1. Note that the scales on the two axes are conveniently *not* the same. From the figure it is clear that the zeros are located as suggested in the statement of the example.

x	-3	-2	-1	0	1	2	$2\frac{1}{2}$	3	4
y	52	-6	-4	10	12	2	$-\frac{15}{16}$	4	66

In Example 1 the fourth degree function has four real zeros. This is not always the case, for some of the zeros may be imaginary. An imaginary zero of a function cannot be approximated from its graph.

EXAMPLE 2. Draw the graph of the function $y = f(x) = x^4 - x^3 - x^2 - 2x - 6$, and approximate its real zeros.

Solution. Again the table of values is constructed, the points are plotted, and the graph is drawn (Fig. 11–2).

x	-2	-1	0	1	2	3
y	18	-3	-6	-9	-6	33

Although the function is of the fourth degree, its graph only crosses the x-axis twice. These two real zeros are between -2 and -1, and between 2 and 3, while the other two are imaginary.

There is, unfortunately, no simple method for approximating the imaginary zeros of a general polynomial function.

PROBLEMS

Draw the graphs of each of the following functions, and thus verify the statement given in Problems 1–4.

1. $f(x) = x^3 - x^2 - 2x + 1$ has one zero between -2 and -1, 0 and 1, and 1 and 2.

2. $f(x) = x^3 - 3x + 1$ has one zero between -2 and -1, 0 and 1, and 1 and 2.

3. $f(x) = x^4 - 2x^2 + 12x - 17$ has one zero between -3 and -2, and one between 1 and 2.

4. $f(x) = x^4 - 4x^3 + x^2 + 6x + 2$ has two zeros between 3 and 2, and two between 0 and -1.

Draw the graphs of the following functions, showing the location of all the real zeros:

5. $f(x) = x^4 - 20x^2 + 48x - 32$
6. $f(x) = x^3 + x^2 - 3x - 4$
7. $f(x) = 4x^3 + 8x^2 - 11x + 3$
8. $f(x) = x^4 - 2x^3 + 3x^2 + x + 6$
9. $f(x) = x^5 - 3x^3 + 9x^2 - 8x + 11$
10. $f(x) = -x^4 + 2x^2 + 8x + 3$

11–3 General remarks on zeros and roots. We recall that the zeros of any function are identical with the roots of the equation formed by equating the function to zero. Consequently, all our previous remarks about the zeros of the polynomial function apply also to the roots of the associated equation.

In Chapters 5 and 6 we found specific methods for solving any polynomial equation

$$a_0x^n + a_1x^{n-1} + a_2x^{n-2} + \cdots + a_{n-1}x + a_n = 0, \qquad a_0 \neq 0$$

when $n = 1$ (linear equation) and $n = 2$ (quadratic equation). There are also formulas for solving this type of equation when $n = 3$ and 4, but these are beyond the scope of this book. Tartaglia was the first to obtain formulas for the solution of the general cubic equation. These were published in 1545 by Cardan and are known as *Cardan's formulas*. Shortly thereafter Ferrari obtained formulas for the solution of the general quartic or fourth degree equation. For equations when $n \geq 5$, it has been proved that in general no algebraic formulas for the roots in terms of the coefficients exist. Many attempts were made to obtain general formulas, but finally, in 1824, N. H. Abel (1802–1829), a Norwegian, proved that in the general case no such formulas exist. Later, E. Galois (1811–1832), a Frenchman, was able to show that such formulas did exist under certain conditions.

It is comparatively simple, however, to find all the rational roots of a polynomial equation and approximate any irrational roots. Imaginary roots will be discussed briefly in Chapter 17.

11–4 Rational roots. With regard to the rational roots of an equation with integral coefficients, we have the following theorem:

THEOREM 11–8. *If the rational number p/q, a fraction in lowest terms, is a root of the equation*

$$a_0x^n + a_1x^{n-1} + a_2x^{n-2} + \cdots + a_{n-1}x + a_n = 0, \qquad (11\text{–}8)$$

where a_i ($i = 0, 1, 2, \ldots, n$) are integral coefficients, then p is an exact divisor of a_n and q is an exact divisor of a_0.

Proof. Since p/q is a root of Eq. (11–8), we have

$$a_0\left(\frac{p}{q}\right)^n + a_1\left(\frac{p}{q}\right)^{n-1} + a_2\left(\frac{p}{q}\right)^{n-2} + \cdots + a_{n-1}\left(\frac{p}{q}\right) + a_n = 0.$$

Multiplying each term of this equation by q^n, we get

$$a_0p^n + a_1p^{n-1}q + a_2p^{n-2}q^2 + \cdots + a_{n-1}pq^{n-1} + a_nq^n = 0. \qquad (11\text{–}9)$$

If we transpose a_nq^n to the right side and divide both members by p,

$$a_0p^{n-1} + a_1p^{n-2}q + a_2p^{n-3}q^2 + \cdots + a_{n-1}q^{n-1} = \frac{-a_nq^n}{p}.$$

Since each a_i, p, and q is an integer, the left member, and therefore the right member, is an integer. Also, p and q have no common factor, so that p does not divide q^n. Thus p is an exact divisor of a_n.

If, in Eq. (11–9), we take the term a_0p^n to the opposite side of the equation and divide both members by q, we get

$$a_1p^{n-1} + a_2p^{n-2}q + \cdots + a_{n-1}pq^{n-2} + a_nq^{n-1} = \frac{-a_0p^n}{q}.$$

By the same type of argument, we have the fact that q is an exact divisor of a_0.

A direct corollary of this is clearly the following theorem.

THEOREM 11–9. *Any rational root of the equation*

$$x^n + a_1x^{n-1} + a_2x^{n-2} + \cdots + a_{n-1}x + a_n = 0, \qquad (11\text{–}10)$$

where each a_i is an integral coefficient, must be an integer which is an exact divisor of the constant term a_n.

We are now prepared to find all the rational roots of any polynomial equation of the type given by Eq. (11–8).

EXAMPLE 1. Solve the equation

$$x^4 - x^3 - 7x^2 - 14x - 24 = 0$$

by first finding the rational roots.

Solution. In examining the equation for possible rational roots, we find by Theorem 11–9 that they are ± 1, ± 2, ± 3, ± 4, ± 6, ± 8, ± 12, and ± 24. By synthetic division we find that 1, 2, and 3 are not roots. For $x = 4$,

$$
\begin{array}{rrrrr|r}
1 & -1 & -7 & -14 & -24 & \underline{4} \\
  & 4 & 12 & 20 & 24 & \\
\hline
1 & 3 & 5 & 6 & 0 &
\end{array}
$$

Putting this result in algebraic form [Eq. (1–17)], we get

$$x^4 - x^3 - 7x^2 - 14x - 24 \equiv (x^3 + 3x^2 + 5x + 6)(x - 4).$$

Since $x - 4$ is a factor of the original equation, $x = 4$ is one root, and our problem reduces to finding the roots of the depressed equation $x^3 + 3x^2 + 5x + 6 = 0$. Since all the signs in this equation are plus, there are no positive roots. (Why?) By using synthetic division, we find -1 is not a root but $x = -2$ is a root.

$$
\begin{array}{rrrr|r}
1 & 3 & 5 & 6 & \underline{-2} \\
  & -2 & -2 & -6 & \\
\hline
1 & 1 & 3 & 0 &
\end{array}
$$

The new depressed equation is $x^2 + x + 3 = 0$. Solving this by the quadratic formula [Eq. (6–6)], we have $x = (-1 \pm \sqrt{-11})/2$, so that our complete solution is

$$x = 4, \quad -2, \quad \frac{-1 \pm \sqrt{-11}}{2},$$

with the last two roots imaginary.

EXAMPLE 2. Solve for the exact roots of

$$4x^5 - 16x^4 + 17x^3 - 19x^2 + 13x - 3 = 0.$$

Solution. Since the signs of the terms alternate, this equation has no negative roots. (Why?) Its possible rational roots are 1, 3, $\frac{1}{2}$, $\frac{3}{2}$, $\frac{1}{4}$, and $\frac{3}{4}$.

By using synthetic division, we find that 1 is not a root but $\frac{1}{2}$ is.

$$
\begin{array}{rrrrrr|l}
4 & -16 & 17 & -19 & 13 & -3 & \frac{1}{2} \\
  & 2 & -7 & 5 & -7 & 3 & \\
\hline
4 & -14 & 10 & -14 & 6 & 0 &
\end{array}
$$

Since the depressed equation has a common factor of 2 in each term, it may be divided out, reducing to $2x^4 - 7x^3 + 5x^2 - 7x + 3 = 0$. Again we find that $\frac{1}{2}$ is a root, so that it is a double root of the original equation.

$$
\begin{array}{rrrrr|l}
2 & -7 & 5 & -7 & 3 & \frac{1}{2} \\
  & 1 & -3 & 1 & -3 & \\
\hline
2 & -6 & 2 & -6 & 0 &
\end{array}
$$

Again, factoring out the common 2, we find that the new depressed equation becomes $x^3 - 3x^2 + x - 3 = 0$. The only possible remaining rational root is the integer 3. (Why?)

$$
\begin{array}{rrrr|l}
1 & -3 & 1 & -3 & 3 \\
  & 3 & 0 & 3 & \\
\hline
1 & 0 & 1 & 0 &
\end{array}
$$

We see that 3 is a root, and the solution of the depressed equation $x^2 + 1 = 0$ gives the final two imaginary roots $\pm\sqrt{-1}$. Thus the complete solution is $x = \frac{1}{2}, \frac{1}{2}, 3, \pm\sqrt{-1}$.

PROBLEMS

Find the exact roots of the following equations:

1. $2x^3 - 3x^2 - 11x + 6 = 0$
2. $x^3 - 6x^2 + 11x - 6 = 0$
3. $x^4 - 16x^3 + 86x^2 - 176x + 105 = 0$
4. $x^3 + x^2 - 24x + 36 = 0$
5. $x^4 - x^3 - 19x^2 + 49x - 30 = 0$
6. $x^4 - 4x^3 + 4x - 1 = 0$
7. $4x^4 + 8x^3 - 7x^2 - 21x - 9 = 0$
8. $2x^4 + 5x^3 - 11x^2 - 20x + 12 = 0$
9. $x^4 - 4x^3 + 6x^2 - 4x + 1 = 0$
10. $10x^4 - 13x^3 + 17x^2 - 26x - 6 = 0$
11. $8x^5 - 12x^4 + 14x^3 - 13x^2 + 6x - 1 = 0$
12. $12x^3 - 52x^2 + 61x - 15 = 0$

Solve each of the following for all positive values of θ less than 2π.

13. $4 \sin^4 \theta - 12 \sin \theta \cos^2 \theta - 7 \cos^2 \theta + 9 \sin \theta + 5 = 0$. [*Hint:* Use the identity $\cos^2 \theta \equiv 1 - \sin^2 \theta$ and then simplify by letting $x = \sin \theta$.]

14. $4 \sin^4 \theta - 4 \sin \theta \cos^2 \theta - 11 \cos^2 \theta + 3 \sin \theta + 8 = 0$

15. $3 \tan \theta \sec^2 \theta + 3 \sec^2 \theta - 4 \tan \theta - 4 = 0$

11–5 Irrational roots. There are several well-known approximation methods* for solving polynomial equations for irrational roots. We shall consider the most elementary method. In Article 11–2 we noticed that any simple root of $f(x) = 0$ could be isolated. If $f(a)$ and $f(b)$ are opposite in sign, there is at least one value of x between a and b where $f(x) = 0$. It is this basic idea that will be used in the following example.

EXAMPLE.   Find the approximate value of the largest positive root of $x^3 - x^2 - 3x + 1 = 0$.

Solution. By first plotting the graph of the function $y = x^3 - x^2 - 3x + 1$, as shown in Fig. 11–3, we note that the root which we wish to approximate is between 2 and 3. If we divide this interval in ten equal parts and successively use synthetic division for the values $x = 2.1, 2.2, 2.3, \ldots, 2.9, 3$, we find $f(2.1) = -0.45$, while $f(2.2) = 0.21$, so that the root lies between 2.1 and 2.2. If we repeat this process for the values 2.11, 2.12, 2.13, $\ldots$, 2.19, 2.2, we find $f(2.17) = -0.0006$ but $f(2.18) = 0.0678$, so that $x = 2.17$ represents the root correct to two decimal places. In fact, $f(2.171) = 0.00621$, which indicates that $x = 2.170$ is correct to three decimal places. This process may, of course, be continued indefinitely.

The amount of work involved in approximating such a root may be greatly reduced by the method of *linear interpolation*, similar to that used in Article 4–13. We found that the root in question lay between 2.1 and

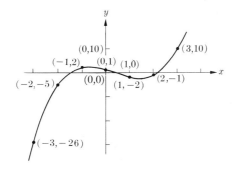

FIGURE 11–3

---

* Methods such as Graeffe's, Horner's, or Newton's appear in most books on the theory of equations.

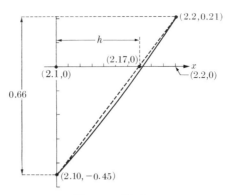

FIGURE 11–4

2.2. This section of the curve appears in Fig. 11–4, with the location of the two points whose abscissas are 2.1 and 2.2. If we assume that the curve approximates a straight line between the two points, by similar triangles

$$\frac{h}{0.45} = \frac{0.1}{0.66},$$

so that $h = 0.07$ approximately. Therefore a good estimate for x is $2.1 + 0.07 = 2.17$. We now evaluate $f(2.17)$ and find it negative. From the way in which the curve is drawn, we realize that the root in question is greater than 2.17. By evaluating $f(2.18)$, we isolate this root without trying all the other eight possible values. This method of linear interpolation can be carried out for each new decimal, until the desired accuracy is obtained.

The beauty of this method is its simplicity. Moreover, it can be used to approximate any real root, provided the graph of the function actually crosses the x-axis, rather than merely being tangent to it.

PROBLEMS

Plot the graphs of each of the functions associated with the following equations and find, accurately to two decimals, the value of the indicated real roots.

1. $x^3 - 3x^2 - x + 2 = 0$ (the least positive)
2. $x^3 + 3x^2 - 6x - 3 = 0$ (the greatest positive)
3. $x^3 - x^2 - 2x + 1 = 0$ (the least positive)
4. $x^3 - 3x + 1 = 0$ (the three real roots)
5. $x^3 - 7x + 7 = 0$ (the two roots between 1 and 2)
6. $x^4 - x^3 + 2x^2 - 3x - 3 = 0$ (all)
7. $x^4 - 2x^3 + x^2 - 1 = 0$ (all)
8. $x^4 - 4x^3 - 4x + 12 = 0$ (all)

Find accurately to three decimals the indicated principal roots:

9. $\sqrt[3]{6}$ 10. $\sqrt[3]{15}$ 11. $\sqrt[4]{2}$ 12. $\sqrt[5]{-9}$

CHAPTER 12

SOME APPLICATIONS OF DIFFERENTIATION

12–1 Extreme values of a function. In discussing the graph of $y = \sin \theta$ in Article 4–3, we mentioned that this function was an increasing function. Let us give a precise definition.

DEFINITION 12–1. *The function $f(x)$ is an* increasing *function at $x = x_1$ if for x sufficiently near x_1 but less than x_1, $f(x) < f(x_1)$, and for x sufficiently near x_1 but greater than x_1, $f(x) > f(x_1)$.*

A similar definition exists for a decreasing function. Either property can be stated in terms of $f'(x_1)$.

THEOREM 12–1. *If $f'(x_1) > 0$, then $f(x)$ is an increasing function at $x = x_1$.*

Proof. Since $f'(x_1) > 0$, we have $f'(x_1) = A$, where $A > 0$. By the definition of the derivative,

$$\frac{f(x) - f(x_1)}{x - x_1} > 0, \qquad (12\text{–}1)$$

for all x sufficiently close to x_1. For such x, if $x < x_1$ then $x - x_1 < 0$, and for (12–1) to hold, $f(x) - f(x_1) < 0$, or $f(x) < f(x_1)$.

On the other hand, for x sufficiently near x_1, if $x > x_1$ then $x - x_1 > 0$, and $f(x) - f(x_1) > 0$ for (12–1) to be satisfied. Thus, if $x > x_1$, $f(x) > f(x_1)$, so that $f(x)$ is increasing at x_1.

THEOREM 12–2. *If $f'(x_1) < 0$, then $f(x)$ is a decreasing function at $x = x_1$.*

Proof. This proof follows the same steps as that for Theorem 12–1.

EXAMPLE. Find where the function $f(x) = 4x^3 + 3x^2 - 18x + 6$ is increasing and where it is decreasing.

Solution. Since $f'(x) = 12x^2 + 6x - 18 = 6(2x + 3)(x - 1)$, we see that $f'(x)$ changes its sign at $x = 1$ and $-\frac{3}{2}$. By using the method for inequalities in Article 6–3, we find $f'(x) > 0$, that is, $f(x)$ is increasing if $x < -\frac{3}{2}$ or $x > 1$, and $f'(x) < 0$, or $f(x)$ is decreasing if $-\frac{3}{2} < x < 1$. See Fig. 12–1.

We are now ready to consider the extreme values of a function. These were specified for the very special quadratic function in Article 6–1.

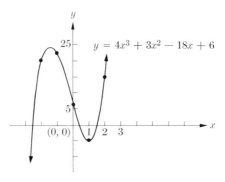

FIGURE 12–1

DEFINITION 12–2. *The function f(x) has an* absolute maximum *at x = x_1 if $f(x_1) \geq f(x)$ for any x in the domain of definition of f(x).*

The *absolute minimum* may be defined in a corresponding fashion.

DEFINITION 12–3. *The function f(x) has a* relative maximum *at x = x_1 if $f(x_1) \geq f(x)$ for all x which are neighboring values of x_1.*

Again, a corresponding definition can be given for a *relative minimum* of a function.

DEFINITION 12–4. *The* extreme values *of a function are the relative maximum and minimum values of the function.*

Although there are many types of maxima or minima for functions that are not too well behaved, we shall limit ourselves in this article to functions which have continuous derivatives at all values of their domains and are therefore continuous. Other slightly more complicated functions will be considered in Article 12–3.

We are interested in finding the values of x at which a function has a relative maximum or minimum. It should be clear from the definitions that a relative minimum of a function may be greater than a relative maximum, and vice versa. For example, in Fig. 12–2 the relative minimum

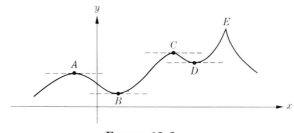

FIGURE 12–2

of the function at D is greater than the relative maximum at A. In this figure it is clear geometrically that the tangent to the curve is horizontal at A, B, C, and D, and thus the slope of the tangent line, or $f'(x)$ evaluated at the corresponding value of x, is zero. This fact, which is evident graphically, may be stated as an important theorem.

THEOREM 12–3. *If $f(x)$ is a differentiable function and has an extreme value at $x = x_1$, then $f'(x_1) = 0$.*

Proof. Suppose the extreme value is a relative maximum. Then for x sufficiently near x_1, $f(x) - f(x_1) \leq 0$. We know that

$$\lim_{x \to x_1} \frac{f(x) - f(x_1)}{x - x_1} = f'(x_1).$$

(1) If $f'(x_1) > 0$, then

$$\frac{f(x) - f(x_1)}{x - x_1} > 0,$$

for all x sufficiently near x_1. However, since $f(x) - f(x_1) \leq 0$ and yet for any $x > x_1$, $x - x_1 > 0$, we would have

$$\frac{f(x) - f(x_1)}{x - x_1} \leq 0,$$

which is an impossible situation.

(2) If $f'(x_1) < 0$, then

$$\frac{f(x) - f(x_1)}{x - x_1} < 0$$

for all x sufficiently near x_1. In this case, since $f(x) - f(x_1) \leq 0$ and yet for $x < x_1$, $x - x_1 < 0$, we would have

$$\frac{f(x) - f(x_1)}{x - x_1} \geq 0,$$

again an impossible situation.

Therefore the fact that $f'(x_1)$ is either greater than or less than zero leads to an impossibility, and $f'(x_1) = 0$.

We can correspondingly treat the case of a relative minimum.

DEFINITION 12–5. *The values of x for which $f'(x) = 0$ are called* critical values.

It is important to note that the converse of Theorem 12–3 is *not* true. As is shown in Fig. 12–3, there is a critical value of x at $x = x_1$, but $f(x_1)$ is not an extreme value of the function. It is therefore important to obtain additional conditions for determining the nature of the function at its

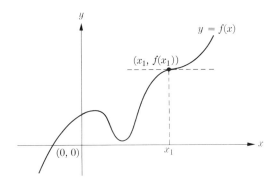

FIGURE 12–3

critical values. One method involves the first derivative of the function, another the second derivative. We shall consider both methods.

THEOREM 12–4. *If $f(x)$ is a function whose derivative exists and is continuous and if as x increases through the critical value $x = x_1$, $f'(x)$ changes sign from positive to negative, then $f(x_1)$ is a relative maximum of the function.*

Proof. Since for x sufficiently near x_1 but less than x_1, $f'(x) > 0$, so that by Theorem 12–1, $f(x)$ is an increasing function. Also, for x sufficiently near x_1 but greater than x_1, $f'(x) < 0$ and, therefore, $f(x)$ is a decreasing function. Thus, if $f'(x)$ changes sign from plus to minus when x increases through $x = x_1$,* then at $x = x_1$, $f(x)$ stops increasing and begins decreasing; that is, $f(x_1)$ is a relative maximum.

There is clearly a corresponding theorem for relative minimum whose proof follows in the same way.

THEOREM 12–5. *If $f(x)$ is a function whose derivative exists and is continuous and if as x increases through the critical value $x = x_1$, $f'(x)$ changes sign from negative to positive, then $f(x_1)$ is a relative minimum of the function.*

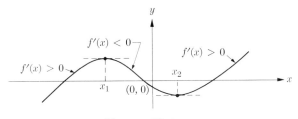

FIGURE 12–4

* An important property of continuous functions implies that this can only occur at a value such as $x = x_1$ where $f'(x_1) = 0$.

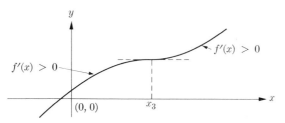

FIGURE 12–5

These theorems should be intuitively clear from the curve in Fig. 12–4. Note that in Fig. 12–5 $f(x)$ has neither a maximum nor a minimum at the critical value $x = x_3$, since $f'(x)$ does not change its sign as x increases through x_3.

The first-derivative test for determining the nature of the function at critical values may be summarized as follows:

1. Solve the equation $f'(x) = 0$ for all real roots x_i in order to obtain the critical values.

2. For each root x_i, determine whether $f'(x)$ changes sign as x increases through the root x_i.

3. $f(x_i)$ is a relative maximum if $f'(x_i) = 0$ and $f'(x)$ changes from plus to minus.

4. $f(x_i)$ is a relative minimum if $f'(x_i) = 0$ and $f'(x)$ changes from minus to plus.

5. $f(x_i)$ is neither a relative maximum nor minimum if $f'(x_i) = 0$ and $f'(x)$ does not change sign.

EXAMPLE 1. Find the extreme values of the function

$$f(x) = 2x^3 - 3x^2 - 36x + 30.$$

Solution. We find

$$f'(x) = 6x^2 - 6x - 36$$
$$= 6(x^2 - x - 6)$$
$$= 6(x - 3)(x + 2).$$

Therefore $f'(x) = 0$ at $x = 3$ or -2. If

$$\begin{array}{ll} x < -2, & f'(x) > 0; \\ -2 < x < 3, & f'(x) < 0; \\ x > 3, & f'(x) > 0. \end{array}$$

Thus $f(-2) = 74$ is a relative maximum and $f(3) = -51$ is a relative minimum.

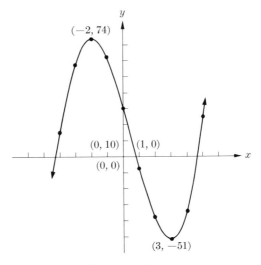

FIGURE 12–6

The advantage in plotting polynomial functions (Article 11–2) with the help of this material may be seen in Fig. 12–6.

EXAMPLE 2. Find the relative maxima and minima of the function

$$f(x) = x^2 + \frac{2}{x}.$$

Solution. We have

$$f'(x) = 2x - \frac{2}{x^2} = \frac{2(x^3 - 1)}{x^2}.$$

The only real zero of this function is $x = 1$. Also, if

$$x < 1, \qquad f'(x) < 0,$$

and if

$$x > 1, \qquad f'(x) > 0.$$

Therefore the only extreme value of $f(x)$ is where $x = 1$, and $f(1) = 3$ is a relative minimum. See Fig. 12–7.

The other simple method for determining the nature of the extreme values of a function at a particular value of the domain involves the second derivative. In order to establish a useful theorem we must define the notion of concavity of a curve.

DEFINITION 12–6. *A curve is* concave upward *at $x = x_1$ if the slope of the tangent to the curve is increasing at that value. It is* concave downward *at $x = x_1$ if this slope is decreasing.*

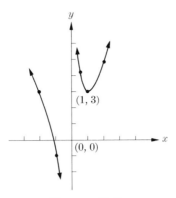

FIGURE 12–7

We might observe that geometrically the tangent to the curve is "turning clockwise" with increasing x as the slope decreases. From the definition we immediately have the following theorem.

THEOREM 12–6. *If $f(x)$ is a function such that $f''(x_1) > 0$, the graph of $f(x)$ is concave upward at $x = x_1$, but if $f''(x_1) < 0$, the graph is concave downward.*

Proof. (a) Since $f''(x_1) > 0$, the function $f'(x)$, the derivative of $f(x)$, is increasing at x_1. But since this function $f'(x)$ is the slope of the tangent to the curve, by Definition 12–6 the graph is concave upward. (b) The other half of the proof is similar.

The following corollary of this theorem gives the important test for extreme values involving the second derivative of a function. This result is often easier to apply than the first-derivative test.

THEOREM 12–7. *If $f''(x_1) < 0$ where x_1 is a critical value, then $f(x)$ has a relative maximum at $x = x_1$; and if $f''(x_1) > 0$ where x_1 is a critical value, $f(x)$ has a relative minimum at $x = x_1$.*

EXAMPLE 3. Test the critical values determined in Example 1 by the second-derivative test.

Solution. We found in Example 1 $f'(x) = 6x^2 - 6x - 36$. Therefore,

$$f''(x) = 12x - 6 = 6(2x - 1).$$

For the critical value $x = 3$, $f''(3) = 30$, which is positive. Thus, at $x = 3$, the curve is concave upward and $f(x)$ has a relative minimum. Moreover, at $x = -2$, $f''(-2) = -30$, which is negative. Thus, at $x = -2$, $f(x)$ has a relative maximum. Note that this is consistent with the results of the solution of Example 1.

Problems

Find the relative maxima and minima of the given functions, testing by both the first- and second-derivative tests.

1. $f(x) = x^2 - 2x + 3$
2. $f(x) = 3x^2 + 6x - 7$
3. $f(x) = 2x^2 - 4x + 3$
4. $f(x) = -2x^2 - 4x + 3$
5. $f(x) = (x + 1)^2(x - 2)$
6. $f(x) = 2x^3 + 5x^2 - 3x$
7. $f(x) = (x + 1)^3$
8. $f(x) = (x - 1)^2(2x + 3)^3$
9. $f(x) = x^2 + 1/x$
10. $f(x) = x^3 + 3/x$
11. $f(x) = x^4 - 4x + 5$
12. $f(x) = ax^2 + bx + c$
13. $f(x) = \sqrt{1 - x^2}$
14. $f(x) = x\sqrt{1 - x^2}$
15. $f(x) = x^2\sqrt{1 - x^2}$
16. $f(x) = x^5 - 5x$
17. $f(x) = \sin x \ (0 \le x \le 2\pi)$
18. $f(x) = \sin x + \cos x \ (0 \le x \le 2\pi)$
19. $f(x) = 3\cos 2x \ (0 \le x \le \pi)$
20. $f(x) = 4\sin^2 x \ (0 \le x \le 2\pi)$

12–2 Applied maximum and minimum problems. There are many problems in everyday life whose solution is a maximum or minimum value of some function. We often wish to find "the smallest or largest" or "the least or most" of something. It is frequently possible to find such a solution by examining the appropriate function. This can be illustrated best by means of several examples. One might also recall Problems 9–13 in Article 6–1.

EXAMPLE 1. A man with 160 feet of fencing wishes to fence off an area in the shape of a rectangle. What should be the dimensions of the area if the enclosed space is to be as large as possible?

Solution. Letting one side of the rectangular area be x feet long, the other sides will be x, $80 - x$, and $80 - x$ feet long, and the area can be expressed as a function of x, namely,

$$f(x) = x(80 - x), \quad \text{where} \quad 0 < x < 80.$$

We are asked to find the values of x and $80 - x$ for which $f(x)$ has a maximum. Since

$$f'(x) = 80 - 2x,$$

a possible value for x would be $x = 40$. To be certain that the function has a maximum at $x = 40$, we note that $f''(x) = -2$ for all values of x, and in particular at $x = 40$. Thus the solution is the square with each side 40 feet long.

EXAMPLE 2. A cylindrical tin can without a top is to have a volume of 20 cubic inches. Find the radius of the base and the height of the can if its shape is such that the least amount of tin will be used.

Solution. Since the volume is fixed (constant), we have $20 = \pi r^2 h$, where r is the radius of the base of the can and h is its height. The total area of the required cylinder is given by the sum of the area of the base and lateral area,

$$A = \pi r^2 + 2\pi r h.$$

Since $20 = \pi r^2 h$, $h = 20/\pi r^2$, so that A can be expressed as a function of the one variable r,

$$A(r) = \pi r^2 + 2\pi r \left(\frac{20}{\pi r^2}\right)$$

$$= \pi r^2 + \frac{40}{r}.$$

We wish to find the value of r (and h) for which A is a minimum.

$$A'(r) = 2\pi r - \frac{40}{r^2}.$$

Setting this equal to zero, we have

$$\frac{2\pi r^3 - 40}{r^2} = 0, \quad \text{or} \quad r = \sqrt[3]{\frac{20}{\pi}}.$$

To show that this value for r gives a minimum for A, we find

$$A''(r) = 2\pi + \frac{80}{r^3},$$

which is positive for the required value of r. To find h, we recall $h = 20/\pi r^2$, in which we substitute the value of $r = \sqrt[3]{20/\pi}$. Thus,

$$h = \frac{20}{\pi \left(\dfrac{20}{\pi}\right)^{2/3}} = \sqrt[3]{\frac{20}{\pi}}.$$

It is interesting to see that the values of h and r are equal and that such would be the case for any value of the constant volume.

This second example illustrates a general problem frequently encountered in physical applications. Often it is possible to express quickly the quantity to be maximized or minimized as a function of two variables. Then, with an additional relationship between these two variables, the original function may be expressed as a function of one variable. The methods developed previously in this chapter are then easily applied. We must always take into account the domain of the function and any relevant physical conditions.

Problems

1. A man has 240 rods of fencing with which to surround a rectangular area and divide it into two plots by running a fence parallel to one side. To ensure an enclosed maximum area, what must be the dimensions of this area?

2. A page in a certain book is to contain 54 square inches. The margins at the top and bottom are $1\frac{1}{2}$ inches, and on the sides, 1 inch. What must be the length of a printed line if the area of text is to be a maximum?

3. What must be the dimensions of the most economical shape for a box of square base and perpendicular sides if it is to hold 12 cubic feet?

4. A covered box is to hold 270 cubic yards, but must have a square base. The material for the base will cost $3 per square yard, but the sides and top only $2 per square yard. What must be the dimensions in order to spend the least amount of money?

5. If a rectangle is inscribed in a circle of radius R, express its dimensions in terms of R (a) if the rectangle's area must be maximum; (b) if the rectangle's perimeter must be maximum.

6. Find the rectangle of largest area which can be inscribed between the curve $x^2 = 8y$ and $y = 4$.

7. Find the dimensions of the largest right circular cylinder which can be inscribed in a given sphere of radius R.

8. Find the dimensions of the largest right circular cylinder which can be inscribed in a given right circular cone of height H and radius R.

9. Find the ratio between the size of the radius and height of a right circular cylinder of constant total area if the cylinder's volume is to be a maximum.

10. Find the ratio between the size of the radius and height of a right circular cylinder of constant volume if the total surface area of the cylinder is to be a maximum.

11. An open box is to be made from a flat piece of metal 24 inches on each side by cutting out equal squares from each corner and turning up the projecting pieces. Find the length of the sides of the squares to be removed if the box thus formed is to be of maximum volume.

12. A man can rent all of his 40 apartments if he rents them for $100 each per month. However, for each $5 increase in rent he will rent one less. How much rent must be charged per month to guarantee the best return?

13. Solve Problem 12 if, in addition to the facts stated, the owner also must pay $10 worth of repairs per month on each rented apartment.

14. A certain television manufacturer estimates that he can sell 50 sets at $200 per set, but for each additional set turned out, the selling price will be reduced $3. How many sets should be manufactured in order to receive the most money? [*Hint:* The result must be an integer.]

15. Show that for any right circular cylinder of constant volume the diameter must equal the height if the surface area (including top and bottom) is to be a minimum.

16. In a given isosceles triangle with base B and height H find the dimensions of the largest rectangle that can be inscribed with one side on the base of the triangle.

17. What point on the curve $y = x^2$ is nearest the point $(2, 0)$? Nearest $(0, 2)$?

18. Find the point on the circle $x^2 + y^2 = 1$ which is nearest the point $(4, 3)$.

19. Find the points on the curve $x^4 + y^4 = 32$ that are nearest and farthest from the origin.

20. A cup is to be constructed from a fixed amount of material by fastening an open circular cylinder on a flat circular base (disc) whose radius is twice that of the cylinder. What will be the ratio of the height of the cylinder to its radius if the cup is to have maximum capacity? (See Fig. 12–8.)

FIGURE 12–8

12–3 Curve tracing. We can now undertake a rather complete analysis of the shape of the graph of a given function. Such an analysis will enable us to "trace" the curve representing the function. We can combine the methods used in Chapters 9 and 11 with the concepts of Chapter 10. Also, other information may be obtained by purely algebraic procedures. We do not wish to engage in detailed calculations unless necessary. Ordinarily we shall confine our discussion of a function and its curve to the following important questions.

1. *Where does the curve intersect the two principal axes?*

To find the points of intersection with the axes [recall Eq. (5–11)], it usually suffices to solve ordinary equations in one variable. At a point where the curve meets the x-axis its y-coordinate is zero. Thus we set $y = 0$ in the equation of the curve and solve for the corresponding values of x. Likewise, if we set $x = 0$ and solve for y, we obtain the coordinates of the points where the curve meets the y-axis.

DEFINITION 12–7. *The intercepts of a curve are the points where the curve meets the axes.*

ILLUSTRATION 1. In the equation $y^2 - x - 16 = 0$, when $x = 0$, $y = \pm 4$, and when $y = 0$, $x = -16$. Thus the graph of the equation $y^2 - x - 16 = 0$ intersects the x-axis at $(-16, 0)$ and the y-axis at $(0, 4)$ and $(0, -4)$. The x-intercept of the curve is -16, and the two y-intercepts are 4 and -4. (See Fig. 12–9.)

2. *Is the curve symmetric with respect to either coordinate axis or the origin?*

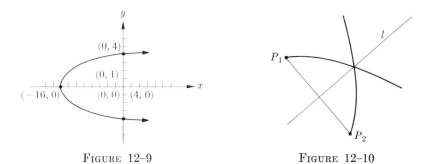

FIGURE 12–9   FIGURE 12–10

DEFINITION 12–8. *Two points, P_1 and P_2, are symmetric with respect to the line l if this line l is the perpendicular bisector of the line segment P_1P_2. Moreover, an entire curve is symmetric with respect to a line l if, corresponding to each point P_1 on the curve, there is a point P_2 also on the curve and symmetric to P_1 with respect to l. (See Fig. 12–10.)*

Let us consider the important case where the line l is the x-axis. If the coordinates of P_1 are (a, b), then by the definition, the coordinates of P_2 are $(a, -b)$. Thus, if whenever the coordinates (a, b) satisfy an equation, the coordinates $(a, -b)$ also satisfy the equation, the curve is symmetric to the x-axis. Likewise, if $(-a, b)$ satisfy an equation whenever (a, b) do, the curve is symmetric to the y-axis. We therefore have the following theorem.

THEOREM 12–8. *A curve is symmetric to the x-axis if its equation is unchanged when y is replaced by $-y$. Also, a curve is symmetric to the y-axis if its equation is unchanged when x is replaced by $-x$.*

The converse of this theorem is also true. (Why?)

DEFINITION 12–9. *Two points P_1 and P_2 are symmetric with respect to a point P_3 if P_3 is the mid-point of the line segment P_1P_2. Likewise, an entire curve is symmetric with respect to a point P_3 if, corresponding to each point P_1 on the curve, there is a point P_2 also on the curve symmetric to P_1 with respect to P_3. (See Fig. 12–11.)*

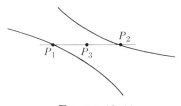

FIGURE 12–11

The following theorem and its converse follow immediately for the important case where the point under consideration is the origin. Its proof is left as an exercise.

THEOREM 12–9. *A curve is symmetric with respect to the origin if its equation is unchanged when x is replaced by $-x$ and, simultaneously, y is replaced by $-y$.*

ILLUSTRATION 2.   The curve representing $y^2 - x - 16 = 0$ (see Fig. 12–9) is symmetric to the x-axis since $(-y)^2 - x - 16 \equiv y^2 - x - 16$, but is not symmetric either to the y-axis or the origin. (Why?)

If a curve is symmetric with respect to both axes, it follows immediately that it must be symmetric with respect to the origin. An example is the curve whose equation is $x^2 - y^2 = 1$. The converse of this statement, however, does not hold. Consider the curve representing $xy = 1$. It is symmetric to the origin (use Theorem 12–8) but to neither axis.

3. *What is the extent of the curve? Are there any excluded regions?*

As was shown in Article 10–6, many functional relationships can be written explicitly $y = f(x)$ or $x = g(y)$. By this procedure the extent of the curve or any excluded regions can usually be determined. Consider the following examples.

EXAMPLE 1.   Discuss the intercepts, symmetry, and extent of the graph of the equation $y^2 = x(x + 1)(x + 2)$.

Solution. (a) When $x = 0$, $y = 0$; when $y = 0$, $x = 0$, -1, or -2. Thus the intercepts are $(0, 0)$, $(-1, 0)$, and $(-2, 0)$.

(b) Since $(-y)^2 \equiv y^2$, the graph is symmetric to the x-axis.

(c) Since $y = \pm\sqrt{x(x + 1)(x + 2)}$ and the expression under the radical must be positive for real values of y, the curve will only exist for x, where $x \geq 0$ or $-2 \leq x \leq -1$. However, the curve will exist for all y-values.

4. *How does the curve behave as either variable increases without limit? Does it have vertical or horizontal asymptotes?* (See the following definitions.)

This question can be answered by using the material in Articles 9–2 and 9–5.

If the curve has an equation in the form $y = f(x)$ and $\lim_{x \to +\infty} f(x) = +\infty$ or $-\infty$, we realize that as x increases without bound, the function either increases or decreases without bound. The case of $\lim_{x \to -\infty} f(x)$ follows the same reasoning, as does the case where $x = g(y)$. If, however, $\lim_{x \to +\infty} f(x)$ or $\lim_{x \to -\infty} f(x)$ equals a constant k, the graph of the function $y = f(x)$ gets close to k as x gets large (or large negatively). Such a line $y = k$ is called a *horizontal asymptote*.

DEFINITION 12–10. *A horizontal asymptote of a curve whose equation is* $y = f(x)$ *is the horizontal line* $y = k$, *where as* x *becomes numerically large without bound,* y *approaches* k.

A vertical asymptote may also be defined.

DEFINITION 12–11. *A vertical asymptote of a curve whose equation is* $y = f(x)$ *is the vertical line* $x = h$, *where as* x *approaches* h, y *becomes numerically large without bound.*

There are two methods for finding these asymptotes (if they exist) for any curve.

EXAMPLE 2. Find the horizontal and the vertical asymptotes of the curve representing $x^2y - y - 4x^2 = 0$ and plot.

Solution. (a) If $x^2y - y - 4x^2 = 0$ is solved for y, we have

$$y = \frac{4x^2}{x^2 - 1} = \frac{4x^2}{(x - 1)(x + 1)}.$$

Since the factors of the denominator are $(x - 1)$ and $(x + 1)$, $x = \pm 1$ are vertical asymptotes. This should be clear, since for values of x approaching either 1 or -1, the denominator approaches zero, so that the numerical value of y increases without bound. To obtain the horizontal asymptote, we find

$$\underset{x \to +\infty}{\text{limit}} \frac{4x^2}{x^2 - 1} = 4.$$

Thus $y = 4$ is the horizontal asymptote.

(b) These methods can be reversed by solving $x^2y - y - 4x^2 = 0$ for x. If this is done, we have $x^2 = y/(y - 4)$, or

$$x = \pm \sqrt{\frac{y}{y - 4}}.$$

Since the only factor of the denominator is $y - 4$, as y approaches 4 (through values of y greater than 4) x increases without bound, and $y - 4$ is the only horizontal asymptote. Also, since $\text{limit}_{y \to +\infty} \pm \sqrt{y/(y - 4)} = \pm 1$, $x = \pm 1$ are the vertical asymptotes. Note that both methods (a) and (b) give the same result.

To obtain the actual graph of this function, we use the methods recently outlined as well as consider the asymptote. We note that $(0, 0)$ is the only intercept, and that the graph is symmetric to the y-axis. (Why?) Also, from $x = \pm \sqrt{y/(y - 4)}$, the curve does not exist for y between 0 and 4.

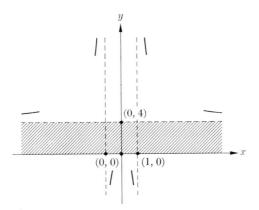

FIGURE 12–12

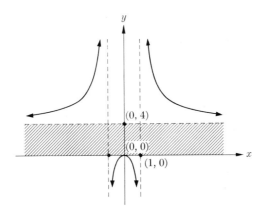

FIGURE 12–13

Thus, for large values of x, y is slightly larger than 4. Moreover, for values of x near 1 but larger than 1, y is large positively, but for values of x near 1 but less than 1, y is large negatively. With this information we can draw our graph as in Fig. 12–12.

Since the curve is continuous except at $x = \pm 1$ and has no other intercepts than $(0, 0)$, it must appear as in Fig. 12–13. For a check or more accurate figure, other points may be located.

5. *Where are the critical values, and what are the extreme values of the function?*

The material in Article 12–1 will enable us to answer these questions.

6. *For what values of x is the curve concave upward, and for what values is it concave downward? What are the inflection points?* (See the following definition.)

By recalling Definition 12–6 and Theorem 12–6, it is possible to determine where the curve is concave upward and where it is concave downward.

DEFINITION 12–12. *A point* $(x_1, f(x_1))$ *is an* inflection point *of a curve if for values of* x *sufficiently near* x_1 *but less than* x_1 *the curve is concave upward, and for each* x *sufficiently near* x_1 *but greater than* x_1 *the curve is concave downward, or vice versa.*

By this definition and Theorem 12–6, any point $(x_1, f(x_1))$ for which $f''(x_1) = 0$ is an inflection point if $f''(x)$ changes its sign as x passes through x_1.

Let us now examine the nature of two more functions, keeping in mind the questions mentioned in this article.

EXAMPLE 3. Sketch the curve of the function $y = 2x^2/\sqrt{x^2 + 1}$.

Solution. Let us answer the questions in this article in the order mentioned, and then sketch the curve.

1. The only intercept is $(0, 0)$.
2. The curve is symmetric to the y-axis since $(-x)^2 = x^2$.
3. Since $x^2 + 1 > 0$ for all real x, the curve exists for all x. Moreover, since the radical and x^2 are both positive, y takes on only positive values.
4. Since $\lim_{x \to +\infty} 2x^2/\sqrt{x^2 + 1} = +\infty$, y increases as x increases. Since $\lim_{x \to -\infty} 2x^2/\sqrt{x^2 + 1} = +\infty$, y increases as x increases negatively. (This we knew because of the symmetry of the function.) Thus there are no horizontal asymptotes. Also, there are no vertical asymptotes, for the denominator cannot equal zero.
5. If $y = 2x^2/\sqrt{x^2 + 1}$,

$$y' = \frac{(x^2 + 1)^{1/2}(4x) - 2x^2 \cdot \frac{1}{2}(x^2 + 1)^{-1/2} \cdot 2x}{x^2 + 1}$$

$$= \frac{2x^3 + 4x}{(x^2 + 1)^{3/2}}.$$

If this is set equal to zero, we have $x = 0$ as the only real root, so that $(0, 0)$ is the only critical point.

$$y'' = \frac{(x^2 + 1)^{3/2}(6x^2 + 4) - (2x^3 + 4x) \cdot \frac{3}{2}(x^2 + 1)^{1/2} \cdot 2x}{(x^2 + 1)^3}$$

$$= \frac{4 - 2x^2}{(x^2 + 1)^{5/2}}.$$

If we evaluate this at $x = 0$, we have $y''(0) > 0$, so that $(0, 0)$ is a minimum point on the curve.

6. Since

$$y'' = \frac{4 - 2x^2}{(x^2 + 1)^{5/2}} = \frac{2(\sqrt{2} + x)(\sqrt{2} - x)}{(x^2 + 1)^{5/2}},$$

$y''(x) = 0$ if $x = \pm\sqrt{2}$.   Moreover, $y''(x) > 0$ if $-\sqrt{2} < x < \sqrt{2}$, but $y''(x) < 0$ if $x > \sqrt{2}$ or $< -\sqrt{2}$.   The corresponding value of y on the curve for either value of x is $y = 4/\sqrt{3} = 2.31$ (approximately). Thus $(\pm 1.41, 2.31)$ are the inflection points.   Also, the curve is concave upward if $-\sqrt{2} < x < \sqrt{2}$ and concave downward if $x > \sqrt{2}$ or $x < -\sqrt{2}$. (Why?)   With the use of this material, we have Fig. 12–14.

EXAMPLE 4.   Discuss and sketch the curve representing

$$y = \frac{(x - 1)(x - 3)}{x^2}.$$

Solution.   1. The x-intercepts are $(1, 0)$ and $(3, 0)$.   There is no y-intercept.

2. There is no simple symmetry.

3. y has real values for all real values of x except $x = 0$.

4. The horizontal asymptote is $y = 1$, and the only vertical asymptote is $x = 0$.   Note that whether x is slightly less than or greater than zero, y is large positively.

5. Since

$$y' = \frac{x^2(2x - 4) - (x^2 - 4x + 3)2x}{x^4} = \frac{4x - 6}{x^3},$$

$x = \frac{3}{2}$ is a critical value.   The corresponding $y = -\frac{1}{3}$.   The point $(\frac{3}{2}, -\frac{1}{3})$ is a minimum point. (Why?)

6. Since $y'' = (-8x + 18)/x^4$, the curve is concave upward if $x > \frac{9}{4}$, but concave downward if $x < \frac{9}{4}$, and $(\frac{9}{4}, -\frac{5}{27})$ is an inflection point.   See Fig. 12–15.

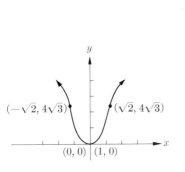

FIGURE 12–14

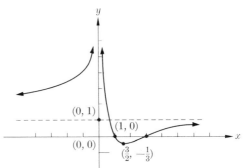

FIGURE 12–15

PROBLEMS

Sketch the graphs of the following expressions, and answer any of the questions in this article which seem appropriate.

1. $xy = 1$

2. $x - 2 = 1/(y - 3)$

3. $xy + 3y - 4 - 12 = 0$

4. $xy - 5y + 2x - 10 = 0$

5. $16x^2 + 25y^2 - 400 = 0$

6. $x^2 - y^2 = 1$

7. $9y^2 - 16x^2 = 144$

8. $x^2 + 4y^2 = 16$

9. $x^2 - 2xy + y^2 + 2x - 3y + 2 = 0$

10. $4x^2 + 4y^2 - 12x - 10y + 5 = 0$

11. $2xy + 4y - 6x = 0$

12. $x^2 + 2xy + y^2 - 2x - 2y = 1$

13. $x^2 + xy + y^2 - 3y - 3 = 0$

14. $2x^2 + 3xy - 2y^2 - 5 = 0$

15. Solve graphically Example 2, Article 6–7

16. Solve graphically Problem 7, Article 6–7

17. Solve graphically Problem 9, Article 6–7

18. Solve graphically Problems 8 and 10, Article 6–7

Sketch the graphs of the following expressions.

19. $y = \dfrac{1}{1 + x^2}$

20. $y = \dfrac{x}{1 + x^2}$

21. $y = \dfrac{x^2 - 2x + 1}{x^2}$

22. $\dfrac{x^2 - 5x + 4}{x^2}$

23. $y = \dfrac{(x - 2)(x - 1)^2}{x(x + 1)}$

24. $\dfrac{x^3 + x}{(x - 1)(x - 2)(x + 2)}$

25. $y^2 = x(x - 1)(x - 2)$

26. $y^2 = (x^2 - 9)(1 - x)$

27. $y^2 = \dfrac{1}{1 + x^2}$

28. $y^2 = \dfrac{x}{1 + x^2}$

29. $y^2 = \dfrac{(x + 1)(x + 2)}{(x - 1)}$

30. $y^2 = \dfrac{x + 1}{(x - 1)^2}$

12–4 Velocities and related rates. In Article 10–1 we examined two specific limits, one interpreted as instantaneous velocity and the other as slope of the tangent line. Following this introduction of the derivative, we have emphasized the geometric interpretation of slope, with its applications. We now wish to return to the notion of velocity and consider its generalization.

We recall that the definition of instantaneous velocity was obtained by considering average velocities, that is, average rates of change of distance with respect to time. Of course, it is not necessary to restrict the variables to measures of distance and time. In fact, any case in which there is a functional relation between two variables may be handled in the same way. If the measure of one quantity is the functional value corresponding to the measure of another quantity, we may consider the ratio of the change in the value of the function over an interval to the length of the interval itself as the average rate of change of the first variable with respect to the second. In this way we have another useful physical interpretation of the derivative.

DEFINITION 12–13. *For any functional relation* $y = f(x)$, *the rate of change of* y *with respect to* x *at the value* x_1 *is the derivative of* $f(x)$ *evaluated at* x_1, *that is,* $f'(x_1)$.

Let us illustrate by considering three examples.

EXAMPLE 1. Recall the motion of a particle along a straight line, discussed in Article 10–1. Let s be the distance in feet, along a straight line, through which a particle has passed from its original position in t seconds. Specifically, if $s(t) = t^3 - 9t^2 + 24t - 5$, find when and where the velocity $v(t)$ is zero, and indicate the motion graphically. (The motion of any object along a line, such as described in this example, is called *rectilinear motion*.)

Solution. Since the velocity $v(t)$ is the rate, the distance $s(t)$ changes with respect to the time t, that is, $s'(t)$, we have

$$s'(t) = v(t) = 3t^2 - 18t + 24 = 3(t - 2)(t - 4).$$

Thus the velocity is zero at $t = 2$ and 4. When

$$
\begin{aligned}
t &= -2, & s(t) &= -97 \\
t &= 0, & s(t) &= -5 \\
t &= 2, & s(t) &= 15 \\
t &= 4, & s(t) &= 11.
\end{aligned}
$$

Moreover, when $t < 2$, $v(t) > 0$, so that the particle is increasing (moving to the right) for two seconds. When $2 < t < 4$, $v(t) < 0$, so that $s(t)$ is decreasing (moving to the left) for two more seconds. When $t > 4$, $v(t) > 0$, so that $s(t)$ is increasing. This is represented in Fig. 12–16.

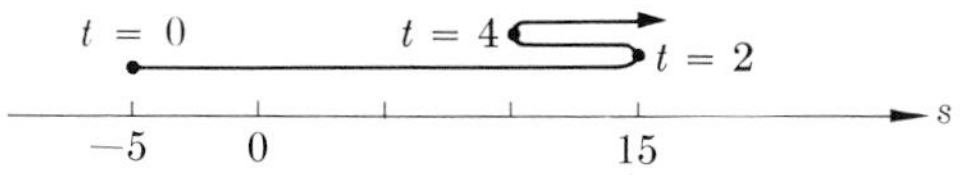

FIGURE 12–16

EXAMPLE 2. How fast is the volume of a spherical balloon increasing when the radius is 3 inches if the radius is increasing at the rate of 5 inches per second?

Solution. We recall that the volume of a sphere is a function of the radius, namely, $V = \frac{4}{3}\pi R^3$. However, both V and R are functions of the time t, so that we may write

$$V(t) = \frac{4}{3}\pi[R(t)]^3.$$

If we take the derivative with respect to t [recall Eq. (10–12)], we have

$$V'(t) = \frac{4}{3}\pi \cdot 3[R(t)]^2 \cdot R'(t),$$

where $V'(t)$ represents the rate the volume is changing with respect to the time, and $R'(t)$ the rate the radius is changing with respect to the time. Since we wish to find $V'(t)$ when $R(t) = 3$ and $R'(t) = 5$, we substitute and obtain

$$V'(t) = 4\pi \cdot 3^2 \cdot 5 = 180\pi \text{ inches per second.}$$

EXAMPLE 3. An automobile traveling at the constant rate of 64 miles per hour crosses a railroad track which is perpendicular to the highway. Five minutes later a train crosses this intersection at the constant rate of 72 miles per hour. At what rate are the train and car separating 10 minutes after the train crosses the highway?

Solution (1): If t minutes represents the time the train travels after crossing the highway, $t + 5$ minutes is the time the automobile travels after crossing. Thus t minutes after the train crosses, its distance from the intersection is $\frac{72}{60}t$ or $\frac{6}{5}t$ miles, while that for the automobile is $\frac{64}{60}(t + 5)$ or $\frac{16}{15}(t + 5)$ miles. Thus the distance between them expressed in terms of t is

$$s(t) = \sqrt{(\tfrac{6}{5}t)^2 + [\tfrac{16}{15}(t + 5)]^2} = \tfrac{1}{15}\sqrt{580t^2 + 2560t + 6400}.$$

Therefore the rate that $s(t)$ is changing is

$$s'(t) = \frac{1}{15} \cdot \frac{1}{2} \frac{1160t + 2560}{\sqrt{580t^2 + 2560t + 6400}}$$

and, evaluated at $t = 10$, we have

$$s'(10) = \frac{1}{30} \cdot \frac{14160}{300} = 1.573 \text{ mi/min} = 94.4 \text{ mi/hr.}$$

Solution (2): This example can also be solved using the notion of the composite function. Let x miles and y miles be the distances covered by the train and car respectively, and s miles the distance between them at any instant. Then

$$s^2 = x^2 + y^2,$$

and since s, x, and y are functions of t, taking the derivative with respect to t, we have

$$2s \cdot s' = 2xx' + 2yy'.$$

Substituting the values $s = 20$, $x = 12$, $y = 16$, $x' = 72$, and $y' = 64$ (why?), we have

$$2 \cdot 20s' = 2 \cdot 12 \cdot 72 + 2 \cdot 16 \cdot 24,$$

or

$$s'(t) = \frac{1728 + 2048}{40} = 94.4 \text{ mi/hr.}$$

Problems

1. Find the rate of change of the area of a square when a side is 6 inches and is increasing at the rate of 2 inches per second.

2. Find the rate of change of the volume of a cube when a side is 6 inches and is increasing at the rate of 2 inches per second.

3. At what rate is the surface area of the sphere in Example 2 increasing when the radius is 3 inches?

The following equations represent rectilinear motion of a point, where s expresses the particular function of t. Discuss the motions described in Problems 4–9, telling when and where the velocity is zero, and represent the motion graphically.

4. $s = 8t$

5. $s = 4 - t^2$

6. $s = t^2 - 6t + 3$

7. $s = \dfrac{4}{t+1}$

8. $s = 2t^3 - 9t^2 + 12t + 6$

9. $s = t^3 - 9t^2 + 15t - 12$

10. If acceleration is defined as the rate the velocity changes with respect to the time, that is, acceleration equals $v'(t) = s''(t)$, find the acceleration in Problems 4–9.

11. Water flows at the rate of 2 cubic inches per second into a cistern in the form of a right circular cone with vertex down. If the radius of the top and the height of the cistern are 5 and 10 inches, respectively, find the rate the water is rising (a) when it is halfway to the top, (b) when the cistern is half full.

12. If the cistern in Problem 11 is being filled with water at the rate of 49π cubic inches per minute, what is the depth of water when the water level is rising 36 inches per minute?

13. One end of a 20 foot ladder rests against a house and the other on the ground. If the foot of the ladder is drawn away from the house along the ground horizontally at the constant rate of 2 feet per second, at what rate is the top descending when the foot is 12 feet from the house?

14. A boy is walking along horizontal ground toward the base of a 60-foot tower at the rate of 5 feet per second. When he is 80 feet from the tower, at what rate is he approaching (a) the top of the tower, (b) a point halfway up the tower?

15. A point moves along the curve $y = 8x^2$ in a way such that its ordinate is increasing at the rate of 4 units per second. At what rate is the abscissa changing when (a) $x = 2$, (b) $y = 2$?

16. Find how rapidly the area of an equilateral triangle is changing if each side is 6 inches and is increasing at the rate of 4 inches per minute.

17. An airplane is flying horizontally at the rate of 300 miles per hour. If it is one mile above the ground and flying north, at what rate is it approaching a point on the ground $1\frac{1}{2}$ miles from the airplane but in the same vertical plane of flight?

18. If the airplane in Problem 17 passes directly over an automobile driving south at the rate of 60 miles per hour, how fast is the distance between them increasing 2 minutes later?

19. If the airplane in Problem 17 passes directly over an automobile driving east at the rate of 60 miles per hour, how fast is the distance between them increasing 2 minutes later?

20. An automobile driving due north at 60 miles per hour passes the intersection of two straight roads. One minute later a second automobile passes the intersection, driving due west at 40 miles per hour. How fast is the distance between the two increasing 5 minutes after the first automobile has crossed the intersection?

21. A walk is perpendicular to the side of a building. A lamp is located a feet from the walk and b feet from the building. If a man walks along the walk toward the building, his shadow moves along the building. How far from the building will he be when his constant rate of speed and that of his shadow are numerically equal?

CHAPTER 13

INVERSE FUNCTIONS

13–1 Inverse functions. In Article 10–6 we discussed functions implicitly defined by an equation. Let us concern ourselves with the second and third columns of the illustrations in that article. We say that $f(x)$ and $g(y)$ are *inverse functions*, each obtainable from the other and both originating in the same equation in two variables. Since it is customary to use the variable x as the independent variable and y as the dependent variable, we must interchange the x's and y's to follow the usual notation. Thus, if $y = f(x)$ represents any function, its inverse function may be obtained (if such exists) by interchanging variables x and y, so that $x = f(y)$, and then solving for y. The range of $f(x)$ will be the domain for the inverse function, and the domain of $f(x)$ will be the range for the inverse function. Certain difficulties may arise from this procedure,* and great care must be taken in choosing the domains and ranges of each function.

Let us look further at the illustrations of Article 10–6.

(a) In illustration (a) the domain and range of the function consist of all real values, so that the domain and range of the inverse function must also consist of all real values.

(b) For this function and its inverse neither x nor y can be zero, but both are defined for all other real values.

(c) More care must be taken in this illustration. Since in the expression $x = (y \pm \sqrt{y^2 + 4})/2$, $\sqrt{y^2 + 4} > |y|$, $x > 0$ if the plus sign is chosen, but $x < 0$ if the minus sign is chosen. Thus, if the domain for the function $y = (x^2 - 1)/x$ is all real positive numbers, its inverse must be $y = (x + \sqrt{x^2 + 4})/2$. What is the domain for the function $y = (x^2 - 1)/x$ if its inverse is $y = (x - \sqrt{x^2 + 4})/2$?

(d) There are two possibilities in choosing the domain for the function $y = \sqrt{1 - x^2}$. (There are also two for $y = -\sqrt{1 - x^2}$.) If, for example, $y = \sqrt{1 - x^2}$ has for its domain $0 \leq x \leq 1$, then the range for its inverse must be the same, so that the positive square root must be chosen for the inverse; but if the function's domain is $-1 \leq x \leq 0$, the minus sign must be chosen for the inverse function. (Why?) These functions and their inverses are shown in the following table, where $f_I(x)$ denotes the inverse of $f(x)$.

---

* We may not be able to solve for y (as for example in $x = y - \sin y$), or our solution may result in a relation and not a function. Recall Definition 3–3.

	$y = f(x)$		$y = f_I(x)$	
(a)	$y = \dfrac{12 - 3x}{4}$	$(-\infty < x < \infty)^*$	$y = \dfrac{12 - 4x}{3}$	$(-\infty < x < \infty)$
(b)	$y = \dfrac{1}{x}$	$(x \neq 0)$	$y = \dfrac{1}{x}$	$(x \neq 0)$
(c)	$y = \dfrac{x^2 - 1}{x}$	$(0 < x)$	$y = \dfrac{x + \sqrt{x^2 + 4}}{2}$	$(-\infty < x < \infty)$
		$(x < 0)$	$y = \dfrac{x - \sqrt{x^2 + 4}}{2}$	$(-\infty < x < \infty)$
(d)	$y = \sqrt{1 - x^2}$	$(0 \leq x \leq 1)$	$y = \sqrt{1 - x^2}$	$(0 \leq x \leq 1)$
		$(-1 \leq x \leq 0)$	$y = -\sqrt{1 - x^2}$	$(0 \leq x \leq 1)$
	$y = -\sqrt{1 - x^2}$	$(0 \leq x \leq 1)$	$y = \sqrt{1 - x^2}$	$(-1 \leq x \leq 0)$
		$(-1 \leq x \leq 0)$	$y = -\sqrt{1 - x^2}$	$(-1 \leq x \leq 0)$

The graphs of $f(x)$ and $f_I(x)$ for illustrations (a) and the first function in (c) are shown in Fig. 13–1. Note that the curves for $y = f(x)$ and $y = f_I(x)$ are symmetric with respect to the line $y = x$. Considering how the inverse function is obtained, in the light of Definition 12–8, would you expect this always to be the case?

In Article 10–6 it was stated that $y = f(x)$ may not have an inverse, readily expressed $(y = x - \sin x)$. Also these illustrations emphasize that in other cases, although $y = f(x)$ may not have an inverse because of the definition of its domain, the domain may be so restricted that the new restricted function does have an inverse. This is especially important in dealing with the concept of inverse function for the circular functions.

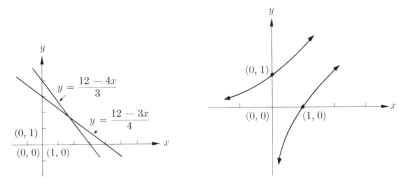

FIGURE 13–1

---

* The notation $-\infty < x < \infty$ means all finite real values of x, both positive and negative.

PROBLEMS

Find the inverse of each of the following functions (Problems 1–12), discussing domain and range in all cases.

1. $y = 5x - 6$

2. $y = x^2$

3. $y = x^2 - 4x$

4. $y = \dfrac{x}{x - 3}$

5. $y = \dfrac{x^2 - 1}{x^2}$

6. $y = \dfrac{x^2 - 1}{x}$

7. $y = x^n$

8. $y = x^{2n} + 2x^n + 1$

9. $y = \sqrt{x^2 - 4}$

10. $y = \dfrac{-3\sqrt{25 - x^2}}{5}$

11. $y = x - 1 + \sqrt{x - 3}$

12. $y = \dfrac{2x - 1 - \sqrt{3x - 4}}{2}$

13–2 Inverse circular functions. The concept of an inverse relation or function is particularly important in studying the circular functions and their properties. In considering the function $y = \sin \theta$, we may wish to talk about y, the sine of θ, but we might also wish to consider or emphasize the angle θ, that is, θ whose sine is y. This emphasis is required so frequently that "θ an angle whose sine is y," or the inverse relation of $y = \sin \theta$, is given a name and a notation. About 1730, Daniel Bernoulli and Leonhard Euler introduced the notation

$$\theta = \arcsin y \qquad (13\text{–}1)$$

to denote an angle whose sine is y, and thus the name for this expression became *arcsine of y*. This was the first suitable notation for an inverse circular relation. Later, in 1813, John Herschel introduced another notation which has also remained in common use, $\theta = \sin^{-1} y$. When -1 is used in this manner, it must be understood that -1 is not an exponent.

From the above definition, if $y = \arcsin \frac{1}{2}$, y is an angle whose sine is $\frac{1}{2}$. Thus, y may be equal to $\pi/6$, $5\pi/6$, $13\pi/6$, $-7\pi/6$, and so forth, or, in general, $y = \pi/6 \pm 2n\pi$, or $5\pi/6 \pm 2n\pi$, where $n = 0, 1, 2, \ldots$ Moreover, these are the only values which y may have. This will be clear from the graph of the relation. From this one observation, we see that although $y = \sin x$ is a (single-valued) function, the inverse relation, $y = \arcsin x$, is infinitely many-valued.

The remaining inverse circular relations are defined in a corresponding way. The expression $\arccos x$ denotes an angle whose cosine is x; $\arctan x$ denotes an angle whose tangent is x; and so forth. The other three inverse circular relations, $\text{arccot } x$, $\text{arcsec } x$, and $\text{arccsc } x$, are of less importance.

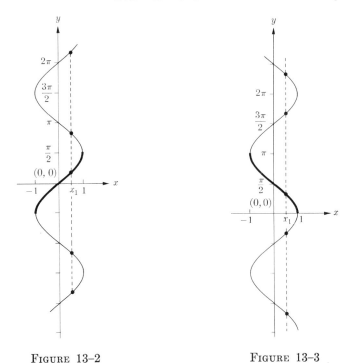

FIGURE 13–2   FIGURE 13–3

They can readily be expressed in terms of arctan x, arccos x, and arcsin x, respectively, by using (4–11), (4–12), and (4–13). Thus the expression arccsc x may be considered equivalent to arcsin $1/x$. More specifically,

$$\text{arccsc } 2 = \text{arcsin } \tfrac{1}{2} = \pi/6, \qquad \text{and so on.}$$

The graphs of the inverse circular relations show their behavior quite clearly. In considering the graph of $y = \text{arcsin } x$, we merely think of the equivalent expression $x = \sin y$ and recall its graph. (This graph was shown in Fig. 4–7, with x and y for y and θ.) If we graph $x = \sin y$ on transparent paper with the x-axis vertical and the y-axis horizontal, turn the paper over, and rotate it clockwise through 90°, the result is the graph of $y = \text{arcsin } x$, shown in Fig. 13–2. The graphs of $y = \text{arccos } x$ and $y = \text{arctan } x$, obtained in a similar way, are shown in Fig. 13–3 and Fig. 13–4. Note that arcsin x and arccos x are defined only for the domain where x is between -1 and 1, inclusive, although arctan x is defined for all finite values of x. Thus arcsin 2 has no meaning,* since there is no

---

* This is true in the present context of real values. In more advanced mathematics the circular functions may be treated in the context of complex values (see Chapter 17), and in such context arcsin 2 is a complex number.

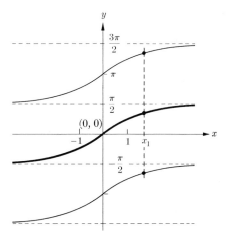

FIGURE 13–4

angle whose sine is 2, but arctan 2 does have meaning. From the graphs we observe once more that these inverse relations have infinitely many values for one value of x. Note this property in the case of each relation.

If the sine of a specific value of y, let us say y_1, is equal to x_1, what other values of y have the same sine? We recall that the addition or subtraction of integral multiples of 2π does not change the circular function of an angle. Also, in the case of the sine function, we found that $\sin(\pi - y) = \sin y$. Therefore $\pi - y + 2n\pi$ will have the same sine as y. In other words, an even multiple of π must be added to y, or an even multiple of π must be added to $\pi - y$, for the angle to have the same sine. Put into one equation, this results in

$$\arcsin x_1 = (-1)^n y_1 + n\pi \quad (-1 \leq x_1 \leq 1) \qquad \text{if} \quad \sin y_1 = x_1. \qquad (13\text{–}2)$$

This is true for every integral value of n and gives a different value of $\arcsin x_1$ for each value of n. For example, when $n = 0$, $\arcsin x_1 = y_1$; when $n = 1$, $\arcsin x_1 = \pi - y_1$; when $n = -1$, $\arcsin x_1 = -(\pi + y_1)$; and so forth. That the formula gives all values of $\arcsin x_1$ should be clear from Fig. 13–3. These are indicated by the intersection of the dotted vertical line and the curve.

Since $\cos(2\pi + y) = \cos y$, and $\cos(-y) = \cos y$, it is easy to verify that the following expression gives all the values for $\arccos x_1$.

$$\arccos x_1 = \pm y_1 + 2n\pi \quad (-1 \leq x_1 \leq 1) \qquad \text{if} \quad \cos y_1 = x_1. \qquad (13\text{–}3)$$

From the fact that both $\tan(\pi + y)$ and $\tan(2\pi + y) = \tan y$, we get the expression

$$\boxed{\arctan x_1 = y_1 + n\pi \quad (-\infty < x_1 < \infty) \qquad \text{if} \quad \tan y_1 = x_1} \qquad (13\text{--}4)$$

for all the values of $\arctan x_1$.

As examples of specific values of such inverse relations, we have

$$\arcsin \tfrac{1}{2} = (-1)^n \frac{\pi}{6} + n\pi,$$

$$\arccos \tfrac{1}{2} = \pm \frac{\pi}{3} + 2n\pi,$$

$$\arctan (-1) = -\frac{\pi}{4} + n\pi,$$

where n is any integer.

We have emphasized in this discussion that the circular inverse relations are many-valued. However, under suitable restrictions, these inverse relations may be made single-valued, and in this way, we obtain the important *arc functions*. As is seen by the graph of $y = \arcsin x$ (Fig. 13–2), if the range of the relation is limited to $-\pi/2 \leq \arcsin x \leq \pi/2$, there is a unique value of y for each x of the domain. In a similar manner, the range for each of the other arc functions is restricted to distinguish between the inverse relations and functions. The capital letter A is used in writing the arc functions. Thus the range of each of the inverse circular functions is as follows:

$$\boxed{\begin{aligned} -\pi/2 \leq \text{Arcsin } x \leq \pi/2, & \qquad (13\text{--}5) \\ 0 \leq \text{Arccos } x \leq \pi, & \qquad (13\text{--}6) \\ -\pi/2 < \text{Arctan } x < \pi/2. & \qquad (13\text{--}7) \end{aligned}}$$

The graphs of these functions are indicated in the figures by heavy lines. In the case of the functional values, the examples listed above become

$$\text{Arcsin } \tfrac{1}{2} = \pi/6, \qquad \text{Arccos } \tfrac{1}{2} = \pi/3, \qquad \text{Arctan } (-1) = -\pi/4.$$

Other examples of functional values are

$$\text{Arcsin } (-\tfrac{1}{2}) = -\pi/6, \qquad \text{Arccot } (-\sqrt{3}) = -\pi/6,$$

$$\text{Arccos } (-\tfrac{1}{2}) = 2\pi/3, \qquad \text{Arcsec } (-2/\sqrt{3}) = 5\pi/6.$$

Problems

Find the values of the following without using tables:

1. $\arcsin \sqrt{3}/2$ [*Hint:* We know $\sin \pi/3 = \sqrt{3}/2$. Therefore, $\arcsin \sqrt{3}/2$
   $= (-1)^n \pi/3 + n\pi$.]

2. $\arctan 1$ 3. $\arccos (-\frac{1}{2})$
4. $\arcsin 0$ 5. $\arctan 0$
6. $\arccos (-1)$ 7. $\mathrm{arcsec}\ \sqrt{2}$
8. $\mathrm{arccot}\ (-\sqrt{3})$ 9. $\mathrm{Arccos}\ 0$
10. $\mathrm{Arctan}\ (-1)$ 11. $\mathrm{Arcsin}\ (-1)$
12. $\mathrm{Arccsc}\ 2$

Find the value of the following with the help of Table I:

13. $\arcsin 0.4067$ 14. $\arctan 1.5399$
15. $\arccos 0.6293$ 16. $\mathrm{Arccos}\ 0.8450$
17. $\mathrm{Arcsin}\ 0.9951$ 18. $\mathrm{Arctan}\ 0.3281$

Solve each of the following for θ:

19. $y = \sin 4\theta$ [*Hint:* We know $4\theta = \arcsin y$. Therefore, $\theta = (\arcsin y)/4$.]
20. $y = \cos 3\theta$ 21. $y = 3 \tan 2\theta$
22. $y = \sin (\theta/2)$ 23. $2y = 4 \sec 2\theta$
24. $3y = 2 + \sin 3\theta$
25. Explain why the value of $y = \mathrm{Arccos}\ x$ cannot be taken in the interval $-\pi/2 \leq y \leq \pi/2$.

Solve each of the following for x:

26. $y = \arcsin 2x$ 27. $y = \frac{1}{3} \arccos (4x - 4)$
28. $y = \arctan (x - 2)$ 29. $y = \arctan x - 2$
30. $y = \pi + 2 \arcsin x$ 31. $8y = (\pi/3) - 4 \arccos (2x + 1)$

13–3 Operations involving inverse circular functions. The most convenient way of considering various operations with the inverse relations and functions is to analyze several examples. Since the inverse circular functions are the same angles for which we have established many formulas, it is sometimes clearer to substitute for an arc function or relation an angle θ or ω. This type of substitution will be illustrated in the examples.

EXAMPLE 1. Find the value of $\sin (\arccos \frac{3}{5})$.

Solution. This example, similar to many problems in Chapter 4, asks for the sine of an angle whose cosine is $\frac{3}{5}$. Let θ be this angle. Then $\cos \theta = \frac{3}{5}$, and $\sin \theta = \pm\sqrt{1 - (\frac{3}{5})^2} = \pm\frac{4}{5}$.

EXAMPLE 2. Find the value of $\cos (\mathrm{Arcsin}\ u + \mathrm{Arccos}\ v)$.

Solution. If we let $\mathrm{Arcsin}\ u = \theta_1$ and $\mathrm{Arccos}\ v = \theta_2$, the example reduces to expressing $\cos (\theta_1 + \theta_2)$ in terms of u and v, where

$$\sin \theta_1 = u, \qquad \cos \theta_2 = v,$$

and therefore,

$$\cos \theta_1 = \sqrt{1 - u^2}, \qquad \sin \theta_2 = \sqrt{1 - v^2}.$$

(Explain why both radicals are positive.) Thus

$$\begin{aligned}
\cos (\text{Arcsin } u + \text{Arccos } v) &= \cos (\theta_1 + \theta_2) \\
&= \cos \theta_1 \cos \theta_2 - \sin \theta_1 \sin \theta_2 \\
&= v\sqrt{1 - u^2} - u\sqrt{1 - v^2}.
\end{aligned}$$

EXAMPLE 3. Prove that Arctan $\frac{1}{2}$ + Arctan $\frac{1}{3}$ = $\pi/4$.

Solution. Since each of the two angles on the left side is less than $\pi/4$, the left side represents an angle between 0 and $\pi/2$, as does the angle $\pi/4$ on the right side. If the tangents of two such angles are equal, the angles themselves are equal. Let us take the tangent of each member of the suspected equality, and if they are equal, we have proved the original relation. It should be emphasized that this will be true only because the tangent function between 0 and $\pi/2$ is single-valued.

$$\tan (\text{Arctan } \tfrac{1}{2} + \text{Arctan } \tfrac{1}{3}) \overset{?}{=} \tan \frac{\pi}{4}$$

$$\frac{\tan (\text{Arctan } \tfrac{1}{2}) + \tan (\text{Arctan } \tfrac{1}{3})}{1 - \tan (\text{Arctan } \tfrac{1}{2}) \tan (\text{Arctan } \tfrac{1}{3})} \overset{?}{=} 1$$

$$\frac{\tfrac{1}{2} + \tfrac{1}{3}}{1 - \tfrac{1}{2} \cdot \tfrac{1}{3}} = 1.$$

If we recall the method of differentiating implicitly defined functions (Article 10–6), it is not difficult to find the derivatives of certain of the inverse circular functions. We shall limit our discussion to the Arc sine and Arc tangent functions.

If $y = \text{Arcsin } x$, $x = \sin y$. If we take the derivative of each member of this equation with respect to x, we have $1 = \cos y \cdot Dy$ or

$$Dy = \frac{1}{\cos y}. \tag{13–8}$$

This may be expressed in terms of x, since $\cos^2 y = 1 - \sin^2 y$, and $\sin y = x$. Thus, $\cos y = \pm\sqrt{1 - x^2}$. But since y is between $-\pi/2$ and $\pi/2$, $\cos y \geq 0$, and we have

$$D (\text{Arcsin } x) = \frac{1}{\sqrt{1 - x^2}}. \tag{13–9}$$

It is interesting to note that this expression is positive for all x where

$-1 < x < 1$. This is evident from the graph of the function in Fig. 13–2 if the slope of the tangent line to the curve at any point is considered.

Generalizing this result by using Eq. (10–12), we have

$$D\,[\text{Arcsin } g(x)] = \frac{Dg(x)}{\sqrt{1 - [g(x)]^2}}.$$ (13–10)

If $y = \text{Arctan } x$, $x = \tan y$. Again, by implicit differentiation with respect to x, we have $1 = \sec^2 y \cdot Dy$, or

$$Dy = \frac{1}{\sec^2 y}.$$ (13–11)

But $\sec^2 y = 1 + \tan^2 y = 1 + x^2$, so that

$$D\,(\text{Arctan } x) = \frac{1}{1 + x^2}.$$ (13–12)

As in (13–10), this result can be generalized to read

$$D\,[\text{Arctan } g(x)] = \frac{Dg(x)}{1 + [g(x)]^2}.$$ (13–13)

EXAMPLE 4.   Find the equation of the tangent line to the curve $y = \text{Arcsin } x$ at $(\frac{1}{2}, \pi/6)$.

Solution.   Since $y' = 1/\sqrt{1 - x^2}$, the slope of the tangent line is $1/\sqrt{1 - \frac{1}{4}} = 2/\sqrt{3}$. Thus,

$$\frac{y - (\pi/6)}{x - \frac{1}{2}} = \frac{2}{\sqrt{3}},$$

or

$$12x - 6\sqrt{3}y = 6 - \sqrt{3}\pi.$$

PROBLEMS

Find the values of the following without the use of tables:

1. $\sin (\arctan \frac{3}{4})$
2. $\cos (\arcsin \frac{7}{25})$
3. $\tan (\arccos \frac{5}{13})$
4. $\sin [\arccos (-\frac{24}{25})]$
5. $\cos (\text{Arcsin } \frac{5}{6})$
6. $\tan [\text{Arcsin } (-\frac{3}{4})]$
7. $\sin (\arcsin u)$
8. $\cos (\text{Arccos } v)$
9. $\tan (\arccos u)$
10. $\sin (\arctan v)$
11. $\text{Arcsin } (\sin \pi/7)$
12. $\text{Arccos } [\cos (-\pi/5)]$
13. $\text{Arctan } (\cot 4\pi/9)$
14. $\text{Arcsin } (\cos \pi/7)$

15. Arccos $(\sin \pi/10)$
16. Arccot $[\tan (-\pi/5)]$
17. Arcsin $(\tan \pi)$
18. Arctan $(\sin 7\pi/2)$
19. $\sin (\arcsin u + \arccos v)$
20. $\cos (\arccos u + \arcsin v)$
21. $\sin (\arccos \frac{4}{5} + \pi)$
22. $\cos (\pi/2 - \arcsin \frac{5}{13})$
23. $\sin (\arcsin \frac{1}{4} + \arccos \frac{1}{4})$
24. $\cos (\arctan \frac{9}{40} - \arccos \frac{15}{17})$
25. $\tan [\text{Arcsin} \frac{5}{13} + \text{Arctan} (-\frac{3}{4})]$
26. $\cos [\text{Arccos} (-\frac{1}{2}) + \text{Arcsin} (-\frac{1}{3})]$
27. $\sin [2 \text{ Arcsin} \frac{4}{5} + \frac{1}{2} \text{ Arccos} \frac{1}{9}]$
28. $\cos (\text{Arcsin} \frac{3}{5} + \text{Arccos} \frac{5}{13} + \text{Arctan} \frac{8}{15})$

Verify the following equations without the use of tables:

29. $\text{Arctan } 3 + \text{Arctan } \frac{1}{3} = \pi/2$
30. $\text{Arcsin } \frac{3}{5} + \text{Arccos } \frac{12}{13} = \text{Arcsin } \frac{56}{65}$
31. $\text{Arctan } \frac{1}{3} + \text{Arctan } \frac{1}{5} = \text{Arctan } \frac{4}{7}$
32. $\text{Arctan } \frac{1}{7} + 2 \text{ Arctan } \frac{1}{3} = \pi/4$
33. $\text{Arctan } \frac{1}{8} + \text{Arctan } \frac{1}{5} + \text{Arctan } \frac{1}{2} = \pi/4$

34. Is the following equation true? $\text{Arctan } 2 + \text{Arctan } 3 = -\pi/4$. Explain your answer.

35. Note that in Problems 11 through 18 only functions were involved. Find all possible values of $\arcsin (\cos \theta)$. [*Hint:* Let $y = \arcsin (\cos \theta)$. Then $\sin y = \cos \theta = \sin (\frac{1}{2}\pi - \theta)$. Therefore, $y = \frac{1}{2}\pi - \theta + 2n\pi$ or $y = \pi - (\frac{1}{2}\pi - \theta) + 2n\pi = \frac{1}{2}\pi + \theta + 2n\pi$. Thus, combining these into a single expression, we have $y = \frac{1}{2}\pi \pm \theta + 2n\pi$.]

Find all possible values of the following:

36. $\arcsin (\sin \theta)$
37. $\arccos (\sin \theta)$
38. $\arccos (\cos \theta)$
39. $\arctan (\tan \theta)$

Solve the following equations for all possible values of x without using tables, and check carefully.

40. $\text{Arctan } x + 2 \text{ Arctan } 1 = 3\pi/4$
41. $\text{Arccos } x + 2 \text{ Arcsin } 1 = \pi$

42. $\text{Arcsin } x + \text{Arccos } 2x = \pi/6$. [*Hint:* Let $\text{Arcsin } x = \alpha$, $\text{Arccos } 2x = \beta$, and use $\sin (\alpha + \beta) = \sin \alpha \cos \beta + \cos \alpha \sin \beta$.]
43. $\text{Arcsin } x + \text{Arccos } (1 - x) = 0$
44. $\text{Arcsin } x + \text{Arccos } (1 - x) = \pi/2$
45. $\text{Arctan } (1 + x) + \text{Arctan } (1 - x) = \pi/2$

Find the derivatives of the following functions in Problems 46–51.

46. $y = \text{Arcsin } (1 + x)$
47. $y = \text{Arctan } (x + 2)$
48. $y = \text{Arctan } \sqrt{x}$
49. $y = x \text{ Arcsin } x$
50. $y = \dfrac{\text{Arctan } x}{x}$
51. $y = \text{Arcsin } \sqrt{1 - x^2}$

52. Derive an expression (in terms of x) for the derivative of $y = \text{Arccos } x$.

Find the equation of the tangent line to the given curve at the indicated point in Problems 53–55.

53. $y = \text{Arcsin } x$ at $(\sqrt{3}/2, \pi/3)$
54. $y = \text{Arctan } x$ at $(-1, \pi/4)$
55. $y = \text{Arccos } x$ at $(-\frac{1}{2}, 2\pi/3)$

CHAPTER 14

EXPONENTIAL AND LOGARITHMIC FUNCTIONS

We have considered in some detail the algebraic functions and one type of transcendental function, the circular functions. The inverse functions of the circular functions were also discussed. There are two other important transcendental functions, the exponential function and its inverse function, the logarithmic function. In this chapter we shall examine these two functions, their properties, and simple applications.

14–1 The exponential function $y = a^x$. Before we define an exponential function, we must define a^x, where a is any positive number and x is an irrational number. Since any irrational number may be approximated by rational numbers (Article 1–1), we may define a^x for x irrational as the limiting value of a^r as r approaches x through rational values. This is a direct application of Theorem 9–5, where $f(x)$ is the constant a and $g(x)$ is the function x [Eq. (9–15)]. For example, since 1, 1.4, 1.41, 1.414, 1.4142 ... are rational values which approach $\sqrt{2}$, we define $5^{\sqrt{2}}$ ($= 9.738$, approximately) to be the limiting value of 5 raised to these powers. It is possible to show that such a definition of irrational exponents obeys the laws of exponents set up in Article 2–5, although the proof is beyond the scope of this book.

With this understanding of the meaning of any real exponent, whether rational or irrational, let us consider the simplest exponential function,

$$y = f(x) = a^x, \qquad a > 0, \tag{14–1}$$

where a is any positive constant. This function exists for all real values of x. Now let us examine the graphs of the two special cases of this type of function, $y = 2^x$ and $y = 3^x$. These are sketched by plotting points whose coordinates satisfy the equations (Fig. 14–1).

x	-2	-1	0	1	2	3
y	$\frac{1}{4}$	$\frac{1}{2}$	1	2	4	8

$$y = 2^x$$

x	-2	-1	0	1	2
y	$\frac{1}{9}$	$\frac{1}{3}$	1	3	9

$$y = 3^x$$

The following properties of the function $y = a^x$ should be apparent from the graphs.

1. The function is positive (its graph lies above the x-axis) for all values of x.

269

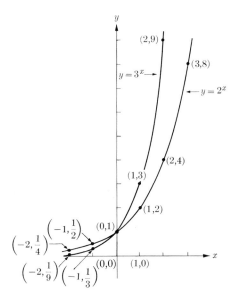

FIGURE 14–1

2. If $a > 1$, the function is an increasing function. As x takes on larger and larger values, so does the function, and as x decreases algebraically, the function approaches but never attains the value zero. The proof of this is apparent when Da^x is found.

3. For all values of a, the function has the value 1 when $x = 0$.

4. There are no zeros of the function.

PROBLEMS

Sketch the graphs of the functions in 1–6:

1. 4^x 2. 10^x 3. 2^{-x} 4. $(\frac{1}{2})^x$ 5. 3^{-x} 6. $(\frac{1}{3})^x$

7. For the function $y = a^x$ state a property corresponding to Property 2 if $0 < a < 1$.

14–2 Geometric progressions. We recall (Article 5–2) that a sequence is the range, or functional values of a function, the domain of which is either all or a part of the set of positive integers. We are now able to define a geometric progression by using the exponential function a^x.

DEFINITION 14–1. *A geometric progression is a sequence in which each term after the first is obtained by multiplying the same fixed number, called the common ratio, by the preceding term.*

ALTERNATE DEFINITION. *A geometric progression is any sequence for which the defining function is of the form a^u, where u is a linear function of x. (See Problem 28 of this article.)*

ILLUSTRATION 1. The sequence $2, 4, 8, \ldots, 2^n$ is a geometric progression with the common ratio 2. The function defining this sequence is 2^x.

ILLUSTRATION 2. The sequence $3, 1, \frac{1}{3}, \frac{1}{9}, \ldots$ is a geometric progression, with $\frac{1}{3}$ the common ratio. Its defining function is 3^{2-x}.

The general notation used for the geometric progression is similar to that of Article 5–2:

a, the first term,
r, the common ratio,
n, the number of terms,
l, the last or nth term.

Since each term is multiplied by the common ratio r to give its succeeding term, a geometric progression may be represented by

$$a, \quad ar, \quad ar^2, \quad ar^3, \quad \ldots, \quad ar^{n-1},$$

with the last value giving the expression for the nth term,

$$l = ar^{n-1}. \tag{14–2}$$

EXAMPLE 1. Find the 10th term of the geometric progression $-8, 4, -2, \ldots$

Solution. With $a = -8$, $r = -\frac{1}{2}$, and $n = 10$, we have

$$l = (-8)(-\tfrac{1}{2})^9$$
$$= (-8)(-\tfrac{1}{512}) = \tfrac{1}{64}.$$

EXAMPLE 2. If the 8th term of a geometric progression is 243 and the 5th term is 9, write the first three terms.

Solution. We have for $n = 8$,

$$243 = ar^7,$$

and for $n = 5$,

$$9 = ar^4.$$

If we divide the members of the first equation by those of the second, we get

$$r^3 = 27, \quad \text{or} \quad r = 3.$$

If we substitute this value in the second equation, we have

$$9 = a(3)^4, \quad \text{or} \quad 81a = 9,$$

$$a = \tfrac{1}{9}.$$

Therefore the first three terms of the required series are

$$\tfrac{1}{9}, \tfrac{1}{3}, \text{ and } 1.$$

The expression for the value of the sum of n terms of any geometric progression is easily obtained. Writing out the sum and multiplying this expression by r, we have

$$S_n = a + ar + ar^2 + \cdots + ar^{n-2} + ar^{n-1},$$

and

$$rS_n = ar + ar^2 + \cdots + ar^{n-1} + ar^n.$$

Subtracting the members of the second equation from those of the first, we have

$$S_n - rS_n = a - ar^n,$$

or

$$(1 - r)S_n = (1 - r^n)a,$$

and solving for S_n,

$$S_n = a\frac{1 - r^n}{1 - r}^* \quad (r \neq 1),$$

which proves the following theorem:

THEOREM 14–1. *The sum of n terms of any geometric progression is given by the expression*

$$S_n = \frac{a(1 - r^n)}{1 - r} \quad (r \neq 1), \tag{14–3}$$

where a is the first term, r the common ratio, and n the number of terms.

Since the last or nth term $l = ar^{n-1}$, $rl = ar^n$, we also have

$$S_n = \frac{a - rl}{1 - r} \quad (r \neq 1). \tag{14–4}$$

We note that in Eqs. (14–3) and (14–4) $r \neq 1$. What can be said about any geometric progression when $r = 1$?

* This expression can also be proved by mathematical induction. See Problem 16, Article (8–1).

Problems

Write out the next three terms in each of the following geometric progressions, and find l and S_n:

1. $1, 4, 16, \ldots$ to 8 terms
2. $27, 9, 3, \ldots$ to 9 terms
3. $\frac{1}{125}, -\frac{1}{25}, \frac{1}{5}, \ldots$ to 7 terms
4. $P(1 + r), P(1 + r)^2, P(1 + r)^3, \ldots$ to 10 terms

In Problems 5–11, three of the elements a, l, r, n, and S_n of the geometric progression are given. Find the missing elements in each case.

5. $a = 2, r = 3, n = 6$ 6. $a = 2, n = 4, l = 16$
7. $a = 1, n = 3, S_n = 13$ 8. $r = -3, n = 5, l = 162$
9. $r = \frac{1}{3}, n = 5, S_n = \frac{4}{9}$ 10. $a = 3, r = \frac{2}{5}, S_n = \frac{609}{125}$
11. $a = -2, r = 2, l = -64$

12. Find the value of k so that $2k + 2$, $5k - 11$, and $7k - 13$ will form a geometric progression.

13. What are the first three terms of the geometric progression whose third term is $\frac{25}{4}$ and whose 7th term is $\frac{4}{25}$.

14. The second term of a geometric progression is $\frac{5}{4}$ and its 4th term is $\frac{1}{5}$. Find its third term.

15. In the geometric progression $18, -12, 8 \ldots$, which term is $\frac{512}{729}$?

*16. The terms between any two terms of a geometric progression are called the *geometric means* between these two terms. Insert four geometric means between $\frac{25}{4}$ and $\frac{8}{125}$.

17. Insert three geometric means between $\frac{27}{8}$ and $\frac{2}{3}$.

*18. Insert one geometric mean between $\frac{7}{8}$ and $\frac{175}{32}$. A single number of this kind is called the *geometric mean of two numbers*.

19. What is the geometric mean of the two numbers a and b?

20. Find the geometric mean of (a) 12 and $\frac{4}{3}$, (b) 28 and 112.

21. Prove that for the two unequal positive numbers a and b, the arithmetic mean is greater than the geometric mean.

22. The population of a certain town is 5000. If it increases 5% every year, what will the approximate population be at the end of 10 years?

23. A rubber ball is dropped from a height of 9 feet. If it rebounds one-third of the distance it has fallen after each fall, how far will it rebound the 6th time? Through what distance has it traveled when it strikes the ground the 7th time?

24. A man accepts a position at $3600 with the understanding that he will receive a 2% increase every year. What will his salary be after 10 years of service?

25. An automobile purchased for $3000 depreciates in value 12% every year. Find its value at the end of 5 years.

26. If a paper napkin 0.01 inch thick could be folded so that it was half as large but twice as thick, folded again in the same manner, and again until the process has been repeated 30 times, approximately how thick would the resulting piece of paper be?

27. If you had the choice of a salary of \$1000 a day for a month of 31 days, or \$1 for the first day's work, \$2 for the second, \$4 for the third, and each day thereafter for the rest of the month your salary would be doubled, which choice would result in the larger salary?

28. By using Eq. (14–2), prove that the two definitions of a geometric progression are equivalent.

14–3 Geometric progressions with infinitely many terms.

In the discussion so far we have considered only the sum of the terms of a finite sequence. If we consider the definition of the arithmetic progression, it should be clear that such a progression with an infinite number of terms has no finite sum. The same is true for a geometric progression with r greater than 1. Each term being larger than the preceding one, no definite value representing such an infinite sum can exist. In fact, even if $r = 1$, each term being the same, no such infinite sum can exist.

If $|r| < 1$, we have a different situation. Consider the sum of the geometric progression

$$S_n = \frac{1}{2} + \frac{1}{4} + \frac{1}{8} + \cdots + \frac{1}{2^n}, \tag{14–5}$$

where $r = \frac{1}{2}$.

One interpretation of S_n may be seen in Fig. 14–2, which represents a line segment one unit in length. The brackets denote the sum of the terms, and the numbers below denote the sum of the progression at any stage. Each term that is added represents a length of half the total length remaining between the point representing the finite sum and the point 1.

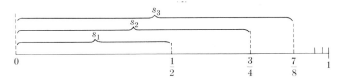

FIGURE 14–2

The more terms considered in Eq. (14–5), the closer we get to the point 1. In fact, we may get as close as we please to 1 by considering a sufficient number of terms, but no matter how many terms are considered, the sum will never exceed 1. Thus we say the limiting value of S_n is 1, and we write

$$S = \operatorname*{limit}_{n \to \infty} S_n = 1. \tag{14–6}$$

This may be shown algebraically. Equation (14–3) may be written

$$S_n = \frac{a}{1 - r} - \frac{ar^n}{1 - r}. \tag{14–7}$$

In the progression (14–5), $a = r = \frac{1}{2}$, so that

$$S_n = \frac{\frac{1}{2}}{1 - \frac{1}{2}} - \frac{\frac{1}{2}(\frac{1}{2})^n}{1 - \frac{1}{2}}$$

$$= 1 - (\tfrac{1}{2})^n.$$

Since the limit of a (finite) sum is the sum of the limits (Theorem 9–1),

$$\lim_{n \to \infty} S_n = \lim_{n \to \infty} 1 - \lim_{n \to \infty} (\tfrac{1}{2})^n.$$

But $\lim_{n \to \infty} (\frac{1}{2})^n = 0$, so that again we have

$$\lim_{n \to \infty} S_n = 1.$$

The same process holds for any geometric progression where $|r| < 1$. Using Eq. (14–7), we have

$$S_n = \frac{a}{1 - r} - \frac{ar^n}{1 - r}.$$

If we let n increase without limit, since a and r are fixed, and $|r| < 1$,

$$\lim_{n \to \infty} \frac{ar^n}{1 - r} = 0.$$

THEOREM 14–2. *The sum S of a geometric progression with infinitely many terms exists if $|r| < 1$, and*

$$\boxed{S = \lim_{n \to \infty} S_n = \frac{a}{1 - r}.} \tag{14–8}$$

EXAMPLE 1. Find the sum of the infinite geometric progression $\frac{3}{2}$, 1, $\frac{2}{3}$, $\frac{4}{9}$, · · ·

Solution. With $a = \frac{3}{2}$ and $r = \frac{2}{3}$, we find

$$S = \frac{a}{1 - r} = \frac{\frac{3}{2}}{1 - \frac{2}{3}} = \frac{\frac{3}{2}}{\frac{1}{3}} = 4\tfrac{1}{2}.$$

EXAMPLE 2. Convert the repeating decimal 3.242424... into an equivalent common fraction.

Solution. We can represent the number 3.242424... as the number 3 plus a geometric progression with $a = 0.24$ and $r = 0.01$, since

$$3.242424... = 3 + (0.24 + 0.0024 + 0.000024 + \cdots).$$

The sum S, in the parentheses, may be given

$$S = \frac{a}{1-r} = \frac{0.24}{1-0.01} = \frac{0.24}{0.99} = \frac{8}{33}.$$

Thus

$$3.242424... = 3 + \tfrac{8}{33} = \tfrac{107}{33}.$$

This result may be checked by actually dividing 107 by 33.

Any infinite repeating decimal can be converted into an equivalent common fraction. Moreover, any common fraction may be written as a periodic decimal (see Article 1–1).

PROBLEMS

Find the sum of each of the following infinite geometric progressions:

1. $1, \tfrac{1}{3}, \tfrac{1}{9}, \ldots$
2. $128, 48, 18, \ldots$
3. $16, -4, 1, \ldots$
4. $\tfrac{4}{3}, 1, \tfrac{3}{4}, \ldots$
5. $2, \sqrt{2}, 1, \ldots$
6. $\sqrt{2}+1, 1, \sqrt{2}-1, \ldots$

Convert each of the repeating decimals into equivalent common fractions:

7. $3.333...$
8. $6.272727...$
9. $0.555...$
10. $8.690909...$
11. $5.818181...$
12. $0.142857142857...$

13. The sum of an infinite geometric progression is $\tfrac{7}{2}$ and the first term is 3. What is the common ratio?

14. The length of the side of a square is 4 inches. A second square is inscribed by connecting the mid-points of the sides of the first square, a third by connecting the mid-points of the sides of the second, and so on. Find the sum of the areas of the infinitely many squares thus formed, including the first.

15. Find the sum of the perimeters of all the squares described in Problem 14.

16. If the original figure in Problem 14 were an equilateral triangle, with sides 4 inches long, and new equilateral triangles were formed in the same way, what would the sum of their areas be, including the area of the original figure?

17. A ball is dropped from a height of 48 feet and rebounds two-thirds of the distance it falls. If it continues to fall and rebound in this way, how far will it travel before coming to rest?

18. The middle third of a line 1 foot long is erased. From each of the two remaining thirds, the middle thirds are erased. From each of the four remaining ninths, the middle thirds are erased. If this process is continued indefinitely, what will be the sum of the lengths of the remaining line segments?

14–4 The logarithmic function. Since for any positive number x and any positive number $a \neq 1$, there is one and only one real value of y which satisfies the equation $a^y = x$,* we can solve this equation for y, and have y equal to the power to which a must be raised in order to obtain the number x. We thus obtain the following definition:

---

* The proof of this statement is beyond the scope of this book, but it should be evident from Fig. 14–2.

DEFINITION 14–2. *The exponent or power y to which the number a is raised to give the number x is called the* logarithm *or* logarithmic function *of x to the base a, and is written*

$$y = \log_a x, \tag{14–9}$$

where $x > 0$, and $a > 0$, and $\neq 1$.

Since $y = \log_a x$ and $y = a^x$ are inverse functions of each other, many of the logarithmic properties should be evident. It is most important to keep in mind that the two expressions

$$x = a^y \quad \text{and} \quad y = \log_a x \tag{14–10}$$

are equivalent.

ILLUSTRATION.

$$\log_3 9 \ = 2 \quad \leftrightarrow 3^2 \ = 9.*$$
$$\log_2 32 = 5 \quad \leftrightarrow 2^5 \ = 32.$$
$$\log_6 1 \ = 0 \quad \leftrightarrow 6^0 \ = 1.$$
$$\log_2 \tfrac{1}{16} = -4 \leftrightarrow 2^{-4} = \tfrac{1}{16}.$$
$$\log_8 4 \ = \tfrac{2}{3} \quad \leftrightarrow 8^{2/3} = 4.$$

Let us sketch the graphs of two logarithmic functions $y = \log_2 x$ and $y = \log_3 x$ and, with the help of these graphs (Fig. 14–3), consider some of the fundamental properties of the function $y = \log_a x$.

x	$\frac{1}{4}$	$\frac{1}{2}$	1	2	4	8
y	-2	-1	0	1	2	3

x	$\frac{1}{9}$	$\frac{1}{3}$	1	3	9
y	-2	-1	0	1	2

$$y = \log_2 x \leftrightarrow 2^y = x \qquad\qquad y = \log_3 x \leftrightarrow 3^y = x$$

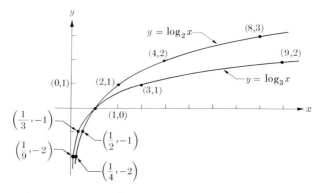

FIGURE 14–3

---

*The symbol $\leftrightarrow$ denotes "is the same as" or that the two expressions are equivalent.

1. The function is positive for all values of x greater than 1, but negative for all values of x less than 1. It is not defined for negative values of x.

2. The function is an increasing function. This will be proved when we find $D \log_a x$.

3. The logarithm of any number with respect to itself as base is equal to 1. Graphically, all such curves pass through the point $(a, 1)$.

4. The function has $x = 1$ for its only zero.

There are several additional properties of logarithms which may be easily derived if we recall that a logarithm is an exponent. They will be stated and proved as theorems.

THEOREM 14–3.   *The logarithm of the product of two quantities is equal to the logarithm of the first quantity plus the logarithm of the second,*

$$\log_a uv \equiv \log_a u + \log_a v. \tag{14–11}$$

Proof. Let u and v be any two positive quantities whose logarithms are x and y, respectively,

$$x = \log_a u \quad \text{and} \quad y = \log_a v,$$

or

$$a^x = u \quad \text{and} \quad a^y = v.$$

Multiplying the corresponding members of these equations, we have

$$uv = a^x a^y = a^{x+y},$$

which by the definition of a logarithm reduces to

$$\log_a uv = x + y = \log_a u + \log_a v.$$

THEOREM 14–4.   *The logarithm of the quotient of two quantities is equal to the logarithm of the first quantity minus the logarithm of the second,*

$$\log_a \frac{u}{v} \equiv \log_a u - \log_a v. \tag{14–12}$$

Proof. With the same assumptions as in Theorem 14–3, we have

$$\frac{u}{v} = \frac{a^x}{a^y} = a^{x-y}.$$

Written in terms of logarithms, this becomes

$$\log_a \frac{u}{v} = x - y = \log_a u - \log_a v.$$

THEOREM 14-5. *The logarithm of a power of a quantity is equal to the power multiplied by the logarithm of the quantity, that is,*

$$\log_a u^p \equiv p \log_a u. \qquad (14\text{--}13)$$

Proof. Let u be any quantity and its logarithm be x. Then $x = \log_a u$ or $a^x = u$. If we raise both members to the p power, we have

$$(a^x)^p = a^{xp} = u^p,$$

or, in terms of logarithms,

$$\log_a u^p = xp = p \log_a u.$$

ILLUSTRATION 1. Theorem 14-3 implies that

$$\log_{10} (47)(93) = \log_{10} 47 + \log_{10} 93$$

or

$$\log_{10} 4700 = \log_{10} 47 \cdot 100 = \log_{10} 47 + \log_{10} 100.$$

ILLUSTRATION 2. Theorem 14-4 implies that

$$\log_{10} \tfrac{82}{53} = \log_{10} 82 - \log_{10} 53.$$

Theorems 14-3 and 14-4 imply that

$$\log_{10} \frac{(48)(96)}{23} = \log_{10} 48 + \log_{10} 96 - \log_{10} 23.$$

ILLUSTRATION 3. Theorem 14-5 is used for both integral powers and roots.

$$\log_{10} 28^5 = 5 \log_{10} 28,$$

$$\log_{10} \sqrt[3]{472} = \log_{10} (472)^{1/3} = \tfrac{1}{3} \log_{10} 472.$$

PROBLEMS

Express the following in logarithmic notation, using (14-10):

1. $3^3 = 27$
2. $5^4 = 625$
3. $4^0 = 1$
4. $10^3 = 1000$
5. $8^{4/3} = 16$
6. $2^{-6} = \frac{1}{64}$
7. $10^{-3} = 0.001$
8. $b^z = w$
9. $4^1 = 4$

Express in exponent notation using (14-10):

10. $\log_2 \tfrac{1}{8} = -3$
11. $\log_{36} 6 = \tfrac{1}{2}$
12. $\log_{10} 1 = 0$

Find by inspection the value of x, a, or u in the following expressions:

13. $x = \log_4 16$
14. $x = \log_7 1$
15. $x = \log_9 \tfrac{1}{9}$

16. $x = \log_{\sqrt{6}} 36$ 17. $\log_5 u = 2$ 18. $\log_a 16 = 4$

19. $x = \log_2 4^7$ 20. $\log_a 32 = -\frac{5}{7}$ 21. $\log_a \frac{2}{3} = -\frac{1}{3}$

Sketch the graphs of the following functions:

22. $y = \log_5 x$ 23. $y = \log_{1/2} x$

24. $y = \log_{10} x$ 25. $y = \log_{1/3} x$

Express as a single logarithm, using Theorems 14–3, 4, and 5:

26. $\log_a x + \log_a y - \log_a z$ 27. $\log_b (a + 2) - \log_b (a - 3)$

28. $4 \log_{10} x - 3 \log_{10} y$ 29. $\frac{1}{2} \log_a x - \frac{2}{3} \log_a y$

30. $\log_b 2x + 3 (\log_b x - \log_b y)$

31. $-\log_a x + 6 \log_a (x - 1) + 3 \log_a x^2$

Write the logarithm of the given expression in terms of the logarithms of its factors:

32. $\log_{10} (895)(1.47)$ 33. $\log_{10} (60.3)^4$

34. $\log_{10} (68)^7(\sqrt{147})$ 35. $\log_{10} \dfrac{(54.3)^3(67)}{(93.9)(32.5)^2}$

14–5 Common logarithms. After the discussion in the previous article, it should be clear that any positive number other than 1 can be used as the base for a system of logarithms. For computational purposes, the most convenient system is that with 10 as its base. The first table of logarithms with 10 as the base was composed by Henry Briggs (1560–1631). The advantages of this system will become apparent as we proceed. In writing

$$10^3 = 1000$$
$$10^2 = 100$$
$$10^1 = 10$$
$$10^0 = 1$$
$$10^{-1} = 0.1$$
$$10^{-2} = 0.01$$
$$10^{-3} = 0.001$$

and considering this list as extending upward and downward indefinitely, we have a method for representing certain numbers as powers of ten. Although these special numbers are the only ones which can be written as 10 with an integral exponent, all positive numbers can be represented approximately as 10 with some exponent. This exponent, we realize from our definition of a logarithm (14–9), is the logarithm of the number to the base 10, and will be called the *common logarithm of a number*. Throughout the rest of this book, the base 10 will be assumed when no base is indicated. Thus, $\log 1000 = 3$, $\log 10 = 1$, or $\log 0.001 = -3$.

Not only do the powers of ten listed above have logarithms, but all positive numbers do. The values of the logarithms to the base ten of all positive numbers every hundredth of a unit between 1 and 10 have been approximated to four decimal places in Table II in the Appendix. For example, to find log 7.63, we look down the first column N of the table for 7.6 and then move to the right of 7.6 to the number which appears in the column headed by 3. Finding 0.8825, we have log 7.63 = 0.8825, which means, of course, $10^{0.8825} = 7.63$ (approximately).

Actually, by making use of the method of *linear interpolation*, similar to that used in Articles 4–13 and 11–5, as well as Table II, we can find the logarithm of a number with four significant digits. If N lies between x and $x + 0.01$, then $N = x + 0.01r$, with r between 0 and 1, so that, assuming the graph of the logarithmic function is a straight line between x and $x + 0.01$,

$$\log N = \log x + r \left[\log (x + 0.01) - \log x\right]. \qquad (14\text{–}14)$$

EXAMPLE 1. Find log 3.476.

Solution. Since $3.47 < 3.476 < 3.48$, we have

$$\begin{aligned}
\log 3.476 &= \log 3.47 + 0.6 \, (\log 3.48 - \log 3.47) \\
&= 0.5403 + 0.6 \, (0.5416 - 0.5403) \\
&= 0.5403 + 0.0008 \\
&= 0.5411.
\end{aligned}$$

This number can have only four significant figures, since the logarithms in the table are only four-figure approximations.

If the logarithm of a number is given to four decimal places, it is also possible to find the number by using Table II. If log N appears in the middle of the table, the process used to find N is reversed. If log N lies between log x and log $(x + 0.01)$, then $N = x + 0.01r$, with

$$r = \frac{\log N - \log x}{\log (x + 0.01) - \log x}, \qquad (14\text{–}15)$$

rounded to the nearest tenth. (Why?)

EXAMPLE 2. Find N if log N = 0.7281.

Solution. If we look in the middle of the table, we find

$$0.7275 < 0.7281 < 0.7284,$$

where

$$\log 5.35 = 0.7284,$$
$$\log 5.34 = 0.7275.$$

Therefore we have

$$r = \frac{0.7281 - 0.7275}{0.7284 - 0.7275} = 0.7 \quad \text{(rounded off)},$$

and $N = 5.347$.

PROBLEMS

Using Table II, find the logarithm of each of the following numbers:

1. 2.57	2. 3.89	3. 6.92	4. 7.65
5. 4.71	6. 9.80	7. 6.875	8. 8.924
9. 3.276	10. 1.892	11. 7.689	12. 5.873

Using Table II, find N in each of the following if log N is equal to:

13. 0.3856	14. 0.8756	15. 0.6149	16. 0.6405
17. 0.9415	18. 0.7657	19. 0.2675	20. 0.5217
21. 0.9229	22. 0.7578	23. 0.5069	24. 0.6745

In general, the logarithm of N has two parts: a whole number, called the *characteristic*, and a positive decimal (a number n such that $0 \leq n < 1$), called the *mantissa*. If the decimal point in a number is just to the right of the first nonzero digit, the logarithm of that number has 0 for its characteristic. All the numbers between 1 and 10 in Table II are of this type. Such a number is said to have its *decimal point in standard position*.

If any number is multiplied by 10, the decimal point is moved one place to the right, or if divided by 10, one place to the left. But each time a number is multiplied by 10, since

$$\log 10N = \log N + \log 10$$
$$= \log N + 1,$$

the logarithm of the number is increased by one. Likewise, if a number is divided by 10, its logarithm is decreased by one, for

$$\log \frac{N}{10} = \log N - \log 10$$
$$= \log N - 1.$$

Thus the general rule for obtaining the characteristic can be stated: *The characteristic of the logarithm of a number is equal to the number of places the decimal point has been moved from standard position. The characteristic is positive if the point has been moved to the right, negative if to the left.* It is because of this property of our number system, and the corresponding ease of determining the characteristic, that logarithms to the base ten are used for computation.

The mantissa, that part of the logarithm which appears in the table, is not affected by the position of the decimal point in the number, but depends only on its succession of digits. Thus, because of the result of Example 1, log 347.6 = 2.5411, since its characteristic is 2, while

$$\log 0.003476 = -3 + 0.5411.$$

The characteristic -3 is usually written $7 - 10$ (it is common practice for computational purposes to write any negative characteristic as a positive integer minus a multiple of 10), so that

$$-3 + 0.5411 = 7.5411 - 10.$$

PROBLEMS

Give the characteristic and mantissa of each of the following logarithms:

1. $\log N = 1.3782$
2. $\log N = 3.4729$
3. $\log N = 0.5728 - 3$
4. $\log N = 9.6847$
5. $\log N = 5.8723$
6. $\log N = 6.7253 - 10$
7. $\log N = -3.7285$
8. $\log N = -0.6892$

Find the logarithms of each of the following numbers, using Table II:

9. 329
10. 0.00874
11. 4728
12. 32.46
13. 0.07284
14. 0.6877

Find N in each of the following, using Table II:

15. $\log N = 3.8228$
16. $\log N = 0.9643 - 2$
17. $\log N = 2.4268$
18. $\log N = 9.8818 - 10$
19. $\log N = 7.5627 - 10$
20. $\log N = -1.4892$

In trigonometry there are frequently computations involving a large amount of multiplication and division. To shorten such work, the logarithms of the circular functions have been tabulated in Table III. Although the entries are logarithms (with the characteristics included), the form of the table is the same as that of Table I, and it is used in exactly the same manner (see Article 4–13).

EXAMPLE 3. Find $\log \sin 36°17'$.

Solution. Since the angle $36°17'$ lies between $36°10'$ and $36°20'$,

$$\begin{aligned}
\log \sin 36°17' &= \log \sin 36°10' + \tfrac{7}{10} [\log \sin 37°20' - \log \sin 37°10'] \\
&= (9.7710 - 10) + \tfrac{7}{10}[(9.7727 - 10) - (9.7710 - 10)] \\
&= (9.7710 - 10) + \tfrac{7}{10}(0.0017) \\
&= (9.7710 - 10) + 0.0012 \\
&= 9.7722 - 10.
\end{aligned}$$

EXAMPLE 4. Find the angle θ between $0°$ and $90°$ if $\log \tan \theta = 0.1947$.

Solution. We locate 0.1947 in the log tangent column between

$$\log \tan 57°20' = 0.1930 \quad \text{and} \quad \log \tan 57°30' = 0.1958.$$

Thus,

$$\frac{r}{10} = \frac{0.1947 - 0.1930}{0.1958 - 0.1930},$$

or

$$r = 10(\tfrac{17}{28}) = 6,$$

so that $\theta = 57°26'$, approximated to the nearest minute.

PROBLEMS

1. By using Table III, and interpolation if necessary, find the value of each of the following:

(a) log sin 13°20',   (b) log cos 45°30',
(c) log sin 67°32',   (d) log cos 38°21',
(e) log tan 72°47',   (f) log sin 115°18',
(g) log cos 68°56',   (h) log sin 51°49'.

2. Find the value of θ between 0° and 90° to the nearest minute by using Table III, and interpolation if necessary, for the following:

(a) log sin θ = 9.2870 $-$ 10,   (b) log cos θ = 9.8365 $-$ 10,
(c) log tan θ = 9.7353 $-$ 10,   (d) log cos θ = 9.7316 $-$ 10,
(e) log sin θ = 9.2278 $-$ 10,   (f) log tan θ = 0.4937,
(g) log cos θ = 9.9797 $-$ 10,   (h) log sin θ = 9.8761 $-$ 10.

14–6 Computation by the use of logarithms. We are now prepared to show how any computation involving multiplication, division, raising to a power, or extracting roots is greatly simplified through the use of logarithms. The work should be outlined systematically before any actual computation is carried out. An orderly arrangement is most helpful, not only in simplifying the work but also in checking the result.

EXAMPLE 1. Use logarithms to compute $(1280 \cdot 0.849)/62.8$.

Solution. By letting $N = (1280 \cdot 0.849)/62.8$, we have, using Theorems 14–3 and 14–4, log N = log 1280 + log 0.849 $-$ log 62.8. The work should then be arranged as follows:

$$
\begin{aligned}
\log 1280 &= \ \ 3.1072 \\
(+) \log 0.849 &= \ \ 9.9289 - 10 \\
\hline
\log \text{numerator} &= 13.0361 - 10 \\
(-) \log 62.8 &= \ \ 1.7980 \\
\hline
\log N &= 11.2381 - 10 \\
N &= 17.3.
\end{aligned}
$$

N is given with three significant figures because the original numbers were of this type.

EXAMPLE 2. Compute by using logarithms: $\sqrt{0.01278}/(0.4825)^3$.

Solution. We know $\log N = \frac{1}{2}\log 0.01278 - 3\log 0.4825$. Arranging our work, we have

$$
\begin{aligned}
\log 0.4825 &= 9.6834 - 10 \\
3\log 0.4825 &= 29.0502 - 30 \\
&= 9.0502 - 10
\end{aligned}
\qquad
\begin{aligned}
\log 0.01278 &= 18.1065 - 20 \\
\tfrac{1}{2}\log 0.01278 &= 9.0532 - 10 \\
(-)\ 3\log 0.4825 &= 9.0502 - 10 \\
\hline
\log N &= 0.0030 \\
N &= 1.007.
\end{aligned}
$$

EXAMPLE 3. Find the value of b by using logarithms if

$$ b = \frac{32.86 \sin 27°42'}{\sin 54°17'}. $$

Solution. We have

$$ \log b = \log 32.86 + \log \sin 27°42' - \log \sin 54°17'. $$

Arranging our work, we get

$$
\begin{aligned}
\log 32.86 &= 1.5167 \\
(+)\ \log \sin 27°42' &= 9.6673 - 10 \\
\hline
\log \text{numerator} &= 11.1840 - 10 \\
(-)\ \log \sin 54°17' &= 9.9095 - 10 \\
\hline
\log b &= 1.2745 \\
b &= 18.81.
\end{aligned}
$$

EXAMPLE 4. Find the value of $x = 52.8 \log 6.79$.

Solution. It is important to note that this example asks for the product of the two factors 52.8 and $\log 6.79$, *not* 52.8 and 6.79. Thus,

$$ \log x = \log 52.8 + \log [\log 6.79]. $$

$$
\begin{aligned}
\log 52.8 &= 1.7226 \\
(+)\ \log [\log 6.79] = \log 0.832 &= 9.9201 - 10 \\
\hline
\log x &= 1.6427 \\
x &= 43.9.
\end{aligned}
$$

PROBLEMS

Using logarithms, compute the value of the following to the correct number of significant figures:

1. $(367)(87.2)$

2. $(47.2)(0.897)$

3. $\dfrac{32.7}{(0.892)^{1/2}}$

4. $\dfrac{(245)(8.62)}{(7.84)^2}$

5. $(32.79)(497.2)(9.738)$

6. $\sqrt{756.9}\ (4.796)$

7. $(-0.8472)^4$*

8. $(-3.472)^{-3}$

9. $\dfrac{(6.892)(-0.9245)^{2/3}}{2.475}$

10. $\left(-\dfrac{47.2}{6.783}\right)^3$

11. $\dfrac{\sqrt{738.2}\ (38.74)}{(0.9576)^2(8743)}$

12. $\left[\dfrac{\sqrt{8453}\ (0.002477)}{347.9}\right]^{1/2}$

13. $4.72 \log 63.9$

14. $\log\ (\log 82.4)$

15. $\dfrac{\log 48.5}{\log 67.2}$

16. $\dfrac{\log 0.8924}{\log 5.237}$

17. $48.7 \tan 58°30'$

18. $\dfrac{68.2 \sin 37°20'}{\sin 49°50'}$

19. $897.2 \cos 63°48'$

20. $(189)(256) \cos 27°11'$

14–7 Compound interest and its generalization. The study of compound interest makes use of logarithmic computation, and it also logically introduces another important system of logarithms.

If an amount of money P is invested at an interest rate of r (expressed in decimals) per year, the amount of interest at the end of one year is Pr, so that the total amount is $P + Pr = P(1 + r)$. If this amount then draws interest for a second year, at the end of two years the total amount is $P(1 + r) + P(1 + r)r = P(1 + r)[1 + r] = P(1 + r)^2$. This represents the compound amount of money at the end of two years due to its investment at the interest rate r. If we continue this process, the amount P, invested for n years and compounded annually at the rate r, is given by

$$A = P(1 + r)^n. \qquad (14\text{–}16)$$

EXAMPLE 1. Find the compound amount at the end of eight years on an original principal of $500 at 6% compounded annually.

---

* Although the logarithm of a negative number is not defined, the calculation may be carried out by considering all factors positive and prefixing the appropriate sign to the result.

Solution. Using (14–16), we have $P = 500$, $r = 0.06$, and $n = 8$. Thus,

$$A = 500(1 + 0.06)^8 = 500(1.06)^8.$$

$\log 1.06 = 0.0253$	$\log 500 = 2.6990$
$8 \log 1.06 = 0.2024$	$(+) \ 8 \log 1.06 = 0.2024$
	$\log A = 2.9014$
	$A = \$796.80.$

Since n represents the number of years and r the rate per year, we can consider the result due to amounts compounded annually, semiannually, quarterly, and so on, if we let s denote the number of conversion periods each year. Thus, in n years, with s conversion periods per year, the number of such periods is ns and the rate per period r/s, or

$$\boxed{A = P\left(1 + \frac{r}{s}\right)^{ns}.} \tag{14–17}$$

EXAMPLE 2. If the \$500 in Example 1 were invested for eight years at 6% compounded quarterly, how large would the result be?

Solution. Since 6% compounded quarterly for eight years is $1\frac{1}{2}\%$ per period, with 32 periods, we have

$$A = 500(1.015)^{32},$$

which results in $A = \$804.20$.

Both this result and that in the first example are not very accurate, since four-place logarithm tables were used. For accurate results, since the exponent is large, either seven-place logarithmic or compound interest tables should be used.

One of the most important exponential functions is a direct result of a generalization of Eq. (14–17), which is sometimes called the *law of natural growth*. It has frequent applications in biology, chemistry, and economics, as well as in mathematics. Let us suppose that the number of conversion periods s increases indefinitely, so that the amount is compounded continuously. Letting $r/s = x$, and therefore $s/r = 1/x$, we have, from Eq. (14–17),

$$A = P\left[\left(1 + \frac{r}{s}\right)^{s/r}\right]^{rn} = P[(1 + x)^{1/x}]^{rn}. \tag{14–18}$$

With s increasing indefinitely, for a fixed r, $r/s = x$ decreases indefinitely through positive values and approaches zero. If Eq. (14–18) is expanded by the binomial theorem (see Problem 4, Article 8–3),

$$A = P\left[1^{1/x} + \frac{1}{x} \cdot 1^{(1/x)-1} \cdot x + \frac{\frac{1}{x}\left(\frac{1}{x} - 1\right)}{2!} \cdot 1^{(1/x)-2} \cdot x^2\right.$$

$$\left. + \frac{\frac{1}{x}\left(\frac{1}{x} - 1\right)\left(\frac{1}{x} - 2\right)}{3!} \cdot 1^{(1/x)-3} \cdot x^3 \cdots\right]^{rn}$$

$$= P\left[1^{1/x} + 1^{(1/x)-1} + \frac{1 - x}{2!} \cdot 1^{(1/x)-2}\right.$$

$$\left. + \frac{(1 - x)(1 - 2x)}{3!} \cdot 1^{(1/x)-3} + \cdots\right]^{rn},$$

and if we take the limit of each term of this expression as x approaches zero, we get

$$A = P\left(1 + 1 + \frac{1}{2} + \frac{1}{3!} + \cdots\right)^{rn}. \qquad (14\text{–}19)$$

Although we have by no means shown that this infinite sum has a definite value,* it would seem probable that the expression within the brackets of Eq. (14–18) does have a definite value if x is allowed to approach zero. Such is the case. This constant value, denoted by e, is a nonterminating, nonrepeating decimal, and therefore irrational (Article 1–1). To six significant figures,

$$e = \lim_{x \to 0} (1 + x)^{1/x} = \left(1 + 1 + \frac{1}{2!} + \frac{1}{3!} + \cdots\right) = 2.71828. \qquad (14\text{–}20)$$

We thus have the function

$$\boxed{A = Pe^{rn},} \qquad (14\text{–}21)$$

representing the amount of P compounded continuously for n years at a rate r.

EXAMPLE 3. The population of a certain locality is 20,000 and is increasing continuously at a rate $r = 0.037$, according to the law of natural growth, Eq. (14–21). Find the approximate population after 25 years.

Solution. With the formula $A = Pe^{rn}$, we have $P = 20,000$, $r = 0.037$, and $n = 25$. Therefore,

$$A = 20,000e^{(0.037)(25)}.$$

---

* As in Article 8–3, any proof, in general, of the existence of a definite value for an infinite sum is beyond the scope of this book.

Solving by logarithms, we have

$$\log A = \log 20{,}000 + (0.037)(25) \log e.$$

$$\log 20{,}000 = 4.3010$$

$$(+) \ (0.037)(25) \log e = 0.4017$$

$$\log A = 4.7027$$

$$A = 50{,}430 \ \text{(approximate) population.}$$

PROBLEMS

1. Find the compound amount at the end of 10 years on an original principal of $200 at 4% (a) compounded annually, (b) compounded semiannually, (c) compounded quarterly, (d) compounded continuously.

2. Find the compound amount at the end of 20 years on an original principal of $3000 at 6% (a) compounded annually, (b) compounded monthly, (c) compounded continuously.

3. What time is required to double a certain amount (a) compounded annually at 6%, (b) compounded continuously at 6%? [*Hint:* Let $P = 1$ and $A = 2$.]

In Problems 4–8, we shall assume the law of natural growth [Eq. (14–21)].

4. The population of a certain town is 80,000 and has been increasing continuously for the past 20 years at the rate $r = 0.025$. What was the population 20 years ago?

5. There are originally 1000 bacteria in a culture, and 4 hours later there are 4000. Find the rate of increase per hour of the bacteria.

6. If the growth of a certain bacteria in a culture increases at the rate $r = 0.24$ per hour, how long will it take 50 bacteria to become 1,000,000?

7. In a certain chemical reaction, the original concentration of 0.03 is reduced to 0.01 in 4 minutes. (a) What is the rate of decrease in the concentration per minute? (b) What will the concentration be in 10 minutes?

8. If radium decomposes according to the relation $y = y_0 e^{-0.04t}$, where y_0 grams of radium reduce to y grams in t centuries, how long will it take one gram to reduce to one-half a gram?

14–8 Applications of the exponential functions. In the last article we saw one important application of the exponential function. Before examining other uses of this function, we shall discuss the method for finding the numerical value of a logarithm to any base and for changing from one base to another. Actually, the exponential function can be used to find the logarithm of a number to any base.

EXAMPLE 1. Find the value of $\log_4 15$.

Solution. If $y = \log_4 15$, we have the equivalent equation

$$4^y = 15.$$

Any such equation may be solved by taking the common logarithm of each member and finding the required value of y. Thus,

$$\log 4^y = \log 15,$$
$$y \log 4 = \log 15.$$

Solving for y, we have

$$y = \frac{\log 15}{\log 4} = \frac{1.1761}{0.6021} = 1.953.$$

If the logarithm of a number to one base is known, it is often desirable to find the logarithm of this number to a different base. Let

$$y = \log_a N.$$

Writing this in the equivalent form

$$a^y = N,$$

and taking the logarithm to the base b of each member, we have

$$\log_b a^y = \log_b N,$$

or

$$y \log_b a = \log_b N.$$

Recalling that $y = \log_a N$, we have

$$\boxed{\log_a N \cdot \log_b a = \log_b N.} \qquad (14\text{--}22)$$

Because of the importance of the case where one base is 10 and the other e, we note that in this case, with $a = e$ and $b = 10$, Eq. (14--22) reduces to

$$\log_{10} N = \log_e N \cdot \log_{10} e = 0.4343 \log_e N, \qquad (14\text{--}23)$$

and

$$\log_e N = \frac{1}{\log_{10} e} \cdot \log_{10} N = 2.303 \log_{10} N. \qquad (14\text{--}24)$$

These two expressions are used extensively in analytic work to change from the common logarithmic system to the logarithm system with base e, and vice versa.

EXAMPLE 2. Find $\log_e 3.24$.

Solution 1. By (14--24),

$$\log_e 3.24 = 2.303 \log 3.24$$
$$= (2.303)(0.5105)$$
$$= 1.175.$$

Solution 2. This example may, of course, be solved as in Example 1. If we let

$$y = \log_e 3.24,$$
$$e^y = 3.24.$$

Taking the common logarithm of each member, we get

$$\log e^y = \log 3.24,$$

or

$$y \log e = \log 3.24.$$

Solving for y, we have

$$y = \frac{\log 3.24}{\log e} = \frac{0.5105}{0.4343} = 1.175.$$

The method used in solving Example 1 and in the second solution of Example 2 is similar to that used in solving many exponential as well as logarithmic equations.

EXAMPLE 3. Solve $4^{x+3} = 7^{x-1}$ for x.

Solution. If we take the common logarithms of both members,

$$\log 4^{x+3} = \log 7^{x-1}.$$

By using Theorem 14–5, we have

$$(x + 3) \log 4 = (x - 1) \log 7.$$

Solving this linear equation for x, we get

$$x \log 4 + 3 \log 4 = x \log 7 - \log 7,$$
$$x(\log 4 - \log 7) = -\log 7 - 3 \log 4,$$
$$x = \frac{\log 7 + 3 \log 4}{\log 7 - \log 4}$$
$$= \frac{2.6514}{0.2430} = 10.92 \text{ (approximately)}.$$

EXAMPLE 4. Solve $\log (x + 3) - \log x = 2$.

Solution. If we use Theorem 14–4,

$$\log (x + 3) - \log x = \log \frac{x + 3}{x} = 2,$$

so that

$$\frac{x + 3}{x} = 100, \qquad x + 3 = 100x,$$
$$99x = 3, \qquad \text{or} \qquad x = \tfrac{1}{33}.$$

PROBLEMS

Find the following logarithms:

1. $\log_2 14$ 2. $\log_5 27$ 3. $\log_7 128$ 4. $\log_{27} 15$
5. $\log_e 7$ 6. $\log_e 12$ 7. $\log_e 1.79$ 8. $\log_e 3.78$

Find the value of x in each of the following:

9. $\log_4 x = 23$
10. $\log_{12} x = 17$
11. $\log_e x = 3.28$
12. $\log_e x = 1.72$
13. $\log_e x = 0.8473$
14. $\log_e x = 2.547$

*15. Prove the relation $\log_b a = 1/(\log_a b)$.

Solve the following exponential equations for x:

16. $3^x = 27$
17. $2^x = 32$
18. $2^x = 27$
19. $3^x = 32$
20. $3^{x+1} = 4^{x-7}$
21. $5(6^x) = 21^{x-2}$
22. $17^{2x-3} = 25^{x-1}$
23. $2.78^x = 7.38^{3x-1}$
24. $e^x + e^{-x} = 2$ [*Hint:* This is quadratic in e^x.]
25. $e^x - e^{-x} = 2$

Solve the following logarithmic equations for x:

26. $\log x - 2 \log 4 = \log 32$
27. $\log (x + 2) - \log x = \log 12$
28. $\log (3x + 2) = \log (x - 4) + 1$
29. $\log (x + 1) - \log x = 2.4742$

14–9 Differentiation of the logarithmic and exponential functions. We are now prepared to differentiate the functions discussed in this chapter. If we consider $f(x) = \log_a x$ and recall the definition of the derivative of $f(x)$ at any value x_1 (Eq. 10–5), then we are interested in the expression

$$\frac{f(x) - f(x_1)}{x - x_1} = \frac{\log_a x - \log_a x_1}{x - x_1}, \quad \text{for} \quad x \neq x_1.$$

But

$$\frac{\log_a x - \log_a x_1}{x - x_1} = \frac{1}{x - x_1} \log_a \frac{x}{x_1} = \frac{1}{x_1} \cdot \frac{x_1}{x - x_1} \log_a \frac{x}{x_1}$$

$$= \frac{1}{x_1} \log_a \left(\frac{x_1 + x - x_1}{x_1}\right)^{x_1/(x-x_1)}$$

$$= \frac{1}{x_1} \log_a \left(1 + \frac{x - x_1}{x_1}\right)^{x_1/(x-x_1)}$$

If we let $u = (x - x_1)/x_1$, this expression becomes

$$\frac{1}{x_1} \log_a (1 + u)^{1/u}.$$

Let us assume that the limit of the logarithm of a function is equal to the logarithm of the limit of the function (an application of Theorem 9–5). Since $\lim_{u \to 0} (1 + u)^{1/u} = e$, Eq. (14–20), we have

$$\lim_{x \to x_1} \frac{\log_a x - \log_a x_1}{x - x_1} = \lim_{x \to x_1} \frac{1}{x_1} \log_a \left(1 + \frac{x - x_1}{x_1}\right)^{x_1/(x-x_1)}$$

$$= \lim_{u \to 0} \frac{1}{x_1} \log_a (1 + u)^{1/u}$$

$$= \frac{1}{x_1} \log_a \lim_{u \to 0} (1 + u)^{1/u}$$

$$= \frac{1}{x_1} \log_a e,$$

and since the logarithm of e exists, we have proved the following theorem.

THEOREM 14–6. *At any positive value x, the derivative of $\log_a x$ is given by*

$$D \log_a x = \frac{1}{x} \log_a e. \tag{14–25}$$

It is because of this important result that the system of logarithms with e for the base is extensively used in calculus. For with this base, since $\log_e e = 1$, Eq. (14–25) becomes greatly simplified and reduces to the following:

COROLLARY 14–6(a). *For any real positive value x, the derivative of $\log_e x$ is given by*

$$D \log_e x = \frac{1}{x}. \tag{14–26}$$

Logarithms to the base e are called *natural logarithms,* or sometimes *Napierian logarithms,* in honor of John Napier (1550–1617), a Scotsman who published the first logarithmic table of any kind in 1614. Many calculus books use the notation $\log_e = \ln$ for the natural logarithm system.

Again, if we use Eq. (10–12), this corollary can be generalized so that we have the following:

COROLLARY 14–6(b). *For any differentiable function $g(x)$ whose range is positive,*

$$D \log_e g(x) = \frac{Dg(x)}{g(x)}. \tag{14–27}$$

ILLUSTRATION 1. (a) $D \log_e x^4 = 4x^3/x^4 = 4/x$. This can also be simplified, recalling that $\log_e x^4 = 4 \log_e x$. $D \log_e x^4 = D(4 \log_e x) = 4/x$. (b) $D \log \sqrt{1 + x^2} = D[\frac{1}{2} \log (1 + x^2)] = x/(1 + x^2)$.

By using the notion of implicit differentiation, we can obtain the derivative of the function $y = a^x$ and its generalization.

THEOREM 14–7. *The derivative at any value x of a^x is given by*

$$Da^x = a^x \log_e a. \tag{14-28}$$

Proof. If $y = a^x$, $x = \log_a y$, and differentiating each member with respect to x, we have

$$1 = \frac{Dy}{y} \log_a e,$$

or

$$Dy = \frac{y}{\log_a e}.$$

The expression of y in terms of x and the use of the result of Problem 15 (Article 14–8) gives the required result,

$$Da^x = a^x \log_e a. \tag{14-29}$$

We immediately have a very important corollary if e is substituted for a in (14–29).

COROLLARY 14–7(a). *The derivative at any value x of e^x is given by*

$$De^x = e^x. \tag{14-30}$$

Thus we have a function which is its own derivative at any value x. This, of course, may be generalized by using Eq. (10–12):

COROLLARY 14–7(b). *For any differentiable function $g(x)$,*

$$De^{g(x)} = e^{g(x)} Dg(x). \tag{14-31}$$

Again, a comparison of Eqs. (14–29) and (14–30) shows the great advantage in using the exponential function to the base e.

ILLUSTRATION 2.

(a) $De^{x^2} = 2xe^{x^2}$

(b) $D(2^{3x-1}x^4) = (2^{3x-1})(4x^3) + x^4 \cdot 2^{3x-1}(3)\log_e 2$

$\qquad = 2^{3x-1}x^3(3x\log_e 2 + 4).$

Let us return to Eq. (14–21) in the general form

$$y = Ce^{kx}, \tag{14–32}$$

where C and k are constants, and prove the property that actually characterizes (and names) the function, *the law of natural growth.*

THEOREM 14–8. *The exponential function* $y = Ce^{kx}$ *increases at a rate proportional to itself.*

Proof. Since the rate of change of any function is defined as its derivative, and $Dy = Cke^{kx} = ky$, the theorem is proved.

Its converse is also true, namely:

CONVERSE 14–8. *If a function* $f(x)$ *increases at a rate proportional to itself, then it is an exponential function.*

Proof. Since $Df(x) = kf(x)$, then $Df(x)/f(x) = k$. If we use Eq. (14–27), we have

$$D\log_e f(x) = k.$$

Thus $\log_e f(x) = kx + c$, which may be verified by differentiating each member of this equation. If we write $\log_e f(x) = kx + c$ in exponential form, we have $e^{kx+c} = f(x)$. But $e^{kx+c} = e^{kx}e^c$, and with e^c written as a new constant C, we have our result, $f(x) = Ce^{kx}$.

PROBLEMS

Find the derivatives of each of the functions in Problems 1–14.

1. $y = \log_e (1/x)$
2. $y = \log_e (x^2 + 1)^2$
3. $y = \log_e \cos x$
4. $y = \log_e \sin x$
5. $y = \log_e \tan x$
6. $y = \log_e (\log_e x)$
7. $y = (\log_e x)/x$
8. $y = \log_e (x + \sqrt{x^2 + 9})$
9. $y = \log_e (\sec x + \tan x)$
10. $y = x^2 e^x$
11. $y = e^x \cos x$
12. $y = x^2 e^{-x}$
13. $y = e^x/x$
14. $y = e^{\log_e x}$

Find the maximum and minimum points, points of inflection, and intercepts, and sketch the curves in Problems 15–19.

15. $y = e^{1/x}$
16. $y = e^{-x}$

17. $y = e^x + e^{-x}$. The graph represented by this function, called the *catenary*, is the curve in which a homogeneous rope or chain between two points of support hangs under its own weight. Knowledge of this function is important in construction of suspension bridges.

18. $y = e^{-x^2}$. This curve is the simplest form of the probability curve and plays a very important part in the theory of probability and statistics.

19. $y = xe^x$.

20. In Article 14–1 the statement was made that $y = a^x$ for $a > 1$ was an increasing function. Prove this statement.

21. In Article 14–4 the statement was made that $y = \log_a x$, $x > 0$, $a > 0$ but $\neq 1$, was an increasing function. Prove this statement.

22. Prove that the rectangle of maximum area inscribed under the curve $y = e^{-x^2}$, with one side on the x-axis, and two adjacent sides perpendicular to it, has two of its vertices at the points of inflection of the curve. See Problem 18.

CHAPTER 15

APPLICATIONS OF THE CIRCULAR FUNCTIONS
IN SOLVING TRIANGLES

There are two general types of applications of the circular functions which are of importance. One of these is the solution of triangles and the establishing of relationships between the sides and angles of a triangle. In the present chapter we shall consider this application.

15–1 General discussion of triangle solutions. The entire point of view with regard to solving triangles has changed during the last few years. Many numerical methods, numerous formulas, and detailed study with many exercises had been considered an important part of trigonometry. More recently, however, the analytic part of trigonometry, with its applications in advanced mathematics and science, has become more important. New developments have produced extremely accurate graphical methods and have also made possible the use of high-speed numerical calculators. We shall concentrate our attention on the fundamental theorems and not emphasize long and detailed processes.

If a certain number of the sides and angles of a triangle are known, the triangle can be solved by finding the remaining sides and angles. We shall derive two of the many formulas used in solving triangles and consider certain special cases of these formulas. Other formulas and relations between the sides and angles of a triangle appear in the examples and problems.

While deriving these relations, it is important to recall that a triangle is determined when

(1) two angles and one side are given,
(2) two sides and the included angle are given,
(3) three sides are given if the longest side is less than the sum of the other two.

Also, there are at most two triangles when

(4) two sides and an angle opposite one of them is given.

These are the four types of problems we wish to solve. We shall denote the three angles at the vertices of any triangle ABC by α, β, and γ, respectively, and the corresponding opposite sides by a, b, and c.

15–2 The Law of Sines. Let us derive the first of two general laws, the Law of Sines. This law involves the sides of the triangle and the sines of its angles, and it will be proved by analytic methods. If we choose a

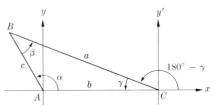

FIGURE 15–1

rectangular coordinate system so that the angle α of the triangle ABC is in standard position (see Fig. 15–1), the coordinates of B are ($c \cos \alpha$, $c \sin \alpha$). (Recall Problem 53, Article 4–2.) If, however, the origin of the coordinate system is at C, with ($180° - \gamma$) in standard position, the coordinates of B are

$$[a \cos (180° - \gamma), \qquad a \sin (180° - \gamma)].$$

Since in either case the y-coordinates of B are equal (the same distance above the x-axis), we have

$$c \sin \alpha = a \sin (180° - \gamma)$$
$$= a \sin \gamma.$$

Dividing each member of this equation by $\sin \alpha \sin \gamma$, we obtain

$$\frac{c}{\sin \gamma} = \frac{a}{\sin \alpha}.$$

With a different choice of the x-axis, $b/\sin \beta = a/\sin \alpha$, and hence we have proved the following theorem.

THEOREM 15–1. *In any triangle with angles α, β, and γ and corresponding opposite sides a, b, and c the following relationship is true:*

$$\boxed{\frac{a}{\sin \alpha} = \frac{b}{\sin \beta} = \frac{c}{\sin \gamma}.} \qquad (15–1)$$

This relationship enables us to solve the problems mentioned in (1) and (4) of Article 15–1. However, before we consider general problems solved by (15–1), let us consider an extremely important special case. The more general problems will be discussed in Article 15–5.

15–3 Solution of right triangles. If γ is a right angle equal to 90°, in (15–1) the equations reduce to $\sin \alpha = a/c$ and $\sin \beta = b/c$. But with $\gamma = 90°$ and $\alpha + \beta + \gamma = 180°$, $\beta = 90° - \alpha$, so that $\cos \alpha = b/c$. Since $\tan \alpha = \sin \alpha/\cos \alpha$, we also have $\tan \alpha = a/b$. From these special conditions, an important corollary should be clear. It may also be considered a direct consequence of the original definitions of these circular functions.

COROLLARY 15–1. *In any right triangle with* $\gamma = 90°$,

$$\sin \alpha = \frac{a}{c} = \frac{side\ opposite\ \alpha}{hypotenuse}, \tag{15–2}$$

$$\cos \alpha = \frac{b}{c} = \frac{side\ adjacent\ \alpha}{hypotenuse}, \tag{15–3}$$

$$\tan \alpha = \frac{a}{b} = \frac{side\ opposite\ \alpha}{side\ adjacent\ \alpha}. \tag{15–4}$$

The following remarks on significant figures will also be helpful in the solving of triangles.

1. Results can be no more accurate than the given sides and angles. We agree to set up the following table for accuracy.

Significant figures for sides:	Angles to the nearest:
2	degree
3	ten minutes
4	minute
5	tenth of a minute

2. If the results are required to only two or three significant digits, the slide rule should be used for the computation. The slide rule can also be employed as a check on the work, unless the answers are to be more accurate than the slide rule will allow.

3. If the results are to be correct to several significant digits, tables should be used. When calculating machines are available, the natural functions and arithmetical methods are usually employed. But since the majority of students do not have access to machines, the logarithmic solution is the logical one. This is the method used in most of the examples.

4. In solving problems, it is advisable to draw the triangle, label the known parts, and make a complete systematic outline of the work before any computation is done.

EXAMPLE 1. In the right triangle ABC, $b = 47.25$, $\alpha = 41°19'$. Find the remaining parts and the area.

Solution. We first draw the triangle and label numerically the parts that are given, as in Fig. 15–2. Then $\beta = 90° - \alpha = 48°41'$. To find a,

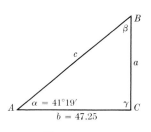

FIGURE 15-2

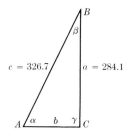

FIGURE 15-3

we use the relation $\tan \alpha = a/b$, and to find c, we use $\cos \alpha = b/c$.

$$a = 47.25 \tan 41°19' \qquad\qquad c = \frac{47.25}{\cos 41°19'}$$

$$
\begin{array}{ll}
\log 47.25 = \quad 1.6744 & \log 47.25 = 11.6744 - 10 \\
(+) \log \tan 41°19' = \quad 9.9440 - 10 & (-) \log \cos 41°19' = \quad 9.8757 - 10 \\
\hline
\qquad \log a = 11.6184 - 10 & \qquad \log c = \quad 1.7987 \\
\qquad\quad a = 41.54 & \qquad\quad c = 62.90
\end{array}
$$

The area of the triangle is $K = \frac{1}{2}ab$.

$$
\begin{array}{l}
\log 41.54 = 1.6184 \\
(+) \log 47.25 = 1.6744 \\
\hline
\log ab = 3.2928 \\
(-) \log \; 2 = 0.3010 \\
\hline
\log K = 2.9918 \\
\qquad K = 981.2
\end{array}
$$

Here the results are correct to four significant figures, as in Table III.

EXAMPLE 2. Solve the right triangle in which $a = 284.1$ and $c = 326.7$.

Solution. Draw the triangle and label numerically the parts that are known, as in Fig. 15–3. Since a and c are given, we use the relation $\sin \alpha = a/c$ to find α and then $\cos \alpha = b/c$ to find b.

$$\sin \alpha = \frac{284.1}{326.7} \qquad\qquad b = 326.7 \cos 60°24'$$

$$
\begin{array}{ll}
\log 284.1 = 12.4534 - 10 & \log 326.7 = \quad 2.5141 \\
(-) \log 326.7 = \quad 2.5141 & (+) \log \cos 60°24' = \quad 9.6937 - 10 \\
\hline
\log \sin \alpha = \quad 9.9393 - 10 & \qquad \log b = 12.2078 - 10 \\
\qquad\quad \alpha = 60°24' & \qquad\quad b = 161.4 \\
\qquad\quad \beta = 29°36'
\end{array}
$$

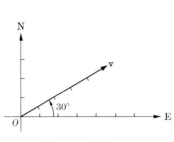

FIGURE 15–4   FIGURE 15–5

Log cos α can be found in the table when log sin α is located. This is one of the advantages in first arranging the work systematically.

Vectors. In science and engineering, physical entities such as velocity, acceleration, or force require not only magnitude but also direction for their complete determination. They are represented by line segments with an arrowhead on one end to show direction. The length of the segment, by reference to some scale, denotes magnitude. Such line segments are called *vectors*. For example, with a scale of 40 pounds to the unit, the vector in Fig. 15–4 might represent a force of 200 pounds acting in the direction 30° with the positive x-axis. A bold-face letter **v** will denote the vector, while the ordinary v will designate its length.

Since **v**, with its initial point at O, as in Fig. 15–5, has v for its length and makes an angle θ with the positive x-axis, its terminal point P has coordinates ($v \cos \theta$, $v \sin \theta$). These coordinates, denoted by v_x and v_y, are called the x- and y-components of **v** and satisfy the relations

$$\begin{aligned} v_x &= v \cos \theta, & v^2 &= v_x^2 + v_y^2, \\ v_y &= v \sin \theta, & \tan \theta &= \frac{v_y}{v_x}. \end{aligned}$$ (15–5)

EXAMPLE 3. Find v_x and v_y for the vector with $v = 247$ and $\theta = 37°40'$.

Solution. $v_x = 247 \cos 37°40' = (247)(0.7916) = 196,$
$v_y = 247 \sin 37°40' = (247)(0.6111) = 151.$

By considering $\mathbf{v}_x$ and $\mathbf{v}_y$ vectors, we can think of **v** as the single vector equivalent to these two. More generally, a vector **v** is the resultant or sum of two vectors $\mathbf{v}_1$ and $\mathbf{v}_2$ if as a single force it will produce the same result as the two forces acting together. If $\mathbf{v}_1$ and $\mathbf{v}_2$ are two nonparallel vectors emanating from the same point, their resultant **v** is the vector from that point having the length and direction of the diagonal of the parallelogram determined by $\mathbf{v}_1$ and $\mathbf{v}_2$. This notion is first used in Problem 22.

Problems

In solving the problems, a calculating machine should be used for some of the computations if possible. Logarithms should be used for others. All solutions should be checked.

1. Find the unknown sides and angles of each of the following triangles. In each, $\gamma = 90°$.

(a) $\alpha = 37°20'$, $a = 243$;   (b) $\alpha = 62°40'$, $b = 796$;
(c) $a = 3.28$, $b = 5.74$;   (d) $b = 68.4$, $c = 96.2$;
(e) $\beta = 51°10'$, $c = 0.832$;   (f) $\alpha = 37°40'$, $a = 54.8$;
(g) $a = 37.9$, $b = 57.3$;   (h) $\beta = 41°25'$, $c = 3265$;
(i) $a = 5429$, $c = 6294$;   (j) $a = 3.273$, $b = 7.647$;
(k) $\beta = 62°57'$, $a = 0.8263$;   (l) $\beta = 47°23'$, $b = 72.55$;
(m) $b = 3572$, $c = 4846$;   (n) $\alpha = 24°47'$, $b = 318.4$.

2. In a circle of radius 96.4 inches, what is the central angle that subtends a chord of 40.3 inches?

3. A rectangular lot is 102 by 296 feet. Find the length of the diagonal and the angle it makes with the longest side.

4. A telegraph pole is braced by wires from the ground which are attached at a point 18.6 feet up the pole. Find the length of a wire that makes an angle of 26°20′ with the vertical.

5. Find the area of a parallelogram whose sides are 33.7 and 15.2 inches if the angle between them is 67°40′.

6. One of the equal sides of an isosceles triangle is 6.73 inches and one of the base angles is 27°10′. Find the base and altitude.

7. A 36-foot ladder is used to reach the top of a 28-foot wall. If the ladder extends 2 feet past the top of the wall, find its inclination to the horizontal.

8. A hemispherical bowl of inside radius 8.00 inches is level and is filled with water to a depth of 2.00 inches. Through what angle may it be tilted before the water spills?

9. A piece of wire 24.78 inches long is bent so as to form an isosceles triangle with one angle 97°26′. Find the length of each side of the triangle formed.

*10. From a point on the ground 152.3 feet away from the foot of a flagpole, the *angle of elevation* of the top of the pole is 31°46′. How high is the flagpole? [*Hint:* When the object observed is above the horizontal plane, the angle between the line of sight from the eye to the object and the horizontal is called the *angle of elevation*. When the object observed is below the horizontal plane, the angle is called the *angle of depression*.]

11. From a lighthouse 75.3 feet above the level of the water, the angle of depression of a boat is 23°40′. How far is the boat from a point at water level directly under the point of observation?

12. Find the height of a balloon directly above a town A if the angle of depression of town B, 6.23 miles from A, is 15°20′.

13. From a lookout tower 80.0 feet high, a man observes from a position 6.5 feet below the top of the tower that the angle of elevation of the top of a certain tree is 12°40′ and that the angle of depression of its base is 72°20′. If the base of the tower and tree are at the same level, what is the height of the tree?

14. From a point 20.75 feet above the surface of the water, the angle of elevation of a building at the edge of the water is 38°16′, while the angle of depression of its image in the water is 56°28′. Find the height of the building and the horizontal distance from the point of observation.

15. From a mountain 1780 feet high, the angle of depression of a point on the nearer shore of a river is 48°40′ and of a point directly across on the opposite side is 22°20′. What is the width of the river between the two points?

16. At a certain point the angle of elevation of a mountain peak is 40°20′. At a point 9560 feet farther away in the same horizontal plane, its angle of elevation is 29°50′. Find the distance of the peak above the horizontal plane.

*17. Lighthouse B is 6.56 miles directly east of lighthouse A. A ship at O observes that A is due north and that the bearing of OB is N 46°10′ E. How far is the ship from A? From B? [*Hint:* The *bearing* of a line in a horizontal plane is the acute angle made by this line with a north-south line. In giving the bearing of a line, the letter N or S is written before the value and E or W follows the value. Thus, in Fig. 15–6, the bearing of OB is read "north 46°10′ east."]

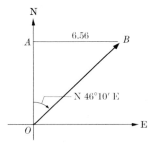

FIGURE 15–6

18. An airplane is 115 miles due east of radio station A; a second radio station is 136 miles due north of A. What are the distance and bearing of the second radio station from the airplane?

19. Because of a certain wind, a boat sails 4728 feet in the direction S 47°29′ W. How far south has it gone? How far west has it gone?

20. Find v_x and v_y for each of the vectors with v and θ given as follows:

(a) $v = 75,\ \theta = 60°$;   (b) $v = 48,\ \theta = 136°$;
(c) $v = 4.72,\ \theta = 217°10′$;   (d) $v = 58.47,\ \theta = 47°18′$.

21. Find the length and direction for each of the vectors if

(a) $v_x = 3,\ v_y = 4$;   (b) $v_x = 23,\ v_y = 45$;
(c) $v_x = -16.2,\ v_y = 28.7$;   (d) $v_x = 382.4,\ v_y = -768.3$.

22. If a force of 658.4 pounds is acting east and another of 316.2 pounds is acting north, what are the magnitude and direction of their resultant?

23. A balloon is rising at the rate of 12 ft/sec and at the same time is being blown horizontally by a wind at 18 ft/sec. Find the angle its path makes with the vertical and determine its actual velocity.

24. A river runs directly east at 1.28 mi/hr. If a swimmer can swim at the rate of 1.75 mi/hr in still water and he starts swimming north directly across the river, in what direction is he actually moving? Where does he hit the opposite bank if the river is one mile wide?

25. In which direction should the swimmer in Problem 24 head in order to reach a point directly across the river?

26. An airplane travels with a speed of 145 mi/hr in calm air. The wind is blowing with a velocity of 23 mi/hr from N 27° E. (a) If the plane is headed in a direction N 63° W, find the magnitude of the speed and the direction of the airplane with reference to the ground. (b) In what direction must the airplane be headed in order to fly in the direction N 63° W, and what would be its actual speed in the air?

27. Find the resultant of the following sets of forces, where f is the magnitude and θ the angle each force makes with the positive x-axis:

(a) $f_1 = 15, \theta_1 = 65°, f_2 = 37, \theta_2 = 142°$;
(b) $f_1 = 6280, \theta_1 = 37°10', f_2 = 2840, \theta_2 = -16°40'$;
(c) $f_1 = 6800, \theta_1 = 210°, f_2 = 7200, \theta_2 = 315°, f_3 = 5600, \theta_3 = 90°$.

[*Note:* Although we could find the resultant as the diagonal of the parallelogram, it is simpler in such problems to work with components. Obtain the sum of the x-components as one force, the sum of the y-components as another, and then find the resultant of these two.]

28. The circle with center at O in Fig. 15–7 is circumscribed about the triangle and OD is drawn perpendicular to BC. What is the relation of $\angle BOD$ to α? Using the right triangle BDO, prove $\sin \alpha = a/2R$. With the necessary additional construction, prove the Law of Sines.

29. In the right triangle ABC, with $\alpha = 30°$, $AB = 2$. D is chosen on AC so that $DC = BC$, and from D a line is drawn perpendicular to AB, meeting AB at K. Show $\angle DBK = 15°$ and, by finding the lengths of the various lines, prove

$$\sin 15° = \frac{\sqrt{6} - \sqrt{2}}{4}.$$

*30. Using Fig. 15–8, where the inscribed circle in triangle ABC has r for its radius, prove the area $K = rs$, where $s = (a + b + c)/2$.

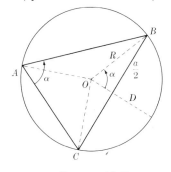

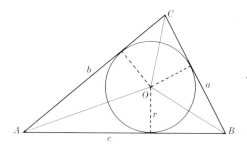

FIGURE 15–7   FIGURE 15–8

15–4 The Law of Cosines. We shall now prove another important relationship, *the Law of Cosines.*

THEOREM 15–2. *In any triangle, with angles α, β, and γ and corresponding opposite sides a, b, and c,*

$$a^2 = b^2 + c^2 - 2bc \cos \alpha. \qquad (15\text{–}6)$$

Proof. Refer to Fig. 15–1, where the angle α of the triangle ABC is in standard position, with the vertex C at $(b, 0)$. If we recall that the coordinates of B are $(c \cos \alpha, c \sin \alpha)$, we have by Eq. (3–9) the distance between $B(c \cos \alpha, c \sin \alpha)$ and $C(b, 0)$:

$$\sqrt{(c \cos \alpha - b)^2 + (c \sin \alpha - 0)^2}.$$

But this length is the length of a, so that

$$a = \sqrt{c^2 \cos^2 \alpha - 2bc \cos \alpha + b^2 + c^2 \sin^2 \alpha},$$

or

$$a^2 = b^2 + c^2 - 2bc \cos \alpha.$$

Similarly, we obtain

$$b^2 = a^2 + c^2 - 2ac \cos \beta, \qquad (15\text{–}7)$$

$$c^2 = a^2 + b^2 - 2ab \cos \gamma. \qquad (15\text{–}8)$$

These three relations make up the Law of Cosines. They hold for all triangles and are used to solve problems of types (2) and (3) in Article 15–1. If $\gamma = 90°$ in (15–8), $c^2 = a^2 + b^2$. For this reason, the Law of Cosines is sometimes called *the generalization of the Pythagorean Theorem.*

15–5 Applications involving oblique triangles. To clarify the use of the Laws of Sines and Cosines, let us consider the following examples.

EXAMPLE 1. Solve the triangle ABC of Fig. 15–9 if $a = 524.7$, $\beta = 46°24'$, and $\gamma = 98°41'$.

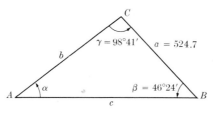

FIGURE 15–9

Solution. First, $\alpha = 180° - (46°24' + 98°41') = 34°55'$. With the value of α known, we can use the Law of Sines to find b and c:

$$b = \frac{a}{\sin \alpha} \sin \beta \qquad\qquad\qquad c = \frac{a}{\sin \alpha} \sin \gamma$$

$\log 524.7 =$	$12.7199 - 10$	$\log \dfrac{a}{\sin \alpha} =$	2.9622
$(-) \log \sin 34°55' =$	$9.7577 - 10$	$(+) \log \sin 98°41' =$	$9.9950 - 10$
$\log \dfrac{a}{\sin \alpha} =$	2.9622	$\log c =$	$12.9572 - 10$
$(+) \log \sin 46°24' =$	$9.8599 - 10$	$c =$	906.2
$\log b =$	$12.8221 - 10$		
$b =$	663.9		

This example illustrates type (1) in Article 15–1.

EXAMPLE 2. Find all triangles for $a = 62.48$, $b = 89.72$, and $\alpha = 32°16'$.

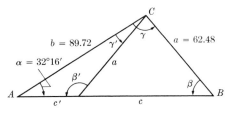

FIGURE 15–10

Solution. The *ambiguous type* of problem (4) is illustrated here. We have the possibility of two solutions, since $\sin(180° - \beta) = \sin \beta$. If we use the Law of Sines and solve for β, we find two values, for each of which there is a corresponding γ and c. Thus we have two distinct solutions, as is suggested in Fig. 15–10.

$$\sin \beta = b \frac{\sin \alpha}{a}$$

$$\log \sin 32°16' = 9.7274 - 10$$
$$(-) \log 62.48 = 1.7958$$
$$\log \frac{\sin \alpha}{a} = 7.9316 - 10$$
$$(+) \log 89.72 = 1.9529$$
$$\log \sin \beta = 9.8845 - 10$$
$$\beta_1 = 50°2' \qquad \text{or} \qquad \beta_2 = 129°58'$$

Thus,

$$\gamma_1 = 180° - (\alpha + \beta_1) \qquad \gamma_2 = 180° - (\alpha + \beta_2)$$
$$= 97°42' \qquad\qquad = 17°46'$$

Then

$$c_1 = \frac{a}{\sin \alpha} \sin \gamma_1 \qquad\qquad c_2 = \frac{a}{\sin \alpha} \sin \gamma_2$$

$$\log \frac{a}{\sin \alpha} = \quad 2.0684 \qquad\qquad \log \frac{a}{\sin \alpha} = \quad 2.0684$$

$$(+) \log \sin 97°42' = \quad 9.9961 - 10 \qquad (+) \log \sin 17°46' = \quad 9.4845 - 10$$

$$\log c_1 = \quad 12.0645 - 10 \qquad\qquad \log c_2 = 11.5529 - 10$$

$$c_1 = 116.0 \qquad\qquad\qquad c_2 = 35.72$$

EXAMPLE 3.   Find the third side of the triangle with $b = 47$, $c = 58$, and $\alpha = 63°$.

Solution. For this problem, type (2) of Article 15–1, we use the Law of Cosines. It should be emphasized that with four-place tables this law produces no more than two significant figures for the third side, since a square root is involved.

$$a^2 = (47)^2 + (58)^2 - 2 \cdot 47 \cdot 58 \cos 63°$$
$$= 2209 + 3364 - 2475.2$$
$$= 3097.8.$$

Thus,

$$a = 56 \text{ (approximately).}$$

The other angles can be found by using the Law of Sines.

It is clear from Example 3 that the Law of Cosines does not lend itself to problems of this type when more than two significant figures are desired. Another law, called the *First Law of Tangents*, can be used in such cases. From the relationship $a/\sin \alpha = b/\sin \beta$, it is not difficult to show that

$$\frac{\sin \alpha - \sin \beta}{\sin \alpha + \sin \beta} = \frac{a - b}{a + b}.$$

If we use this and Problem 25, Article 4–9, we have

$$\boxed{\frac{\tan \frac{1}{2}(\alpha - \beta)}{\tan \frac{1}{2}(\alpha + \beta)} = \frac{a - b}{a + b},} \qquad (15\text{--}9)$$

This equation and the five similar formulas obtained by interchanging and rotating letters constitute the *First Law of Tangents*. (See Problem 7.)

EXAMPLE 4. Solve the triangle with $a = 16.47$, $b = 25.49$, and $c = 33.77$.

Solution. This example of type (3) again requires the use of the Law of Cosines. We find

$$a^2 = 271.26 \qquad 2ab = 839.64$$
$$b^2 = 649.74 \qquad 2ac = 1112.4$$
$$c^2 = 1140.4 \qquad 2bc = 1721.6$$

so that

$$\cos \alpha = \frac{b^2 + c^2 - a^2}{2bc} = 0.8823, \qquad \text{or} \qquad \alpha = 28°5',$$

$$\cos \beta = \frac{a^2 + c^2 - b^2}{2ac} = 0.6850, \qquad \text{or} \qquad \beta = 46°46',$$

$$\cos \gamma = \frac{a^2 + b^2 - c^2}{2ab} = -0.2613, \qquad \text{or} \qquad \beta = 105°9'.$$

The solution is easily checked, since $\alpha + \beta + \gamma = 180°$.

Example 4 could be solved using five-place tables of logarithms, but the process is long because of the form of the Law of Cosines. However, the *Second Law of Tangents* lends itself to large numbers as well as logarithmic computation. By adding 1 to both members of the expression for $\cos \alpha$ in Example 4, dividing each side by 2, and factoring the right side, we get

$$\frac{1 + \cos \alpha}{2} = \frac{(b + c + a)(b + c - a)}{4bc}.$$

Also,

$$\frac{1 - \cos \alpha}{2} = \frac{(a + b - c)(a - b + c)}{4bc}.$$

Now, letting $(a + b + c)/2 = s$ in these expressions, and recalling Eqs. (4–49) and (4–51), we have

$$\sin \frac{\alpha}{2} = \sqrt{\frac{(s - b)(s - c)}{bc}}$$

and

$$\cos \frac{\alpha}{2} = \sqrt{\frac{s(s - a)}{bc}}.$$

If we divide we get

$$\boxed{\tan \frac{\alpha}{2} = \frac{r}{s - a},} \qquad\qquad (15\text{–}10)$$

where

$$r^* = \sqrt{\frac{(s-a)(s-b)(s-c)}{s}}.$$

Formula (15–10) and the analogous formulas

$$\tan\frac{\beta}{2} = \frac{r}{s-b} \quad\text{and}\quad \tan\frac{\gamma}{2} = \frac{r}{s-c}$$

are called the *Second Law of Tangents* and give the angles of any triangle in terms of its three sides. (See Problem 10.)

PROBLEMS

1. Solve the following triangles ABC, given

    (a) $\alpha = 62°40'$, $\beta = 79°20'$, $a = 147$;
    (b) $\beta = 81°43'$, $\gamma = 57°51'$, $c = 47.35$;
    (c) $\alpha = 47°57'$, $\gamma = 118°11'$, $b = 87270$;
    (d) $\beta = 14°36'$, $\gamma = 53°8'$, $b = 8.367$.

2. Find and draw all triangles with $a = 62.48$, $b = 43.17$, and $\alpha = 32°16'$. Compare Example 2. [*Hint:* It is impossible to have two solutions, since $\beta_2 + \alpha > 180°$.]

3. Is there a triangle with $a = 62.48$, $b = 143.4$, and $\alpha = 32°16'$? Compare Example 2, and draw the figure. [*Hint:* Can $\sin\beta$ be greater than one?]

4. In the type of problem where two sides and an angle less than 90° and opposite one of these sides are given, we note various possibilities by comparing Example 2 with Problems 2 and 3. Assuming a, b, and α are given, explain the following with the aid of Fig. 15–11:

$\alpha < 90°$	$\alpha > 90°$
$a < b \sin\alpha$ gives no solution.	$a \le b$ gives no solution.
$a = b \sin\alpha$ gives a special right triangle.	$b < a$ gives one solution.
$b \sin\alpha < a < b$ gives two solutions.	
$a \ge b$ gives one solution.	

5. In each of the following either show that there is no solution or find all solutions:

    (a) $b = 59.4$, $c = 72.3$, $\beta = 38°40'$;
    (b) $a = 49.3$, $c = 8.72$, $\alpha = 45°10'$;
    (c) $a = 14.72$, $b = 25.64$, $\beta = 147°47'$;
    (d) $b = 4.927$, $c = 5.764$, $\gamma = 57°18'$.

---

* With the results of Problem 30, Article 15–3, and Problem 12 of this article, r is found to be the expression for the radius of the inscribed circle of any triangle.

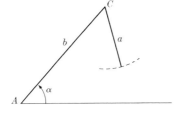
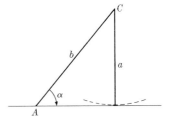

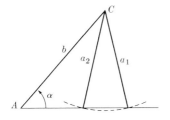
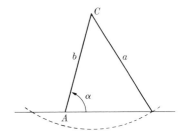

FIGURE 15–11

6. Solve each of the following triangles for the side opposite the given angle:

(a) $a = 4$, $b = 7$, $\gamma = 30°$;

(b) $a = 7.6$, $c = 9.2$, $\beta = 47°$;

(c) $b = 8.3$, $c = 4.4$, $\alpha = 138°$.

*7. Solve the following triangles with

(a) $b = 18.62$, $c = 35.61$, $\alpha = 52°18'$.

[*Hint:* Use the First Law of Tangents with $c - b = 16.99$, $c + b = 54.23$, $\frac{1}{2}(\gamma + \beta) = 63°51'$, and find $\frac{1}{2}(\gamma - \beta)$. Then $\frac{1}{2}(\gamma + \beta) + \frac{1}{2}(\gamma - \beta) = \gamma$, and so on.]

(b) $a = 463$, $b = 628$, $\gamma = 57°40'$.

8. Solve the following triangles with

(a) $a = 356.8$, $c = 551.4$, $\beta = 87°48'$;

(b) $b = 321.0$, $c = 672$, $\alpha = 124°16'$.

9. Solve the following triangles by the Law of Cosines:

(a) $a = 4$, $b = 5$, $c = 6$;

(b) $a = 32$, $b = 56$, $c = 63$.

*10. Solve the following triangles by the most convenient method:

(a) $a = 18.76$, $b = 25.31$, $c = 29.65$.

Hint: If using logarithms and the Second Law of Tangents, arrange your work systematically:

$$2s = 73.72 \qquad \log(s-a) =$$
$$s = 36.86 \qquad \log(s-b) =$$
$$s-a = 18.10 \qquad (+)\log(s-c) =$$
$$s-b = \qquad \log \text{ numerator} = 3.1782$$
$$s-c = \qquad (-)\log s =$$
$$\log r^2 =$$
$$\log r = 0.8058$$

$$\log r = \qquad\qquad \log r = \qquad\qquad \log r =$$
$$(-)\log(s-a) = \qquad (-)\log(s-b) = \qquad (-)\log(s-c) =$$
$$\log \tan \frac{\alpha}{2} = \qquad \log \tan \frac{\beta}{2} = \qquad \log \tan \frac{\gamma}{2} =$$
$$\frac{\alpha}{2} = \qquad\qquad \frac{\beta}{2} = \qquad\qquad \frac{\gamma}{2} =$$

(b) $a = 523,$ $b = 576,$ $c = 615;$
(c) $a = 0.8147,$ $b = 0.6834,$ $c = 0.3449;$
(d) $a = 4.32,$ $b = 5.78,$ $c = 13.44.$

*11. Prove that the area of the triangle in Fig. 15–1 is given by the formula

$$K = \tfrac{1}{2}bc \sin \alpha.$$

Rotation of letters yields

$$K = \tfrac{1}{2}ac \sin \beta = \tfrac{1}{2}ab \sin \gamma.$$

*12. Using the values for $\sin \theta/2$ and $\cos \theta/2$ given in the discussion which follows Example 4 and also the formula $\tfrac{1}{2}\sin \alpha = \sin \alpha/2 \cos \alpha/2$ [Eq. (4–43)], prove

$$K = \sqrt{s(s-a)(s-b)(s-c)}.$$

It is from this expression and the result $K = rs$, Problem 30, Article 15–3, that we establish the value

$$r = \sqrt{\frac{(s-a)(s-b)(s-c)}{s}},$$

where r is the radius of the inscribed circle.

13. Use the results of Problem 11 and the Law of Sines to show that

$$K = \frac{a^2 \sin \beta \sin \gamma}{2 \sin \alpha} = \frac{b^2 \sin \gamma \sin \alpha}{2 \sin \beta} = \frac{c^2 \sin \alpha \sin \beta}{2 \sin \gamma}.$$

14. Find the areas of the triangles in previous problems designated by the instructor.

15. Find the lengths of the sides of a parallelogram if its diagonal, which is 72.83 inches long, makes angles with the sides of 27°52′ and 16°41′, respectively.

16. What angle does the slope of a hill make with the horizontal if a tree 74.3 feet tall, growing on the slope of the hill, is found to subtend an angle of 19°30′ from a point 147 feet from the foot of the tree? (The distance is measured along the slope straight down the hill.)

17. Two airways cross each other at an angle of 49°. At a certain instant, airplane A is 32 miles from the crossing, while B is 76 miles from the crossing. What is the distance between them at this instant? (Two solutions.)

18. Two sides of a parallelogram are 68 and 83 inches and one of the diagonals is 42 inches. Find the angles of the parallelogram.

19. From a point in the same horizontal plane with the base of a building, the angles of elevation of the top and the bottom of a flagpole on top of the building are 64°40′ and 59°50′ respectively. If the building is 112 feet high, how tall is the flagpole?

20. As a train is traveling due north on a certain track, the engineer observes a column of smoke in a direction N 20°20′ E. After traveling 475 feet, he observes the same smoke in a direction S 71°40′ E. How far was the smoke from the first point of observation? From the second? How far was it from the track?

21. A battleship is moving along the shoreline in a direction N 18°40′ E, at a constant rate of 36.5 mi/hr. If a squadron of airplanes traveling 186 mi/hr is due east of the battleship, in what direction should they fly in order to reach the battleship as quickly as possible?

*22. If $\mathbf{R}$ is the resultant of two forces $\mathbf{f}_1$ and $\mathbf{f}_2$, and R, f_1, and f_2 represent their respective magnitudes, explain the formula $R^2 = f_1^2 + f_2^2 + 2f_1f_2 \cos \theta$, where θ is the angle between the two forces. Recall Problem 22, Article 15–3. Find the magnitude and direction of the resultant of two forces: 75 pounds acting due north and 93 pounds acting N 63° W.

23. An airplane travels with a speed of 153 mi/hr in calm air. If the wind is blowing with a velocity of 27 mi/hr from S 21° W and the plane is headed in a direction S 53° E, find the magnitude of the speed of the airplane and its direction with reference to the ground.

24. The resultant of two forces of 61.3 pounds and 34.9 pounds is a force of 73.7 pounds. What angle does the resultant make with each of the two forces?

CHAPTER 16

FURTHER APPLICATIONS OF THE CIRCULAR FUNCTIONS

The second general type of application of circular functions stems from the fact that the solutions of a large number of the problems with which science deals today are periodic in nature. Problems with such solutions are found in astronomy and mechanics, and in dealing with the phenomena of light, sound, and electricity. The analysis of these problems requires, among other things, the frequent use of the circular functions, with special emphasis on certain of their properties and graphs. In this chapter we shall examine these properties and graphs in some detail. In addition, we shall consider certain applications which naturally arise.

16–1 Graphs of the curves $y = a \sin kx$. In drawing the graph of $y = \sin x$ (Fig. 4–7, Article 4–3), we might have plotted directly by assigning arbitrary values of x, computing the corresponding value of y for each x, and finding the points of the coordinates thus obtained. Although such a method can be used for sketching the graph of any circular function, it is seldom used for more general expressions, since it is more convenient to generalize from the simple curves already plotted. Occasionally, a few points are used for checking purposes.

The graphs of the function $y = a \sin kx$ for different values of the constants a and k can be considered the graphs of the general "sine curves" of which $y = \sin x$ is a special case. Since the function $y = \sin x$ is periodic with a period of 2π [recall Eq. (4–5)], its graph has its greatest ordinate, one, when $x = \pi/2 \pm 2n\pi$. Thus the general function $y = a \sin kx$ (assuming $a > 0$ and $k > 0$) is also periodic, and repeats itself each time kx varies over a length of 2π, or x over the length $2\pi/k$. Thus its period is $2\pi/k$, and its graph will have its greatest ordinate when $x = \pi/2k \pm 2n\pi/k$. This greatest ordinate a, or maximum of the function, is called the *amplitude* of the function, and the length of one complete *cycle*, $2\pi/k$, is called its *period*.

To sketch the graph of any sine curve of the type $y = a \sin kx$, mark off from the origin on the positive x-axis a distance equal to one period. As in Fig. 4–7, the two end points and the mid-point of this interval are points on the curve. The graph takes on its greatest value at the x-value midway between the first two points, and its numerically greatest negative value midway between the last two points (see Problems 13 and 14). These points will suffice to sketch the graph with fair accuracy. It will frequently be convenient to have the subdivisions on the two axes of

313

different length. It may also be clearer to express the horizontal units in terms of π.

EXAMPLE. Give the amplitude and period of the function

$$y = 3 \sin (\tfrac{1}{2}\pi x)$$

and sketch its graph.

Solution. The amplitude is 3 and its period is $2\pi/(\pi/2) = 4$. The distance marked off from the origin for one period of this graph is 4; the end points of this distance are $(0, 0)$ and $(4, 0)$ and the mid-point is $(2, 0)$. Since $a = 3$, the points of maximum value and of minimum value are $(1, 3)$ and $(3, -3)$, respectively. With this one period sketched, any number of additional periods can be added to the right or left. The graph of this function appears in Fig. 16–1.

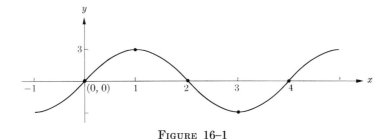

FIGURE 16–1

This discussion has assumed that a and k are positive. If $k < 0$, the relationships between functions of positive and negative values of the angles* can be used to change kx to a positive value when x is positive. Thus, to complete the discussion, we need only consider $y = -a \sin kx$, where a and k are positive. This function has precisely the same graph as $y = a \sin kx$, except that for each value of x those values of y which were positive are now negative, and vice versa. In other words, the graph of $y = -a \sin kx$ might be described as a reflection about the x-axis of $y = a \sin kx$.

The same procedure which is used in plotting $y = a \sin kx$ may be used with slight modification in sketching $y = a \cos kx$. Its curve also has an amplitude of a and a period $2\pi/k$. The cosine curve differs from the corresponding sine curve, however, in that it is shifted to the left a distance equal to one-quarter of its period, since $\sin (x + \pi/2) = \cos x$. Compare Figs. 4–7 and 4–8.

---

* $- \sin x = \sin (-x)$, $\cos x = \cos (-x)$, and so forth.

PROBLEMS

Find the amplitude and period of each of the following and sketch their graphs:

1. $y = 5 \sin 2\pi x$
2. $y = 2 \sin \frac{1}{2}x$
3. $y = 3 \sin \pi x/3$
4. $y = 0.5 \cos 4x$
5. $y = 1.5 \cos \frac{3}{2}x$
6. $y = \sin 6x$
7. $y = 2 \sin (-\frac{1}{4}x)$; how does this compare with $y = 2 \sin (\frac{1}{4}x)$?
8. $y = 2 \cos (-\frac{1}{4}x)$; how does this compare with $y = 2 \cos (\frac{1}{4}x)$?
9. $y = -0.5 \sin 3t$
10. $y = 2 \sin 0.001\pi t$
11. $y = 100 \cos 0.0314t$
12. $y = \sin 0.0025t$

13. Prove that $y = a \sin kx$ has its critical values at $x = (\pi/2k) \pm (2n\pi/k)$ and $x = (3\pi/2k) \pm (2n\pi/k)$, by finding Dy and solving this expression set equal to zero.

14. By finding D^2y, show that at $x = (\pi/2k) \pm (2n\pi/k)$ the function $y = a \sin kx$ has relative maxima, but at $x = (3\pi/2k) \pm (2n\pi/k)$ it has relative minima.

15. By setting D^2y equal to zero, for $y = a \sin kx$, prove that the points of inflection of the curve are at $x = \pm n\pi/k$.

16–2 Graphs of the curves $y = a \sin (kx + b)$. In a discussion of the graphing of the circular functions the more generalized sine function $y = a \sin (kx + b)$ should be considered. We have noticed that $\cos x = \sin (x + \pi/2)$ differs from $\sin x$ merely by a shift to the left a distance $\pi/2$. Similarly, the graph of $y = a \sin (kx + b) = a \sin k(x + b/k)$ differs from $y = a \sin kx$ only in its shift in the horizontal direction a distance b/k. Assuming $k > 0$, this shift, or displacement, is to the right or left according as $b/k < 0$ or $b/k > 0$. We call $|b/k|$ the *phase displacement*, and b the *phase constant* or *phase difference*. The function has the same amplitude a and period $2\pi/k$.

The graph of $y = a \cos (kx + b)$ can be sketched either by considering it a generalization of $y = a \cos kx$ or a "shifted" sine curve.

EXAMPLE 1.   Give the amplitude, period, and phase displacement and sketch the graph of $y = 4 \sin (2x - \pi/3)$.

Solution. This function has an amplitude of 4 and a period of π. Since its phase displacement is $\pi/6$ (why?), its graph goes through the point $(\pi/6, 0)$ and continues to the right, completing one period as it passes through $(7\pi/6, 0)$. The graph is shown in Fig. 16–2.

EXAMPLE 2.   Sketch the graph of $y = 3 \sin x + 4 \cos x$.

Solution. In Example 5, Article 4–9, we showed that

$$3 \sin x + 4 \cos x = 5 \sin (x + \theta_1),$$

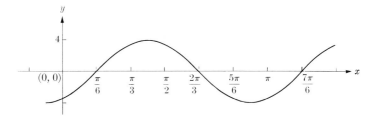

FIGURE 16–2

where $\sin \theta_1 = \frac{4}{5}$ and $\cos \theta_1 = \frac{3}{5}$. Thus, using Table I, $\theta_1 = 0.93$ (approximately), so that we may sketch the graph by considering the expression

$$y = 5 \sin (x + 0.93).$$

Be sure that the location of $(-0.93, 0)$ is consistent with the length of the period $2\pi = 6.28$, as in Fig. 16–3.

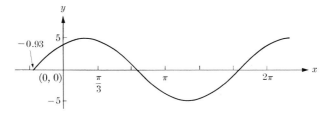

FIGURE 16–3

16–3 Graphing by addition of ordinates. Another very useful method of sketching is known as *composition of ordinates*. In Article 16–6 this method of graphing will be used in connection with certain applications.

EXAMPLE. Sketch the graph of $y = \sin x + \sin 2x$.

Solution. First, sketch on the same axes the graphs of the two separate functions $y = \sin x$ and $y = \sin 2x$. Then the ordinate for any value of x is the sum of the ordinates for that value of x from each of the graphs, $y = \sin x$ and $y = \sin 2x$. This amounts to finding the height of the curve $y = \sin x + \sin 2x$ by adding the heights of the other two curves. Of course, the sign must be taken into account. The period of one of these functions is 2π and the other is π. Thus the period of the function $y = \sin x + \sin 2x$ is 2π. The required graph appears in Fig. 16–4.

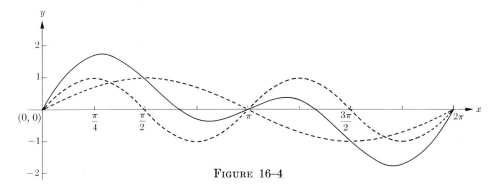

FIGURE 16-4

PROBLEMS

Sketch the graphs of the following functions, giving their amplitudes, periods, and phase displacements:

1. $y = 2 \sin (x - \pi/6)$ 2. $y = 4 \sin (x - 1)$
3. $y = 0.5 \sin (2x + \pi/8)$ 4. $y = 3 \cos (t/2 - 1)$
5. $y = \sin (t + 0.25)$ 6. $y = 2 \sin [(t - 1)/3]$
7. $13y = 5 \sin x + 12 \cos x$ 8. $y = \sin x + \cos x$
9. $y = 15 \sin x + 8 \cos x$ 10. $y = 24 \sin x + 7 \cos x$
11. $y = 2 \sin x - 5 \cos x$ 12. $y = 0.6 \sin 2x + 0.5 \cos 2x$

Sketch the graphs of the following functions by the method of addition of ordinates and give the period of each:

13. $y = \sin x + \cos x$ (Compare this curve with Problem 8.)
14. $y = 2 \sin x + 3 \cos 2x$ 15. $y = 4 \cos x/2 - 3 \sin 2x$
16. $y = 0.26 \sin x + 0.47 \cos 3x$ 17. $y = \sin x + \sin 2x + \sin 3x$

Sketch the graphs of the following functions:

18. $y = 2(\sin x - \frac{1}{2} \sin 2x + \frac{1}{3} \sin 3x)$
19. $y = \sin x + \frac{1}{3} \sin 3x + \frac{1}{5} \sin 5x$ 20. $y = \dfrac{4}{\pi}\left(\sin x - \dfrac{1}{3^2} \sin 3x\right)$

16-4 Use of the derivatives of the circular functions. Many problems in graphing expressions involving the circular functions may be simplified by use of the derivative. Applied maximum and minimum problems as well as problems containing related rates are among those that involve the circular functions. Consider the following examples.

EXAMPLE 1. Find the relative maximum and minimum and the points of inflection of the curve representing the function

$$y = 2 \sin x - \sin^2 x \quad (0 \le x \le 2\pi)$$

and sketch the curve.

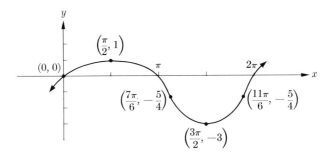

FIGURE 16–5

Solution. Since

$$Dy = 2 \cos x - 2 \sin x \cos x = 2 \cos x\,(1 - \sin x),$$

the critical values are $x = \pi/2$ and $3\pi/2$. Moreover,

$$D^2y = -2 \sin x + 2 \sin^2 x - 2 \cos^2 x = 4 \sin^2 x - 2 \sin x - 2$$
$$= 2(2 \sin x + 1)(\sin x - 1).$$

By Theorem 12–7, the function has a minimum at $x = 3\pi/2$. This theorem, however, does not apply for the critical value $x = \pi/2$. (Why?) By Theorem 12–4 we find that at $x = \pi/2$ the function has a maximum. Solving $D^2y = 0$, we have $x = 7\pi/6$ and $11\pi/6$, and $x = \pi/2$. We have already found that the function has a maximum at $x = \pi/2$, and, by Definition 12–12, there are inflection points at both $7\pi/6$ and $11\pi/6$. The graph of this function appears in Fig. 16–5.

EXAMPLE 2. From a dock 10 feet above the water, a man is pulling a boat along the surface of the water toward the dock by hauling in a rope, tied to the front of the boat, at the rate of 5 ft/sec. If θ represents the angle the rope makes with the surface of the water, find the rate θ is changing when the boat is 24 feet (along the water level) from the foot of the dock.

Solution. From Fig. 16–6, showing the position of the boat, we have

$$\sin \theta = \frac{10}{y}.$$

Differentiating with respect to t (time), we have

$$\cos \theta \cdot \frac{d\theta}{dt} = \frac{-10}{y^2} \frac{dy}{dt},$$

from which we may find $d\theta/dt$ since $dy/dt = -5$ and, when $x = 24$, $y = 26$ and $\cos \theta = \frac{12}{13}$.

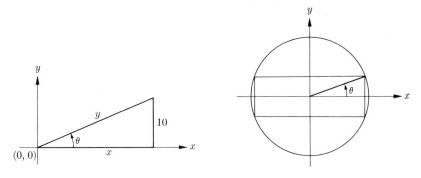

FIGURE 16–6   FIGURE 16–7

Thus,

$$\frac{d\theta}{dt} = \frac{-10}{\cos\theta \cdot y^2}\frac{dy}{dt} = \frac{-10(-5)}{\frac{12}{13}(26)^2} = \frac{25}{312},$$

or θ is increasing approximately 0.08 radians per second.

EXAMPLE 3. Consider all possible rectangles which may be inscribed in a circle of radius a. By using circular functions, find which one of these rectangles has the largest perimeter. (See Fig. 16–7.)

Solution. If θ represents the angle from the positive x-axis to a corner of the rectangle, the length of the horizontal side of the rectangle is $2a\cos\theta$, while the length of the vertical side is $2a\sin\theta$. Thus the perimeter, $4a(\cos\theta + \sin\theta)$, is a function of θ, for which we wish to find a maximum.

$$P(\theta) = 4a(\cos\theta + \sin\theta)$$

and

$$DP(\theta) = 4a(-\sin\theta + \cos\theta).$$

Setting this equal to zero and solving, we find that at the critical value $\theta = \pi/4$ the second derivative of $P(\theta)$ is negative. Hence $P(\theta)$ has a maximum, and this maximum value is

$$P_{\max} = 4a\left(\frac{1}{\sqrt{2}} + \frac{1}{\sqrt{2}}\right) = 4\sqrt{2}a;$$

the rectangle is a square (why?).

PROBLEMS

1. Find equations of the tangent and the normal line to the curve at the indicated point on the curve.

(a) $y = \cos x$ where $x = \pi/3$,   (b) $y = \sin^2 x/\cos x$ where $x = \pi/3$.

2. Find the angle between the curves $y = \sin x$ and $y = \tan x$ at each of their points of intersection in the interval $0 \le x \le \pi$.

3. Prove that the magnitude of the slope of the curve $y = \tan x$ is never less than one.

4. At what points on the curve $y = \sin x$ does the slope equal the value of the function?

5. A line segment of constant length lies in the first quadrant with its ends on the coordinate axes. Find the position where its distance from the origin is as large as possible. [*Hint:* Let θ be the acute angle between the line segment and the x-axis.]

6. A line segment AB is 13 inches long and lies in the first quadrant with A on the x-axis and B on the y-axis. How fast is the acute angle between the line segment and the x-axis changing when A has coordinates $(12, 0)$ and is moving to the right 3 inches per second?

7. A balloon leaving the ground 80 feet from an observer rises 15 feet per second. If no wind is moving the balloon horizontally, how fast is the angle of elevation of the balloon (from the observer) changing after 4 seconds?

8. Find the maximum and minimum values of the function $y = A \sin \omega x + B \cos \omega x$, where A, B, and ω are constants. (Recall Example 5, Article 4–9, and Example 2, Article 16–2. We shall also see a more general use of this in Article 16–6.)

9. Sketch the graph of the functions $y = x + \sin x$, where $0 \leq x \leq 2\pi$, indicating the maximum, minimum, and points of inflection on the curve.

10. Do the same for the function $y = 2 \cos x + \cos^2 x$, where $0 \leq x \leq 2\pi$.

11. By the method of composition of ordinates (Article 16–3), sketch the graph of the function given in Problem 9.

12. Recalling that $\sin^2 x = (1 - \cos 2x)/2$, sketch the graph of the function discussed in Example 1 by the method of composition of ordinates.

13. By making use of angle θ, find the area of the largest rectangle that can be cut from a circular quadrant, as in Fig. 16–8.

14. Two points A and B are located distances a and b from a straight line of length c, as shown in Fig. 16–9. Locate point C on the line so that the distance $AC + CB$ will be a minimum, by first finding the relationship between α and β for each location.

15. A wall 8 feet high is 27 feet from a house. Find the length of the shortest pole that will reach from the ground outside the wall to the side of the house. [*Hint:* Use an angle. (Recall Problem 21, Article 12–2.)]

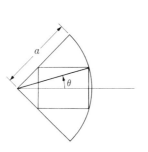

FIGURE 16–8

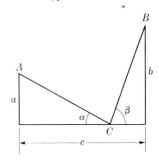

FIGURE 16–9

16. Under ideal conditions the range of a bullet fired across level ground is $R = (v_0^2/2g) \sin 2\alpha$, where v_0 is the initial velocity of the projectile, g is the acceleration due to gravity, and α is the angle of elevation of the gun. Find the value of α for the greatest range.

17. A straight line passes through the point (a, b) and intersects both axes. Show that the minimum length of its segment between its intercepts is $(a^{2/3} + b^{2/3})^{3/2}$. (Recall Problem 22, Article 12–2.)

18. A man who can row 4 ft/sec and can run 8 ft/sec is in a small boat 600 feet from the nearest point on a straight shore. If he wishes to reach a point on the shore 1000 feet from his present position in the shortest possible time (see Fig. 16–10), in which direction should he go?

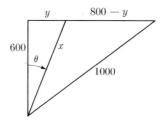

FIGURE 16–10

19. A man walks at the rate of 4 mi/hr and rows at the rate of 2 mi/hr. He wishes to get from a point on the edge of a circular pond to a point directly opposite. He can row to any point and walk along the edge the rest of the way, row straight across, or walk along the edge all the way. How shall he proceed if he is to make the trip in the least time? In the greatest time?

20. A ship leaves a dock at the rate of 8 mi/hr, sails north for two hours, and then turns on a course E 30° S. If a searchlight at the dock tracks the ship, how fast is the light rotating (a) just after the turn, (b) after the ship has traveled 3 hours? [*Hint:* Use the Law of Sines.]

16–5 Simple harmonic motion. The notion of simple harmonic motion is fundamental to any discussion of periodic phenomena. Examples of bodies which move approximately according to the laws of harmonic motion are the bob of a simple pendulum, a floating cork in turbulent water, a particle in a vibrating violin string, a point on the prong of a tuning fork, a particle of air during the passage of a simple sound wave, and a particle of earth during a small earthquake. Actually, any body whose position d on a straight line is given at any instant t by the equation $d = a \sin \omega t$ is said to describe *simple harmonic motion*.

Although the independent variable of the circular functions has been considered the measure of an angle, this is by no means always the case. The circular functions are defined where the domain is any set of real values. In the function $\sin \omega t$, for example, ωt is a real number which might be considered the radian measure of an angle or a measure of any other quantity. In the case of simple harmonic motion it is a measure of time. Hence we need only recall the properties of this circular function to recognize some of the features of simple harmonic motion.

Simple harmonic motion is oscillatory in character, repeating itself in definite intervals of time. Thus it is periodic. The *amplitude* of the motion is the magnitude of the maximum value of $a \sin \omega t$, or a, that is, the magnitude of the displacement from the central point of the motion. The time required for one complete vibration or one cycle is called the *period* $(2\pi/\omega)$. The number of complete periods per unit time, namely $1/(2\pi/\omega)$ or $\omega/2\pi$, is called the *frequency* of the simple harmonic motion. The *phase* at any instant is the fractional part of the period which has elapsed since the body passed through its central position in the positive direction. Actually, the position of the body need not be given from the time when $t = 0$, but may be given from any time t_0. Thus the more general equation may be written $d = a \sin \omega(t - t_0)$. We have learned that this more general equation represents the same curve, except for a shift along the t-axis. This equation also describes simple harmonic motion, for it can be written $d = a \sin \omega t'$, where $t' = t - t_0$. Since $y = a \sin kt$ and $y = a \cos kt$ differ only in phase, $d = a \cos \omega t$ also is used to describe simple harmonic motion.

It is interesting to observe that a graph of a simple harmonic motion can be obtained directly from a demonstration of such motion. Let us consider, for example, the swinging of a simple pendulum from a fixed point and the marking of its trace on a sheet of paper moving at a constant velocity. From Fig. 16–11 it is clear that the displacement of the bob from its central position is a sine function of the time.

One of the most elementary examples of simple harmonic motion is a point moving at uniform speed around the circumference of a circle. Consider the circle with center at O and a radius a in Fig. 16–12. If the point P is thought of as moving with constant or uniform velocity on the circle,

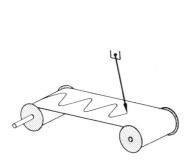

FIGURE 16–11

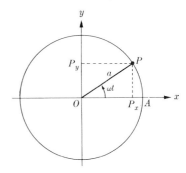

FIGURE 16–12

the question arises as to the type of motion of the point P_x or P_y, that is, the projection of P on the x-axis or the projection of P on the y-axis. Suppose the constant angular velocity of P is ω radians per second,* and the point P starts at A. Then the measure of the angle traveled by P in any time t, expressed in seconds, is ωt; thus P_y moves so that its y-coordinate is given by $y = a \sin \omega t$, and the projection of P on the y-axis describes simple harmonic motion. It is interesting to note that P_y is at the origin when $t = 0$ and, as P_y moves up, its speed decreases until it is 0 at C. The point P_y then moves down, increasing in speed until it attains its maximum as it passes through O, diminishing again in speed until it becomes 0 at C'; it then moves up with increasing speed to its starting point O. Then the whole motion is repeated. Actually, the speed of any body describing simple harmonic motion increases and decreases in the manner described.

PROBLEMS

1. What can be said about the motion of the point P_x in Fig. 16–12? Obtain an expression of its position at any time t.

2. The following equations represent simple harmonic motions. Give their amplitudes, their periods, their frequencies, and sketch their graphs.

(a) $y = 8 \sin 2x$,
(b) $y = 10 \sin (t/3)$,
(c) $y = \frac{1}{4} \sin 3t$,
(d) $y = 7 \cos 5x$,
(e) $y = 4 \sin 2\pi x$,
(f) $y = a \sin \omega t$.

3. A particle moves along a line in such a way that its displacement from a fixed point of the line is given by $d = 2 \sin^2 t$. Can this motion be expressed as simple harmonic motion? What is its period? [*Hint:* Can $\sin^2 \theta$ be expressed in terms of $\cos 2\theta$?]

4. Quantity of electric current is measured in amperes, a unit proportional to the number of electrons which pass a fixed point in a wire during one second. For a simple generator this quantity of current is expressed by

$$I = a_1 \sin \omega t.$$

Give the expression for I if the amplitude is 10 and the current is 60-cycle. Sketch the graph of this expression. The 60-cycle current (i.e. current with a frequency of 60 cycles per second) is the one in most common use at the present time in this country.

5. The flow of electricity is dependent upon the *electromotive force*, measured in volts. The expression for the electromotive force for a simplified generator is given by

$$E = a_2 \sin \omega t.$$

---

* It is left as an exercise to distinguish between angular velocity expressed in radians per second and linear velocity expressed in linear units per second. [*Hint:* Recall $s = r\theta$.]

How can E be expressed in terms of t if the amplitude is 8 and the current is 60-cycle?

6. The amount of power of an electric current to light lamps, generate heat, or operate machinery is dependent on its energy at any time t. This electrical power is usually expressed in kilowatts and is given by the expression $P = EI$. For the 60-cycle current mentioned in Problems 4 and 5, show that P can be written in the form

$$P = a_1 a_2 \sin^2 \omega t.$$

Find the period of this periodic function. Note that P, E, and I, in Problems 4, 5, and 6, are all examples of *simple harmonic behavior*.

7. If a flute is played softly in the middle register, the sound that is produced closely approximates a *simple sound*. A simple sound is defined as one which produces on the oscillograph a wave that may be represented by a simple harmonic curve, that is, by $y = a \sin \omega t$. Give the expression for such a sound and draw the graph of its equation if the given frequency is 400 cycles per second and the amplitude is 0.001 inch.

8. The pressure in a traveling sound wave is given by

$$p = 10 \sin 200\pi \left(t - \frac{x}{1000} \right) \text{ dynes/cm}^2,$$

where t is in seconds and x in centimeters. Sketch p as a function of x at the following definite times: $t = 0, 1/400, 2/400, 3/400,$ and $4/400$ sec.

9. The equation of a traveling transverse wave in a certain chord is given by the expression

$$y = 25 \sin \pi (0.20t - 0.01x),$$

where x is in centimeters and t is in seconds. Graph this equation when $x = 10$, 25, and 100 cm.

16–6 Addition of two general sine functions. In order to observe certain applications of graphing, let us consider the combining of two sine functions.

(1) Any two general sine functions of the same period are represented by

$$y_1 = a \sin (\omega t + \alpha)$$

and   (16–1)

$$y_2 = b \sin (\omega t + \beta).$$

Their amplitudes are a and b, their phase difference is $\beta - \alpha$, and their common period is $2\pi/\omega$. We shall show that the sum of these two functions of the same period is itself a sine function of that period.

$$y = y_1 + y_2 = a \sin (\omega t + \alpha) + b \sin (\omega t + \beta)$$
$$= a (\sin \omega t \cos \alpha + \cos \omega t \sin \alpha) + b (\sin \omega t \cos \beta + \cos \omega t \sin \beta)$$
$$= A \sin \omega t + B \cos \omega t, \qquad\qquad (16-2)$$

where
$$A = a \cos \alpha + b \cos \beta \quad \text{and} \quad B = a \sin \alpha + b \sin \beta.$$

We recall that $A \sin \omega t + B \cos \omega t = r \sin (\omega t + \delta)$, where

$$
\begin{aligned}
r &= \sqrt{A^2 + B^2} \\
&= \sqrt{(a^2 \cos^2 \alpha + 2ab \cos \alpha \cos \beta + b^2 \cos^2 \beta)} \\
&\qquad\qquad + (a^2 \sin^2 \alpha + 2ab \sin \alpha \sin \beta + b^2 \sin^2 \beta) \\
&= \sqrt{a^2 + b^2 + 2ab(\cos \alpha \cos \beta + \sin \alpha \sin \beta)} \\
&= \sqrt{a^2 + b^2 + 2ab \cos (\beta - \alpha)},
\end{aligned}
$$

and where
$$\sin \delta = \frac{B}{r} \quad \text{and} \quad \cos \delta = \frac{A}{r}.$$

Hence, $y = a \sin (\omega t + \alpha) + b \sin (\omega t + \beta) = r \sin (\omega t + \delta)$, where r and δ have the values just found.

We have proved an important theorem:

THEOREM 16–1. *The sum of any two general sine curves of the same period, regardless of their phase and amplitude, is a general sine curve with that same period.*

This result may be generalized to include the sum of any finite number of general sine curves of the same period. It is especially useful in the fields of electricity and sound, as the problems of this article will indicate.

(2) The equations of two general sine functions of *different frequencies*, when they are in phase at $t = 0$, can be given by

$$y_1 = a \sin 2\pi n_1 t$$

and   (16–3)

$$y_2 = a \sin 2\pi n_2 t.$$

The resulting sine function is then obtained by combining these functions, $y = y_1 + y_2$. Thus,

$$y = y_1 + y_2 = a(\sin 2\pi n_1 t + \sin 2\pi n_2 t),$$

and by Eq. (4–54), Article 4–12, with $\alpha + \beta = 2\pi n_1 t$ and $\alpha - \beta = 2\pi n_2 t$,

$$y = 2a \sin 2\pi \frac{n_1 + n_2}{2} t \cos 2\pi \frac{n_1 - n_2}{2} t. \qquad (16\text{–}4)$$

This result does not represent an exact sine function, but it does under certain conditions approximate the sine function. If $n_1 - n_2$ is small compared with n_1 and n_2, the resulting equation may be regarded as a "sine function with a slowly varying amplitude." Let

$$n = \frac{n_1 + n_2}{2}, \qquad \gamma = \frac{n_1 - n_2}{2}.$$

Thus γ is small compared with n and, as a result of this substitution, we have

$$y = 2a \cos 2\pi\gamma t \sin 2\pi nt. \tag{16-5}$$

Since γ is small in comparison with n, $\cos 2\pi\gamma t$ varies very slowly compared with $\sin 2\pi nt$; that is, the number of oscillations of the frequency n is large during the time it takes the cosine to go through one period. Thus the resultant curve becomes a sine curve of slowly varying amplitude. In the case of sound waves, this periodic variation of amplitude is heard as "beats." The number of beats per second is equal to the number of times per second the wave, $y = \sin 2\pi nt$, has a value of 1 and -1. The principle of beating is used in connection with radio, television, wireless waves, telephone, and high-frequency electric current.

EXAMPLE. Sketch the graph of the curve $y = \sin 50\pi t + \sin 60\pi t$.

Solution. By using (16-5), we have

$$y = \sin 50\pi t + \sin 60\pi t$$
$$= 2 \cos 5\pi t \sin 55\pi t.$$

Since $\sin 55\pi t$ always lies between 1 and -1, the curve lies between the two curves $y = \pm 2 \cos 5\pi t$, touching them at the points where $\sin 55\pi t = \pm 1$. Thus it touches when $t = 1/110, 3/110, 5/110$, and so forth. The graph is shown in Fig. 16-13.

It is important to understand that this discussion has been based on two sine functions with the *same* amplitudes. In the case when the amplitudes are not the same, not only is the amplitude of the resultant a varying amplitude, but also the frequency varies. Thus there is no similarity of this behavior to that of a simple sine function.

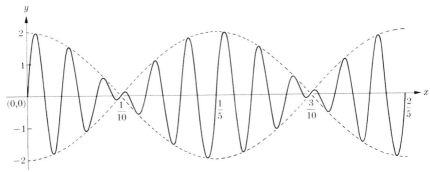

FIGURE 16-13

PROBLEMS

1. Two atmospheric waves give rise to pressure variations at a given point in space according to the equations

$$p_1 = a \sin 2\pi nt$$

and

$$p_2 = a \sin \left(2\pi nt - \frac{2\pi}{3} \right).$$

Calculate the amplitude of the resultant wave at this point in space.

2. Express $y = 4 \sin (\theta + \pi/6) + 5 \sin (\theta - \pi/3)$ in the form

$$y = r \sin (\theta + \delta).$$

3. The electromotive force E (recall Problem 5, Article 16–5) in a circuit is given by $E = 80 + 8.2 \sin \omega t + 4.8 \cos \omega t - 0.8 \sin 3\omega t + 1.2 \cos 3\omega t$. Express E in the form $A_0 + A_1 \sin (\omega t + \alpha_1) + A_2 \sin (3\omega t + \alpha_2)$, finding the values of A_0, A_1, A_2, α_1, and α_2.

4. Sketch the graphs of Problems 2 and 3. The graphs may be completed by the method of Article 16–3 called *composition of ordinates* or the *principle of superposition*.

5. Moving or traveling waves are sometimes reflected from the boundaries of the bodies in which they move and thus introduce waves that travel in the opposite direction. These add to the original waves to produce the resulting wave according to the principle of superposition. Consider a column of air in which the equation of the original wave is given by

$$y_1 = a \sin 2\pi n \left(t - \frac{x}{V} \right)$$

and the equation of the reflected wave is

$$y_2 = a \sin 2\pi n \left(t + \frac{x}{V} \right).$$

The resulting wave is $y = y_1 + y_2$. Prove by using Eq. (4–54), Article 4–12, with $\alpha + \beta = 2\pi n(t - x/V)$ and $\alpha - \beta = 2\pi n(t + x/V)$, that

$$y = 2a \sin 2\pi nt \cos \frac{2\pi nx}{V}.$$

This is the equation for the so-called *standing wave*. It is thus named because at certain positions in the body in which the waves are moving y is always 0; these values for x are the values for which $\cos 2\pi nx/V = 0$, that is,

$$\frac{2\pi nx}{V} = \frac{\pi}{2}, \frac{3\pi}{2}, \frac{5\pi}{2}, \text{ etc.}$$

For what values of x is $y = 0$? It is interesting to note that this resulting wave at any given time t is a simple harmonic expression in x; at any position x, it represents a simple harmonic expression of t. In all musical instruments sound is produced by standing waves.

By making use of the method described in (2) of this article, sketch the graphs of:

6. $y = \sin 200t + \sin 210t$ 7. $y = \sin 80t + \sin 100t$

16–7 Harmonic analysis and synthesis. It can be demonstrated mathematically that any periodic piecewise continuous* curve may be approximated by a finite sum of sine and cosine curves, where the lowest frequency in the sum produces the period of the curve itself, while the remaining terms have frequencies which are integral multiples of the lowest. This extremely useful method of analyzing a curve or function, known as *harmonic analysis*, was first announced by J. B. J. Fourier in 1807 and first published in Paris in 1822. It might be expected that the method was discovered through the study of sound and wave motion but, although the result is extremely useful in such studies, the principle was actually found in the course of Fourier's study of the conduction of heat.

Fourier's Theorem may be stated in mathematical form for the periodic curve y by the approximate equality

$$y \approx a_0 + a_1 \sin \theta + a_2 \sin 2\theta + a_3 \sin 3\theta + \cdots + a_n \sin n\theta$$
$$+ b_1 \cos \theta + b_2 \cos 2\theta + b_3 \cos 3\theta + \cdots + b_n \cos n\theta.$$

In this expression y is the ordinate of the original curve for any particular value x, and θ, expressed in terms of x, is $2\pi x/L$. Thus the use of values of x ranging from 0 to L, where L is the period of the curve, is equivalent to letting θ range from 0 to 2π. With the exception of a_0, which simply denotes the displacement of the entire curve from the original reference axis, each individual sine or cosine curve enters into the composite. In passing, we might mention that there are machines, called *harmonic analyzers*, which can obtain the expressions for all Fourier coefficients of any given curve. That is, from the curve as a drawing, it is possible with such a machine to obtain the equation of the curve.

The converse of the analytic process which we have discussed is also useful. This process, called *harmonic synthesis*, might be described as the combining of several simple curves in order to obtain their resultant or composite curve. In some cases this may be accomplished by calculations. It may always be accomplished, although only approximately, by the

---

* A function is piecewise continuous in a finite interval if that interval can be subdivided into a finite number of intervals in each of which the function is continuous and has finite limits as the variable approaches either end point from the interior.

graphical method of adding the measured ordinates of the individual curves and plotting the results, as suggested in Article 16–3.

Great advances in various fields have been made through the use of harmonic analysis. In the study of musical sound waves the tones of different musical instruments have been recorded, their waves produced on the oscillograph, and the results discussed mathematically by means of harmonic analysis. One of the results of this study was the development of the electric organ. The science of *seismology*, which deals with the phenomena and origins of earthquakes, employs harmonic analysis because of the nature of the earthquake's vibratory motion and resulting wave form. When the vibrations are not large, the motion is essentially a simple harmonic motion; in the more general case, the wave is a composite wave. The waves are recorded by an instrument called the *seismograph*, and from this record the amplitude, direction of motion, and amount of periodicity of each vibration may be computed. Harmonic analysis and synthesis are used in predicting the tides. One of the important functions of the United States Coast and Geodetic Survey is the annual preparation and publication of a tidal calendar. This "Tide Table," issued one to two years in advance, predicts every high and low water at most of the principal seaports of the world. The time of the predicted occurrences is correct to the nearest minute, and the height to the nearest tenth of a foot. These predictions are made mechanically by using the circular functions in connection with the periodic movements of the sun and moon.

CHAPTER 17

COMPLEX NUMBERS

The possibility of extensions or generalizations of the real number system was mentioned in Chapter 1. One of these extensions is the algebra of all ordered pairs of real numbers. We shall briefly discuss this very useful generalization, and then we shall consider one of its most common interpretations in some detail.

17–1 Algebra of ordered pairs. With the set of all ordered pairs of numbers (x, y) as elements, where x and y are real numbers, we can set up an algebra.

DEFINITION 17–1. *Two ordered pairs (x_1, y_1) and (x_2, y_2) are said to be equal* if and only if $x_1 = x_2$ and $y_1 = y_2$.*

Thus, $(x + 2y, 2x - y) = (4, 3)$ if and only if $x + 2y = 4$ and $2x - y = 3$ or, specifically, $x = 2$ and $y = 1$.

We next define the fundamental operations of addition and multiplication, and their inverse operations, subtraction and division.

DEFINITION 17–2. *The sum of two ordered pairs (x_1, y_1) and (x_2, y_2) is the ordered pair $(x_1 + x_2, y_1 + y_2)$ and is written*

$$(x_1, y_1) + (x_2, y_2) = (x_1 + x_2, y_1 + y_2). \qquad (17\text{–}1)$$

As in the case of real numbers, where the solution for x of the equation $a + x = b$, written $b - a$, is called the *difference*, the solution for (x, y) in the equation

$$(x_1, y_1) + (x, y) = (x_2, y_2) \qquad (17\text{–}2)\dagger$$

is called the *difference of the two ordered pairs* (x_2, y_2) and (x_1, y_1). Since (17–2) implies

$$x_1 + x = x_2, \qquad y_1 + y = y_2,$$

or

$$x = x_2 - x_1, \qquad y = y_2 - y_1,$$

the difference (x, y) is written as the ordered pair $(x_2 - x_1, y_2 - y_1)$, or

---

* These definitions of equality, addition, and multiplication are by no means the only possible ones for ordered pairs, but have been chosen specifically for the introduction of the complex number system.

† Equations (17–2) and (17–5) have unique solutions for (x, y).

$$(x_2, y_2) - (x_1, y_1) = (x_2 - x_1, y_2 - y_1). \qquad (17\text{–}3)$$

The definition of multiplication is not so obvious as that of addition.

DEFINITION 17–3.   *The product of two ordered pairs is defined by the equation*

$$(x_1, y_1) \cdot (x_2, y_2) = (x_1 x_2 - y_1 y_2, x_1 y_2 + x_2 y_1). \qquad (17\text{–}4)$$

For example,

$$(2, 1) \cdot (3, 2) = (2 \cdot 3 - 1 \cdot 2, 2 \cdot 2 + 3 \cdot 1) = (4, 7).$$

In the case of real numbers, division is defined in terms of multiplication, and the definition for the quotient of two ordered pairs follows the same pattern. Since the real number $x = a/b$ is defined by the equation $bx = a$, we define the quotient of two ordered pairs (x_1, y_1) and (x_2, y_2) as the ordered pair (x, y), which is the solution of the equation

$$(x_2, y_2) \cdot (x, y) = (x_1, y_1), \qquad (x_2, y_2) \neq (0, 0). \qquad (17\text{–}5)$$

Using (17–4), we get

$$(xx_2 - yy_2, xy_2 + x_2 y) = (x_1, y_1),$$

and therefore

$$x_2 x - y_2 y = x_1, \qquad y_2 x + x_2 y = y_1.$$

Solving for x and y, we find the solution

$$x = \frac{x_1 x_2 + y_1 y_2}{x_2^2 + y_2^2}, \qquad y = \frac{x_2 y_1 - x_1 y_2}{x_2^2 + y_2^2}.$$

Thus the quotient of two ordered pairs may be written

$$\frac{(x_1, y_1)}{(x_2, y_2)} = \left(\frac{x_1 x_2 + y_1 y_2}{x_2^2 + y_2^2}, \frac{x_2 y_1 - x_1 y_2}{x_2^2 + y_2^2} \right). \qquad (17\text{–}6)$$

For example,

$$\frac{(4, 8)}{(3, 1)} = (2, 2).$$

It can easily be verified that the elements of this algebra of ordered pairs satisfy the first five properties stated in Article 1–3.

17–2 Complex numbers. One of the most common interpretations of the algebra of ordered pairs discussed in Article 17–1 is the algebra of complex numbers. The expression $x + yi$, where x and y are real numbers and i has the property that $i^2 = -1$, is called a *complex number.* If $y = 0$, of course the complex number is real; but if $y \neq 0$, the complex number is said to be *imaginary.* With $y \neq 0$ and $x = 0$, $x + yi$ is a *pure imaginary.*

With the numbers x and y obeying the ordinary laws for real numbers, and the new element i obeying the law

$$i^2 = -1,$$

the complex numbers $x + yi$ may be thought of as an abbreviation for the ordered pairs. To show that this is the case, the reader should verify that the complex numbers $x + yi$ satisfy the same laws as the ordered pairs (x, y). Specifically, in considering the sum of two complex numbers, we have

$$(x_1 + y_1 i) + (x_2 + y_2 i) = (x_1 + x_2) + (y_1 + y_2)i. \qquad (17\text{–}7)$$

The product of two complex numbers is given by

$$\begin{aligned}
(x_1 + y_1 i) \cdot (x_2 + y_2 i) &= x_1 x_2 + x_1 y_2 i + x_2 y_1 i + y_1 y_2 i^2 \\
&= (x_1 x_2 - y_1 y_2) + (x_1 y_2 + x_2 y_1)i. \qquad (17\text{–}8)
\end{aligned}$$

We see in this equation the reason for defining the product of two ordered pairs as in (17–4). The quotient of two complex numbers is given by

$$\begin{aligned}
\frac{x_1 + y_1 i}{x_2 + y_2 i} &= \frac{(x_1 + y_1 i)(x_2 - y_2 i)}{(x_2 + y_2 i)(x_2 - y_2 i)} \\
&= \frac{x_1 x_2 - x_1 y_2 i + x_2 y_1 i - y_1 y_2 i^2}{x_2^2 - x_2 y_2 i + x_2 y_2 i - y_2^2 i^2} \\
&= \frac{x_1 x_2 + y_1 y_2}{x_2^2 + y_2^2} + \frac{x_2 y_1 - x_1 y_2}{x_2^2 + y_2^2} i. \qquad (17\text{–}9)
\end{aligned}$$

Thus the ordered pair (x, y) may be regarded as representing the complex number $x + yi$.

Two complex numbers which differ only in the sign of their imaginary parts are called *conjugates* of each other. Thus, $3 + 2i$ and $3 - 2i$ or $5i$ and $-5i$ are conjugate complex numbers or, more generally, $x + yi$ and $x - yi$ are numbers of this type. Note Problems 24 and 25.

It is unfortunate that the word "imaginary" has been applied to the numbers $x + yi$ where $y \neq 0$. Although these numbers were originally introduced to solve quadratic equations, they have been extremely useful in physics and engineering, especially in the description of certain electrical phenomena. Used in these fields, the "imaginary" numbers have significance which is quite as real as that of the "real" numbers.

A few quadratic equations in Chapter 6 and other equations in Chapter 11 have imaginary numbers as solutions. These were given as square roots of negative numbers, with no additional explanation at that time. Graphically, we noticed that the functions involved had real zeros only where the corresponding curves crossed or touched the horizontal axis. We are now able to write such solutions in terms of the imaginary symbol i.

EXAMPLE. Solve the equation $x^2 - 4x + 6 = 0$.

Solution. Using the quadratic formula Eq. (6–6), with $a = 1$, $b = -4$, and $c = 6$, we have

$$x = \frac{-(-4) \pm \sqrt{(-4)^2 - 4(1)(6)}}{2(1)}$$

$$= \frac{4 \pm \sqrt{16 - 24}}{2} = \frac{4 \pm \sqrt{-8}}{2}$$

$$= \frac{4 \pm 2\sqrt{-2}}{2} = 2 \pm \sqrt{2}\, i.$$

PROBLEMS

In the algebra defined for ordered pairs, show that

1. $(x, y) \cdot (0, 0) = (0, 0)$
2. $(x, y) + (0, 0) = (x, y)$
3. $(x, y) \cdot (1, 0) = (x, y)$
4. $(x, y) = (y, x)$ if and only if $x = y$
5. $(0, 1)^2 = (0, 1) \cdot (0, 1) = (-1, 0)$
6. What ordered pair in the algebra of ordered pairs takes the place of zero in our ordinary number system? What ordered pair takes the place of one?

Find the value of (x, y) in Problems 7 through 15.

7. $(x, y) = (2, 3) + (4, 5)$
8. $(x, y) = (-2, 1) + (3, -7)$
9. $(x, y) = (3, -1) - (4, -2)$
10. $(3, 1) = (x, y) + (5, -1)$
11. $(x, y) = (3, 1) \cdot (2, 3)$
12. $(x, y) = (-1, 2) \cdot (3, -5)$
13. $(x, y) = (2, -1)/(-1, 3)$
14. $(x, y) = (23, 11)/(5, -1)$
15. $(x, y) = (-\frac{1}{2}, \sqrt{3}/2)^3$

In Problems 16 through 19, give the expression as a single complex number.

16. (a) $(2 + 5i) + (4 - i)$,   (b) $(2 + 5i) - (4 - i)$.
17. (a) $(2 + 5i)(4 - i)$,   (b) $(2 + 5i)(4 + i)$.
18. (a) $\dfrac{2 + 5i}{4 - i}$,   (b) $\dfrac{2 + 5i}{4 + i}$.
19. (a) $i^3 = i \cdot i^2$, (b) $i^4 = i^2 \cdot i^2$, (c) i^5, (d) $1/i$.

20. Prove, for any positive integer n,

(a) $i^{4n} = 1$,   (b) $i^{4n+1} = i$,   (c) $i^{4n+2} = -1$,

(d) $i^{4n+3} = -i$,   (e) $i^{n+4} = i^n$.

In the following problems, use the ordinary properties of the real numbers, and the fact that $i^2 = -1$.

21. State Problems 7, 11, and 13, interpreting the ordered pairs as complex numbers, and solve.

22. If the complex number $x + yi = 0$, show algebraically that $x = 0$ and $y = 0$. [*Hint:* Since $x = -yi$, $x^2 = -y^2$. What can be said about x and y?]

23. If $x_1 + y_1 i$ and $x_2 + y_2 i$ are two complex numbers such that $x_1 + y_1 i = x_2 + y_2 i$, show by using algebra that $x_1 = x_2$ and $y_1 = y_2$. [*Hint:* Transpose so that $x_1 - x_2 + (y_1 - y_2)i = 0$. Then use Problem 22.]

24. Prove that the sum and product of two conjugate complex numbers are both real.

25. Prove that if the sum and product of two imaginary numbers are real, the numbers are conjugate complex numbers.

17–3 Complex roots of an equation. In the example of the preceding article the roots of the equation were the two conjugate imaginary numbers $2 + \sqrt{2}\,i$ and $2 - \sqrt{2}\,i$. In any polynomial equation with real coefficients, such roots always occur in pairs. This result may be stated as a fundamental theorem.

THEOREM 17–1. *If the complex number $a + bi$, $b \neq 0$, is a root of the polynomial equation*

$$f(x) = a_0 x^n + a_1 x^{n-1} + a_2 x^{n-2} + \cdots + a_{n-1}x + a_n = 0, \quad (17\text{–}10)$$

where $a_0 \neq 0$, n is a positive integer, and a_i are real constants, then its conjugate $a - bi$ is also a root.

Proof. Since $a + bi$ is a root of $f(x) = 0$, $a + bi$ is a factor of $f(x)$. Let us divide $f(x)$ by the product $[x - (a + bi)][x - (a - bi)] \equiv x^2 - 2ax + a^2 + b^2$ until the remainder is of degree less than $x^2 - 2ax + a^2 + b^2$. The remainder will therefore be of the first degree at most. Symbolically, this can be expressed

$$\frac{f(x)}{x^2 - 2ax + a^2 + b^2} \equiv q(x) + \frac{Rx + S}{x^2 - 2ax + a^2 + b^2}, \quad (17\text{–}11)$$

or

$$f(x) \equiv [x^2 - 2ax + a^2 + b^2]q(x) + Rx + S,$$

where R and S are real constants. Since this equality is true for all x, it is true for $x = a + bi$. Thus,

$$f(a + bi) = 0 \cdot q(a + bi) + R(a + bi) + S = 0.$$

Consequently, by the property stated in Problem 22,

$$Ra + S = 0 \quad \text{and} \quad Rbi = 0.$$

Since $b \neq 0$, $R = 0$, and therefore $S = 0$, which shows that the division in (17–11) is exact. Hence $a - bi$ is also a factor of $f(x)$; that is, $a - bi$ is a root of $f(x) = 0$.

As a result of the theorem, we note several properties of the roots of Eq. (17–10).

(1) The imaginary roots of such an equation occur in pairs.

(2) Any such equation has an even number of imaginary roots.

(3) If the degree of such an equation is odd, the equation has at least one real root.

PROBLEMS

Find the third degree equation with integral coefficients having the given numbers as roots.

1. $3, 2 - i$ 2. $-4, 6i$ 3. $\frac{1}{2}, -5 + i$
4. $\frac{3}{2}, i - 4$ 5. $-\frac{1}{3}, 3 + \sqrt{2}\,i$ 6. $\frac{2}{3}, (-3 + \sqrt{5}\,i)/2$

Solve the following equations given the one root in parentheses. [*Hint:* Use division.]

7. $x^3 - 4x^2 + 9x - 36 = 0$, $(3i)$
8. $2x^3 + 9x^2 + 14x + 5 = 0$, $(-2 + i)$
9. $x^3 - 8x^2 + 23x - 22 = 0$, $(3 - \sqrt{2}\,i)$
10. $2x^3 - 8x^2 + 11x - 5 = 0$, $\frac{1}{2}(3 + i)$

17–4 Graphical representation of complex numbers. The interpretation of the ordered pair (x, y) as the complex number $x + yi$ lends itself to a simple graphical representation of the complex numbers. Since (x, y) may be plotted as a point in the rectangular coordinate system, every complex number $x + yi$ may be associated with some point in the plane, and every point in the plane with some complex number. This plane is called the *complex plane*, and the figure on which the complex numbers are plotted is called the *Argand diagram*.* The real numbers lie on the x-axis, the pure imaginaries on the y-axis, and a number such as $5 - 2i$ is represented by the point $(5, -2)$.

Any point $P(x, y)$ in the plane, other than $(0, 0)$, lies on some circle with center at $(0, 0)$ and radius r, where $r = \sqrt{x^2 + y^2}$. Let θ be the angle in standard position having OP as its terminal side (see Fig. 17–1), so that

$$x = r \cos \theta, \quad y = r \sin \theta. \tag{17–12}$$

---

* The system of representing complex numbers graphically was discovered independently by Wessel (Norwegian), Argand (French), and Gauss (German) about 1800.

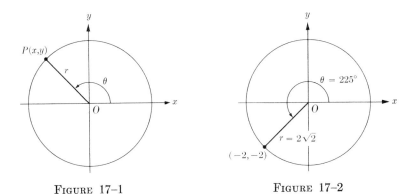

FIGURE 17–1   FIGURE 17–2

Thus the complex number, $x + yi$, may be written in trigonometric form,

$$x + yi = r\,(\cos\theta + i\sin\theta). \qquad (17\text{–}13)*$$

Since $\sin\theta$ and $\cos\theta$ are both periodic with period $2\pi = 360°$, for $r > 0$ and any integer k,

$$r\,[\cos\,(\theta + k\,360°) + i\sin\,(\theta + k\,360°)]$$

is also a trigonometric form for $x + yi$. We note that r must be greater than zero. The value

$$r = \sqrt{x^2 + y^2} \qquad (17\text{–}14)$$

is called the *absolute value* or *modulus* of $x + yi$. The angle θ is called the *amplitude* or *argument* of $x + yi$.

EXAMPLE 1.   Express the complex number $-2 - 2i$ in trigonometric form.

Solution. By locating the point $(-2, -2)$ which corresponds to $-2 - 2i$ (see Fig. 17–2), we have

$$r = \sqrt{(-2)^2 + (-2)^2} = 2\sqrt{2}$$

and $\tan\theta = 1$, with θ terminating in the third quadrant. Thus,

$$\theta = 225°,$$

and

$$-2 - 2i = 2\sqrt{2}\,(\cos 225° + i\sin 225°).$$

---

* The form $r\,(\cos\theta + i\sin\theta)$ is sometimes abbreviated r cis θ.

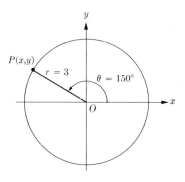

FIGURE 17-3

EXAMPLE 2.   Express the complex number $3 (\cos 150° + i \sin 150°)$ in the form $x + yi$.

Solution. On the terminal side of the angle of 150°, in standard position, locate the point P three units from the origin, as in Fig. 17-3. Since $P(x, y)$ represents the complex number, we have

$$x = 3 \cos 150° = \frac{-3\sqrt{3}}{2}$$

and

$$y = 3 \sin 150° = \tfrac{3}{2}.$$

Hence,

$$3 (\cos 150° + i \sin 150°) = -\frac{3\sqrt{3}}{2} + \frac{3}{2} i.$$

One of the advantages of the trigonometric form for complex numbers is its usefulness in obtaining products. By letting $r_1 (\cos \theta_1 + i \sin \theta_1)$ and $r_2 (\cos \theta_2 + i \sin \theta_2)$ be two complex numbers, we have the following theorem.

THEOREM 17-2.   *The modulus of the product of two complex numbers is the product of the moduli, and the amplitude is the sum of the amplitudes.*

Proof.

$$r_1 (\cos \theta_1 + i \sin \theta_1) \cdot r_2 (\cos \theta_2 + i \sin \theta_2)$$

$$= r_1 r_2 (\cos \theta_1 \cos \theta_2 + i \cos \theta_1 \sin \theta_2 + i \sin \theta_1 \cos \theta_2$$
$$+ i^2 \sin \theta_1 \sin \theta_2)$$

$$= r_1 r_2 [(\cos \theta_1 \cos \theta_2 - \sin \theta_1 \sin \theta_2)$$
$$+ i (\sin \theta_1 \cos \theta_2 + \cos \theta_1 \sin \theta_2)]$$

$$= r_1 r_2 [\cos (\theta_1 + \theta_2) + i \sin (\theta_1 + \theta_2)]. \qquad (17\text{-}15)$$

Problems

1. Locate the point representing graphically each of the following complex numbers. Give the trigonometric form for each, using the least positive or zero value of its amplitude.

(a) 2,

(b) −2,

(c) $3i$,

(d) $-i$,

(e) $2 - 2i$,

(f) $-2 + 2i$,

(g) $-\dfrac{1}{2} + \dfrac{\sqrt{3}}{2}i$,

(h) $-\dfrac{1}{2} - \dfrac{\sqrt{3}}{2}i$.

2. Express each of the following in the form $x + yi$.

(a) $3(\cos 0° + i \sin 0°)$,

(b) $2(\cos 90° + i \sin 90°)$,

(c) $\cos 180° + i \sin 180°$,

(d) $2(\cos 225° + i \sin 225°)$,

(e) $2(\cos 270° + i \sin 270°)$,

(f) $8(\cos 135° + i \sin 135°)$,

(g) $4(\cos 300° + i \sin 300°)$,

(h) $6(\cos 150° + i \sin 150°)$.

3. Perform the indicated multiplications, expressing the final result in the form $x + yi$. Check your result by expressing each of the given numbers in the form $x + yi$ and then performing the multiplication algebraically.

(a) $3(\cos 60° + i \sin 60°) \cdot 2(\cos 30° + i \sin 30°)$,

(b) $4(\cos 120° + i \sin 120°) \cdot 2(\cos 90° + i \sin 90°)$,

(c) $3(\cos 135° + i \sin 135°) \cdot 4[\cos(-45°) + i \sin(-45°)]$,

(d) $[2(\cos 120° + i \sin 120°)]^3$.

*4. Prove that the quotient of the two complex numbers $r_1(\cos \theta_1 + i \sin \theta_1)$ and $r_2(\cos \theta_2 + i \sin \theta_2)$ is given by

$$\frac{r_1}{r_2}[\cos(\theta_1 - \theta_2) + i \sin(\theta_1 - \theta_2)]. \tag{17-16}$$

5. Use (17–16) to perform the following divisions. Check as in Problem 3.

(a) $4(\cos 60° + i \sin 60°) \div 2(\cos 30° + i \sin 30°)$,

(b) $6(\cos 0° + i \sin 0°) \div 3(\cos 240° + i \sin 240°)$.

6. Prove that the reciprocal of $r(\cos \theta + i \sin \theta)$ is

$$\frac{1}{r}(\cos \theta - i \sin \theta).$$

7. Prove that $[r(\cos \theta + i \sin \theta)]^2 = r^2(\cos 2\theta + i \sin 2\theta)$.

8. In considering formula (17–12), we recall a similar formula, (15–5), given in Chapter 15. These are indeed the same, if in the ordered pairs considered in this chapter the x and y are thought of as representing the x- and y-components of a vector from the origin to the point (x, y). The algebra of ordered pairs may be interpreted as a study of vectors in the plane. By plotting the following num-

ber pairs with their sum and drawing
the appropriate vectors, show that the
parallelogram law for the sum of two
vectors is satisfied (see last paragraph
in Article 15–3).

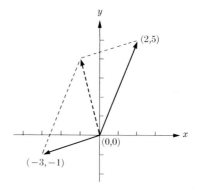

   (a) $(2, 5) + (-3, -1) =$ [*Hint:*
      See Fig. 17–4.]
   (b) $(-1, 2) + (4, -5) =$
   (c) $(3, -2) + (-2, 3) =$
   (d) $(-3, -2) + (6, 4) =$

FIGURE 17–4

17–5 Powers and roots of complex numbers. In Article 17–4,
we obtained an expression for the product of two complex numbers in
trigonometric form. By using (17–15), we immediately have

$$[r \, (\cos \theta + i \sin \theta)]^2 = r^2 \, (\cos 2\theta + i \sin 2\theta),$$

and then,

$$[r \, (\cos \theta + i \sin \theta)]^3 = r^3 \, (\cos 3\theta + i \sin 3\theta).$$

In fact, we can prove by mathematical induction a general theorem
known as De Moivre's Theorem, discovered by Abraham De Moivre
(1667–1754).

THEOREM 17–3. *If n is any positive integer,*

$$[r \, (\cos \theta + i \sin \theta)]^n = r^n \, (\cos n\theta + i \sin n\theta). \qquad (17\text{–}17)$$

This theorem holds for rational, irrational, and even complex values of the
exponent, but we shall make use of it only with integral values.

Proof. Part (a). Verification. This has been done at the beginning of
this article.

   Part (b). Assuming

$$[r \, (\cos \theta + i \sin \theta)]^k = r^k \, (\cos k\theta + i \sin k\theta), \qquad (17\text{–}18)$$

we must show

$$[r \, (\cos \theta + i \sin \theta)]^{k+1} = r^{k+1} \, [\cos \, (k+1)\theta + i \sin \, (k+1)\theta]. \qquad (17\text{–}19)$$

Multiplying each member of (17–18) by $r \, (\cos \theta + i \sin \theta)$, we have

$$[r \, (\cos \theta + i \sin \theta)]^{k+1} = r^k \, (\cos k\theta + i \sin k\theta) r(\cos \theta + i \sin \theta),$$

and by Eq. (17–15),

$$[r \, (\cos \theta + i \sin \theta)]^{k+1} = r^{k+1} \, [\cos (k\theta + \theta) + i \sin (k\theta + \theta)]$$
$$= r^{k+1} \, [\cos (k + 1)\theta + i \sin (k + 1)\theta],$$

which is exactly (17–19).

Part (c) follows immediately.

EXAMPLE 1. Show that $z^3 = 1$ if $z = -\frac{1}{2} + (\sqrt{3}/2)i$.

Solution. Putting z in trigonometric form, we have

$$z = \cos 120° + i \sin 120°.$$

Thus,

$$z^3 = (\cos 120° + i \sin 120°)^3$$
$$= \cos 3(120°) + i \sin 3(120°)$$
$$= \cos 360° + i \sin 360° = 1.$$

A more important use of (17–17) is made in finding the roots of complex numbers. In our discussion we should recall that for r positive the notation $\sqrt[n]{r}$ represents the principal nth root of r, that is, the only nth root of r which is positive and real.

EXAMPLE 2. Find the three cube roots of $-2 - 2\sqrt{3}\, i$.

Solution. We wish to find values of r and θ such that

$$[r \, (\cos \theta + i \sin \theta)]^3 = -2 - 2\sqrt{3}\, i.$$

If we use Theorem 17–3, and express $-2 - 2\sqrt{3}\, i$ in trigonometric form, this becomes

$$r^3 \, (\cos 3\theta + i \sin 3\theta) = 4 \, (\cos 240° + i \sin 240°).$$

When two complex numbers are equal, their moduli are equal and their amplitudes are either equal or differ by integral multiples of 360°. Thus,

$$r^3 = 4 \quad \text{and} \quad 3\theta = 240° + k \, 360°,$$

or

$$r = \sqrt[3]{4} \quad \text{and} \quad \theta = 80° + k \, 120°,$$

where k is any positive or negative integer, or zero. Hence

$$r \, (\cos \theta + i \sin \theta)$$

will be

$$\sqrt[3]{4} \, (\cos \ 80° + i \sin \ 80°), \quad \text{for} \quad k = 0,$$
$$\sqrt[3]{4} \, (\cos 200° + i \sin 200°), \quad \text{for} \quad k = 1,$$
$$\sqrt[3]{4} \, (\cos 320° + i \sin 320°), \quad \text{for} \quad k = 2.$$

These three values are all distinct, and they represent the three different cube roots of $-2 - 2\sqrt{3}\, i$. For any other integral value of k, the expression will reduce to one of these three values, so that these three numbers are the only cube roots. A complex number has three and only three cube roots, four and only four fourth roots, and in general, n and only n nth roots. Should it be required to reduce our answers to the form $x + yi$, we can use tables to find $\sqrt[3]{4}$ and the values of the functions of $80°, 200°,$ and $320°$.

The general theorem concerning such roots should now be apparent.

Theorem 17–4. *For any complex number* $r (\cos \theta + i \sin \theta)$ *and any positive integer* n,

$$\sqrt[n]{r}\, (\cos \theta_k + i \sin \theta_k), \qquad\qquad (17\text{–}20)$$

where

$$\theta_k = \frac{\theta + k\, 360°}{n}, \qquad k = 0, 1, 2, \ldots (n - 1),$$

represents the n *distinct* nth *roots of* $r (\cos \theta + i \sin \theta)$.

Proof. To show that (17–20) is an nth root of $r (\cos \theta + i \sin \theta)$ for each k, we merely use (17–17) to raise it to the nth power:

$$[\sqrt[n]{r}\, (\cos \theta_k + i \sin \theta_k)]^n = r (\cos n\theta_k + i \sin n\theta_k)$$
$$= r [\cos (\theta + k\, 360°) + i \sin (\theta + k\, 360°)]$$
$$= r (\cos \theta + i \sin \theta).$$

Also we must note that the n complex numbers given by (17–20) for the n different values of k are distinct, since no two of their amplitudes differ by a multiple of $360°$.

The use of formula (17–20) will enable us to find the n nth roots of any complex number directly by substitution.

Problems

Write each of the expressions in Problems 1–7 in the form $x + yi$.

1. $[2 (\cos 15° + i \sin 15°)]^6$

2. $[3 (\cos 120° + i \sin 120°)]^5$

3. $[2 (\cos 315° + i \sin 315°)]^3$

4. $(\cos 36° + i \sin 36°)^{10}$

5. $\left(-\dfrac{\sqrt{3}}{2} + \dfrac{i}{2}\right)^5$

6. $(1 - i)^8$

7. $\left(\dfrac{1}{\sqrt{2}} + \dfrac{i}{\sqrt{2}}\right)^{200}$

Find and represent graphically the required roots in Problems 8–15.

8. The square roots of $4 + 4\sqrt{3}\, i$

9. The square roots of $-16i$

10. The cube roots of 1

11. The cube roots of -8

12. The fourth roots of $4 - 4\sqrt{3}\,i$

13. The fourth roots of 16 $(\cos 120° + i \sin 120°)$

14. The cube roots of 8 $(\cos 300° + i \sin 300°)$

15. The tenth roots of 1. Compare the figure with Fig. 4–14.

Solve the equations in Problems 16–19, expressing the roots in the form $x + yi$, and represent them graphically.

16. $z^6 = 64$ 17. $z^4 = 1$

18. $z^3 + i = 0$ 19. $z^5 + 32 = 0$

CHAPTER 18

CONIC SECTIONS

18–1 General discussion. In many of the preceding articles we have considered the graphs of various curves. In Article 12–3 we discussed general methods that apply to all curves. In this chapter we shall consider in some detail four important special curves which occur so frequently in science that they deserve special mention. Each will be described geometrically, and it will then be shown that each is a graph of some quadratic equation in x and y; that is, each may be represented as a special case of the general equation

$$Ax^2 + Bxy + Cy^2 + Dx + Ey + F = 0, \qquad (18\text{–}1)$$

where A, B, and C are not all zero.

These four curves, the circle, parabola, ellipse, and hyperbola, are called *conic sections* (or simply *conics*) because they can be described as the curve of intersection of a plane and a right circular cone. In fact, this was the method first used in studying these curves and in establishing many of their properties.

18–2 The circle. The circle is the simplest of the conic sections. Geometrically (Fig. 18–1), it is the intersection of a right circular cone and a plane perpendicular to the axis of the cone.

We recall from Article 3–4 the definition of a circle:

DEFINITION 18–1. *A circle is the locus of all points in the plane which are at a constant distance from a fixed point.*

From this definition we obtained, by using Eq. (3–4), the general equation of a circle with center (h, k) and radius r [recall Eq. (3–4)],

$$(x - h)^2 + (y - k)^2 = r^2. \qquad (18\text{–}2)$$

It would be helpful to recall the discussion and problems in Article 3–5.

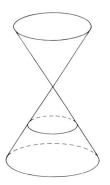

FIGURE 18–1

343

EXAMPLE 1. Identify and sketch the curve represented by the equation $x^2 + y^2 + 6x - 4y = 12$.

Solution. We merely write this equation in the form of (18–2) by completing the square. (Recall Article 6–1.) We have

$$x^2 + y^2 + 6x - 4y = 12,$$
$$(x^2 + 6x + \quad) + (y^2 - 4y + \quad) = 12.$$

By adding 9 and 4 to both members of the equation, we get

$$(x^2 + 6x + 9) + (y^2 - 4y + 4) = 12 + 9 + 4,$$

or

$$(x + 3)^2 + (y - 2)^2 = 5^2.$$

The equation is now in the form of Eq. (18–2), with $h = -3$, $k = 2$, and $r = 5$, so that it represents a circle with center at $(-3, 2)$ and radius 5. Its graph is shown in Fig. 18–2.

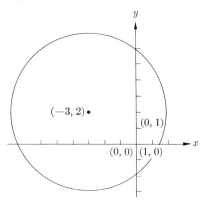

FIGURE 18–2

This example indicates the use of two fundamental circle theorems and their methods of proof.

THEOREM 18–1. *An equation of any circle may be written*

$$\boxed{x^2 + y^2 + Dx + Ey + F = 0.} \qquad (18\text{–}3)$$

Proof. If Eq. (18–2), which represents any circle, is expanded to

$$x^2 - 2hx + h^2 + y^2 - 2ky + k^2 = r^2$$

or

$$x^2 - 2hx + y^2 - 2ky = r^2 - h^2 - k^2,$$

by letting $-2h = D$, $-2k = E$, and $h^2 + k^2 - r^2 = F$, we have the desired result.

THEOREM 18–2. *Conversely, if Eq. (18–3) is satisfied by more than one point, it is an equation of a circle.*

Proof. As in Example 1, we can complete the squares and put this equation in the form of Eq. (18–2).

$$x^2 + Dx + \frac{D^2}{4} + y^2 + Ey + \frac{E^2}{4} = \frac{D^2}{4} + \frac{E^2}{4} - F,$$

or

$$\left(x + \frac{D}{2}\right)^2 + \left(y + \frac{E}{4}\right)^2 = \frac{D^2 + E^2 - 4F}{4}.$$

If $D^2 + E^2 - 4F < 0$, the coordinates of no point will satisfy this equation. (Why?) If $D^2 + E^2 - 4F = 0$, only the point $(-D/2, -E/2)$ will satisfy the equation. (This is sometimes called a *point circle.*) If, however, $D^2 + E^2 - 4F > 0$, we have the equation of a circle whose center is $(-D/2, -E/2)$ and whose radius is $\frac{1}{2}\sqrt{D^2 + E^2 - 4F}$.

With this result, we may think of either Eq. (18–2) or (18–3) as representing any circle. The three independent constants h, k, and r, or D, E, and F, represent implicitly the fact that a circle is determined by three independent conditions, a familiar fact to students of plane geometry. This will be emphasized in the following examples as well as in the problems.

EXAMPLE 2. Find an equation of the circle which passes through the three points $(7, -5)$, $(-1, 1)$, and $(0, -6)$.

Solution (1). Let us consider Eq. (18–3) as the solution to this example. Since the coordinates of any point which lies on a curve satisfy the equation of that curve, we must have the following three conditions satisfied:

$$49 + 25 + 7D - 5E + F = 0,$$
$$1 + 1 - D + E + F = 0,$$
$$36 - 6E + F = 0.$$

Solving this system of equations, we find $D = -6$, $E = 4$, and $F = -12$, so that an equation of the required circle is

$$x^2 - 6x + y^2 + 4y - 12 = 0.$$

Recall Problem 15, Article 5–7.

Solution (2). Observing Fig. (18–3), we know that the center of the required circle lies on the perpendicular bisector of P_1P_3 and also of P_2P_3.

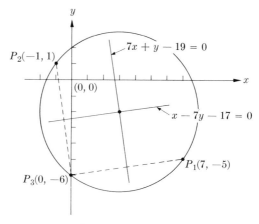

FIGURE 18-3

An equation of the perpendicular bisector of P_1P_3 is $7x + y - 19 = 0$, and of P_2P_3 is $x - 7y - 17 = 0$. Since the center (h, k) lies on both these lines, it lies at their point of intersection; hence $(h, k) = (3, -2)$. The radius r is the distance between $(3, -2)$ and any one of the three given points, that is, 5. Thus, using Eq. (18-2), we have the result

$$(x - 3)^2 + (y + 2)^2 = 25.$$

It is easily seen that the two results are the same (why?).

Many problems of this general type are solved by finding two independent conditions that the coordinates of the center must satisfy, that is, two lines on which the center must lie. The solution of these two equations determines the center. Having found the center and the radius, we can use Eq. (18-2) to obtain the required equation of the circle.

PROBLEMS

1. Find equations of the circles whose centers and radii are given:

(a) center $(2, 3)$, radius 1;   (b) center $(-6, 4)$, radius 6;
(c) center $(-\frac{2}{3}, \frac{3}{2})$, radius $\frac{1}{4}$;   (d) center $(2\sqrt{3}, -\sqrt{2})$, radius $\sqrt{5}$.

2. Determine whether the equation represents a circle, a point, or no locus. In the case of a circle, give the coordinates of the center and the radius and sketch.

(a) $x^2 + y^2 + 4x - 6y + 9 = 0$,
(b) $x^2 + y^2 - 6x + 8y + 24 = 0$,
(c) $x^2 + y^2 + 8x - 14y + 65 = 0$,
(d) $x^2 + y^2 - 3x + 7y - 14 = 0$,
(e) $2x^2 + 2y^2 - 8x + 12y - 31 = 0$,
(f) $36x^2 + 36y^2 - 48x - 36y + 16 = 0$.

In each of Problems 3–16 find equations of all circles satisfying the given conditions.

3. Center at the origin, passing through the point $(4, -5)$.

4. Center at $(-3, 2)$, passing through the point $(1, -4)$.

5. One of its diameters joins the points $(6, -8)$ and $(-2, 4)$.

6. One of its diameters joins the points $(3, 1)$ and $(-5, 7)$.

7. Center $(3, 2)$ and tangent to the line $x - 3y + 4 = 0$. [*Hint:* Recall Eq. (5–17).]

8. Center $(-4, 1)$ and tangent to the line $2x + 3y - 7 = 0$.

9. Passing through the points $(5, 1)$, $(3, 3)$, and $(-1, -5)$.

10. Passing through the points $(5, 3)$, $(7, 1)$, and $(8, 2)$.

11. Passing through the points $(4, 9)$, $(5, 8)$, and $(-3, 2)$.

12. Passing through the points $(6, -6)$, $(-1, -5)$, and $(7, -5)$.

13. Passing through the point $(-2, 4)$ and tangent to the line $x - 2y = 2$ at the point $(6, 2)$.

14. Passing through the point $(3, -1)$ and tangent to the line $3x + 2y = 5$ at the point $(1, 1)$.

15. Passing through the points $(5, -3)$ and $(1, 3)$, with center on

$$x - 2y - 2 = 0.$$

16. Passing through the points $(2, 4)$ and $(1, -3)$, with center on $x + 2y = 0$.

17. Find the coordinates of the points of intersection of the circle $x^2 + y^2 - 4x + 6y - 12 = 0$ and the line $2x - y + 3 = 0$. (Recall Problem 11, Article 6–7.)

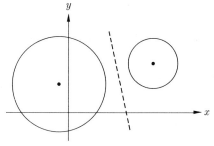

FIGURE 18–4

18. Find the coordinates of the points of intersection of the circle $x^2 + y^2 - 3x + y - 4 = 0$ and the line $2x + 3y + 5 = 0$.

19. If, as in Fig. 18–4,

$$x^2 + y^2 + D_1x + E_1y + F_1 = 0$$

and

$$x^2 + y^2 + D_2x + E_2y + F_2 = 0$$

represent two nonconcentric circles, show that (a) $D_1 = D_2$ and $E_1 = E_2$ cannot both be possible; (b) if each member of the second equation is subtracted from the first equation, the resulting equation is a linear equation. The straight line represented by this equation is called the *radical axis of the two circles*. Find the radical axis of these two circles.

20. Prove that the radical axis of two circles is perpendicular to the line joining their centers. Choose the coordinate axes and the equations of the circles so as to make the work general and yet as simple as possible.

21. Find the radical axis of the circles $x^2 + y^2 - 4y = 0$ and $x^2 + y^2 - 6x + 8y + 24 = 0$. Does this radical axis pass through $(6, 1)$?

22. If the centers of three nonconcentric circles lie on a straight line, what can be said about the three radical axes of these circles, taken in pairs?

23. If their centers do not lie on a straight line, prove that the radical axes of three circles, taken in pairs, meet in a point. This point is called the *radical center*. Recall Problem 21, Article 7–1.

24. Find the radical center of the three circles

$$x^2 + y^2 - 4x = 0, \qquad x^2 + y^2 - 2y = 0, \qquad x^2 + y^2 + 8x + 2y - 32 = 0.$$

25. If the two circles in Problem 19 actually intersect, state why the corresponding radical axis must pass through the points of intersection of the two circles. This radical axis is then called the *line of their common chord*. The *common chord* is the line segment between the two points of intersection. See Fig. 18–5.

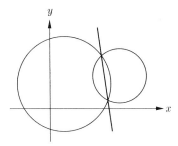

FIGURE 18–5

26. Find an equation of the common chord of the following circles and thus find the coordinates of their points of intersection. Then find the length of this common chord.

$$x^2 + y^2 - 2x - 4y = 20 \qquad \text{and} \qquad x^2 + y^2 + 2x = 52.$$

Find equations of all circles satisfying the given conditions in Problems 27–31. [*Hint:* Find two independent conditions which the coordinates of the center must satisfy.]

27. Passing through the points $(2, -2)$ and $(3, 5)$ and having 5 for its radius.

28. Passing through the points $(-1, -3)$ and $(3, 5)$, and tangent to the line $2x + y - 13 = 0$. [*Hint:* The center of the required circle is equidistant from each of these points and the given line.]

29. Passing through the point $(6, 0)$ and tangent to the lines $4x - 3y - 12 = 0$ and $3x - 4y - 12 = 0$.

30. Passing through the point $(4, 1)$, tangent to the line $x - y + 7 = 0$, and having a radius $\sqrt{32}$.

31. Passing through the point $(1, 2)$, tangent to the line $x - 2y - 2 = 0$, and having a radius $\sqrt{5}$.

32. Find an equation of the tangent to each of the following circles at the point indicated on the circle (recall Article 10–4):

(a) $x^2 + y^2 = 10$ at $(1, 3)$,

(b) $x^2 + y^2 - x + 7y + 6 = 0$ at $(3, -3)$,

(c) $x^2 + y^2 + 2x = 0$ at $(0, 0)$,

(d) $(x - 2)^2 + (y + 3)^2 = 25$ at $(-1, 1)$.

33. Find equations of the tangents to the circles

$$x^2 + y^2 - 3x + y = 0, \qquad x^2 + y^2 + 4x - 2y = 0$$

at one of their points of intersection and the angle of intersection of the circles at that point. Recall Problem 14, Article 10–4.

34. Prove that the circles

$$x^2 + y^2 - 4x + 2y - 4 = 0, \qquad x^2 + y^2 - 2x - 10y + 10 = 0$$

intersect at right angles.

35. Find equations of the tangents to the circle $x^2 + y^2 = 13$ through the point $(1, 5)$, as shown in Fig. 18–6. [*Hint:* Find the slope at any point (x_0, y_0), on the circle. Then find (x_0, y_0), since the line through (x_0, y_0) and $(1, 5)$ is tangent to the circle and has this slope, and since (x_0, y_0) lies on the circle.]

36. Find equations of the tangents to the circle $x^2 + y^2 + 4x - 4y - 2 = 0$ through the point $(2, 4)$.

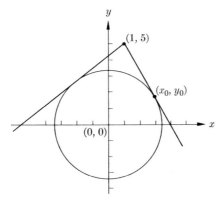

FIGURE 18–6

18–3 The parabola. As was mentioned in Article 18–1, each of the conic sections can be described geometrically as the intersection of a plane and a right circular cone. This intersection (see Fig. 18–7) is a parabola

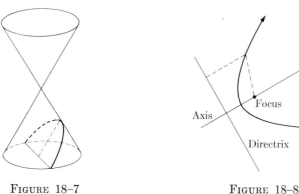

FIGURE 18–7   FIGURE 18–8

when the plane is parallel to a generator of the cone. However, as in the case of the circle, we shall define the parabola as a locus of points.

DEFINITION 18–2. *A parabola is the locus of all points in the plane which are equidistant from a fixed line and a fixed point not on the line.*

The fixed line is called the *directrix*, while the fixed point is called the *focus* (Fig. 18–8). The line through the focus and perpendicular to the directrix is called the *axis of the parabola*, since the locus is clearly symmetric with respect to this line. The point on the axis midway between the directrix and the focus is the *vertex* of the curve.

To obtain an equation for this locus, and to make the work and also the result as simple as possible, let us choose the x-axis as the axis of the parabola and its vertex at the origin. Letting the distance between the vertex and focus be p, we may choose the focus F on the positive x-axis, with coordinates $(p, 0)$. Then the directrix will have $x = -p$ for its equation. By definition, any point $P(x, y)$ which lies on the curve of the parabola must be equidistant from the line $x = -p$ and the point $(p, 0)$ (Fig. 18–9). Therefore, recalling Eq. (5–17), we have

$$|x + p| = \sqrt{(x - p)^2 + (y - 0)^2}.$$

If we square both members and simplify, this equation becomes

$$y^2 = 4px. \tag{18–4}$$

Since the above algebraic steps may be reversed, any point whose coordinates satisfy Eq. (18–4) is a point satisfying the original definition. Thus Eq. (18–4) is an equation of a parabola with focus at $(p, 0)$ and directrix $x = -p$.

In Eq. (18–4), since $y^2 \geq 0$, $4px \geq 0$, so that if $p > 0$ the curve lies to the right of the y-axis. If $p < 0$, x must be negative, and the curve will lie to the left of the y-axis. The chord through the focus, perpendicular

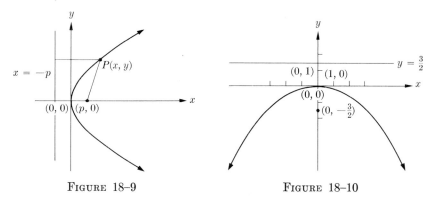

FIGURE 18–9   FIGURE 18–10

to the axis of the parabola, is called the *latus rectum* of the parabola. Since the ends of this chord are on the curve, and therefore are equidistant from the focus and directrix, the length of the latus rectum is $|4p|$. A rough sketch of any parabola in this form can be shown by using these two points together with the vertex, although other points should be located if a more accurate figure is required.

If, in deriving Eq. (18–4), the axis of the parabola had been chosen as the y-axis, the point $(0, p)$ as the focus, and thus $y = -p$, as the directrix, the corresponding equation would be

$$x^2 = 4py. \qquad (18\text{–}5)$$

The parabola whose equation is given by Eq. (18–5) would lie above the x-axis if $p > 0$, but below if $p < 0$.

EXAMPLE. Find the focus, directrix, and the length of the latus rectum of the parabola $x^2 = -6y$ and sketch.

Solution. Since this equation is in the form of Eq. (18–5) with $p = -\frac{3}{2}$, its axis is the y-axis, and it "opens down." Its focus has coordinates $(0, -\frac{3}{2})$; the directrix is $y = \frac{3}{2}$ and the length of the latus rectum is 6. The graph of the curve appears in Fig. 18–10.

It should be emphasized that the parabolas discussed in this article have one of the coordinate axes as their axis, and the origin as their vertex. In general, parabolas can have much more complicated equations, as will be seen in Articles 18–8 and 18–9.

PROBLEMS

Find the focus, directrix, length of the latus rectum, and sketch the graph of the parabolas in Problems 1–6.

1. $y^2 = 8x$ 2. $x^2 = 9y$ 3. $x^2 = -y$
4. $y^2 = -24x$ 5. $2x^2 + 3y = 0$ 6. $3y^2 + 7x = 0$

Find equations of the parabolas described in Problems 7–12.

7. Focus, $(2, 0)$; directrix, $x = -2$.
8. Focus, $(0, -3)$; directrix, $y = 3$.
9. Vertex, $(0, 0)$; focus, $\left(-\frac{3}{2}, 0\right)$.
10. Vertex $(0, 0)$; length of latus rectum 7; focus on the negative y-axis.
11. Vertex $(0, 0)$; focus on the x-axis; passing through $(2, 3)$.
12. Vertex $(0, 0)$; focus on the y-axis; passing through $(-3, 4)$.

Find equations of the parabolas described in Problems 13–16, using the original definition.

13. Focus $(1, 1)$; directrix $x + y + 2 = 0$.
14. Focus $(0, 0)$; directrix $x + y - 2 = 0$.
15. Focus $(3, 4)$; directrix $x = 2$.
16. Focus $(2, -3)$; directrix $y = -5$.

17. Using Definition 18–2, demonstrate that the equation $(y - k)^2 = 4p(x - h)$ represents the parabola whose vertex is at (h, k) and whose focus is p units to the right of (h, k). This equation will be discussed further in Article 18–8.

18. What would the conditions on the coefficients of Eq. (18–1) be if Eq. (18–1) represented the parabola in Problem 17?

19. The line segment between the focus F and any point P on the parabola is called a *focal radius*. Prove that for any point $P(x_0, y_0)$ on the parabola $y^2 = 4px$, the length of the focal radius is $|x_0 + p|$.

20. Find the locus of the center of a circle which is tangent to the line $y = -3$ and the circle $x^2 + y^2 = 4$.

21. Find the locus of the center of a circle which is tangent to the line $x = 2$ and the circle $x^2 + y^2 = 16$.

22. Find equations of the tangent and normal lines to the parabola $x^2 + 8y = 0$ at $(-4, -2)$, a point on the parabola.

23. Find equations of the tangents to the parabola $y^2 - 6x = 10$ through the external point $(5, 7)$. Draw the figure.

Problems 24–26 represent certain properties that are important in the use of the parabola.

24. Prove that the circle drawn with a focal radius of the parabola $y^2 = 4px$ as its diameter is tangent to the y-axis.

25. If PQ represents a chord of the parabola $y^2 = 4px$ passing through the focus, prove that the circle drawn with PQ as diameter is tangent to the directrix.

26. If any line is drawn tangent to the parabola $y^2 = 4px$ at $P(x_0, y_0)$, a point on the curve, prove that the angle between this tangent and the focal radius of the point $P(x_0, y_0)$ is equal to the angle between this tangent and the line through P, parallel to the x-axis. See Fig. 18–11.

18–4 The ellipse. Geometrically, the ellipse can also be described as the intersection of a plane and a right circular cone. If the plane is inclined, but not parallel to a generator, so that it intersects only one nappe (section) of the cone, this intersection is an ellipse (see Fig. 18–12).

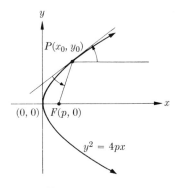

FIGURE 18–11   FIGURE 18–12

We again prefer to make use of a definition in terms of a locus of points:

DEFINITION 18–3. *An ellipse is the locus of all points in the plane such that the sum of its distances from two fixed points is a constant.*

The two fixed points, usually denoted by F and F', are called the *foci* of the ellipse. The mid-point of the line segment FF' is called the *center* of the ellipse. If the length of this line segment is denoted by $2c$, and the sum of the distances (or constant mentioned in the definition) by $2a$, we have $2a > 2c$ or $a > c$. (Why?)

As in the case of the parabola, we wish to choose the coordinate axes so as to obtain an equation for the general ellipse in as simple a form as possible. If we take the center as the origin and the points $F(c, 0)$ and $F'(-c, 0)$ on the x-axis (Fig. 18–13), the definition requires that the coordinates of the point $P(x, y)$ satisfy the condition

$$|F'P| + |FP| = 2a,$$

or

$$\sqrt{(x + c)^2 + (y - 0)^2} + \sqrt{(x - c)^2 + (y - 0)^2} = 2a. \quad (18\text{–}6)$$

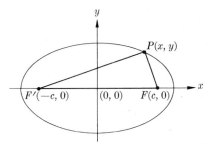

FIGURE 18–13

If we transpose the first radical to the right side of the equation and square each member, we have

$$x^2 - 2cx + c^2 + y^2 = 4a^2 - 4a\sqrt{(x + c)^2 + y^2} + x^2 + 2cx + c^2 + y^2,$$

which becomes

$$4a\sqrt{(x + c)^2 + y^2} = 4a^2 + 4cx.$$

Dividing each member by 4, and again squaring, we eliminate the radical and have

$$a^2(x^2 + 2cx + c^2 + y^2) = a^4 + 2a^2cx + c^2x^2,$$

which reduces to

$$(a^2 - c^2)x^2 + a^2y^2 = a^2(a^2 - c^2). \tag{18-7}$$

Since $a > c$, $a^2 - c^2 > 0$. By denoting $a^2 - c^2$ by b^2 and dividing each member of Eq. (18-7) by a^2b^2, we get the result

$$\boxed{\frac{x^2}{a^2} + \frac{y^2}{b^2} = 1.} \tag{18-8}$$

This calculation shows that any point $P(x, y)$ which lies on the ellipse has coordinates that satisfy Eq. (18-8). We also must show the converse, namely, that any point whose coordinates satisfy Eq. (18-8) lies on the ellipse. This may be done by reversing the steps of the above proof. Therefore Eq. (18-8) is the required equation and is called the *standard equation of the ellipse* with its center at the origin.

By considering the graph of this equation, as in Article 12-3, we find:

(a) it is symmetric with respect to both axes, and thus to the origin;
(b) its intercepts are $(\pm a, 0)$ and $(0, \pm b)$;
(c) it lies in the rectangle where $|x| \leq a$ and $|y| \leq b$.

The points $V(a, 0)$ and $V'(-a, 0)$ are called the *vertices* of the ellipse, and the line segment VV' of length $2a$ is called the *major axis* of the ellipse. The line segment between the y-intercepts of length $2b$ is called its *minor axis*. The chord through either focus perpendicular to the major axis is called the *latus rectum*; it is of length $2b^2/a$ (why?). By using this length and the intercepts, one is able to sketch the graph of the curve with comparative ease.

As in the case of the parabola, if the foci had been located on the y-axis, namely $F(0, c)$ and $F'(0, -c)$, the major axis would lie along the y-axis, again of length $2a$, and the equation would become

$$\boxed{\frac{y^2}{a^2} + \frac{x^2}{b^2} = 1,}$$ (18–9)

with the vertices $V(0, a)$ and $V'(0, -a)$. In either case, Eq. (18–8) or (18–9), $b^2 = a^2 - c^2$, so that $a > b$.

EXAMPLE 1.   Sketch the graph of the ellipse whose equation is $9x^2 + 4y^2 = 36$, giving the coordinates of the foci, ends of the major and minor axes, and length of each latus rectum.

Solution. Dividing each member by 36, in order to put the equation in standard form, we have

$$\frac{x^2}{4} + \frac{y^2}{9} = 1,$$

so that $a = 3$ and $b = 2$, and the ellipse has its major axis along the y-axis (why?). Since $a^2 - c^2 = b^2$, $c = \sqrt{9 - 4} = \sqrt{5}$. The coordinates of the foci are $F(0, \sqrt{5})$ and $F'(0, -\sqrt{5})$, the vertices are $V(0, 3)$ and $V'(0, -3)$, and the ends of the minor axis are $(2, 0)$ and $(-2, 0)$. The length of each latus rectum is $2b^2/a = 2 \cdot \frac{4}{3} = \frac{8}{3}$. The required graph appears in Fig. 18–14.

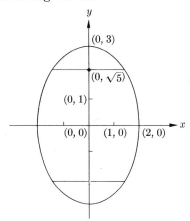

FIGURE 18–14

It should be clear that two ellipses would be similar (the same shape, but possibly of different sizes) if the ratio of b and a were constant. If, however, one of these remains fixed and the other changes, the actual shape of the ellipse would change. It is more useful to consider the ratio c/a. Since

$$\frac{c}{a} = \frac{\sqrt{a^2 - b^2}}{a} = \sqrt{1 - \frac{b^2}{a^2}},$$

if b/a remains constant, so does c/a, and conversely. This ratio c/a, denoted by e, is called the *eccentricity* of the ellipse. For any ellipse, the quantity e always has a value such that $0 \le e < 1$. If we keep a fixed, that is, the location of the two vertices V and V', the shape of the ellipse ranges from a circle (where F and F' coincide, and $c = 0$, so $e = 0$) to a long, thin ellipse, hardly distinguishable from a straight line (where F and F' are close to V and V', or c is almost equal a). The limiting case where $c = a$ and $e = 1$ would indeed be the straight-line segment VV'. One of the important uses of the eccentricity appears in Problem 24.

EXAMPLE 2. Find an equation of the ellipse with center $(0, 0)$, one focus $(4, 0)$, and eccentricity $\frac{2}{5}$.

Solution. Since $c = 4$ and $c/a = \frac{2}{5}$, $a = 10$. Also $b^2 = a^2 - c^2 = 100 - 16 = 84$. Therefore the required equation is

$$\frac{x^2}{100} + \frac{y^2}{84} = 1.$$

PROBLEMS

Sketch the graphs of each of the following equations (Problems 1–6), giving the center, foci, length of each axis, and eccentricity.

1. $\dfrac{x^2}{25} + \dfrac{y^2}{16} = 1$ 2. $\dfrac{x^2}{36} + \dfrac{y^2}{100} = 1$

3. $x^2 + 2y^2 = 6$ 4. $4x^2 + 3y^2 = 12$

5. $36x^2 + 100y^2 = 1$ 6. $9x^2 + 4y^2 = 1$

In Problems 7–14 find an equation of the ellipse satisfying the following conditions:

7. Ends of minor axis are $(0, \pm 2)$; distance between foci is 6.

8. Foci are $(3, 0)$ and $(-3, 0)$; length of either latus rectum is 9.

9. Vertices are $(\pm 6, 0)$; foci are $(\pm 4, 0)$.

10. Foci are $(0, \pm 2)$; eccentricity is $\frac{2}{3}$.

11. Center at the origin; one vertex is $(4, 0)$; passes through the point $(2, \frac{1}{2}\sqrt{3})$.

12. Center at the origin; major axis along x-axis; passes through the two points $(4, 3)$ and $(6, 2)$.

13. Center at the origin; symmetrical with respect to axes; passes through $(1, -4)$ and $(2, 2)$.

14. Center at the origin; symmetrical with respect to axes; length of latus rectum is $\frac{2}{3}$; eccentricity is $\frac{2}{3}$.

15. Derive Eq. (18–9) showing all steps.

16. Using Definition 18–3, determine an equation of the ellipse with foci $(2, 3)$ and $(8, 3)$ and length of major axis 10.

17. Using Definition 18–3, determine an equation of the ellipse with foci $(5, 1)$ and $(5, -3)$ and length of minor axis 6.

18. With the help of Definition 18–3, show that the equation

$$\frac{(x-h)^2}{a^2} + \frac{(y-k)^2}{b^2} = 1$$

represents an ellipse with center (h, k), foci $(h \pm c, k)$, and major axis of length $2a$.

19. What would be the conditions on the coefficients of Eq. (18–1) if this equation represented the ellipse given in Problem 18?

20. Find the locus of the centers of all circles which are tangent to the circle $(x+1)^2 + y^2 = 36$ and pass through the point $(1, 0)$. Why is this locus an ellipse?

21. Find the locus of all points P such that the ratio of the distance of P from the point $(4, 0)$ to its distance from the line $x = 6$ is equal to $\sqrt{6}/3$.

22. Find the locus of all points P such that the ratio of the distance of P from the point $(0, \frac{3}{2})$ to its distance from the line $y = 6$ is equal to $\frac{1}{2}$.

23. Find the locus of all points P such that the ratio of the distance of P from the point $(c, 0)$ to its distance from the line $x = a^2/c$ is equal to c/a.

24. The statement of Problem 23, with $e = c/a$ $(0 \le e < 1)$, is sometimes used as the definition of an ellipse. Show that this statement is equivalent to: The ellipse with Eq. (18–8) is the locus of all points P such that the ratio of the distance of P from the point $(ae, 0)$ to its distance from the line $x = a/e$ is equal to the eccentricity e, where $0 \le e < 1$.

25. Find equations of the tangent and normal lines to the ellipse $6x^2 + y^2 = 100$ at $(4, 2)$.

26. As in the case of the parabola (Problem 19, Article 18–3), the line segment between the focus F and any point P on the ellipse is called a focal radius. Prove that any tangent to an ellipse makes equal angles with the focal radii drawn to the point of tangency.

27. Find the coordinates of the point $P(x, y)$ in the first quadrant if the tangent to the ellipse $(x^2/a^2) + (y^2/b^2) = 1$ at this point has equal intercepts.

28. At what points on the ellipse $(x^2/a^2) + (y^2/b^2) = 1$ do the tangent and normal form an isosceles triangle with the x-axis?

18–5 The hyperbola. The hyperbola can be described geometrically as the intersection of a right circular cone and a plane inclined so that it cuts both nappes and does not pass through the vertex of the cone (see Fig. 18–15). We again define this conic section in terms of a locus of points:

DEFINITION 18–4. *A hyperbola is the locus of all points in the plane such that the difference of its distances from two fixed points is a constant.*

FIGURE 18–15

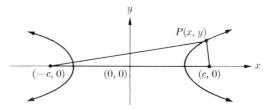

FIGURE 18–16

The two fixed points, usually denoted by F and F', are called the *foci* of the hyperbola. The mid-point of the line segment FF' is called the *center* of the hyperbola. If the length of this line segment is denoted by $2c$, and the numerical difference of the distances (or constant mentioned in the definition) by $2a$, we have $2c > 2a$ or $c > a$. (Why?)

As in the case of the ellipse, we wish to choose the coordinate axes so as to obtain an equation for the general hyperbola in as simple a form as possible. If we choose the center as the origin and the foci $F(c, 0)$ and $F'(-c, 0)$ on the x-axis (Fig. 18–16), the definition requires that the coordinates of the point $P(x, y)$ satisfy the condition

$$|F'P| - |FP| = \pm 2a,$$

or

$$\sqrt{(x + c)^2 + (y - 0)^2} - \sqrt{(x - c)^2 + (y - 0)^2} = \pm 2a.$$

$$(18\text{–}10)$$

Since the difference mentioned in the definition may be taken in either order, the hyperbola consists of two branches. This explains the $\pm$ sign in Eq. (18–10). The plus sign holds on the right branch, the minus sign on the left.

If we repeat the process used with Eq. (18–6), we again obtain

$$(a^2 - c^2)x^2 + a^2y^2 = a^2(a^2 - c^2). \qquad (18\text{–}11)$$

But now $c > a$, so that $c^2 > a^2$, and hence Eq. (18–11) may be written

$$(c^2 - a^2)x^2 - a^2y^2 = a^2(c^2 - a^2), \qquad (18\text{–}12)$$

where $c^2 - a^2 > 0$. Now, letting $c^2 - a^2 = b^2$ and dividing each member by a^2b^2, we have the desired result,

$$\frac{x^2}{a^2} - \frac{y^2}{b^2} = 1. \qquad (18\text{–}13)$$

Since, as in the case of the ellipse, the steps in this calculation are reversible, Eq. (18–13) is the required equation. It is considered the *standard equation of the hyperbola* with its center at the origin.

By discussing the graph of this equation, as in Article 12–3, we find:

(a) it is symmetric with respect to both axes and thus to the origin;

(b) it has $(\pm a, 0)$ for its x-intercepts; it has no y-intercepts;

(c) the curve exists for all real values of y; it exists for all x such that $|x| \geq a$.

The points $V(a, 0)$ and $V'(-a, 0)$ are called the *vertices*, and the line segment VV' of length $2a$ is called the *transverse axis*, since it crosses the curve. The other axis is called the *conjugate axis*. The chord through either focus perpendicular to the transverse axis is again called the *latus rectum*; it has a length of $2b^2/a$. The ratio c/a is again called the *eccentricity*, but $e > 1$ for any hyperbola (why?).

There is one further fact which will help sketch the graph of Eq. (18–13). Let us consider the part of the graph which lies in the first quadrant. (If we use the symmetry of the curve, its behavior in the other quadrants will also be clear.) Since

$$y = \frac{b}{a} \sqrt{x^2 - a^2}, \tag{18–14}$$

as x increases so does y, but we can be more explicit. Consider the line through the center whose equation is $y = (b/a)x$, or $bx - ay = 0$. The distance d from any point (x_1, y_1) to this line is [recall Eq. (5–17)]

$$d = \frac{|bx_1 - ay_1|}{\sqrt{a^2 + b^2}} = \frac{|bx_1 - ay_1|}{c}.$$

If the point (x_1, y_1) is on the hyperbola, its coordinates satisfy the equation, so that

$$b^2 x_1^2 - a^2 y_1^2 = (bx_1 - ay_1)(bx_1 + ay_1) = a^2 b^2,$$

and thus

$$d = \frac{a^2 b^2}{c|bx_1 + ay_1|}. \tag{18–15}$$

As x increases along the curve, so does y [Eq. (18–14)], and thus

$$\lim_{x_1 \to \infty} d = \lim_{x_1 \to \infty} \frac{a^2 b^2}{c|bx_1 + ay_1|} = 0.$$

Thus, as x increases indefinitely, the distance from the curve to the straight line approaches zero. Such a straight line is called an *asymptote* of the hyperbola.* In the same way, the line $y = (-b/a)x$ may be shown

---

* Recall from Article 12–3 the definition of a horizontal or vertical asymptote and note the similarity to the definition given here.

to be an asymptote, so that the two lines

$$\left(\frac{x}{a} + \frac{y}{b}\right)\left(\frac{x}{a} - \frac{y}{b}\right) = 0$$

or

$$\frac{x^2}{a^2} - \frac{y^2}{b^2} = 0 \qquad (18\text{--}16)$$

are asymptotes of the hyperbola, Eq. (18–13). By sketching these lines and using the facts stated in (a), (b), and (c), we can easily draw the graph of Eq. (18–13).

As in the case of the ellipse, if the foci had been located on the y-axis, namely $F(0, c)$ and $F'(0, -c)$, the transverse axis would lie along the y-axis, again of length $2a$, but the equation would become

$$\boxed{\frac{y^2}{a^2} - \frac{x^2}{b^2} = 1,} \qquad (18\text{--}17)$$

with the vertices $V(0, a)$ and $V'(0, -a)$. In either case, Eq. (18–13) or (18–17), $b^2 = c^2 - a^2$, and the asymptotes are the same.

EXAMPLE 1. Sketch the graph of the hyperbola $9x^2 - 16y^2 = 144$, giving the coordinates of the foci and vertices, the eccentricity, length of the latus rectum, and the equations of the asymptotes.

Solution. Dividing each member by 144, we have

$$\frac{x^2}{16} - \frac{y^2}{9} = 1,$$

so that $a = 4$, $b = 3$, and $c = 5$. Since the coefficient of x^2 is positive, the transverse axis is the x-axis. Thus the foci have coordinates $(\pm 5, 0)$, the vertices $(\pm 4, 0)$, the eccentricity is $\frac{5}{4}$, and the length of the latus rectum is $2 \cdot \frac{9}{4} = \frac{9}{2}$. By replacing the constant term by zero, we have the asymptotes $(x^2/16) - (y^2/9) = 0$, or $3x + 4y = 0$ and $3x - 4y = 0$. The graph appears in Fig. 18–17.

EXAMPLE 2. Find an equation of the hyperbola having $(0, \pm 6)$ for foci and $(0, \pm 4)$ for vertices.

Solution. With these coordinates for the foci and vertices, we immediately have $c = 6$ and $a = 4$. Since $b^2 = c^2 - a^2$, $b^2 = 20$. Also, the required hyperbola has y for its transverse axis, so that the required equation is

$$\frac{y^2}{16} - \frac{x^2}{20} = 1.$$

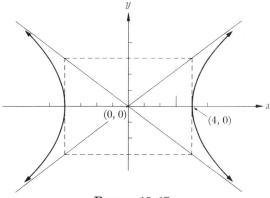

FIGURE 18–17

PROBLEMS

Sketch the graphs of each of the following equations (Problems 1–6), giving the center, foci, length of each axis, equations of the asymptotes, and eccentricity.

1. $\dfrac{x^2}{36} - \dfrac{y^2}{64} = 1$ 2. $\dfrac{y^2}{16} - \dfrac{x^2}{9} = 1$

3. $3x^2 - 4y^2 = 12$ 4. $5x^2 - 16y^2 = 80$

5. $9y^2 - 16x^2 = 1$ 6. $4x^2 - y^2 = 1$

In Problems 7–14 find an equation of the hyperbola satisfying the following conditions:

7. Foci are $(\pm 6, 0)$; length of latus rectum is 18.
8. Vertices are $(0, \pm 4)$; eccentricity is $\frac{5}{2}$.
9. Equations of asymptotes are $x^2 - 4y^2 = 0$; passes through $(3, -1)$.
10. Center at origin; one focus is $(4, 0)$; eccentricity is 8.
11. Center at origin; axes along coordinate axes; latus rectum length is $\frac{4}{3}$; slopes of asymptotes are ± 3.
12. Center at origin; axes along coordinate axes; e is $\sqrt{6}/2$; passes through $(1, 2)$.
13. Center at origin; transverse axis along y-axis; length of latus rectum is $\frac{2}{3}$; passes through $(1, -2)$.
14. Center at the origin; transverse axis along x-axis; passes through $(2, -3)$ and $(-7, 6)$.

15. The hyperbola in whose equation $a = b$ is called a *rectangular hyperbola*. Show that for a rectangular hyperbola: (a) the asymptotes intersect at right angles; (b) the eccentricity is $\sqrt{2}$.

16. Using Definition 18–4, determine an equation of a hyperbola with foci $(-5, 4)$, $(1, 4)$, and length of transverse axis 4.

17. Using Definition 18–4, determine an equation of a hyperbola with vertices $(2, -3)$, $(8, -3)$, and eccentricity $\frac{5}{3}$.

18. With the help of Definition 18–4, show that the equation

$$\frac{(x - h)^2}{a^2} - \frac{(y - k)^2}{b^2} = 1$$

represents a hyperbola with center (h, k), foci $(h \pm c, k)$, and transverse axis of length $2a$.

19. What would be the conditions on the coefficients of Eq. (18–1) if this equation represented the hyperbola given in Problem 18?

20. Find the locus of the center of all circles which are tangent to the circle $(x - 1)^2 + y^2 = 1$ and pass through the point $(-1, 0)$. Why is this locus a hyperbola?

21. Find the locus of all points P such that the ratio of the distance of P from the point $(0, \frac{9}{2})$ to its distance from the line $y = \frac{1}{18}$ is equal to 9.

22. Find the locus of all points P such that the ratio of the distance from the point $(6, 0)$ to its distance from the line $x = \frac{3}{2}$ is equal to 2.

23. The statement of Problem 23, Article 18–4, with $e = c/a$ (but $e > 1$), is sometimes used as the definition of a hyperbola. Show that this statement is equivalent to: The hyperbola with Eq. (18–13) is the locus of all points P such that the ratio of the distance of P from the point $(ae, 0)$ to its distance from the line $x = a/e$ is equal to the eccentricity e, where $e > 1$.

24. Prove that the product of the distances from any point on a hyperbola to the two asymptotes is a constant.

25. Find equations of the tangent and normal lines to the hyperbola $6x^2 - 4y^2 = 38$ at the point $(-3, 2)$.

26. Prove that any tangent to a hyperbola bisects the angle between the focal radii drawn to the point of tangency.

18–6 Summary and applications. We have seen that each of the conic sections may be defined geometrically as the intersection of a right circular cone and a plane in various positions. The definitions we gave for the conics as loci, however, made it possible to study each separately and to emphasize the graphs and properties of each. It seems appropriate at this time to unify the parabola, ellipse, and hyperbola in the light of Problem 24, Article 18–4, and Problem 23, Article 18–5.

DEFINITION 18–5. *For any fixed line l and any fixed point F not on the line l, the locus of all points P in the plane such that the ratio of the distance of P from the point F to the distance from the line l is equal to a constant $e > 0$ is*

$$\begin{aligned} &\textit{an ellipse for } e < 1, \\ &\textit{a parabola for } e = 1, \qquad\qquad (18\text{–}18) \\ &\textit{a hyperbola for } e > 1. \end{aligned}$$

The results of the two problems mentioned above, together with the original definition of the parabola, should indicate the equivalence of Definition 18–5 with those previously used. In each case, the fixed line is called the *directrix*, and the fixed point the *focus*. In fact, as has been mentioned, both the ellipse and hyperbola have two foci, and with these, corresponding directrices.

The following lists some of the many applications of the different conics in various fields of science.

1. Parabola:
    (a) The path of a projectile due to the force of gravity if air resistance is neglected.
    (b) Cable of a suspension bridge if the weight of the bridge is distributed uniformly.
    (c) A parabolic curve which approximates a curve through a set of points (by a method known as "least squares").
    (d) Parabolic reflectors and surfaces used in telescopes, optical instruments, etc.

2. Ellipse:
    (a) Orbits of the planets, including the earth, with the sun at a focus.
    (b) Orbits of some comets.
    (c) Elliptical gears.
    (d) Arches of certain bridges.

3. Hyperbola:
    (a) Certain laws in physics are hyperbolic in nature. Any two quantities that are inversely proportional are governed by a law of this type.*
    (b) Certain hyperbolic lenses.
    (c) Orbits of some comets.
    (d) Families of curves (used to locate position in certain navigational systems).

18–7 Translation of axes. Throughout our discussion of analytic methods we have constantly tried to place our axes relative to the curve, locus, or figure under consideration in a position which will be to our advantage. This was emphasized in Article 5–8, and again in the last few articles. Sometimes, however, we are given an equation with a specific rectangular coordinate system. It may then greatly simplify our work if we change the system of axes. Such a change may consist of a translation of the axes, a rotation of the axes, or both.

DEFINITION 18–6. *If either or both of the two rectangular coordinate axes are moved so that the origin takes on a new position but each axis remains parallel to its original position, the change is called a translation of the axes.*

---

* Article 18–8, where we take up the graph of $xy = k$, makes clear the fact that inverse proportion is hyperbolic.

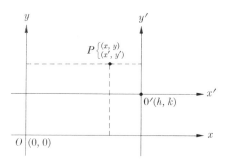

FIGURE 18–18

Let us be more specific. If any fixed point whose original coordinates are (h, k) is denoted by O', and the two lines parallel to the x- and y-axes through O' are regarded as the new x'- and y'-axes respectively, any point P with coordinates (x, y), relative to the original axes, will also have coordinates (x', y') relative to the new axes.

THEOREM 18–3. *As shown in Fig. 18–18, the relation between the new and the old coordinates for this translation is given by*

$$x' = x - h, \qquad y' = y - k, \tag{18–19}$$

or

$$x = x' + h, \qquad y = y' + k. \tag{18–20}$$

Proof. Figure 18–18 may be used in the proof of Eq. (18–19). Equation (18–20) follows directly from (18–19).

With the use of Eq. (18–20), any equation in x and y may be transformed to an equation in x' and y'. Graphically, the curve of the equation in the xy-coordinate system will coincide with that of the new equation in the $x'y'$-coordinate system; that is, the axes are translated, not the curve.

EXAMPLE 1. Find an equation relative to the new set of axes with the new origin located at $(4, -3)$ if the original equation is $x^2 - 8x - 2y + 10 = 0$. Sketch the curve showing both sets of axes.

Solution. Any point $P(x, y)$ whose coordinates (x, y) satisfy $x^2 - 8x - 2y + 10 = 0$ has for its new coordinates $x' = x - 4$ and $y' = y + 3$, since $h = 4$ and $k = -3$. Thus, $x = x' + 4$ and $y = y' - 3$ gives the original coordinates in terms of the new ones. Substituting these values for x and y in the given equation, we have

$$(x' + 4)^2 - 8(x' + 4) - 2(y' - 3) + 10 = 0,$$

the required new equation. Simplifying this, we get

$$x'^2 + 8x' + 16 - 8x' - 32 - 2y' + 6 + 10 = 0,$$

or

$$x'^2 = 2y'.$$

The graph appears in Fig. 18–19 with both sets of axes shown.

In Example 1, the new equation $x'^2 = 2y'$ is much simpler than the original equation $x^2 - 8x - 2y + 10 = 0$. Hence we see one of the important uses of translation of axes, the simplification of the graphing of a given curve.

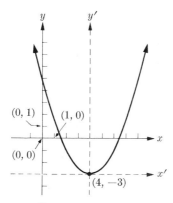

FIGURE 18–19

EXAMPLE 2. Determine the translation to eliminate the x- and y-terms in the equation $4x^2 + 9y^2 - 16x + 18y - 11 = 0$, and find the resulting equation relative to this translation.

Solution (1). Let us complete the square (recall Article 6–1, or Example 1, Article 18–1). We have

$$4x^2 + 9y^2 - 16x + 18y - 11 = 0,$$

or

$$4(x^2 - 4x \quad) + 9(y^2 + 2y \quad) = 11.$$

By adding 4 and 1, inside the first and second parentheses, and therefore 25 to the right member, we have not changed the equation, but may write it in the form $4(x - 2)^2 + 9(y + 1)^2 = 36$ or, dividing the members by 36,

$$\frac{(x - 2)^2}{9} + \frac{(y + 1)^2}{4} = 1.$$

If we let $x' = x - 2$ and $y' = y + 1$, so that $h = 2$ and $k = -1$, the equation relative to the new coordinate system is

$$\frac{x'^2}{9} + \frac{y'^2}{4} = 1,$$

which has no x- or y-terms. This method of choosing a translation is frequently used to facilitate the graphing of conic sections when their axes are parallel to the coordinate axes.

Solution (2). The equation relative to the new axes can be obtained for any translation by substituting $x = x' + h$ and $y = y' + k$ in $4x^2 + 9y^2 - 16x + 18y - 11 = 0$. Thus,

$$4(x' + h)^2 + 9(y' + k)^2 - 16(x' + h) + 18(y' + k) - 11 = 0.$$

Simplifying, we have

$$4x'^2 + 8hx' + 4h^2 + 9y'^2 + 18ky' + 9k^2 - 16x' \\ - 16h + 18y' + 18k - 11 = 0,$$

and then collecting terms, we obtain

$$4x'^2 + 9y'^2 + (8h - 16)x' + (18k + 18)y' \\ + 4h^2 + 9k^2 - 16h + 18k - 11 = 0.$$

Since we desire to eliminate the x'- and y'-terms, we must have their coefficients zero, so that $8h - 16 = 0$ and $18k + 18 = 0$ or $h = 2$ and $k = -1$. Thus the required transformation is $x = x' + 2$ and $y = y' - 1$ [or $x' = x - 2$, $y' = y + 1$, as was found in Solution (1)]. If these values for x and y are substituted in the original equation, we obtain as before

$$\frac{x'^2}{9} + \frac{y'^2}{4} = 1.$$

The graph of the equations with both coordinate systems is shown in Fig. 18–20.

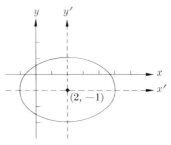

FIGURE 18–20

EXAMPLE 3. Find the coordinates of the vertex, focus, equation of directrix, and length of latus rectum of the parabola $y^2 + 4x - 6y + 13 = 0$.

Solution. By completing the square, we have

$$y^2 - 6y + 9 = -4x - 13 + 9 = -4x - 4,$$

or

$$(y - 3)^2 = -4(x + 1).$$

By letting $y' = y - 3$ and $x' = x + 1$, we have

$$y'^2 = -4x',$$

so that the new origin, and vertex, is $(-1, 3)$ in the original system. Therefore, in the original coordinate system, since $4p = -4$ or $p = -1$, the vertex is $(-1, 3)$, the focus is $(-2, 3)$, the equation of the directrix is $x = 0$, and the length of the latus rectum is 4. Figure 18–21 shows the graph of the given parabola.

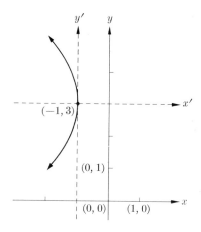

FIGURE 18–21

PROBLEMS

In Problems 1–4 transform the given equation by translating the coordinate axes to the new origin indicated.

1. $2x - 3y + 5 = 0$; $(2, 3)$
2. $x^2 + y^2 - 2x + 6y + 6 = 0$; $(1, -3)$
3. $x^2 - 4y^2 + 6x + 8y + 1 = 0$; $(-3, 1)$
4. $xy - 2y + 3x - 7 = 0$; $(2, -3)$

In Problems 5–10 transform the given equation into another equation lacking terms of the first degree, by a translation of the coordinate axes.

    5. $x^2 - y^2 - 4x + 4y - 1 = 0$
    6. $4x^2 + 9y^2 - 24x + 36y + 36 = 0$
    7. $xy - 7x + 3y - 22 = 0$
    8. $4x^2 + y^2 + 16x - 10y + 37 = 0$
    9. $2y^2 + 4y - 8x + 18 = 0$
    10. $9x^2 - 4y^2 + 36x + 8y - 4 = 0$

In Problems 11–15 find the coordinates of the center (if any), vertices, and foci, the eccentricity, and equations of asymptotes (if any), and sketch the curve.

    11. $x^2 + 4y^2 - 10x - 40y + 109 = 0$
    12. $9x^2 - 24x + 72y + 16 = 0$
    13. $9x^2 - 4y^2 - 54x + 8y + 113 = 0$
    14. $5x^2 - 4y^2 - 20x - 24y - 36 = 0$
    15. $12x^2 + 16y^2 - 12x - 9 = 0$

    16. Do Problem 17, Article 18–3, by the method of this article.

    17. Do Problem 18, Article 18–4, and Problem 18, Article 18–5, by the method of this article.

    18. Note that the graph of Eq. (18–1) with $B = 0$, if it exists and does not consist of just a point or straight line, is one of the conic sections. What are the conditions on the coefficients for a circle, a parabola, an ellipse, and a hyperbola?

18–8 Rotation of axes. Often the rotation of axes is an advantageous procedure.

DEFINITION 18–7. *If, in a rectangular coordinate system with given x- and y-axes, a new set of rectangular coordinate axes x′ and y′ are chosen having the same origin, the change is called* a rotation of axes.

As in the case of a translation of the coordinate axes to a new set of axes, so in the case of rotation of a set of coordinate axes to a new set of axes, there exists a relation between the original coordinates (x, y) of any point P and the new set of coordinates $(x′, y′)$ of this same point. If α denotes the angle from the original positive x-axis to the new positive $x′$-axis, and the coordinates of any point P are denoted before and after the rotation (Fig. 18–22) by (x, y) and $(x′, y′)$, respectively, we have the following theorem.

THEOREM 18–4. *The relation between the new and the old coordinates, if the axes are rotated through an angle α, is given by*

$$\begin{aligned} x &= x' \cos \alpha - y' \sin \alpha, \\ y &= x' \sin \alpha + y' \cos \alpha. \end{aligned} \qquad (18\text{–}21)$$

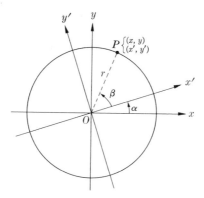

FIGURE 18–22

Proof. In Fig. 18–22 the length of the line between the origin and any point P is denoted by r. The point P has coordinates (x, y) in the original system and (x', y') in the new system, where the angle from the x-axis to the x'-axis is α, and a positive angle is measured in a counterclockwise direction. Let β be the angle from the x'-axis to the line OP. Then the x- and y-coordinates of P may be expressed as follows:

$$x = r \cos (\alpha + \beta),$$
$$y = r \sin (\alpha + \beta) \tag{18–22}$$

or, recalling Eqs. (4–29), (4–30),

$$x = r \cos \alpha \cos \beta - r \sin \alpha \sin \beta,$$
$$y = r \sin \alpha \cos \beta + r \cos \alpha \sin \beta. \tag{18–23}$$

Since

$$x' = r \cos \beta, \qquad y' = r \sin \beta,$$

Eq. (18–23) becomes

$$x = x' \cos \alpha - y' \sin \alpha$$

and

$$y = x' \sin \alpha + y' \cos \alpha.$$

To express x' and y' in terms of x and y, Eq. (18–21) may be solved for x' and y'. We recall Problem 17, Article 5–5, and obtain

$$x' = x \cos \alpha + y \sin \alpha,$$
$$y' = -x \sin \alpha + y \cos \alpha. \tag{18–24}$$

EXAMPLE 1. If the original coordinate axes are rotated through an angle of 45°, find the transformed equation, relative to the $x'y'$-system, of the original curve whose equation is $y^2 - x^2 = 2$.

Solution. Since $\alpha = 45°$, the necessary transformation becomes

$$x = \frac{1}{\sqrt{2}} x' - \frac{1}{\sqrt{2}} y',$$

$$y = \frac{1}{\sqrt{2}} x' + \frac{1}{\sqrt{2}} y'.$$

Substituting these values in $y^2 - x^2 = 2$, we have

$$\frac{(x' + y')^2}{2} - \frac{(x' - y')^2}{2} = 2$$

or, upon simplifying, $x'y' = 1$. The curve is shown in Fig. 18–23 with both sets of coordinate axes.

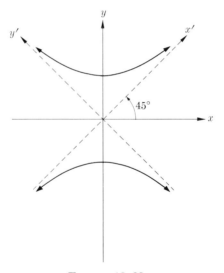

FIGURE 18–23

We recall the difficulty involved in graphing certain curves when xy-terms were present. One of the distinct advantages of a rotation of axes is the possibility of elimination of such terms. We may then sketch the simpler curve in the new rotated system, and thus obtain the graph of the curve in the original system. Consider the next example with this in mind.

EXAMPLE 2. Sketch the graph of the equation $3x^2 + \sqrt{3}\,xy + 2y^2 = 4$ by rotating the coordinate axes through an angle of 30° and using the equation relative to the new axes.

Solution. Since $\alpha = 30°$, we have by using Eq. (18–21),

$$x = \frac{\sqrt{3}}{2}\,x' - \frac{1}{2}\,y',$$

$$y = \frac{1}{2}\,x' + \frac{\sqrt{3}}{2}\,y',$$

which represents the proper transformation. Substituting these values in $3x^2 + \sqrt{3}\,xy + 2y^2 = 4$, we have

$$\frac{3(\sqrt{3}\,x' - y')^2}{4} + \frac{\sqrt{3}\,(\sqrt{3}\,x' - y')(x' + \sqrt{3}\,y')}{4} + \frac{2(x' + \sqrt{3}\,y')^2}{4} = 4,$$

or

$$3(3x'^2 - 2\sqrt{3}\,x'y' + y'^2) + \sqrt{3}\,(\sqrt{3}\,x'^2 + 2x'y' - \sqrt{3}\,y'^2)$$
$$+ 2(x'^2 + 2\sqrt{3}\,x'y' + 3y'^2) = 16.$$

This equation reduces to

$$7x'^2 + 3y'^2 = 8.$$

This is the equation of the same curve, relative to the new rotated axes, and is easily sketched on the $x'y'$-axes, since it represents an ellipse in standard position. See Fig. 18–24.

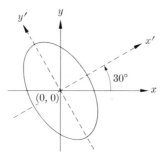

FIGURE 18–24

This example illustrates the simplification of an equation by the proper rotation. Fortunately, such a simplification, the elimination of the xy-term, can always be obtained for any equation of the form

$$Ax^2 + Bxy + Cy^2 + Dx + Ey + F = 0. \qquad (18\text{--}1)$$

Hence the graph of the equation can be recognized and sketched.

THEOREM 18-5. *Given any equation in the form of Eq. (18–1), there exists an angle α, where $\tan 2\alpha = B/(A - C)$ if $A \neq C$ or $\alpha = 45°$ if $A = C$, such that the graph of this equation relative to the new set of axes obtained by rotating through the angle α has a new equation with no $x'y'$-term.*

Proof. In the equation

$$Ax^2 + Bxy + Cy^2 + Dx + Ey + F = 0$$

let us replace x and y by the corresponding values from Eq. (18–21), where the axes are rotated through an angle α. We get

$$A(x' \cos \alpha - y' \sin \alpha)^2 + B(x' \cos \alpha - y' \sin \alpha)(x' \sin \alpha + y' \cos \alpha)$$
$$+ C(x' \sin \alpha + y' \cos \alpha)^2 + D(x' \cos \alpha - y' \sin \alpha)$$
$$+ E(x' \sin \alpha + y' \cos \alpha) + F = 0.$$

If we collect the various like terms, we can easily see that this equation may be written in the form

$$A'x'^2 + B'x'y' + C'y'^2 + D'x' + E'y' + F = 0, \qquad (18\text{–}25)$$

where

$$A' = A \cos^2 \alpha + B \sin \alpha \cos \alpha + C \sin^2 \alpha,$$
$$B' = 2(C - A) \sin \alpha \cos \alpha + B(\cos^2 \alpha - \sin^2 \alpha),$$
$$C' = A \sin^2 \alpha - B \sin \alpha \cos \alpha + C \cos^2 \alpha,$$
$$D' = D \cos \alpha + E \sin \alpha,$$
$$E' = E \cos \alpha - D \sin \alpha.$$

This expression, Eq. (18–25), is the new equation of the same curve, but relative to the new set of axes. It will have no $x'y'$-term if we choose α so that $B' = 0$, that is, so that

$$2(C - A) \sin \alpha \cos \alpha + B(\cos^2 \alpha - \sin^2 \alpha) = 0. \qquad (18\text{–}26)$$

Recalling Eqs. (4–43), (4–44), we may write

$$(C - A) \sin 2\alpha + B \cos 2\alpha = 0.$$

If $A - C = 0$, $\cos 2\alpha = 0$, so that the choice $\alpha = 45°$ will necessitate $B' = 0$. If $A \neq C$, we have

$$\boxed{\tan 2\alpha = \frac{B}{A - C}.} \qquad (18\text{–}27)$$

Since this can always be solved for 2α, and hence for α, such an angle always exists.

Although there are infinitely many values for α (differing from one another by multiples of $\pi/2$) which would satisfy Eq. (18–26) and thus make $B' = 0$, we shall ordinarily choose the smallest positive value.

To obtain the form of Eq. (18–21) for a specific correct rotation, that is, the value of $\sin \alpha$ and $\cos \alpha$ when $\tan 2\alpha$ is given, we must first find $\cos 2\alpha$ and then use Eqs. (4–49), (4–51) in the form

$$\sin \alpha = \sqrt{\frac{1 - \cos 2\alpha}{2}}, \qquad \cos \alpha = \sqrt{\frac{1 + \cos 2\alpha}{2}}. \qquad (18\text{–}28)$$

This will be illustrated in Example 3.

EXAMPLE 3. Sketch the graph of the equation $7x^2 + 12xy - 2y^2 = 5$.

Solution. We rotate the axes through an angle α, determined by Eq. (18–27). Thus

$$\tan 2\alpha = \frac{12}{7 - (-2)} = \frac{4}{3}.$$

Since $\tan 2\alpha = \frac{4}{3}$, $\cos 2\alpha = \frac{3}{5}$. (Why?) Therefore,

$$\sin \alpha = \sqrt{\frac{1 - \frac{3}{5}}{2}} = \frac{1}{\sqrt{5}}$$

and

$$\cos \alpha = \sqrt{\frac{1 + \frac{3}{5}}{2}} = \frac{2}{\sqrt{5}},$$

and Eq. (18–21) becomes

$$x = \frac{2}{\sqrt{5}} x' - \frac{1}{\sqrt{5}} y', \qquad y = \frac{1}{\sqrt{5}} x' + \frac{2}{\sqrt{5}} y'.$$

Substituting these values in $7x^2 + 12xy - 2y^2 = 5$, we have

$$\frac{7(2x' - y')^2}{5} + \frac{12(2x' - y')(x' + 2y')}{5} - \frac{2(x' + 2y')^2}{5} = 5$$

or, simplifying,

$$2x'^2 - y'^2 = 1.$$

This hyperbola may now be sketched (Fig. 18–25) in the $x'y'$-coordinate system and the original axes shown, and we realize that the angle of rotation α is approximately $26°34'$.

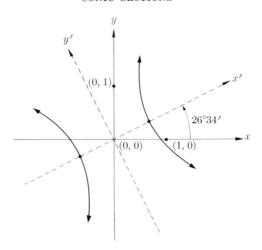

FIGURE 18–25

PROBLEMS

Sketch the graph of each of the following equations, showing each pair of coordinate axes.

1. $xy = 8$
2. $2x^2 + 4xy + 5y^2 = 2$
3. $3x^2 - 2xy + 3y^2 = 2$
4. $4xy + 3y^2 = 4$
5. $5x^2 + 4xy + 8y^2 = 36$
6. $x^2 + 36xy - 14y^2 = 52$
7. $9y^2 + 24xy + 16y^2 - 20x + 15y = 0$
8. $xy + 3x + 2y - 7 = 0$
9. $3x^2 + 2xy + 3y^2 + 16x - 16y + 52 = 0$
10. $4x^2 - 4xy + y^2 - 6x + 3y = 4$
11. $3x^2 - 4xy + 6y^2 + 8x + 4y + 10 = 0$
12. $8x^2 + 12xy + 17y^2 - 28x - 46y + 17 = 0$

13. Prove that the equation of any circle with center at the origin is unchanged under a rotation through any angle α.

14. Show that if Eq. (18–1) is transformed by a rotation through any angle α to the equation given by Eq. (18–25), then $A' + C' = A + C$. [*Hint:* Use the values for A' and C' given in the proof of Theorem 18–5.]

15. Under the same conditions stated in Problem 14, prove that $B'^2 - 4A'C' = B^2 - 4AC$. Quantities such as $A + C$ and $B^2 - 4AC$ which do not change their values are called *invariants* under rotation of axes.

16. Show that the graph of Eq. (18–1), if its curve is not degenerate,* is an ellipse or circle, parabola, or hyperbola according as $B^2 - 4AC$ is negative, zero, or positive. [*Hint:* Use the result of Problem 15.]

17. Using the results of Problem 16, state which conic section is represented by the equations given in Problems 2–12.

* By "degenerate" we mean no curve, a point, or one or two straight lines.

CHAPTER 19

INTEGRATION

19-1 General discussion. Up to this point, in the applications of the calculus we have been concerned with the process of differentiation of a function. In many cases, however, it is necessary to reverse this process; that is, we must find a function which possesses a given derivative. For example, if we are given that $Df(x) = x^3$, we may be required to find $f(x)$. By inspection, recalling the form of the derivative of x^n, we realize that one answer would be $f(x) = x^4/4$, since $D(x^4/4) = 4x^3/4 = x^3$. Moreover, since the derivative of any constant is equal to zero (Theorem 10-2), an equally correct solution for this problem would be $f(x) = x^4/4 + C$, where C is any constant, since $D(x^4/4 + C) = D(x^4/4) + D(C) = 4x^3/4 + 0 = x^3$. We are able to prove a general theorem of which this example is a special case.

THEOREM 19-1. *Any two functions which differ by a constant have the same derivative.*

Proof. Suppose $G(x) = F(x)$ and $H(x) = F(x) + C$. By Theorem 10-2, $DG(x) = DF(x)$, and $DH(x) = D[F(x) + C] = DF(x) + DC = DF(x) + 0 = DF(x)$.

THEOREM 19-2. (*Converse of Theorem 19-1*) *If two functions have the same derivative for all values of x where $a \leq x \leq b$, then they differ at most by a constant.*

Proof. Suppose $DF(x) = f(x)$ and $DG(x) = f(x)$, where $a \leq x \leq b$. Then $DF(x) - DG(x) = f(x) - f(x) = 0$. But $DF(x) - DG(x) = D[F(x) - G(x)]$, so that $D[F(x) - G(x)] = 0$; that is, $F(x) - G(x)$ has a derivative of zero for all these values of x. Thus its graph is a horizontal straight line, or $F(x) - G(x) = C$.

DEFINITION 19-1. *Any function of x whose derivative is $f(x)$ is called an integral of $f(x)$. The process of finding such a function is called* integration.

Since the process of integration is used so frequently, we introduce the special notation. If y is a function of x such that $Dy = f(x)$, then we write $y = \int f(x)\, dx$ and say that y is an integral of $f(x)$. The dx emphasizes that x is the independent variable. The function $f(x)$ is called the *integrand*, and x, the independent variable, is called the *variable of integration*. As a result of Theorem 19–1, we may write

$$\boxed{\int f(x)\, dx = F(x) + C,}$$ (19–1)

where $F(x)$ is any function whose derivative is $f(x)$ and C is any constant. Since C is any arbitrary constant, the expression $\int f(x)\, dx$ is often referred to as an *indefinite integral*.

19–2 Certain standard integration forms. All of the forms which will be used in this book in connection with the applications of integration are direct results of Theorems 19–1 and 19–2. Any of these forms may be verified by differentiating the integral and noting that the result of such differentiation is the integrand. The most important forms are given as theorems below.

THEOREM 19–3. *For any real value of n except $n = -1$*

$$\boxed{\int x^n\, dx = \frac{x^{n+1}}{n+1} + C.}$$ (19–2)

Proof. Since

$$D\left[\left(\frac{x^{n+1}}{n+1}\right) + C\right] = D\left(\frac{x^{n+1}}{n+1}\right) + DC$$

$$= \frac{1}{n+1}\, Dx^{n+1} + 0$$

$$= \frac{1}{n+1} \cdot (n+1)x^n$$

$$= x^n,$$

we have our proof. Note that Theorems 10–2, 4, 7, and 8 are used here.

THEOREM 19–4. *When $n = -1$,*

$$\int x^n\, dx = \int \frac{dx}{x} = \log_e x + C.$$ (19–3)

Proof. This result follows directly by using Corollary 14–6.

THEOREM 19–5. *For the exponential function e^x,*

$$\int e^x\, dx = e^x + C.$$ (19–4)

Proof. Recall Corollary 14–7.

THEOREM 19–6. *For the circular functions* sin *x and* cos *x,*

$$\int \cos x \, dx = \sin x + C, \tag{19-5}$$

$$\int \sin x \, dx = -\cos x + C. \tag{19-6}$$

Proof. For Eq. (19–5), recall Example 3, Article 10–2. For Eq. (19–6), use Problem 12, Article 10–2, and Theorem 10–7 (why?).

There are also two more general theorems which will prove important and useful in the material that follows.

THEOREM 19–7. *If* $\int f(x) \, dx$ *exists, that is, if there exists some function* $F(x)$ *such that* $DF(x) = f(x)$, *then*

$$\int k f(x) \, dx = k \int f(x) \, dx, \tag{19-7}$$

where k is any constant.

Proof. $D(kF(x)) = k \, DF(x)$ by Theorem 10–7, and since $DF(x) = f(x)$, $D(kF(x)) = kf(x)$. This emphasizes that a constant multiplier can be "taken outside" the integral sign.

THEOREM 19–8. *If* $\int f(x) \, dx$ *and* $\int g(x) \, dx$ *exist, then*

$$\int f(x) \, dx + \int g(x) \, dx = \int [f(x) + g(x)] \, dx. \tag{19-8}$$

Proof. Since $f(x) \, dx$ exists, there is a function $F(x)$ such that $DF(x) = f(x)$. Also there is a function $G(x)$ such that $DG(x) = g(x)$. Thus $f(x) + g(x) = DF(x) + DG(x) = D[F(x) + G(x)]$, which gives the required result.

With the help of these theorems we are able to integrate any polynomial, or in fact, any finite sum of terms each of which is a constant multiplied by some real power of the variable of integration.

EXAMPLE 1. Integrate the indefinite integral, $\int (3x^2 + 4x^{-1}) \, dx$.

Solution.
$$\int (3x^2 + 4x^{-1}) \, dx = \int 3x^2 \, dx + \int 4x^{-1} \, dx$$

$$= 3 \int x^2 \, dx + 4 \int \frac{dx}{x}$$

$$= x^3 + 4 \log_e x + C.$$

Note that Theorems 19–3, 4, 7, and 8 were used in this solution.

EXAMPLE 2. Integrate the indefinite integral $\int (2x - 3)^2\, dx$.

Solution.
$$\int (2x - 3)^2\, dx = \int (4x^2 - 12x + 9)\, dx$$

$$= 4 \int x^2\, dx - 12 \int x\, dx + 9 \int dx$$

$$= \frac{4x^3}{3} - 6x^2 + 9x + C.$$

EXAMPLE 3. Integrate $\int [(x^3 + 5x - 1)/\sqrt{x}]\, dx$.

Solution.

$$\int \frac{x^3 + 5x - 1}{\sqrt{x}}\, dx = \int x^{5/2}\, dx + 5 \int x^{1/2}\, dx - \int x^{-1/2}\, dx$$

$$= \frac{2x^{7/2}}{7} + \frac{10x^{3/2}}{3} - 2x^{1/2} + C.$$

PROBLEMS

Find the integrals in Problems 1–20, using the theorems of this article. Check each result by differentiation.

1. $\int (x^3 + 4x)\, dx$

2. $\int x^{-4}\, dx$

3. $\int (4x^2 - 7x + 2)\, dx$

4. $\int (5x + \sqrt{x})\, dx$

5. $\int (x^{1/2} + x^{1/3})\, dx$

6. $\int \frac{x^3 + 6x + 7}{x}\, dx$

7. $\int \frac{x^4 + 8x - 6}{x^2}\, dx$

8. $\int (x^{-3} + x^{-4})\, dx$

9. $\int \left(1 + \frac{1}{x}\right)^2\, dx$

10. $\int \frac{1 - x^2}{x^2}\, dx$

11. $\int (x - 1)^3\, dx$

12. $\int \frac{dx}{3x}$

13. $\int \frac{dx}{\csc x}$

14. $\int \frac{dx}{\sec x}$

15. $2 \int \sin \frac{x}{2} \cos \frac{x}{2}\, dx$

16. $\int \frac{e^{2x}}{e^x}\, dx$

17. $\int (x - 1)(x^2 + 2)\, dx$.   [*Hint:* The integral of a product is *not* the product of the integrals.]

18. $\int \cos x \tan x\, dx$

19. $\int (x^2 + 2x)(2x + 2)\, dx$

20. $\int 3x^2(x^3 + 1)^2\, dx$

21. Prove that $\int a^x\, dx = a^x/\log_e a + C = a^x \log_a e + C$.

22. Prove that $\int dx/\sqrt{1 - x^2} = \text{Arcsin } x + C$.   [*Hint:* Recall Eq. (13–9).]

23. Prove that $\int dx/(1 + x^2) = \text{Arctan } x + C$.   [*Hint:* Recall Eq. (13–13).]

19–3 Integration involving composite functions.   To obtain further general results, we must obtain the generalizations of the theorems of the preceding article. We shall begin by using Theorem 10–9 and, specifically, Eq. (10–12), to state the result for the integration of a composite function. Since

$$h'(x) = f'(g(x)) \cdot g'(x),$$

where $h(x) = f(g(x))$, we may write, using Eq. (19–1),

$$h(x) = \int f'(g(x)) \cdot g'(x)\, dx + C. \tag{19–9}$$

One important special case of this result is that in which $f(g(x))$ is $g(x)$ to a power.

THEOREM 19–9.   *For any real value of n except* $n = -1$

$$\int [g(x)]^n g'(x)\, dx = \frac{[g(x)]^{n+1}}{n + 1} + C. \tag{19–10}$$

Proof.   The proof follows directly by differentiating the right-hand members of this expression, using Eq. (10–12).

EXAMPLE 1.   Integrate $\int 3x^2(x^3 - 7)^4\, dx$.

Solution.   If $x^3 - 7$ is considered $g(x)$, $g'(x) = 3x^2$. Thus,

$$\int 3x^2(x^3 - 7)^4\, dx = \int [g(x)]^4 g'(x)\, dx = (x^3 - 7)^5/5 + C.$$

The term $3x^2$ must appear or the example could *not* have been done by this method.

EXAMPLE 2. Integrate $\int \sqrt{x^2 - 6x + 8}(x - 3)\, dx$.

Solution. If we let $g(x)$ be $x^2 - 6x + 8$, $g'(x) = 2x - 6 = 2(x - 3)$. The integral may then be written

$$\int \sqrt{x^2 - 6x + 8}(x - 3)\, dx = \int \frac{(x^2 - 6x + 8)^{1/2} 2(x - 3)}{2}\, dx,$$

and since the *constant* 2 in the denominator is unnecessary for our integration, it may go outside the integral sign. Thus,

$$\int \sqrt{x^2 - 6x + 8}(x - 3)\, dx = \tfrac{1}{2} \int [g(x)]^{1/2} g'(x)\, dx$$

$$= \frac{1}{2} \frac{[g(x)]^{3/2}}{\frac{3}{2}} = \frac{(x^2 - 6x + 8)^{3/2}}{3} + C.$$

The ability to take a *constant* inside or outside the integral sign is most useful (see the proof of Theorem 19–7). The position of a variable, of course, cannot be changed in this way.

Other special cases where the function $f(g(x))$ is not algebraic follow the same pattern. Proofs of the following theorems make use of Eq. (10–12) and are left as exercises. (It is of course assumed that $g(x)$ is a function which has a derivative.)

THEOREM 19–10.

$$\int \frac{g'(x)\, dx}{g(x)} = \log_e g(x) + C. \tag{19-11}$$

THEOREM 19–11.

$$\int e^{g(x)} g'(x)\, dx = e^{g(x)} + C. \tag{19-12}$$

THEOREM 19–12.

$$\int \cos g(x) \cdot g'(x)\, dx = \sin g(x) + C, \tag{19-13}$$

$$\int \sin g(x) \cdot g'(x)\, dx = -\cos g(x) + C. \tag{19-14}$$

We now give several examples of the use of these theorems.

ILLUSTRATION 1.

$$\int e^{3x}\, dx = \tfrac{1}{3} \int e^{3x} \cdot 3\, dx = \frac{e^{3x}}{3} + C.$$

ILLUSTRATION 2.

$$\int \cos 5x \, dx = \tfrac{1}{5} \int (\cos 5x)5 \, dx = \frac{\sin 5x}{5} + C.$$

ILLUSTRATION 3.

$$\int (e^x + e^{-x})^2 \, dx = \int (e^{2x} + 2 + e^{-2x}) \, dx$$

$$= \tfrac{1}{2} \int e^{2x} 2 \, dx + \int 2 \, dx - \tfrac{1}{2} \int e^{-2x}(-2) \, dx$$

$$= \frac{e^{2x}}{2} + 2x - \frac{e^{-2x}}{2} + C.$$

EXAMPLE 3.   Find the integral $\int \sin x \cos x \, dx$.

Solution (1)   Considering $g(x) = \sin x$, $g'(x) = \cos x$, we have

$$\int \sin x \cos x \, dx = \frac{\sin^2 x}{2} + C.$$

Solution (2)   Considering $g(x) = \cos x$, $g'(x) = -\sin x$, we have

$$\int \sin x \cos x \, dx = -\int \cos x(-\sin x) \, dx = \frac{-\cos^2 x}{2} + C.$$

Solution (3)   Recalling that $2 \sin x \cos x = \sin 2x$, we have

$$\int \sin x \cos x \, dx = \tfrac{1}{2} \int \sin 2x \, dx = \tfrac{1}{4} \int (\sin 2x)2 \, dx$$

$$= \frac{-\cos 2x}{4} + C.$$

Explain the apparent discrepancy in the three results.

PROBLEMS

Find the following integrals (Problems 1–25) by using the theorems of this article. Check each result by differentiating.

1. $\displaystyle \int (x^2 - 1)^2 2x \, dx$

2. $\displaystyle \int \frac{dx}{\sqrt{1 - x}}$

3. $\displaystyle \int x\sqrt{x^2 - 4} \, dx$

4. $\displaystyle \int \frac{x \, dx}{\sqrt{9 - x^2}}$

5. $\displaystyle\int y^2(y^3 + a^3)^{3/2}\,dy$

6. $\displaystyle\int (2x^2 + 3x)^3(8x + 6)\,dx$

7. $\displaystyle\int \sin^2 x \cos x\,dx$

8. $\displaystyle\int \cos^2 x \sin x\,dx$

9. $\displaystyle\int \sin 3x\,dx$

10. $\displaystyle\int \cos 4x\,dx$

11. $\displaystyle\int \frac{dx}{1 - x}$

12. $\displaystyle\int \frac{dx}{2x - 3}$

13. $\displaystyle\int \frac{(\log_e x)^2\,dx}{x}$

14. $\displaystyle\int \frac{2 + \log_e x}{x}\,dx$

15. $\displaystyle\int \frac{x + 3}{x + 1}\,dx$ [*Hint:* Divide $x + 3$ by $x + 1$.]

16. $\displaystyle\int \frac{x^2 + x}{x - 1}\,dx$

17. $\displaystyle\int \frac{2x^2 + 3}{x + 1}\,dx$

18. $\displaystyle\int \tan x\,dx$ $\left[Hint:\ \tan x \equiv \dfrac{\sin x}{\cos x}\cdot\right]$

19. $\displaystyle\int \cos^2 x\,dx$ $\left[Hint:\ \text{Recall } \cos^2 x \equiv \dfrac{1 + \cos 2x}{2}\cdot\right]$

20. $\displaystyle\int \sin^2 x\,dx$

21. $\displaystyle\int (1 + \cos x)^2\,dx$

22. $\displaystyle\int e^{2x-1}\,dx$

23. $\displaystyle\int (e^x - e^{-x})^2\,dx$

24. $\displaystyle\int \frac{e^{1/x}\,dx}{x^2}$

25. $\displaystyle\int \frac{e^x\,dx}{e^x - 1}$

26. Prove
$$\int \frac{g'(x)\,dx}{\sqrt{1 - [g(x)]^2}} = \text{Arcsin } g(x) + C.$$

27. Prove
$$\int \frac{g'(x)\,dx}{1 + [g(x)]^2} = \text{Arctan } g(x) + C.$$

19–4 Two simple applications of integration. We are now prepared to consider some of the simpler applications of integration. We recall from Article 10–4 that if an equation of a curve is given, by differentiation we can find the slope of the curve at any point. By the process of integration we can now find the curve when the slope is given.

EXAMPLE 1. Find a function the curve of whose graph has, at any point (x, y) on the curve, the slope $3x^2 - 2$ and passes through the point whose coordinates are $(1, 3)$.

Solution. By the definition in Article 10–4, the derivative of the function at the point (x, y) is the slope $3x^2 - 2$. Thus,

$$y = \int (3x^2 - 2)\, dx + C, \qquad \text{or} \qquad y = x^3 - 2x + C.$$

This represents a family of curves which all have the same slope for any particular value of x. For the curve that passes through $(1, 3)$, y must be 3 when x is 1, so that $3 = 1^3 - 2 \cdot 1 + C$, or $C = 4$. Therefore the required function is $y = x^3 - 2x + 4$.

Another application in which we can use the notion of integration is that of the motion of bodies under the influence of gravity, assuming the resistance of air to be negligible. With the one assumption that the acceleration of gravity is $32\ \text{ft/sec}^2$, and denoting acceleration by a, we have

$$a = Dv = -32, \tag{19–15}$$

where the derivative of v is with respect to time t. The minus sign indicates that the distance s the body has traveled is measured positively upward from the ground. The fact that the acceleration is negative indicates that the velocity is decreasing as the time increases. Since $Dv = -32$, $v = \int -32\, dt = -32t + C$. At time $t = 0$, $C = v$. We shall denote this initial velocity by v_0. Thus,

$$v = -32t + v_0. \tag{19–16}$$

Recalling that the velocity $v = Ds$ where again the derivative is with respect to time t, we have $Ds = -32t + v_0$, or

$$s = \int (-32t + v_0)\, dt = -16t^2 + v_0 t + C^*.$$

When $t = 0$, $s = C^*$, which we shall denote by s_0, the initial distance. Then

$$s = -16t^2 + v_0 t + s_0. \tag{19–17}$$

Frequently s is measured from the initial position, that is, $t = 0$. In this case, $s_0 = 0$, so that Eq. (19–17) becomes

$$s = v_0 t - 16t^2. \tag{19–18}$$

It is interesting to see how these equations, so frequently encountered in physics as definitions, are derived from a first fundamental assumption.

PROBLEMS

Find a function the curve of whose graph has the given slope and passes through the given point in Problems 1–6.

1. Slope $x^2 - 1$; point $(2, 3)$.   2. Slope $\sqrt{x}$; point $(1, 0)$.
3. Slope $1/\sqrt{x}$; point $(1, 2)$.   4. Slope $1/x$; point $(1, 1)$.
5. Slope $\sin x$; point $(\pi/2, 1)$.   6. Slope e^x, point $(0, 2)$.

In Problems 7–13 find a polynomial function of lowest degree which satisfies the stated conditions.

7. The graph of its curve has a minimum at $(2, 3)$.

8. The graph of its curve has a maximum at $(2, 3)$.

9. The graph of its curve has a minimum at $(2, 3)$ and passes through $(4, 7)$. [*Hint:* Let $Dy = k(x - 2)$.]

10. The graph of its curve passes through $(1, 1)$ with slope 3 and has a minimum where $x = -2$.

11. The graph of its curve has a maximum at $(2, 3)$ and passes through $(4, -1)$. Explain why this could not be a minimum.

12. The graph of its curve has a maximum at $(1, 2)$ and a minimum at $(0, -4)$.

13. The graph of its curve has an inflection point at $(1, 0)$ and passes through $(0, 0)$.

14. Find an equation of the curve for which $D^2y = \sqrt{x}$ and that passes through $(4, 0)$ with an inclination of $45°$.

15. A body was projected upward from the ground with an initial velocity of 64 ft/sec. Express the height of the body above the ground after t seconds. At what time was the body the highest and at this time what was the height?

16. A ball was thrown upward from a window 120 feet above the ground, with an initial velocity of 64 ft/sec. Express the height of this ball above the ground after t seconds. At what time was this ball the highest, and what was this greatest height? How many seconds after it was thrown did the ball reach the ground, and with what velocity?

17. A body falls from rest from a balloon 2000 feet above the ground. How long will it take to reach the ground, and with what velocity will it strike the ground?

18. If a stone is thrown straight down from the balloon in Problem 17 with a velocity of 32 ft/sec, with what velocity will it strike the ground, and in how many seconds after it is thrown?

19. A point moves along a straight line with velocity $3t - 4$. If its displacement is 6 when $t = 2$, what is the displacement when $t = 4$?

20. A particle moves along a straight line with acceleration $3 - 3t$. When $t = 1$, its distance from the origin is 6, but when $t = 2$, its distance from the origin is 10. What is the velocity of the particle when $t = 3$?

19–5 Area as an integral. We shall now turn our attention to one of the most important uses of integration, that of calculating areas. Let us consider the area bounded above by the graph of the function $f(x)$ which is continuous on the interval $a \le x \le b$, below by the x-axis, on the left by the vertical line $x = a$, and on the right by the vertical line $x = b$. We shall assume that such an area exists and denote it by A.

For our purposes, we shall represent this as an area swept over by a vertical line at x, where $a \leq x \leq b$ (see Fig. 19–1), while this line moves from left to right from $x = a$ to $x = b$. The line extends from the x-axis to the curve $y = f(x)$. The length of this moving vertical line is, of course, equal to $f(x)$. The area swept over will depend upon the value x and thus is a function of x, $A(x)$. We are able to show that $A'(x) = f(x)$. Since $A(x)$ has a derivative, it is continuous; and by letting $A(a) = 0$, the value of $A(x)$ at $x = b$, that is $A(b)$ is the required area.

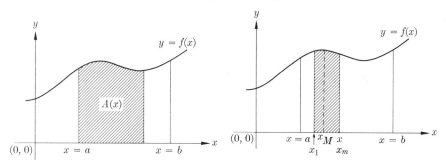

FIGURE 19–1   FIGURE 19–2

THEOREM 19–13. *If the function $A(x)$ represents the area bounded by the graph of the function $y = f(x)$, continuous on $a \leq x \leq b$ and positive, the x-axis, the line $x = a$, and the vertical line at x, then*

$$A'(x) = f(x). \tag{19–19}$$

Proof. Let x_1 be any number such that $a \leq x_1 \leq b$, and consider it held fixed. For any x greater than x_1, $A(x) > A(x_1)$, and $A(x) - A(x_1)$ is the area under the curve and above the x-axis between x_1 and x (it is the shaded area in Fig. 19–2). If $f(x_m)$ denotes the minimum value of $f(x)$ for any value in the interval between x_1 and x, and $f(x_M)$ the maximum in the interval,* we clearly have the inequality

$$f(x_m)(x - x_1) \leq A(x) - A(x_1) \leq f(x_M)(x - x_1).$$

Since $x - x_1 > 0$,

$$f(x_m) \leq \frac{A(x) - A(x_1)}{x - x_1} \leq f(x_M). \tag{19–20}$$

---

* x_m and x_M are the points in the interval from $x = x_1$ to $x = x$ where the function $f(x)$ has its minimum and maximum. Any continuous function on a closed interval has such points.

Since $f(x)$ is continuous, $x_1 \leq x_m \leq x$, and $x_1 \leq x_M \leq x$,

$$\lim_{x \to x_1} f(x_m) = f(x_1) \qquad \text{and} \qquad \lim_{x \to x_1} f(x_M) = f(x_1).$$

Therefore, since the limits of the extremes in (19–20) are equal,

$$\lim_{x \to x_1} \frac{A(x) - A(x_1)}{x - x_1}$$

exists and is equal to $f(x_1)$. Since x_1 was any value between a and b, we have the required result.

It should be mentioned that the vertical line was regarded as moving to the right, so that $x > x_1$ and $A(x) > A(x_1)$. If the line were moving from right to left, the same type of argument could be used, and the result would be the same.

Since $A'(x) = f(x)$,

$$A(x) = \int f(x)\, dx + C, \tag{19–21}$$

where with the original assumptions, we may find not only the value of C for any such area problem, but also the area itself. If we let $F(x)$ be any integral of $f(x)$,

$$A(x) = F(x) + C.$$

We wish to have the value of $A(x)$ at $x = a$ or $A(a) = 0$, so that

$$0 = F(a) + C \qquad \text{or} \qquad C = -F(a).$$

Hence

$$A(x) = F(x) - F(a). \tag{19–22}$$

This expression, satisfying both the conditions imposed just before the statement of Theorem 19–13, gives an expression for the area under the curve $y = f(x)$ and above the x-axis, from a to x. Thus the area from a to b is

$$A(b) = F(b) - F(a). \tag{19–23}$$

The expression in Eq. (19–22) is so important and so frequently used, not only in area problems but also in other applications, that a special name and notation is given to it.

DEFINITION 19–2.

$$F(x) - F(a) = \int_a^x f(x)\, dx, \tag{19–24}$$

where $F'(x) = f(x)$, is called the definite integral *from a to x of $f(x)$.*

The expression given in (19–23) may be written as $\int_a^b f(x)\, dx$ and is called the *definite integral* from a to b. The notation frequently used in such an integration is

$$\int_a^b f(x)\, dx = F(x)\Big|_a^b = F(b) - F(a). \qquad (19\text{-}25)$$

By Theorem 19–13 and Definition 19–2, we have our final result:

THEOREM 19–14. *If the function $f(x)$ is positive and continuous on the interval $a \le x \le b$, the area bounded by $y = f(x)$, the x-axis, and the vertical lines $x = a$ and $x = b$ is expressed*

$$\boxed{\int_a^b f(x)\, dx = F(b) - F(a),}$$

where $F'(x) = f(x)$.

EXAMPLE 1. Find the value of $\int_1^3 (x^2 + x)\, dx$.

Solution. $\displaystyle \int_1^3 (x^2 + x)\, dx = \frac{x^3}{3} + \frac{x^2}{2}\Big|_1^3 = \frac{3^3}{3} + \frac{3^2}{2} - \left(\frac{1}{3} + \frac{1}{2}\right) = \frac{38}{3}.$

This may be considered the area between the graph of $y = x^2 + x$ and the x-axis from $x = 1$ to $x = 3$.

EXAMPLE 2. Find the area bounded by the parabola $y = -x^2 + 6x - 5$ and the x-axis.

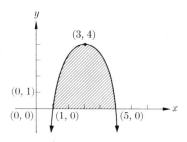

FIGURE 19–3

Solution. Since the curve crosses the x-axis at $x = 1$ and 5, we are interested in the area between the curve and the x-axis between 1 and 5. (See Fig. 19–3.) Therefore,

$$\int_1^5 (-x^2 + 6x - 5)\, dx = -\frac{x^3}{3} + 3x^2 - 5x\Big|_1^5$$

$$= (-\tfrac{125}{3} + 75 - 25) - (-\tfrac{1}{3} + 3 - 5) = \tfrac{32}{3}.$$

EXAMPLE 3. Find the area under one arch of the curve whose equation is
$y = \sin x$.

Solution. Since one arch of the sine curve extends from $x = 0$ to $x = \pi$
(Fig. 4–7), the required area is

$$\int_0^\pi \sin x \, dx = -\cos x \Big|_0^\pi = -[-1 - 1] = 2.$$

PROBLEMS

Evaluate the following definite integrals in Problems 1–12.

1. $\displaystyle\int_1^3 3x^2 \, dx$

2. $\displaystyle\int_0^3 (x^3 - 4x + 5) \, dx$

3. $\displaystyle\int_0^1 (1 - \sqrt{x})^2 \, dx$

4. $\displaystyle\int_0^{\pi/2} \cos x \, dx$

5. $\displaystyle\int_1^2 \frac{dx}{x^2}$

6. $\displaystyle\int_{-2}^0 \frac{dx}{x + 3}$

7. $\displaystyle\int_5^7 \frac{dx}{x - 4}$

8. $\displaystyle\int_0^1 (e^x + e^{-x}) \, dx$

9. $\displaystyle\int_{-1}^1 \sqrt{1 - x} \, dx$

10. $\displaystyle\int_0^1 2x(x^2 + 1)^2 \, dx$

11. $\displaystyle\int_1^4 \frac{dx}{\sqrt{4x - 1}}$

12. $\displaystyle\int_0^2 \sqrt{2x + 5} \, dx$

In each of the following problems draw a figure carefully, indicating the area
to be calculated.

13. Find the area under the curve of $y = x^2$ from $x = 1$ to $x = 4$.

14. Find the area under the curve of $y = \sqrt{x}$ from $x = 1$ to $x = 4$.

15. Find by integration the area of the triangle bounded by the x-axis and
the lines $y = 2x$ and $x = 3$. Check the result by elementary geometry.

16. Find the area below $y = x^2 + 2$ and above the x-axis between $x = -2$
and $x = 2$.

17. Find the area under one arch of the curve $y = 3 \sin 2\pi x$.

In Problems 18–27, find the area bounded by each of the curves and the x-axis.

18. $y = 4x - x^2$

19. $y = 9 - x^2$

20. $y = -x^2 + 4x - 3$

21. $y = -x^2 + 7x - 12$

22. $y = -x^2 - 2x + 3$

23. $y = 3 + x - 2x^2$

24. $y = x^3 + 2x + 1$ from $x = 0$ to $x = 3$

25. $y = x\sqrt{2x^2 + 1}$ from $x = 0$ to $x = 2$

26. $y = \dfrac{x}{\sqrt{2x+1}}$ from $x = 0$ to $x = 4$

27. $y = \dfrac{x}{\sqrt{2x^2+1}}$ from $x = 0$ to $x = 2$

19–6 Area in the plane. We have assumed in all our discussions that $a < b$ and that $f(x) \geq 0$ over the interval $a \leq x \leq b$. Such restrictions, of course, limit considerations. Let us give a more general definition, that is, the same basic one but without the restriction that $f(x) \geq 0$ or that $a < b$, and determine the resulting geometrical meaning.

DEFINITION 19–3. *If $f(x)$ is continuous at all values between a and b, whether $a < b$ or $b < a$,*

$$\int_a^b f(x)\,dx = F(b) - F(a),$$

where $DF(x) = f(x)$.

1. *Conditions on a and b.* To interpret the relationship between a and b geometrically, we make use of the following theorem based on Definition 19–3.

THEOREM 19–15. $\int_a^b f(x)\,dx = -\int_b^a f(x)\,dx.$

Proof. $\int_a^b f(x)\,dx = F(b) - F(a)$ but also, by definition,

$$\int_b^a f(x)\,dx = F(a) - F(b) = -\,[F(b) - F(a)]$$

$$= -\int_a^b f(x)\,dx.$$

Thus interchanging the limits merely changes the sign of the result; that is, if $b < a$, the integral may still be interpreted as an area, when $f(x) \geq 0$. Ordinarily we shall consider $a < b$.

2. *Case where $f(x) < 0$ for $a \leq x \leq b$.* If $f(x) < 0$, let $-f(x) = f^+(x)$ where $f^+ \geq 0$. Then

$$\int_a^b f(x)\,dx = -\int_a^b f^+(x)\,dx,$$

which represents the negative value of the area under the curve $f^+(x)$ and above the x-axis, between a and b. Since $f^+(x)$ is the image of $f(x)$ reflected on the x-axis, the result of the integration of $\int_a^b f(x)\,dx$ where $f(x) < 0$ is the area between the curve and the x-axis with a negative sign.

3. *Case where $f(x) > 0$ for some of the interval $a \leq x \leq b$, but the graph of $y = f(x)$ crosses the x-axis in this interval, so that for some of the interval $f(x) < 0$.* We have the following theorem.

THEOREM 19–16.   *If $f(x)$ is continuous on the interval $a \le x \le b$, $f(x) \ge 0$, $a < c < b$,*

$$\int_a^b f(x)\, dx = \int_a^c f(x)\, dx + \int_c^b f(x)\, dx, \qquad (19\text{–}26)$$

where $F'(x) = f(x)$.

Proof. Since

$$\int_a^c f(x)\, dx = F(c) - F(a), \qquad \text{and} \qquad \int_c^b f(x)\, dx = F(b) - F(c),$$

we have, by adding respective members of these equations,

$$\int_a^c f(x)\, dx + \int_c^b f(x)\, dx = F(c) - F(a) + F(b) - F(c) = F(b) - F(a),$$

which by definition is equal to $\int_a^b f(x)\, dx$. We are now able to use a combination of the original result (Theorem 19–14) and that mentioned in Case 2.

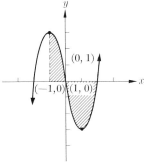

FIGURE 19–4

EXAMPLE. If $f(x) = x^3 - 4x$, find $\int_{-1}^2 f(x)\, dx$ and interpret the result geometrically.

Solution. $\displaystyle \int_{-1}^2 f(x)\, dx = \int_{-1}^2 (x^3 - 4x)\, dx = \frac{x^4}{4} - 2x^2 \Big|_{-1}^2$

$$= (4 - 8) - (\tfrac{1}{4} - 2) = -\tfrac{9}{4}.$$

If we set $f(x) = 0$, we find the graph of the function crosses the x-axis at $(-2, 0)$, $(0, 0)$, and $(2, 0)$. (See Fig. 19–4.)

By Theorem 19–16,

$$\int_{-1}^2 f(x)\, dx = \int_{-1}^0 f(x)\, dx + \int_0^2 f(x)\, dx,$$

and we have

$$\int_{-1}^{0} (x^3 - 4x)\, dx = \left. \frac{x^4}{4} - 2x^2 \right|_{-1}^{0} = -\left(\tfrac{1}{4} - 2\right) = \tfrac{7}{4},$$

$$\int_{0}^{2} (x^3 - 4x)\, dx = \left. \frac{x^4}{4} - 2x^2 \right|_{0}^{2} = 4 - 8 = -4.$$

Thus the area bounded by the curve and the x-axis between -1 and 0 is $\tfrac{7}{4}$, and the area bounded by the curve and the x-axis between 0 and 2 is 4. (Since $f(x) < 0$ for x between 0 and 2, -4 represents the negative of this area.) The magnitude of the answer $-\tfrac{9}{4}$ represents the difference between these areas, while the minus sign indicates that the area below the x-axis is greater than that above. In general, to obtain such areas, where part is below the x-axis and part above, care must be taken to determine where $f(x) > 0$ and where $f(x) < 0$. *Area itself is always considered positive.*

PROBLEMS

Prove, using the general Definition 19–3 and assuming $f(x)$ and $g(x)$ are continuous (Problems 1–5):

1. $\displaystyle \int_{a}^{x} -f(x)\, dx = -\int_{a}^{x} f(x)\, dx$

2. $\displaystyle \int_{a}^{x} kf(x)\, dx = k \int_{a}^{x} f(x)\, dx$

3. $\displaystyle \int_{a}^{x} f(x)\, dx \pm \int_{a}^{x} g(x)\, dx = \int_{a}^{x} [f(x) \pm g(x)]\, dx$

4. $\displaystyle \int_{a}^{a} f(x)\, dx = 0$. With this problem and $a > b$ (the discussion in Case 1) we have considered all cases $a < b$, $a = b$, and $a > b$.

5. $\displaystyle D\left[\int_{a}^{x} f(x)\, dx\right] = f(x)$

6. Find the area bounded by the parabola $y = x^2 - 7x + 10$ and the x-axis.

7. Find the area bounded by the parabola $y = x^2 - 2x - 3$ and the x-axis.

8. Find the area bounded by the curve of $y = x^3 - 6x^2 + 11x - 6$ and the x-axis between $x = 1$ and $x = 3$.

9. Find the value of $\int_{-1}^{1} (x^3 - x)\, dx$. Explain the result geometrically.

10. Find the value of $\int_{1}^{2} (1 - x^2)\, dx$. Explain the result geometrically.

19–7 Area between two curves. Frequently we wish to find the area between two different curves. This is easily accomplished by using the next two theorems, as is shown geometrically in Figs. 19–5 and 19–6.

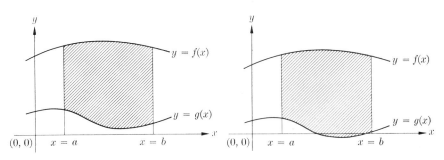

FIGURE 19-5   FIGURE 19-6

THEOREM 19-17. *If $f(x) \geq g(x) > 0$ and both are continuous for all x in the interval $a \leq x \leq b$, the area between $y = f(x)$, $y = g(x)$, and the lines $x = a$ and $x = b$ is given by*

$$A = \int_a^b [f(x) - g(x)]\, dx. \tag{19-27}$$

Proof. Since by Problem 3, Article 19-6,

$$\int_a^b [f(x) - g(x)]\, dx = \int_a^b f(x)\, dx - \int_a^b g(x)\, dx,$$

we have our result, for the first integral on the right represents the area between $y = f(x)$ and the x-axis, and the second integral, the area between $y = g(x)$ and the x-axis (Fig. 19-5).

THEOREM 19-18. *If $f(x) \geq g(x)$, but $g(x) \leq 0$ over all or part of the interval $a \leq x \leq b$, and both functions are continuous, the area between $y = f(x)$, $y = g(x)$, and the lines $x = a$ and $x = b$ is again*

$$A = \int_a^b [f(x) - g(x)]\, dx.$$

Proof. If a constant k sufficiently large to make $g(x) + k > 0$ for all x is added to both $f(x)$ and $g(x)$, the area between the two new functions is left unchanged, but now

$$f(x) + k \geq g(x) + k > 0.$$

Therefore,

$$\int_a^b [(f(x) + k) - (g(x) + k)]\, dx$$

represents the required area and

$$\int_a^b [(f(x) + k) - (g(x) + k)]\, dx = \int_a^b [f(x) - g(x)]\, dx,$$

which is the required result.

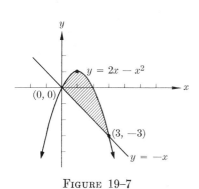

FIGURE 19–7

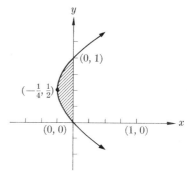

FIGURE 19–8

EXAMPLE 1. Find the area bounded by the parabola $y = 2x - x^2$ and the line $y = -x$ (Fig. 19–7).

Solution. Since the two curves intersect at $(0, 0)$ and $(3, -3)$ (why?), the required area, by Theorem (19–18), is

$$\int_0^3 [(2x - x^2) - (-x)]\, dx.$$

Evaluating this integral, we have

$$\int_0^3 [2x - x^2 - (-x)]\, dx = \int_0^3 (3x - x^2)\, dx$$

$$= \frac{3x^2}{2} - \frac{x^3}{3}\Big|_0^3 = \frac{9}{2}.$$

EXAMPLE 2. Find the area between $x = y^2 - y$ and the y-axis.

Solution (1) As is shown in Fig. 19–8, the vertex of this parabola is $(-\frac{1}{4}, \frac{1}{2})$, since $x = y^2 - y$ or $x + \frac{1}{4} = y^2 - y + \frac{1}{4}$, that is, $(y - \frac{1}{2})^2 = x + \frac{1}{4}$. The required area can be regarded, if we use Theorem 19–7, as the area between the two functions [solving $(y - \frac{1}{2})^2 = x + \frac{1}{4}$ for y]

$$y = \tfrac{1}{2} + \sqrt{x + \tfrac{1}{4}} \qquad \text{and} \qquad y = \tfrac{1}{2} - \sqrt{x + \tfrac{1}{4}}$$

from $x = -\frac{1}{4}$ to $x = 0$. Thus,

$$\int_{-1/4}^0 [(\tfrac{1}{2} + \sqrt{x + \tfrac{1}{4}}) - (\tfrac{1}{2} - \sqrt{x + \tfrac{1}{4}})]\, dx = 2 \int_{-1/4}^0 \sqrt{x + \tfrac{1}{4}}\, dx$$

$$= \frac{4(x + \tfrac{1}{4})^{3/2}}{3}\Big|_{-1/4}^0 = \frac{4}{3}[(\tfrac{1}{4})^{3/2} - 0] = \frac{1}{6}.$$

Solution (2) Frequently, as in this case, problems can be greatly simplified by interchanging the variables x and y in all the previous results. Thus the expression for the negative of the required area is $\int_0^1 f(y)\, dy$, where $x = f(y) = y^2 - y$. Hence

$$\int_0^1 (y^2 - y)\, dy = \frac{y^3}{3} - \frac{y^2}{2}\Big|_0^1 = \frac{1}{3} - \frac{1}{2} = -\frac{1}{6},$$

and the area is $\frac{1}{6}$.

PROBLEMS

Draw graphs and indicate the required area for each problem.

1. Find the area between the curves of the two equations $y = 2 - x^2$ and $x = y$.

2. Find the area bounded by the parabola $x^2 = y$ and $y = 4$.

3. Find the area bounded by the curve whose equation is $y = 2x - x^2$ and the line $y = -2$.

4. Find the area bounded by the parabola $y = x^2$ and the line $3x = 4y$.

5. Find the area bounded by the parabolas

$$x^2 = 2(y - 1) \quad \text{and} \quad x^2 = 4(y - 2).$$

6. Find the total area which is enclosed between the curve whose equation is $y = x(x - 1)(x - 4)$ and the line $y = 4(x - 1)$.

7. Find the area between the curve whose equation is $x = 1 - y^2$ and the y-axis.

8. Find the area bounded by the curve whose equation is $x = y^2 - y^3$ and the y-axis.

9. Find the area bounded by the curve whose equation is $x = 4y - y^2$ and $x + y = 4$. Do this two ways.

10. Find the area in the first quadrant between the two curves whose equations are $y^2 = x$ and $y^2 = x^3$.

19–8 Volumes of solids. A solid of revolution is a volume which is generated by revolving a plane area about a line in the plane of the area. By the very nature of such a solid, the cross-section perpendicular to the line about which it is revolved (its axis) is a circle or circular ring with its center on this line. Such volumes are easily found by integration.

Let us consider the same area as in Article 19–5, that which is bounded above by the graph of the function $y = f(x)$, which is continuous on $a \le x \le b$, bounded below by the x-axis, and between $x = a$ and $x = b$. If this area is revolved about the x-axis, thus generating a volume of revolution (Figure 19–9 shows one-fourth of the generated volume), the volume from $x = a$ to any value of x between a and b will depend on the choice of x. We shall denote such a volume by the function of x, $V(x)$.

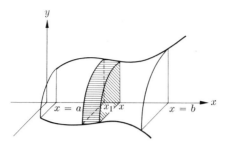

FIGURE 19–9

THEOREM 19–19. *If $V(x)$ represents the volume generated by revolving about the x-axis, the area bounded by the curve of the function $y = f(x)$, continuous on $a \leq x \leq b$ and positive, the x-axis, the line $x = a$, and the vertical line at x, then*

$$V'(x) = \pi[f(x)]^2. \qquad (19\text{–}28)$$

Proof. Let x_1 be any number such that $a < x_1 < b$, and consider it held fixed. For any x greater than x_1, $V(x) > V(x_1)$ and $V(x) - V(x_1)$ is the volume shown in Fig. 19–9 between x_1 and x. If $f(x_m)$ denotes the minimum value of $f(x)$ in the interval between x_1 and x, and $f(x_M)$ the maximum of the function in this interval, we have the inequality

$$\pi[f(x_m)]^2(x - x_1) \leq V(x) - V(x_1) \leq \pi[f(x_M)]^2(x - x_1).$$

To establish this inequality, we should realize that the volume $V(x) - V(x_1)$ lies between the volumes of two cylinders, one with $f(x_m)$ for its radius, the other with $f(x_M)$. In both cases the altitude of the cylinder is $x - x_1$. If we divide each member of the inequality by $x - x_1$,

$$\pi[f(x_m)]^2 \leq \frac{V(x) - V(x_1)}{x - x_1} \leq \pi[f(x_M)]^2. \qquad (19\text{–}29)$$

Since $f(x)$ is continuous, as in the proof of Theorem 19–13,

$$\lim_{x \to x_1} f(x_m) = \lim_{x \to x_1} f(x_M) = f(x_1),$$

so that

$$\lim_{x \to x_1} \frac{V(x) - V(x_1)}{x - x_1}$$

exists and is equal to $\pi[f(x_1)]^2$. Since x_1 was any value between a and b, we have our result. As in Theorem 19–13, the argument is similar and valid whether the vertical line at x is taken on the right or left of x_1.

Since $V(x)$ satisfies (19–28) and $V(a) = 0$,

$$V(x) = \pi \int_a^x [f(x)]^2 \, dx,$$

and the volume of revolution from a to b is

$$\boxed{V = \pi \int_a^b [f(x)]^2 \, dx} \qquad (19\text{–}30)$$

EXAMPLE. Find the volume of the right circular cone with height h and radius r. See Fig. 19–10.

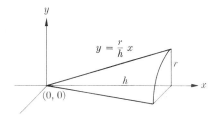

FIGURE 19–10

Solution. Since the function $y = f(x)$ is $y = (r/h)x$ (why?), we have

$$\pi \int_0^h \left(\frac{rx}{h}\right)^2 dx = \frac{\pi r^2}{h^2} \int_0^h x^2 \, dx = \frac{\pi r^2}{h^2} \left[\frac{x^3}{3}\right]\bigg|_0^h$$

$$= \frac{\pi r^2 h}{3}.$$

PROBLEMS

1. Find the volume of the solid obtained by revolving about the x-axis the area bounded by the parabola $y^2 = 4x$, the x-axis, and the line $x = 4$.

2. Find the volume of the solid generated by revolving about the x-axis the area bounded by $y = 3x - x^2$ and $y = 0$.

3. Find the volume of the solid generated by revolving about the x-axis the area bounded by $x^{1/2} + y^{1/2} = a^{1/2}$, $x = 0$, and $y = 0$.

4. Find the volume of a sphere of radius a. [*Hint:* $f(x) = \sqrt{a^2 - x^2}$.]

5. Find the volume of the solid obtained by revolving the area enclosed by the ellipse $(x^2/a^2) + (y^2/b^2) = 1$.

6. Find the volume of the solid generated by revolving about the x-axis the area in the first quadrant bounded by $x^{2/3} + y^{2/3} = a^{2/3}$, $x = 0$, and $y = 0$.

7. Develop the expression for the volume of the solid of revolution if the area revolved is that enclosed by the curve $x = g(y)$, the y-axis, and the lines

$y = a$ and $y = b$,

$$V = \pi \int_a^b [f(y)]^2 \, dy.$$

What conditions are imposed on $x = f(y)$?

8. Find the volume of the solid generated by revolving about the y-axis the area bounded by the parabola $y^2 = 4x$, the y-axis, and the line $y = 4$.

9. Find the volume of the solid generated by revolving about the y-axis the area bounded by the curve $y = \log_e x$, $y = 2$, $x = 0$, and $y = 0$.

10. Find the volume of the solid generated by revolving about the x-axis one arch of the curve $y = \sin x$.

19–9 Work done by a variable force. If a constant force of magnitude f acts in a straight line through a distance s, we recall from elementary physics that the total work done by this force is

$$W = (\text{force})(\text{distance}) = fs. \tag{19–31}$$

This leads to a simple generalization when the force is not constant but a continuous function of its position. If the force is $f(x)$, a function of the distance x, acting along the x-axis from the point where $x = a$ to $x = b$, where $a < b$, the work done in moving from $x = a$ to any position x will also be a function of x, $W(x)$.

> DEFINITION 19–4. *If $f(x)$ is continuous on the interval $a \leq x \leq b$, the work done in moving a body under this force from a to x is given by the expression*
>
> $$W(x) = \int_a^x f(x) \, dx. \tag{19–32}$$

To show the appropriateness of this definition, if $f(x)$ is increasing, let x_1 be any fixed number such that $a < x_1 < b$. Then if $x_1 < x$,

$$f(x_1)(x - x_1) \leq W(x) - W(x_1) \leq f(x)(x - x_1),$$

or

$$f(x_1) \leq \frac{W(x) - W(x_1)}{x - x_1} \leq f(x). \tag{19–33}$$

Again, allowing x to approach x_1, since $f(x)$ is continuous,

$$\lim_{x \to x_1} f(x) = f(x_1).$$

Thus we have

$$\lim_{x \to x_1} \frac{W(x) - W(x_1)}{x - x_1},$$

which is equal to $W'(x)$, so that, with $W(a) = 0$,

$$W(x) = \int_a^x f(x)\,dx. \tag{19-34}$$

The fact that $f(x)$ is increasing is not part of the definition but is used in the explanation merely for convenience.

EXAMPLE. If a force is proportional to the distance that a spring is compressed ($f = kx$), and it takes a force of 10 pounds to compress a certain spring 1 inch, how much work will be done in compressing the spring 3 inches from its natural length?

Solution. Since $f = kx$ and $f = 10$ when $x = 1$, $k = 10$. Thus,

$$W = \int_0^3 10x\,dx = 5x^2 \Big|_0^3 = 45 \text{ inch-pounds.}$$

PROBLEMS

1. A spring of natural length 12 inches requires a force of 8 pounds to stretch it 1 inch. Find the work required to stretch the spring 2 inches.

2. Find the work required to stretch the spring in Problem 1

(a) from length 12 inches to length 15 inches,
(b) from length 13 inches to length 16 inches,
(c) from length 14 inches to length 17 inches.

3. For a spring of natural length 10 inches, compare the work required to stretch it from 11 to 12, and from 12 to 13 inches.

4. If 50 foot-pounds of work is necessary to stretch a spring from 12 to 14 inches, but 80 foot-pounds is necessary to stretch it from 13 to 15 inches, find the natural length of the spring.

5. The force exerted by gas on a piston that encloses it in a cylinder is $f = c/x$, where x is the distance of the piston from the fixed end of the cylinder and c is a constant. If the force exerted is 50 pounds when x is 20 inches, find the work done in decreasing x to 10 inches.

6. The force due to gravity acting on a particle at a distance x from the center of the earth is expressed by $f = c/x^2$, where c is a constant. If x is R, the earth's radius, the force f is the weight W of the body at the earth's surface. Find the work required to move the body from the surface of the earth to a distance R above the surface of the earth.

CHAPTER 20

PERMUTATIONS, COMBINATIONS, AND PROBABILITY

Although an extensive treatment is impossible here, certain elementary aspects of permutations and combinations will be discussed, since these branches of study are so useful in mathematics and in the other natural sciences. The results of our discussions will then be used in certain problems in simple probability.

20–1 The fundamental principle. We shall begin by considering a simple example. Let us find how many numbers of two different digits can be formed from the four integers 1, 2, 3, and 4. Any one of the four may be chosen for the tens digit of the number. With each particular choice of this type, there will remain three integers from which to choose the units digit. Thus, for each of the four choices, there are three more choices, making a total of $4 \cdot 3$ or 12 numbers in all. We have, then,

$$
\begin{aligned}
&41, 42, 43, \text{ (4 for the tens digit)}, \\
&31, 32, 34, \text{ (3 for the tens digit)}, \\
&21, 23, 24, \text{ (2 for the tens digit)}, \\
&12, 13, 14, \text{ (1 for the tens digit)}
\end{aligned} \tag{20–1}
$$

as the possible two-digit numbers.

A slightly more complicated problem would be to find how many numbers of three different digits could be formed with the same integers 1, 2, 3, and 4. Each of the 12 numbers listed in (20–1) can be regarded as representing the hundred and tens digits. Since two of the four integers have already been selected in each case, the possibility for the new units digit must be one of the two remaining integers. For example, with the first number 41, we may have 2 or 3, forming the numbers 412 or 413. We therefore have $(4 \cdot 3) \cdot 2$ or 24 numbers, each containing three digits, which can be formed from the given integers.

These examples have illustrated a fundamental principle.

FUNDAMENTAL PRINCIPLE. *If one thing can be done independently in n_1 different ways, and if a second thing can be done independently in n_2 different ways, and a third thing can be done independently in n_3 different ways, and so on (for any finite number of things), then the total number of ways in which all the things may be done in the stated order is $n_1 n_2 n_3 \ldots$*

EXAMPLE 1. How many different committees consisting of one Democrat and one Republican can be formed from seven Democrats and four Republicans?

Solution. The Democrat can be chosen in any one of seven ways, and independently, the Republican can be chosen in any one of four ways. Thus, by the fundamental principle, the total number of different possible committees is $7 \cdot 4 = 28$.

EXAMPLE 2. If two cubical dice are thrown, in how many ways can they fall?

Solution. Since each cube has six faces, each may fall independently any one of six different ways. Consequently, there are $6 \cdot 6 = 36$ possible ways for them to fall.

EXAMPLE 3. In a certain election, there are three candidates for president, four for vice-president, five for secretary, but only two for treasurer. In how many different ways may the election turn out?

Solution. With each of the three possibilities for president, there are four for vice-president. With each of these $(4 \cdot 3 = 12)$ possibilities, there are five possibilities for secretary, and so on. Thus the total number of different possible election results is

$$4(3)(5)(2) = 120.$$

PROBLEMS

1. A nickel and a dime are tossed on a table. In how many ways can they fall?

2. If all questions are answered in a true-false quiz of ten questions, how many ways are there of answering the entire quiz?

3. How many numbers of three different digits less than 500 can be formed from the integers 1, 2, 3, 4, 5, 6, 7?

4. If there are 12 milers entered in a race, in how many ways can first, second, and third place be awarded?

5. There are five main roads between the cities A and B, and four between B and C. In how many ways can a person drive from A to C and return, going through B on both trips, without driving on the same road twice?

6. How many numbers of at most three different digits can be formed from the integers 1, 2, 3, 4, 5, 6?

7. How many numbers of at least three different digits can be formed from the integers 1, 2, 3, 4, 5, 6?

8. A tennis club consists of 12 boys and 9 girls. How many mixed doubles teams (one boy and one girl) are possible? In how many ways can a mixed doubles match be arranged?

9. A freshman student must take a modern language, a natural science, a social science, and English. If there are four possible different modern languages, five natural sciences, three social sciences, but each student must take the same English course, in how many different ways can he select his course of study?

10. In selecting an ace, king, queen, and jack from an ordinary deck of 52 cards, how many ways may we choose if (a) they must be of different suits, (b) they may or may not be of different suits, (c) they must be of the same suit, (d) they must be in a particular suit?

11. If there are eight outside doors in a dormitory, in how many ways can a student enter one and (a) leave by a different door, (b) leave by any door?

12. A baseball stadium has four entrance gates and nine exits. In how many ways may two men enter together, but leave by different exits?

20–2 Permutations. Each different arrangement or ordered set of things is called a *permutation* of those things. For example, the numbers 423 and 432 use the same numbers, but are different permutations of the three numbers. In general, if we have n things and arrange r of them in a definite order, such an arrangement is a permutation of n things taken r at a time.

A formula for the total number of permutations of n different things taken r at a time is easily established by using the fundamental principle of the last article. This function of the integers n and r will be denoted by $P(n, r)$.* The possible number of arrangements of n things taken r at a time is equivalent to the number of ways of choosing from n different things to fill r positions. There are n choices for the first position, then $n - 1$ choices for the second position, $n - 2$ choices for the third, and so on. The rth position can be filled with any of the $n - (r - 1) = n - r + 1$ remaining things, so that the r positions can be filled in $n(n - 1)(n - 2) \ldots (n - r + 1)$ ways. Thus,

$$P(n, r) = n(n - 1)(n - 2) \ldots (n - r + 1). \qquad (20\text{–}2)$$

If we are interested in the permutation of n things taken n (or all) at a time, we note that $r = n$ in (20–2), and we have

$$P(n, n) = n(n - 1)(n - 2) \ldots 3 \cdot 2 \cdot 1 = n!.\dagger \qquad (20\text{–}3)$$

By multiplying the numerator and denominator of the right member of (20–2) by $(n - r)!$, we obtain an alternate formula for $P(n, r)$,

$$P(n, r) = \frac{n(n - 1)(n - 2) \ldots (n - r + 1)(n - r)!}{(n - r)!}$$

_____

* The symbol $_nP_r$ is also frequently used.

† Recall the definition of factorial n, $n!$ (Article 7–2).

or

$$P(n, r) = \frac{n!}{(n - r)!} \cdot {}^*$$

(20–4)

EXAMPLE 1. Find the number of permutations of the four integers 1, 2, 3, and 4 taken two at a time.

Solution. Since we wish to find the number of permutations of four things taken two at a time,

$$P(4, 2) = 4 \cdot 3 = 12.$$

These twelve arrangements are listed in Article (20–1).

EXAMPLE 2. If four persons enter a bus in which there are ten vacant seats, how many ways are there for the four to be seated?

Solution. Since this represents the arrangement of ten seats taken four at a time,

$$P(10, 4) = 10 \cdot 9 \cdot 8 \cdot 7 = 5040.$$

EXAMPLE 3. In how many ways may five books be arranged on a shelf?

Solution. This represents the permutation of five things taken five at a time. Thus,

$$P(5, 5) = 5! = 120.$$

Although the number of permutations of the eight letters of the word "readings" is clearly 8!, the number of such permutations of the letters of "gargling" is somewhat less, since three of the letters are alike. An example will illustrate the next theorem.

EXAMPLE 4. Find the number of permutations of the eight letters of "gargling."

Solution. Considering all the letters different, we would have P, the required number of permutations, equal to 8!. This might be done by giving each of the g's a different subscript, such as g_1, g_2, and g_3. Actually, however, the three g's could be permuted among themselves in 3! ways. In fact, for each distinct arrangement of the other letters, this would be the case. Thus $3! \, P = 8!$, or

$$P = \frac{8!}{3!}.$$

The proof of the following general theorem parallels the reasoning in Example 4 and is left as an exercise.

---

* Factorial zero, 0!, is by definition equal to 1.

THEOREM 20–1. *If P represents the number of different permutations of n things taken all at a time, when p are of one kind, q are of another kind, r of a third kind, and so on, then*

$$P = \frac{n!}{p!q!r!\ldots}.$$ (20–5)

EXAMPLE 5. How many permutations are there of the 11 letters in "Mississippi" taken all together?

Solution. Since there are four s's, four i's, and two p's, we have

$$P = \frac{11!}{4!4!2!} = 34{,}650.$$

PROBLEMS

1. How many numbers of three different digits each can be formed from the digits 1, 2, 3, 4, 5, 6, 7, 8, 9?

2. How many numbers of three different digits each less than 700 can be formed from the digits in Problem 1?

3. How many numbers of at most three different digits each can be formed from the digits in Problem 1?

4. In how many ways can a class elect a president, vice-president, secretary, and treasurer from a class of 100 students?

5. In how many ways can four boys and three girls be seated in a row containing seven seats (a) if they may sit anywhere, (b) if the boys and girls must alternate?

6. In how many ways can four boys and four girls be seated in a row containing eight seats (a) if they may sit anywhere, (b) if the boys and girls must alternate?

7. A baseball manager insists on having his best hitter bat fourth and the pitcher bat last. In such circumstances, how many batting orders are possible?

8. In how many ways can eight people be seated in a row of eight seats if two people insist on sitting next to each other?

9. A language teacher wants to keep books of the same language together on his shelf. If he has 12 spaces for 5 French, 4 Italian, and 3 German books, in how many ways can they be placed on his shelf?

10. In how many ways can eight people be seated around a table?

11. In how many ways can eight people be seated around a table if two people insist on sitting next to each other?

12. How many license plates can be made using any two letters for the first two places and any of the numbers 0 through 9 for the last three?

13. Do Problem 12, with the condition that no letter or number be repeated.

14. How many permutations are there of the letters of the word (a) "algebra," (b) "college"?

15. How many permutations are there of the letters of the word "Tennessee"?

16. In how many ways can four red beads, five white beads, and three blue beads be arranged in a row?

17. In how many ways can seven different colored beads be made into a bracelet?

18. Show that $P(n + 1, r) \equiv (n + 1)P(n, r - 1)$.

19. Solve the equation $P(n, 5) = 20P(n, 3)$ for n.

20. Find the value of $P(5, 1) + P(5, 2) + P(5, 3) + P(5, 4) + P(5, 5)$.

20–3 Combinations. In contrast to a permutation, which is a certain ordered arrangement of different things, a *combination* is a set or collection of things in no particular order. Thus, by the combinations of n different things taken r at a time, we mean all the possible selections of r different things from the n things, with no regard to order or arrangement. This total number of combinations is written $C(n, r)$.*

The only difference between permutations and combinations is order or arrangement. For any one of the $C(n, r)$ combinations, consisting of r different things, the r elements may be rearranged by permutation in $r!$ different ways. Therefore, for all the possible combinations there will be $C(n, r)r!$ different permutations. Since these are all the possible permutations of the n things taken r at a time, we have the relation

$$C(n, r) \cdot r! = P(n, r),$$

or

$$C(n, r) = \frac{P(n, r)}{r!}. \tag{20–6}$$

This may be written in terms of factorials by using (20–4),

$$C(n, r) = \frac{n!}{(n - r)!r!}. \tag{20–7}$$

If we use (20–7), it is clear that

$$C(n, r) = C(n, n - r) \tag{20–8}$$

(recall Problem 27, Article 8–2). The form given in (20–6) is most frequently used in problems.

EXAMPLE 1. In a class of 15 boys and 10 girls, in how many ways may a committee made up of 3 boys and 2 girls be selected?

---

* Recall Eq. (8–5) and accompanying footnote. The symbol $_nC_r$ is also frequently used.

Solution. Since order has nothing to do with membership on the committee, the boys may be selected in $C(15, 3)$ ways, while the girls may be selected in $C(10, 2)$ ways. By the fundamental principle, we have

$$C(15, 3) \cdot C(10, 2) = \frac{15 \cdot 14 \cdot 13}{1 \cdot 2 \cdot 3} \cdot \frac{10 \cdot 9}{1 \cdot 2}$$
$$= 20{,}475.$$

EXAMPLE 2. On a certain examination, the student must answer 8 out of the 12 questions, including exactly 5 of the first 6. In how many ways may he write the examination?

Solution. Since five of the first six must be answered, this may be done in $C(6, 5)$ ways. Having now answered five questions, he must answer three of the remaining six. This may be done in $C(6, 3)$ ways. Therefore the number of ways in which he can write the examination is given by

$$C(6, 5) \cdot C(6, 3) = 120.$$

Frequently we wish to find the total number of combinations of n things taken 1, 2, 3, . . . , or n at a time. In Problem 29, Article 8–2, we showed

$$2^n = 1 + C(n, 1) + C(n, 2) + C(n, 3) + \cdots + C(n, n),$$

so that the total number of combinations taken 1, 2, 3, . . . , or n at a time is

$$\boxed{C(n, 1) + C(n, 2) + C(n, 3) + \cdots + C(n, n) = 2^n - 1.} \quad (20\text{–}9)$$

EXAMPLE 3. How many different sums of money can be made from a penny, a nickel, a dime, and a quarter?

Solution. Since there are four coins, the number of different amounts of money is

$$C(4, 1) + C(4, 2) + C(4, 3) + C(4, 4) = 2^4 - 1 = 15.$$

PROBLEMS

1. Find the value of (a) $C(7, 4)$, (b) $C(10, 2)$, (c) $C(21, 19)$.
2. Find the value of

$$C(8, 3) + C(8, 4) + C(8, 5) + C(8, 6) + C(8, 7) + C(8, 8).$$

3. In how many ways may a committee of 4 be chosen from a group of 25?
4. From a group of 25 Democrats and 18 Republicans, how many committees consisting of 3 Democrats and 2 Republicans are possible?

5. From the group in Problem 4, if one of two specific Democrats is to be chairman, how many committees are possible with the same balance of Democrats and Republicans as previously stated?

6. How many football games are played if each of the nine football teams in a certain conference plays each of the other teams in that conference once?

7. On a college baseball squad, there are three catchers, five pitchers, seven infielders, and seven outfielders. How many different baseball nines can be formed?

8. In how many ways can a bridge hand of 13 cards be chosen from a deck of 52 cards?

9. In how many ways can a person get a bridge hand consisting of only aces or face cards?

10. In how many ways can a person get a bridge hand which consists of cards seven or lower?

11. In how many ways can a person get a bridge hand consisting of two aces, one king, one queen, three jacks, and the six other cards ten or less?

12. From four red balls, five white balls, and six blue balls, how many selections consisting of five balls can be made if two are to be red, one white, and two blue?

13. Without considering special cases, (a) how many straight lines are determined by nine points, (b) how many circles are determined by nine points?

14. How many triangles are determined by nine points no three of which lie on the same straight line?

15. How many tetrahedrons are determined by nine points no four of which lie in the same plane?

16. From a group of 15 people, how many committees can be formed consisting of two, three, or four people?

17. In how many ways may a college president's wife invite (a) two, (b) three, (c) two or more, of eight faculty wives to a tea?

18. How many different sums of money can be formed from a penny, nickel, dime, quarter, and half dollar if at least two coins are used?

19. Solve for n the equation $C(n + 2, 4) = 6C(n, 2)$.

20. Prove $C(n, r) + C(n, r - 1) \equiv C(n + 1, r)$.

20–4 Probability. The theory of probability, which had its origin in games of chance during the seventeenth century, and at that time was developed mathematically by Pascal (1623–1662) and Fermat (1601–1665), has become one of the most important and useful branches of mathematics. It is extremely helpful in statistical studies of physics, biological and social phenomena, in life insurance, in industry, and, in fact, in most fields of study in which the future is under consideration. Anything more than an introduction to the subject is, unfortunately, beyond the scope of this book.

In considering an event, we say that an act which may result in the event's occurring or failing to occur is a *trial*. If the event occurs, it is called a *success*, but if it fails to occur, it is called a *failure*.

DEFINITION 20–1. *If an event may occur s ways but fail to occur f ways and if each of the s + f ways is equally likely,* the probability of obtaining a success in a trial of the event is*

$$p = \frac{s}{s + f},$$ (20–10)

and the probability of obtaining a failure is

$$q = \frac{f}{s + f}.$$ (20–11)

It is important to note that $0 \le p \le 1$, $0 \le q \le 1$, and $p + q = 1$. If a success is certain, $f = 0$, so that $p = 1$. Also, since $p + q = 1$, $q = 1 - p$. Thus, if the probability that an event will succeed is p, the probability that it will fail is $1 - p$.

In computing a probability according to this definition, we must compute s, f, and $s + f$. To do this, we often make use of the formulas in the last two articles.

EXAMPLE 1. If a die, which is a cube that has spots one through six on its faces, is thrown, what is the probability that a four will show?

Solution. Since $s = 1$ and $s + f = 6$, $p = \frac{1}{6}$.

EXAMPLE 2. If two cards are drawn from an ordinary deck of 52 cards, what is the probability that both are spades?

Solution. The number of ways of drawing two cards from a deck of 52 is $C(52, 2)$, while the number of ways of drawing two spades is $C(13, 2)$. Thus $s + f = C(52, 2)$ and $s = C(13, 2)$, so that

$$p = \frac{C(13, 2)}{C(52, 2)} = \frac{78}{1326} = \frac{1}{17}.$$

EXAMPLE 3. A committee of five is to be selected at random from six Democrats and four Republicans. What is the probability that the committee will consist of three Democrats and two Republicans?

Solution. The total number of possible five-man committees is $C(10, 5)$, while the number of "successful" committees is $C(6, 3) \cdot C(4, 2)$. Thus,

$$p = \frac{C(6, 3)C(4, 2)}{C(10, 5)} = \frac{10}{21}.$$

It must be emphasized that a probability based on theory will *guarantee nothing* in an actual situation. Specifically, in Example 1, the probability

---

* By equally likely, we mean that there is no reason for expecting any one to happen rather than any other.

of $\frac{1}{6}$ for a four's showing does not mean that a four will show exactly once in six throws. Nor will it show exactly ten times in 60 throws. We merely expect, in any large number of throws, to have a four show approximately one-sixth of the time.

PROBLEMS

1. If a die is thrown, what is the probability that a three will turn up? (b) What is the probability that a one or two will turn up?

2. If a card is drawn from an ordinary deck of 52 cards, (a) what is the probability that it is a king, (b) a face card, (c) seven or below, (d) a diamond, (e) a black card?

3. If two dice are thrown, what is the probability of throwing a total of four? (The total may be four if each die shows a two, if one shows a one and the second a three, or vice versa.)

4. If two dice are thrown, what is the probability of throwing a total of seven or eleven?

5. If two dice are thrown, what is the probability of throwing a total of two, three, or twelve?

6. If two dice are thrown and the result is an eight, what is the probability it was thrown with two fours?

7. If two cards are drawn from an ordinary deck of 52 cards, what is the probability that (a) both will be aces, (b) both will be red, (c) both will be below a six?

8. A bag contains eight red and four white balls. What is the probability that a ball drawn out will be red? White?

9. If three balls are drawn from the bag described in Problem 8, what is the probability (a) two will be red and one white, (b) all three will be red?

10. If four men and four women are seated at random in a row, what is the probability that the men and women alternate?

11. If there are six different sections of an algebra course offered, what is the probability that three students, registering independently, will get the same section? Will get Section One?

12. What is the probability of drawing a bridge hand from an ordinary pack of cards (a) all in the same suit, (b) all hearts?

13. Six couples are invited to play bridge. What is the probability that each man will have his wife for a partner?

14. If a family of four takes seats at random in a row, what is the probability the father and mother (a) sit together, (b) sit on the ends?

15. In a group of 30, what is the probability that two people will have their birthday dates coincide? [*Hint:* Find the probability that no one of the group will have coincident birthdays. Use logarithms.]

20–5 Empirical probability. Often when analysis according to probability theory does not yield a satisfactory result, experimental or statistical data on past information may be beneficial in finding the probability of an event. The larger the number of cases considered, the more accurate the results will be; hence care should always be taken to secure as large a sample as possible. We use the following definition:

DEFINITION 20–2. *If an event occurs h times out of n trials, the relative frequency of its occurrence is h/n.*

It has been assumed, and with justification, that for large values of n this relative frequency approximates the mathematical probability of an event. In this way we define what is called *empirical probability.*

DEFINITION 20–3. *If an event occurs h times out of n trials, where n is a large number, then the probability p that the event will occur in any one trial is defined as*

$$p = \frac{h}{n}. \qquad (20\text{–}12)$$

This form of probability is used extensively in the social sciences, industry, and actuarial work.

EXAMPLE 1. An investigator asked 1000 people in a large city which of two candidates they preferred in the coming election for mayor. If 679 preferred the first candidate, what is the probability that a person selected at random would prefer this candidate?

Solution. Since $h = 679$ and $n = 1000$, the desired probability is $679/1000 = 0.679$.

Table V in the back of the book is the American Experience Table of Mortality, which lists the number of persons surviving at different ages, based on an initial group of 100,000 at an age of ten years. It is useful in finding the life expectancy of a person at any age.

EXAMPLE 2. Using Table V, determine the probability that a person aged 21 will live to be 65.

Solution. From Table V, of the 100,000 people considered, 91,914 are living at age 21, and of these 49,341 are still alive at age 65. The desired probability is thus

$$p = \frac{49{,}341}{91{,}914} = 0.54.$$

PROBLEMS

1. In a certain city there were 20,000 automobiles registered. If 625 traffic accidents were reported in that same year of registration, what was the probability of a specific car's being involved in one of the accidents?

2. In the town of Oberlin, in which there were 2000 bicycles registered, 25 bicycle thefts were reported in 1959. If we assume this ratio will continue, what is the probability that a certain individual will have his bicycle stolen in 1960?

3. A certain factory making small resistors finds that out of 100 resistors, three will be faulty. What is the probability that a given resistor from this company will not be accurate?

4. A baseball player had 192 safe hits out of 512 times at bat in the 1959 season. Assume that he will have the same batting average during the next season. What is the probability that he will get a hit any time he goes to bat?

5. A certain inland lake in northern Michigan has been completely frozen over by Christmas Day in 35 of the last 40 years. Based on this fact, what is the probability it will be frozen over by Christmas Day of the next year?

6. In a certain college, one out of every nine students left at the end of their first year because of scholastic difficulty. If next year's freshman class has 360 first-year students, how many of these would be expected to continue for another year?

Use Table V in the following problems.

7. What is the probability that a person 16 years old will live to be 50?

8. What is the probability that a person 50 years old will live to be 80?

9. What is the probability that a person 80 years old will die during the following year?

10. What is the probability that a person 65 years old will die during the next five years?

11. What is the probability that a person 50 years old will die between the ages of 70 and 71?

20–6 Probability of more than one event. The problems discussed thus far have been concerned with only one event. It is also possible to consider probabilities of two or more events. Two or more events are called *mutually exclusive* if not more than one of them can happen in a given trial. For example, a toss of a coin cannot result in both a head and a tail; on a single drawing from a pack of cards, the card drawn cannot be both a king and queen.

THEOREM 20–2. *If two events are mutually exclusive with the probability for the first event's happening p_1, and the probability for the second's happening p_2, then the probability p that one or the other of the two events will happen is $p = p_1 + p_2$.*

Proof. If s is the number of ways in which one or the other event can happen, $s = s_1 + s_2$, where s_1 represents the number of ways the first event can happen, and s_2 the number of ways the second can happen. Letting f be the number of ways neither event can occur, $s + f$ will be the total number of possibilities. Thus,

$$p = \frac{s_1 + s_2}{s + f} = \frac{s_1}{s + f} + \frac{s_2}{s + f},$$

and by definition we have

$$p = p_1 + p_2.$$

EXAMPLE 1. From a bag containing four red, five white, and three blue marbles, a marble is drawn. What is the probability that it is red or blue?

Solution. The probability of drawing a red ball is $\frac{4}{12}$, while the probability of drawing a blue ball is $\frac{3}{12}$. Since these two events or drawings are mutually exclusive,

$$p = \tfrac{4}{12} + \tfrac{3}{12} = \tfrac{7}{12}.$$

Two or more events are called *independent* if the happening of one event in no way affects the happening of any other of the events. For example, in Example 1, if a marble is drawn from the bag, the marble replaced, and a second marble drawn, these drawings or events are said to be *independent*.

THEOREM 20–3. *If two events are independent with the probability of the first's happening p_1, and the probability of the second's happening p_2, then the probability p that both events will happen in a single trial is $p = p_1p_2$.*

Proof. If s_1 and s_2 represent the number of ways the two events can happen, and f_1 and f_2 the number of ways the two can fail to happen, by the fundamental principle s_1s_2 represents the number of ways in which the two events can happen, and $(s_1 + f_1)(s_2 + f_2)$ the total number of ways the two events can either happen or not happen; then,

$$p = \frac{s_1s_2}{(s_1 + f_1)(s_2 + f_2)} = \frac{s_1}{s_1 + f_1} \cdot \frac{s_2}{s_2 + f_2},$$

which by definition is

$$p = p_1p_2.$$

The proof of a fourth theorem is similar. Two or more events are called *dependent* if the happening of any one affects the occurrence of the other events. If in Example 1 the second ball is drawn without replacing the first ball drawn, the probability of drawing a certain colored ball will depend on the result of the first drawing.

THEOREM 20–4. *If two events are dependent, with the probability of the first event's occurring p_1 and, after it happens, the probability of the second's happening p_2, then the probability p that both events will happen is $p = p_1p_2$.*

The proof is left as an exercise.

EXAMPLE 2. From the bag described in Example 1, a marble is drawn and replaced and then a second marble is drawn. What is the probability that both marbles drawn are red?

Solution. These two events are independent, for the probability involved in the second drawing is not affected by the result of the first. Since the probability of drawing a red marble is $\frac{4}{12}$ on either the first or second drawing,

$$p = \tfrac{1}{3}(\tfrac{1}{3}) = \tfrac{1}{9}.$$

EXAMPLE 3. From the bag described in Example 1, a marble is drawn and then, without replacing the first, a second marble is drawn. What is the probability that both are red?

Solution. Again the probability of drawing a red marble on the first drawing is $\frac{1}{3}$. The second drawing, however, is made from eleven marbles, of which three are red (assume the first marble drawn was red). Thus

$$p = \tfrac{1}{3} \cdot \tfrac{3}{11} = \tfrac{1}{11}.$$

Note that the outcome of the second drawing depends on the result of the first.

In any problem involving two or more events, extreme care should be taken to determine whether the events are independent, dependent, or mutually exclusive.

Although each of these theorems is proved for two events, the theorems may clearly be generalized to account for n events.

PROBLEMS

1. If two coins are tossed, what is the probability that both will (a) fall with the same side up, (b) turn up tails?

2. If the mathematics library has three copies of the same book, what is the probability that four students will use the same copy if they borrow it at different times?

3. If a ball player is batting 300 (three hits out of ten times at bat), what is the probability he will get four hits in a row?

4. Find the probability of drawing (a) an ace or queen from an ordinary pack of playing cards if one card is drawn, (b) an ace and a queen if after the first drawing, the card is returned and a second is drawn, (c) an ace and a queen if the cards are drawn in succession, without replacement.

5. If two dice are thrown three times, what is the probability of throwing (a) a seven once and only once, (b) a seven at least once?

6. If two cards are drawn from an ordinary pack of playing cards, what is the probability that (a) both are of the same denomination, (b) both are of the same suit, (c) both are of the same color, (d) each is of a different color?

7. A football team's probability of winning its first game is $\frac{3}{7}$ and its second $\frac{4}{7}$. What is the probability (a) of winning both games, (b) of winning the first but losing the second, (c) losing both games?

8. If the probability of passing the first test in an algebra course is $\frac{2}{3}$, and the second is $\frac{3}{4}$, what is the probability of (a) passing both tests, (b) failing both tests, (c) passing only one test?

9. The top-seeded player in a tennis tournament has probabilities of $\frac{3}{4}$, $\frac{2}{3}$, and $\frac{1}{2}$ of winning his first, second, and third matches. Find the probability that (a) he will win all three, (b) he will win the first two but lose the third.

10. A young man 24 years old marries a young woman of 22. Find the probability that (a) they will both be alive at the age of 70, (b) he will live until 70 and she until 75, (c) they both will die within 25 years of their marriage. [*Hint:* Use **Table V.**]

ANSWERS TO
ODD-NUMBERED PROBLEMS

ANSWERS TO ODD-NUMBERED PROBLEMS

CHAPTER 1

ARTICLE 1–3

1. 36, 14, 275, 25/11
3. $-16, -32, -192, -3$
5. $-4, 4, 0, 0$
7. 5/6, 1/6, 1/6, 3/2
9. $-71/28, -1/28, 45/28, 36/35$
11. $-5/4, 5/4, 0, 0$

ARTICLE 1–4

1. $3a + b - 1, a + 5b - 7$
3. $6x + 6y - z, 2x + 3z$
5. $-8x - 11y, 12x - y$
7. $-2x - 4y$
9. $-6x - 9y - 4$
11. $16x - 3y - 9$
13. $13x - 10y$
15. $a^2 - (b^2 - 2bc + c^2)$
17. $4x^2 - (4y^2 + 4y + 1)$
19. $(c - a)x, -(a - c)x$
21. $(a + b)x, -(-a - b)x$
23. 7
25. 17
27. 5
29. 35

ARTICLE 1–5

1. a^9
3. $3x^{12}$
5. y^{24}
7. a^{20}
9. $125c^3$
11. $32a^{15}$
13. $a^{(r+s)t}$
15. $2^n x^{n^2}$
17. $2x^2 + x - 15$
19. $16x^2 - 4y^2$
21. $r^3 - r^2 s - rs^2 + s^3$
23. $x^3 + y^3$
25. $2x^4 - 3x^3 - 10x^2 + 6x + 8$
27. $x^3 - 2x^2 - 5x + 6$
29. $x^6 - 8y^6$
31. $a^{2n+1} - a^{2n} - 7a^{n+1} + 7a^n + 10a - 10$
33. $x^{4n} - 2x^{2n}y^{2n} + y^{4n}$
35. $x^4 - 4x^3 y + 6x^2 y^2 - 4xy^3 + y^4$

ARTICLE 1–6, (1)

1. $3y^2 - 2x^2$

3. $\dfrac{2x^2}{y} - 3x^3$

5. $3x - 4y + 6x^2 y^2$
7. $x^2 - 7x + 10 \equiv (x - 2)(x - 5)$
9. $3x^2 - 13x + 4 \equiv (3x - 1)(x - 4)$
11. $2x^3 - 7x^2 + 11x - 4 \equiv (x^2 - 3x + 4)(2x - 1)$
13. $x^2 y - 6x^3 - 12xy^2 - 6y^3 \equiv (-3x^2 - 4xy - 12y^2)(2x - 3y) - 42y^3$
15. $4x^3 + 5 + 4x^2 - 13x \equiv (2x^2 - 3x + 1)(2x + 5)$
17. $5x^3 - 2x^2 + 3x - 4 \equiv (5x + 8)(x^2 - 2x + 1) + (14x - 12)$
19. $x^6 - y^6 \equiv (x^5 + x^4 y + x^3 y^2 + x^2 y^3 + xy^4 + y^5)(x - y)$

417

ARTICLE 1–6, (2)

1. $Q = 3x + 7, R = 17$
3. $Q = x^2 - 4x + 8, R = -7$
5. (a) $Q = x^3 - 3x - 10, R = -28$
 (b) $Q = x^3 - 3x^2 - 4, R = -4$
7. (a) $Q = 3x^3 + 6x^2 + 12x + 17, R = 14$
 (b) $Q = 3x^3 - 6x^2 + 12x - 31, R = 42$
9. $x^3 - 2x^2 + 3x - 4 \equiv (x^2 + x + 6)(x - 3) + 14$
11. $x^4 - 5x^3 + x^2 - 6 \equiv (x^3 - 4x^2 - 3x - 3)(x - 1) - 9$

ARTICLE 1–7

1. $6ax - 8ay$
3. $-21x^3y - 28xy^2$
5. $4x^2 - 9y^2$
7. $x^4 - 16y^4$
9. $4x^2 + 28xy + 49y^2$
11. $x^2 - 7x + 10$
13. $x^2y^4 - 2xy^2z^2w + z^4w^2$
15. $28x^2 - 9xy - 9y^2$
17. $4x^2 + 12xy + 9y^2 - 9$
19. $x^2 + 4y^2 + z^2 - 4xy - 2xz + 4yz$
21. $x^3 + 8$
23. $x^2 + 6xy + 9y^2 - 4z^2 + 16zw - 16w^2$
25. $a^2 + b^2 + c^2 + d^2 - 2ab + 2ac - 2ad - 2bc + 2bd - 2cd$
27. $4(x + 2y)^2 + 2(x + 2y) - 12$
29. $8x^3 + 36x^2y + 54xy^2 + 27y^3$

ARTICLE 1–8, (1)

1. $4(x - 5)$
3. $3y(y - 3)$
5. $xyz^2(yz - 3x + 5y^2)$
7. $(2x + 5)(3y - 4x)$
9. $2z(x + 3y)(z - 3x)$
11. $(3 - a)(3 + a)$
13. $(15a^4 - 8b)(15c^4 + 8b)$
15. $x(xy^2 - 5d^3)(xy^2 + 5d^3)$
17. $(x + 2y - z)(x + 2y + z)$
19. $(a + b + c + d)(a + b - c - d)$
21. $[9(4x - 3y) + 5(3z + w)][9(4x - 3y) - 5(3z + w)]$
23. $(x - 4)^2$
25. $(3xy + 11)^2$
27. $5(z - 3w)^2$
29. $(7 - x)^2$
31. $(a - 2)(a^2 + 2a + 4)$
33. $(2x^{2n} + 3y^m)(4x^{4n} - 6x^{2n}y^m + 9y^{2m})$
35. $(x - 5y)(19x^2 - 10xy + 7y^2)$
37. $(x - 4)(x - 3)$
39. $(ab - 5)(ab + 4)$
41. $(7x - 2)(5x - 2)$
43. $(3a - 4)(2a + 5)$
45. $(x + y - 5)(x + y - 2)$
47. $(4x + 2y - 5)(2x + y + 2)$
49. $2(2a + 2b + c + d)(3a + 3b - 5c - 5d)$

ARTICLE 1–8, (2)

1. $(a + b)(x - y)$
3. $(x - 2)(x^2 + 4)$
5. $(a - 3)(2 - b^2)$
7. $(x - 1 + y)(x - 1 - y)$
9. $(2x + y - 2)(2x - y + 2)$
11. $(x + y + z - w)(x + y - z + w)$

13. $(x + 2y - 3)(x + 2y + 2)$
15. $(x^2 - xy - 3y^2)(x^2 + xy - 3y^2)$
17. $(a^2 - 2ab + 3b^2)(a^2 + 2ab + 3b^2)$
19. $(a^4 + b^4)(a^2 + b^2)(a + b)(a - b)$
21. $(x - z)(x + 2y + z)$
23. $3(z - x)(x + 2y + z)$

CHAPTER 2

ARTICLE 2–1

1. $\dfrac{4}{9}$

3. $\dfrac{a^2 x^2}{y^2}$

5. $\dfrac{a}{x + y}$

7. $\dfrac{x + 1}{x}$

9. $\dfrac{x + 4}{x - 4}$

11. $\dfrac{y + 2}{y + 5}$

13. $\dfrac{3a + 1}{2a - 1}$

15. $\dfrac{2(3 - x)}{x + 5}$

17. $\dfrac{x + 6}{x^2 + 6x + 36}$

19. $\dfrac{x^2 + 2xy + y^2}{x^2 + y^2}$

ARTICLE 2–2

1. $\dfrac{6}{5}$

3. $\dfrac{(3x - 4y)(3x + 4y)}{12xy}$

5. $\dfrac{23 - 2x}{18}$

7. $\dfrac{2x^2 - y^2}{x - y}$

9. $\dfrac{x - y}{5x - 3}$

11. $\dfrac{5yz - 4xz + 3xy}{xyz}$

13. $\dfrac{5(1 - x)}{3(x - 4)}$

15. $\dfrac{2x^2 - 9x - 9}{(2x - 3)(x - 5)(x - 6)}$

17. $\dfrac{4a^2 + 9a + 29}{a^3 - 27}$

19. $-\dfrac{5}{(x + 2)(x + 3)}$

21. $\dfrac{8y^4 - 28y^3 + 21y^2 + 27y - 35}{(2y - 3)^2(y + 1)}$

23. $\dfrac{xz - x^2 + xy - y^2 + yz - z^2}{(x - y)(y - z)(z - x)}$

ARTICLE 2–3, (1)

1. $1/4$

3. $7/17$

5. $\dfrac{1}{a + b}$

7. $\dfrac{15x}{4y}$

9. $\dfrac{40x^3}{81}$

11. $\dfrac{x}{x^2 + xy + y^2}$

13. $\dfrac{1}{x + 3}$

15. y

17. 1

19. $-\dfrac{2 + 3x}{x^2(x + 1)}$

ARTICLE 2–3, (2)

1. $-\dfrac{57}{5}$

3. $\dfrac{x}{z}$

5. $\dfrac{2y + 5x}{2y - 5x}$

7. $x - 1$

9. $(3x + 2y)(y - 2x)$

ARTICLE 2–4

1. 8

3. $\dfrac{3y^4}{x^2}$

5. $\dfrac{2x^5}{3y^5}$

7. $\dfrac{cd(a + b)}{ab}$

9. $\dfrac{(a + b)^2}{ab}$

11. $x^{nm} y^{2m}$

ARTICLE 2–5

1. 5

3. 4/7

5. 16/9

7. 1/64

9. 81

11. $\sqrt[20]{x}$

13. $\sqrt[20]{x}$

15. $\sqrt[20]{x}$

17. $\dfrac{1}{64xy^5}$

19. $\dfrac{5x^2}{3y}$

21. $a + 2\sqrt{ab} + b$

23. $x + y$

25. $x^2 + \dfrac{2x}{y} + \dfrac{1}{y^2}$

ARTICLE 2–6

1. $2\sqrt{2}$

3. 5/2

5. $-5\sqrt[3]{5}$

7. $3xy^2\sqrt{3xy}$

9. $3zx^2y\sqrt[3]{3zy^2}$

11. $5\sqrt{35}/21$

13. $b\sqrt{a^2 + c^2}$

15. $\sqrt{3xy}/y^2$

17. $xy\sqrt[4]{27x^3y^2}/9$

19. $\sqrt{5}$

21. $\sqrt[3]{45x}/3x$

23. $x\sqrt{13xz}/y$

ARTICLE 2–7

1. $4\sqrt{3}$

3. $11\sqrt{2}$

5. $-\sqrt{x + y}$

7. $(ac^2 + b^3c + a^4b^2)\sqrt{abc}$

9. $32\sqrt{3}/3$

11. 5, 2

ARTICLE 2–8

1. $\sqrt{65}$

3. $2\sqrt[3]{13}$

5. $(x - y)\sqrt{x + y}$

7. $(x + y)\sqrt{x^2 - xy + y^2}$

9. $2\sqrt[3]{3}$

11. $2(\sqrt{3} + \sqrt{7})$

13. -2

15. $-13 - \sqrt{15}$

17. $(3 - \sqrt{5})/2$

19. 8/3

21. $\sqrt[3]{9}/3$

23. $\sqrt[4]{3a^2b^2}/b$

25. $\sqrt{15}/10$

27. $\sqrt[3]{4}$

29. $(5\sqrt{7} + 5\sqrt{3})/4$

31. $\dfrac{x^2 - x\sqrt{y}}{x^2 - y}$

33. $-(57 + 13\sqrt{21})/12$

35. $2(4 + 2\sqrt[3]{3} + \sqrt[3]{9})/5$

37. $(2\sqrt{3} + 3\sqrt{2} - \sqrt{30})/12$

CHAPTER 3

ARTICLE 3–1

1. $-6.5, -5, -1, 0, 0.333, 1/3, \sqrt{4}, 2.3, 2^3$

5. $(0), (-1), (1), \left(\dfrac{\sqrt{2} + \sqrt{3}}{2}\right), \left(\dfrac{x_1 + x_2}{2}\right)$

7. (a) ± 2 (e) $7, -3$ (i) $6, -2$
   (b) $\pm\sqrt{5}$ (f) 4 (j) None
   (c) ± 3 (g) $9, -3$ (k) None
   (d) $\pm 1/4$ (h) $6, -4$ (l) $8, 2$

11. $|x - a| = r$, or $\sqrt{(x - a)^2} = r$

ARTICLE 3–2

3. (a) $(3, 2)$ 5. II, IV, III, I, II, IV
   (b) $(-4, 6)$
   (c) $(5, 0)$
7. (a) $(8, 4), (4, -4), (-4, 4)$ 11. (a) $(-1, 7/2)$
   (b) $(-1, 6), (3, -2), (-3, -4)$ (b) $(11/2, -9/2)$
                                             (c) $(-1, 0)$

ARTICLE 3–3

1. (a) $\sqrt{34}$ (d) 13
   (b) $\sqrt{106}$ (e) 8
   (c) $3\sqrt{2}/4$ (f) $\sqrt{(x + 1)^2 + (y - 3)^2}$
7. Yes; no
9. $(2\sqrt{3}, -1 - 4\sqrt{3})$ or $(-2\sqrt{3}, -1 + 4\sqrt{3})$
11. $(\pm a\sqrt{2}/2, 0)$ and $(0, \pm a\sqrt{2}/2)$
13. $(1, 0), (0, -1), (1/\sqrt{2}, 1/\sqrt{2}), (-1/2, \sqrt{3}/2)$

ARTICLE 3–4

1. (a) $(x - 3)^2 + (y - 1)^2 = 25$ (c) $(x + 1)^2 + (y - 3)^2 = 9$
   (b) $(x - 4)^2 + (y + 2)^2 = 9$ (d) $(x - 2)^2 + (y + 4)^2 = 25$
3. (a) All points inside or on the circle
   (b) All points outside or on the circle
   (c) The point $(3, -1)$
5. $4\sqrt{3}\, r$

ARTICLE 3–5

5. Problem 2: (a) 1/8   (c) −5/8   (e) 2/3   (g) 2
              (b) 3/8   (d) −5/6   (f) 5/4   (h) −1/3

     Problem 3: (a) 1/12   (c) 1/8   (e) −3/4   (g) 5/24
              (b) 1/3   (d) 2/9   (f) −5/12   (h) −5/2

7. (a) 0.4712   (c) 0.8203   (e) 4.4186
   (b) 2.7285   (d) 3.3080   (f) −6.6116

9. (a) 47°41′   (e) 81°21′   (i) 212°37′
   (b) 33°53′   (f) 85°17′   (j) 206°12′
   (c) 51°   (g) 164°47′   (k) 37°38′
   (d) 151°   (h) 42°22′   (l) 4°26′

11. 3/2 radians, 85°57′   13. 120°, 30°, 172°30′, 108°30′
15. 60 radians   17. 5, 1, θ

ARTICLE 3–6

1. −5, −3, 1, −7
3. 1, −1, −1/4. $f(3)$ does not exist
5. 0, $\sqrt{2}$, 2. All nonnegative values
7. 2, 0, 2, 4. All real values, all nonnegative real values
9. $P = 3x$, $A = x^2\sqrt{3}/4$

ARTICLE 3–7

1. −5/2   3. 0   5. 2, 5
7. 1   9. 1   11. 0, ±1

CHAPTER 4

ARTICLE 4–2

1. +   3. +   5. +
7. −   9. −   11. +
13. +   15. −   17. I or IV
19. III or IV   21. I or IV   23. IV
25. II
27. $\sin \theta = 4/5$ 29. $\sin \theta = 3/5$
      $\cos \theta = 3/5$ $\cos \theta = -4/5$
31. $\sin \theta = -15/17$ 33. $\sin \theta = -1$
      $\cos \theta = -8/17$ $\cos \theta = 0$
35. $\sin \theta = 0$ 37. $\sin \theta = -3/5$
      $\cos \theta = 1$ $\tan \theta = 3/4$
39. $\cos \theta = -\sqrt{5}/3$ 41. $\sin \theta = -\sqrt{11}/6$
      $\tan \theta = -2/\sqrt{5}$ $\tan \theta = -\sqrt{11}/5$
43. $\cos \theta = -4/5$ 45. $\sin \theta = \pm 2/\sqrt{13}$
      $\tan \theta = 3/4$ $\cos \theta = \pm 3/\sqrt{13}$

47. $\cos \theta = \pm\sqrt{95}/12$
   $\tan \theta = \pm 7/\sqrt{95}$
51. $\sin \theta = -15/17$
   $\cos \theta = -8/17$

49. $\sin \theta = -15/17$
   $\cos \theta = -8/17$

ARTICLE 4–3

1. $\sin \theta = 0$
   $\cos \theta = -1$

3. $\sin \theta = 0$
   $\cos \theta = 1$

5. (a) $\sin \theta = 0$
       $\cos \theta = -1$
   (b) $\sin \theta = -1$
       $\cos \theta = 0$
   (c) $\sin \theta = 1$
       $\cos \theta = 0$

   (d) $\sin \theta = 0$
       $\cos \theta = 1$
   (e) $\sin \theta = 0$
       $\cos \theta = -1$
   (f) $\sin \theta = 0$
       $\cos \theta = 1$

   (g) $\sin \theta = 1$
       $\cos \theta = 0$
   (h) $\sin \theta = 0$
       $\cos \theta = 1$
   (i) $\sin \theta = 0$
       $\cos \theta = -1$

13. (a) $\sqrt{2}$, (b) 2

ARTICLE 4–4

11. (a) 1
    (b) 1

13. $-\sqrt{3}$

15. $(5/2) - \sqrt{3}$

17. -1

19. 2

21. $30° = \pi/6$
    $150° = 5\pi/6$

23. $30° = \pi/6$
    $210° = 7\pi/6$

25. $135° = 3\pi/4$
    $315° = 7\pi/4$

27. $45° = \pi/4$
    $135° = 3\pi/4$

29. $150° = 5\pi/6$
    $330° = 11\pi/6$

ARTICLE 4–6

1. $1/\sin \theta$

3. $\pm\sqrt{1 - \sin^2 \theta}$

5. $\pm \sin \theta/\sqrt{1 - \sin^2 \theta}$

7. $1/\cos \theta$

9. $\pm\sqrt{1 - \cos^2 \theta}$

11. $\pm\sqrt{1 - \cos^2 \theta}/\cos \theta$

13. $\sin \theta = \pm \tan \theta/\sqrt{1 + \tan^2 \theta}$, $\cos \theta = \pm 1/\sqrt{1 + \tan^2 \theta}$
    $\cot \theta = 1/\tan \theta$, $\sec \theta = \pm\sqrt{1 + \tan^2 \theta}$, $\csc \theta = \pm\sqrt{1 + \tan^2 \theta}/\tan \theta$

15. $1/(1 - \cos^2 \theta)$

ARTICLE 4–9

1. $\sin 75° = \dfrac{\sqrt{6} + \sqrt{2}}{4}$, $\cos 75° = \dfrac{\sqrt{6} - \sqrt{2}}{4}$, $\tan 75° = 2 + \sqrt{3}$

3. $\cos \dfrac{7\pi}{12} = \dfrac{\sqrt{2} - \sqrt{6}}{4}$, $\tan \dfrac{7\pi}{12} = -(2 + \sqrt{3})$

5. (a) 56/65
   (b) $-33/65$

   (c) $-56/33$
   (d) $-16/65$

   (e) 63/65
   (f) $-16/63$

7. (a) II
   (b) IV

9. $\sin(\alpha + \beta) = -304/425$, $\cos(\alpha + \beta) = 297/425$

11. $\dfrac{\sqrt{3}\tan\theta + 1}{\sqrt{3} - \tan\theta}$ 13. $\dfrac{1 - \tan\theta}{1 + \tan\theta}$

15. $\dfrac{2}{\sqrt{3}\sin\theta - \cos\theta}$ 17. $\dfrac{\sin\theta - \cos\theta}{\sqrt{2}}$

29. $13\sin(\theta + \theta_1)$, where $\sin\theta_1 = 12/13$ and $\cos\theta_1 = 5/13$

31. $5\sin(\theta + \theta_1)$, where $\sin\theta_1 = -3/5$ and $\cos\theta_1 = 4/5$

33. $\sqrt{2}\sin\left(\theta + \dfrac{\pi}{4}\right)$

ARTICLE 4–10

1. $-\sin 16°$ 3. $-\sin 41°$ 5. $-\cot 24°$

7. $\cos 5°$ 9. $-\cot 14°$ 11. $-\sin 16°18'$

13. $-\cos 24°46'$ 15. $\sin 23°21'$ 27. π

ARTICLE 4–11

3. $\sin 7\pi/12 = \sqrt{2 + \sqrt{3}}/2$

   $\cos 7\pi/12 = -\sqrt{2 - \sqrt{3}}/2$

   $\tan 7\pi/12 = -(2 + \sqrt{3})$

5. (a) $-120/169$ (d) $3/\sqrt{13}$

    (b) $-119/169$ (e) $2/\sqrt{13}$

    (c) $120/119$ (f) $3/2$

7. $\dfrac{3 + 4\cos 2\theta + \cos 4\theta}{8}$

ARTICLE 4–12

1. $(\sin 8\theta - \sin 2\theta)/2$ 3. $(\sin 12\theta - \sin 2\theta)/2$

5. $(\sin 7\theta + \sin 3\theta)/2$ 7. $[\sin(3\theta/2) - \sin(2\theta)]/2$

9. $2\sin(\pi/6)\cos(\pi/18)$ 11. $2\cos(\pi/2)\cos(5\pi/18)$

13. $2\sin 6\theta\cos 2\theta$ 15. $2\cos(5\theta/4)\sin(5\theta/12)$

ARTICLE 4–13

3. $33° = 15° + 18°$, $39° = 75° - 36°$, $42° = 60° - 18°$

5. (a) 0.2476   (e) 0.3872   7. (a) 25°10'   (e) 12°10'

    (b) 1.3111   (f) 0.3035   (b) 48°20'   (f) 75°50'

    (c) 0.8760   (g) 0.9026   (c) 27°40'   (g) 20°20'

    (d) 0.8949   (h) −0.9465   (d) 57°40'   (h) 38°20'

CHAPTER 5

ARTICLE 5–1

1. -2 3. $5/6$ 5. -3

7. -7 9. $11/9$ 11. -5

13. $-16/9$ 15. $\pi/3, 2\pi/3$ 17. 0.3217, 3.4633

19. 0.2195, 2.3985, 3.3611, 5.5401

21. $\dfrac{c}{a-b}$

23. $2A/h$

25. $\dfrac{l-a}{n-1}$

27. $\dfrac{Sr+a-S}{r}$

29. $\dfrac{2S-an}{n}$

31. $\dfrac{a\tan\theta_1}{\tan\theta_2-\tan\theta_1}$

33. 18 years

35. $45,000

37. $1\frac{5}{7}$ hr

ARTICLE 5–2

1. 10, 13, 16; $l = 25$, $S_9 = 117$
3. 1, -2, -5; $l = -32$, $S_{15} = -165$
5. $l = 46$, $S_{12} = 288$
7. $d = 48/91$, $l = 34/7$
9. $a = -31/28$, $l = 151/28$
11. $n = 7$, $S_7 = 147$
13. 8, 9, 10
15. 187,026
17. 2, 5, 8, 11
19. $-25/2$, -7, $-3/2$
21. (a) -4; (b) 17/15
25. 27 numbers; $S = 2835$
27. 1092 times
29. 1610 ft
31. $5075

ARTICLE 5–3

1. (a) $-6/7$
   (b) Does not exist (line is vertical)
   (c) 3
   (d) 0
5. 33°40′, 56°20′
7. 56°20′
9. 36°10′, 28°30′, 115°20′
11. AB 5/4, BC $-4/3$, CD 5, AD $-2/3$
15. 3/7

ARTICLE 5–4

1. (a) $3x - y + 2 = 0$ (d) $x - y + 8 = 0$
   (b) $4x + y + 5 = 0$ (e) $x - 2 = 0$
   (c) $y + 2 = 0$ (f) $x + y - 4 = 0$
3. $x + y - 1 = 0$
5. $8x - 6y - 7 = 0$
7. $x - y + 4 = 0$
9. $3x + y - 2 = 0$
11. Slope 2; x-intercept $-1/6$; y-intercept $-1/3$

ARTICLE 5–5

1. $x = 2$, $y = -1$
3. $x = 3$, $y = 5$
5. $x = 2/3$, $y = 3/2$
7. $\alpha = \pi/6, 5\pi/6$
   $\beta = 0$
9. $\alpha = \pi/6, 11\pi/6$
   $\beta = \pi/6, 7\pi/6$
11. $x = 5$, $y = -2$

13. $x = \dfrac{a^3 + a^2b + 3ab^2 + b^3}{a^2 + b^2}$

$y = \dfrac{a^3 - a^2b + ab^2 + b^3}{a^2 + b^2}$

15. $x = \dfrac{a}{\tan k_2 - \tan k_1}$

$y = \dfrac{a \tan k_1}{\tan k_2 - \tan k_1}$

17. $x' = x \cos \alpha + y \sin \alpha$

$y' = y \cos \alpha - x \sin \alpha$

19. $27/36$

21. 150 mi/hr, 10 mi/hr

23. 12 hr, 15 hr

25. $(-1, 2)$, $(2, 5)$, $(3, -1)$

27. $(18/7, 8/7)$, $(30/7, 4/7)$, $(23/7, -10/7)$, $(11/7, -6/7)$

29. $(1, 4)$

31. $18/5$

33. (a) $y = -\dfrac{x}{3} + \dfrac{11}{3}$ (b) $y = -\dfrac{3}{10}x + \dfrac{4}{5}$

ARTICLE 5–6

1. $32/13$

5. $3/\sqrt{13}$

3. $21/\sqrt{37}$

7. $5x + 12y + 7 = 0$

$5x + 12y - 19 = 0$

9. $3x - 4y + 6 = \pm(5/13)(12x - 5y - 9)$. These two equations represent the bisectors of the two angles formed by the two given intersecting lines.

ARTICLE 5–7

1. $x = 1$, $y = 2$, $z = 3$

3. $x = 3$, $y = -1$, $z = 4$

5. $x = 1/3$, $y = -2/5$, $z = 1/2$

7. $x = 5$, $y = 6$, $z = 7$

9. $x = 3$, $y = 4$, $z = 6$

11. 544

13. $90°$, $15°$, $75°$

15. $x^2 + y^2 - x - 7y + 6 = 0$

CHAPTER 6

ARTICLE 6–1

1. Minimum -4, when $x = -3$

3. Minimum $-121/8$, when $x = -5/4$

5. Minimum $-169/24$, when $x = 17/12$

7. Minimum 2, when $x = -3$

9. 8, 8

11. 40 ft, 40 ft

ARTICLE 6–2, (1)

1. -1, -5; 3, 2; $3/2$, 4; 3, $5/2$; $1/3$, $5/2$; -1.1, 3.6; None; None.

3. 4, $-3/2$

5. $\pi/6$, $5\pi/6$, $7\pi/6$, $11\pi/6$

7. $1/2$, -2

9. 0, $\pi/3$, $2\pi/3$, π

11. $3/2$, $3/2$

13. 0, 2.6780, π, 3.6052

15. $-a/4$, $-3a/2$

17. $2\pi/3$, π, $4\pi/3$

19. 3, -4

ARTICLE 6–2, (2)

1. $3/2, -4$

3. $\dfrac{-1 \pm \sqrt{5}}{2}$

5. $0, \pi/3, 5\pi/3$

7. a, b

9. $1, \dfrac{c-a}{a-b}$

11. $3\pi/4, 7\pi/4, 0.5880, 3.7295$

13. $1, -5/4$

15. $0.3142, 0.9425, 2.1991, 2.8275$
$3.4558, 4.0841, 5.3407, 5.9691$

17. $\dfrac{v_0 \pm \sqrt{v_0^2 - 2gs}}{g}$

19. -3

21. $\pm 2/3, \pm\sqrt{-1}$

23. $\pm\sqrt{5}/5, \pm\sqrt{3}/3$

25. Real roots: $2, -1$

27. $25, 16$

29. $1, -3, -1 \pm \sqrt{-3}$

31. $\dfrac{1 \pm \sqrt{-3}}{2}, \dfrac{1 \pm \sqrt{-3}}{2}$

33. $2, 17/4$

35. $3, -2$

37. $3/5$ or $5/3$

39. 1

41. $\dfrac{-27 + \sqrt{909}}{2}$ yd

43. $m = 9/7$ or $-7/9$

45. $3x + y - 6 = 0, x + 3y + 6 = 0$

ARTICLE 6–3, (1)

5. $x < 6$

7. $x > 3$

9. $-7/2 < x < 2$

11. $x > 5/2$ or $x < -7/3$

13. All real values

15. $x > 5$ or $x < 2$

17. $x > 5$ or $x < 2$

19. $x > 5$ or $x < 1$

21. $\dfrac{3\pi}{4} < \theta < \dfrac{5\pi}{4}$ or $0 \le \theta < \dfrac{\pi}{4}$ or $\dfrac{7\pi}{4} < \theta \le 2\pi$

23. $\pi < \theta < 2\pi$

25. $\dfrac{4\pi}{3} < \theta < 2\pi$

27. $0 \le \theta < \dfrac{7\pi}{6}$ or $\dfrac{11\pi}{6} < \theta < 2\pi$

29. All values

31. $\dfrac{\pi}{4} < \theta < \dfrac{5\pi}{4}$

ARTICLE 6–4

1. The sums of the zeros are $-6, -1, -5/2, 11/2, 17/6, 5/2, -6$, and $5/3$
The products of the zeros are $5, -6, -6, 15/2, 5/6, -4, 11, 4/3$

3. $x^2 + x - 20 = 0$

5. $12x^2 + x - 6 = 0$

7. $x^2 - 4x + 1 = 0$

9. $8x^2 + 12x + 1 = 0$

11. $5x^2 - 8x - 4 = 0$

13. $2x^2 + 5x - 3 = 0$

15. $36x^2 + 24x - 5 = 0$

17. $6x^2 - 5x - 1 = 0$

19. $k = -1$

21. $k = 1$

23. $k = 49/12$ 25. $k = -5$
27. $k = 0$ 29. All values of k
31. $-8 < k < 8$ 33. $k = 27/4$
35. $k > 3/2$ or $k < -1$

ARTICLE 6–5

1. $11/2$ 3. $7, 1$
5. 16 7. -5
9. 6 11. $2.09, 6.05$ (approx.)
13. $0, \pi/2$ 15. $3\pi/4, 5.99$ (approx.)

ARTICLE 6–6

1. $z = \dfrac{kx}{y}$ 3. $z = 6xy$ 5. $C = kd$

7. $A = kx^2$ 9. $\dfrac{1}{2}, \dfrac{\sqrt{3}}{2}, 0.6157$ 11. 90

13. 576π sq. in.   15. 72 ergs   17. 2 ft
19. Multiplied by 16

ARTICLE 6–7

1. $x = 0, 2$ 3. No real values
   $y = 0, 16$

5. $x = \dfrac{3 \pm \sqrt{7}}{2}, y = \dfrac{5 \mp \sqrt{7}}{2}$ 7. $x = 2, -8/5; y = 1, -1/5$

9. $x = \dfrac{-2 \pm 2\sqrt{5}}{3}$ 11. $b = \pm a\sqrt{1 + m^2}$
   $y = 1 \pm \sqrt{5}$
13. $23, 32$ 15. $7, 4$

CHAPTER 7

ARTICLE 7–1, (1)

1. -2 3. 3 5. 1 11. $x = 1$
15. Real; equal; imaginary

ARTICLE 7–1, (2)

1. 5 3. 0
15. (a) 5 17. $4x + 3y - 17 = 0$
    (b) $29/2$

ARTICLE 7–2

1. Rows and columns are interchanged
3. Two columns are identical   5. 1008
9. $x = a, b$ 11. $x = 3, 1$

ARTICLE 7–3

1. -110 3. -484 5. 0

ARTICLE 7–4

3. $x = -4,\ y = -3,\ z = 2,\ w = 1$

CHAPTER 8

ARTICLE 8–2

1. $a^7 + 7a^6b + 21a^5b^2 + 35a^4b^3 + 35a^3b^4 + 21a^2b^5 + 7ab^6 + b^7$

3. $32x^5 + 80x^4y^2 + 80x^3y^4 + 40x^2y^6 + 10xy^8 + y^{10}$

5. $625x^4 - 500x^3y^2 + 150x^2y^4 - 20xy^6 + y^8$

7. $x^2 + 6x^{5/3}y^{1/3} + 15x^{4/3}y^{2/3} + 20xy + 15x^{2/3}y^{4/3} + 6x^{1/3}y^{5/3} + y^2$

9. $x^2 - \dfrac{15x^{8/5}}{y^2} + \dfrac{90x^{6/5}}{y^4} - \dfrac{270x^{4/5}}{y^6} + \dfrac{405x^{2/5}}{y^8} - \dfrac{243}{y^{10}}$

11. $\dfrac{x^{24}}{4096} + \dfrac{3x^{22}}{256y^2} + \dfrac{33x^{20}}{128y^4} + \dfrac{55x^{18}}{16y^6} + \cdots$

13. $x^{11/3} - \dfrac{11x^{10/3}}{y^{1/3}} + \dfrac{55x^3}{y^{2/3}} - \dfrac{165x^{8/3}}{y} + \cdots$

15. $1 + kx + \dfrac{k(k-1)}{2}x^2 + \dfrac{k(k-1)(k-2)}{3!}x^3 + \cdots$

17. $59{,}136x^6y^6$ 19. $\dfrac{35y^8}{8}$ 21. $-414{,}720x^7$

23. $(7/2)x^5$

ARTICLE 8–3

1. $1 - x + x^2 - x^3 + \cdots$ 3. $1 + \dfrac{x}{2} + \dfrac{3x^2}{8} + \dfrac{5x^3}{16} + \cdots$

5. 0.9803   7. 1.005   9. 5.745   11. 4.932

CHAPTER 9

ARTICLE 9–1

9. (a) $-1/ax$,   (b) $x + a$,   (c) $(\sqrt{x} - \sqrt{a})/(x - a)$ or $1/(\sqrt{x} + \sqrt{a})$

11. $f(x) = x$ 13. $g(x) = x + 1$

15. $4x^2 + 4x + 1,\ 2x^2 + 1,\ 4x + 3$

ARTICLE 9–2, (1)

1. 7   3. 5   5. 1

7. Does not exist. (See Eq. 9–7.)

9. -3 11. $-1/2048$ 13. -3

15. $2x$

17. (a) $-2/3$ (c) 0
    (b) $-1/4$ (d) Does not exist. (See Eq. 9–7.)
21. Does not exist
23. Does not exist

ARTICLE 9–2, (2)

1. ∞ 3. $-\infty$ 5. ∞ 9. 0
11. 0 13. $3/2$ 15. 0 17. ∞
19. $-1/5$

ARTICLE 9–3

1. -2 3. $\sqrt{2}$ 5. 5

ARTICLE 9–4

1. $0.10414 < \sin \pi/30 < 0.10472$, $1 > \cos \pi/30 > 0.99452$,
   $0.10472 < \tan \pi/30 < 0.10530$

ARTICLE 9–5

1. (1) Not continuous at $x = 0$
   (2) Not continuous at $x = 1$
   (3) Not continuous at $x = \pm 3, \pm 2\frac{1}{2}, \pm 2, \pm 1\frac{1}{2}, \pm 1, \pm \frac{1}{2}, 0$
   (4) Not continuous at $x = 0, \pm 2n/3$
   (5) Not continuous at $x = 0, \pm n/2$
   (6) Not continuous at $x = 2$
   (7) Not continuous at $x = 2, 4$
3. Not continuous at $x = 7$
5. Not continuous at $x = 0$

CHAPTER 10

ARTICLE 10–1

1. 32 3. $32a - 8$ 5. 4 7. -4 9. nx_1^{n-1}

ARTICLE 10–2

1. 2 3. $3a^2$
5. 2 7. $3x^2$
9. $\dfrac{1}{2\sqrt{x}}$ 11. $-\dfrac{1}{2(x - 2)^{3/2}}$
13. $2 \cos 2x$
15. 1 for $x > 0$; -1 for $x < 0$; $f'(0)$ does not exist

ARTICLE 10–3

1. (a) $24x^5$ 3. m
   (b) $15x^2$
   (c) $36x$
5. (a) $\dfrac{x^2 + 4x - 1}{(x + 2)^2}$, (b) $\dfrac{2 - 2x^2}{(x^2 + 1)^2}$, (c) $-\dfrac{1}{x^2}$, (d) $3x^2 - \dfrac{2}{x^3}$

7. (a) $\dfrac{x^{4/3} + x^{2/3}}{3x^2}$, (b) $\dfrac{2}{3\sqrt[3]{x}}$

9. (a) $x \cos x + \sin x$, (b) $6x \cos x - 3x^2 \sin x$

   (c) $\cos^2 \theta - \sin^2 \theta$, (d) $\dfrac{x \cos x - \sin x}{x^2}$

ARTICLE 10–4

1. Tangent $2x - y - 3 = 0$
   Normal $x + 2y - 9 = 0$
3. Tangent $x - y - 9 = 0$
   Normal $x + y - 3 = 0$
5. Tangent $x - 2y - \dfrac{\pi}{3} - \sqrt{3} = 0$

   Normal $2x + y - \dfrac{2\pi}{3} - \dfrac{\sqrt{3}}{2} = 0$

7. Tangent $2x + 3y - 30 = 0$
   Normal $3x - 2y - 19 = 0$
9. $(5/2, -1/4)$ 11. At no point   13. $(\pm\sqrt{2}, \pm 8\sqrt{2})$
15. (a) $(0,0)$; $45°$ (d) $(\pm 2, 0)$; $71°20'$
      $(1, 1)$; $26°30'$; $(-1, -1)$; $26°30'$
   (b) $(0, 0)$; $90°$ (e) $(\pi/4, 1/\sqrt{2})$; $70°30'$
      $(1, 1)$; $36°50'$
   (c) $(\pm 1.03, \pm 0.24)$; $90°$ (f) $(0, 0)$; $53°$
17. $(3, -13/2)$, $(2, -4/3)$
19. $(-3, 3/2)$
21. $(-1, 3)$, $2x - y + 5 = 0$
   $(-7, -45)$, $14x - y + 53 = 0$

ARTICLE 10–5

1. $6x(x^2 + 3)^2$ 3. $4(x - 2)(x^2 - 4x + 6)$
5. $3(x^2 + x)^2(3x + 2)^3(10x^2 + 11x + 2)$

7. $\dfrac{4(3x - 1)}{\sqrt{4x - 5}}$ 9. $\dfrac{1 - 2x}{3\sqrt[3]{(x - x^2)^2}}$

11. (a) $x + \sqrt{3}\,y - 2a = 0$ 13. $16°20'$
   (b) $x - 8y + 5 = 0$
   (c) $8x - 9y - 25 = 0$
   (d) $x + y = \sqrt{2}/2$

ARTICLE 10–6

1. $-\dfrac{4x}{9y}$ 3. $\dfrac{x}{y}$ 5. $-\dfrac{y^{1/2}}{x^{1/2}}$

7. (a) $8x + 9y = 62$ 9. $42°$
   (b) $2x + 2y + p = 0$
   (c) $y_1^{1/3}x + x_1^{1/3}y = x_1^{1/3}y_1^{1/3}a^{2/3}$
11. Tangent $3x - 2y - 1 = 0$
   Normal $2x + 3y - 5 = 0$

ARTICLE 10–7

1. $6x - 10$

3. $2(6x + 1)$

5. $\dfrac{3x - 4}{4(x - 1)^{3/2}}$

7. $\dfrac{4}{(x + 1)^3}$

9. $-\dfrac{25}{y^3}$

11. $\dfrac{2(x + y)}{x^2}$

13. $\dfrac{y^2 - (x - 1)^2}{y^3}$

15. $3 \cos x (9 \cos^2 x - 7)$

17. $5; 12$

19. $8; 30$

21. $7/9; 4/27$

23. $3/\sqrt{2}; 7/\sqrt{2}$

25. $-1/3; -2/9$

27. $\dfrac{(-1)^n n!}{x^{n+1}}$

CHAPTER 11

ARTICLE 11–1, (1)

1. $R = 17$

3. $R = -7$

5. (a) -6,   (b) 57

7. Yes

9. No

11. Yes

ARTICLE 11–1, (2)

1. 2, one; 3, two; -4, three

3. -7, single; $3/2$, three

5. $-5/3$, single; 3, four

7. $x = 2$, double root

9. $x = 1$, triple root

13. Upper limit 3, lower limit -4

15. Upper limit 3, lower limit -2

17. Upper limit 3, lower limit -3

19. Upper limit 2, lower limit -1

21. Upper limit 2, lower limit -3

ARTICLE 11–2

5. 2, double; single between 1 and 2; single between -5 and -6

7. Single at -3; double between 0 and 1

9. Single between -2 and -3

ARTICLE 11–4

1. $-2, 3, 1/2$

3. $1, 3, 5, 7$

5. $1, 2, 3, -5$

7. $-\dfrac{3}{2}, -\dfrac{3}{2}, \dfrac{1 \pm \sqrt{5}}{2}$

9. $1, 1, 1, 1$

11. $1/2, 1/2, 1/2, \pm\sqrt{-1}$

13. $\pi/6, 5\pi/6, 7\pi/6, 11\pi/6, 3\pi/2$

15. $\pi/6, 5\pi/6, 7\pi/6, 11\pi/6, 3\pi/4, 7\pi/4$

ARTICLE 11–5

1. 0.75

3. 0.45

5. 1.36, 1.69

7. $-0.62, 1.62$

9. 1.817

11. 1.189

CHAPTER 12

ARTICLE 12–1

1. At $x = 1, f(1) = 2$ is a relative minimum
3. At $x = 1, f(1) = 1$ is a relative minimum
5. At $x = 1, f(1)$ is a relative minimum
 At $x = -1, f(-1)$ is a relative maximum
7. No relative maximum or minimum
9. At $x = 1/\sqrt[3]{2}, f(x)$ is a relative minimum
11. At $x = 1, f(1)$ is a relative minimum
13. At $x = 0, f(0)$ is a relative maximum

15. At $x = \pm\sqrt{2/3}, f(x)$ is a relative maximum
 At $x = 0, f(x)$ is a relative miminum

17. At $x = \pi/2, f(x)$ is a relative maximum
 At $x = 3\pi/2, f(x)$ is a relative minimum

19. At $x = 0, \pi, f(x)$ is a relative maximum
 At $x = \pi/2, f(x)$ is a relative minimum

ARTICLE 12–2

1. 40 by 60 rods

3. $2\sqrt[3]{2}$ by $\frac{3}{2}\sqrt[3]{2}$ ft

5. $\sqrt{2}R$ by $\sqrt{2}R$ for (a) and (b)

7. $r = \sqrt{2/3}\,R$; $\quad A = \dfrac{2}{\sqrt{3}}\,R$

9. $h = 2r$

11. Length $= 4$

13. \$155 per month

17. (a) $(0.8, 0.7)$, (b) $(\sqrt{3/2}, 3/2)$

19. $(0, \pm 2\sqrt[4]{2})$ or $(\pm 2\sqrt[4]{2}, 0)$ nearest
 $(\pm 2, \pm 2)$ farthest

ARTICLE 12–4

1. 24 square inches per second
3. 120π square inches per second
5. The velocity is zero when $t = 0$ and $s = 4$
7. The velocity is never zero
9. The velocity is zero when $t = 1$ and $s = -5$, and when $t = 5$ and $s = -37$

11. (a) $\dfrac{8}{25\pi}$ feet per second; (b) $\dfrac{8}{\pi(500)^{2/3}}$ feet per second

13. 3/2 feet per second
15. (a) 1/8 units per second; (b) 1/2 units per second
17. $900/\sqrt{13}$ miles per hour
19. $3120/\sqrt{105}$ miles per hour
21. $b \pm \sqrt{ab}$

CHAPTER 13

ARTICLE 13–1

1. $y = \dfrac{x + 6}{5}$

3. $y = 2 \pm \sqrt{x + 4}$

5. $y = \dfrac{1}{\pm\sqrt{1 - x}}$

7. $y = \sqrt[n]{x}$

9. $y = \pm\sqrt{x^2 + 4}$

11. $y = \dfrac{2x + 3 \pm \sqrt{4x - 7}}{2}$

ARTICLE 13–2

3. $\pm 2\pi/3 + 2n\pi$

5. $n\pi$

7. $\pm\pi/4 + 2n\pi$

9. $\pi/2$

11. $-\pi/2$

13. $(-1)^n\, 24° + n180°$

15. $\pm 51° + n360°$

17. $84°20'$

21. $(1/2) \arctan (y/3)$

23. $(1/2) \operatorname{arcsec} (y/2)$

27. $(1/4)(4 + \cos 3y)$

29. $\tan (y + 2)$

31. $\dfrac{\cos \left(2y - \dfrac{\pi}{12}\right) - 1}{2}$

ARTICLE 13–3

1. $\pm 3/5$

3. $\pm 12/5$

5. $\sqrt{11}/6$

7. u

9. $\pm\sqrt{1 - u^2}/u$

11. $\pi/7$

13. $\pi/18$

15. $2\pi/5$

17. 0

19. $uv \pm \sqrt{(1 - u^2)(1 - v^2)}$

21. $\pm 3/5$

23. 1 or $-7/8$

25. $-16/63$

27. $(24\sqrt{5} - 14)/75$

37. $2n\pi \pm (\pi/2 - \theta)$

39. $n\pi + \theta$

41. 1

43. 0

45. 0

47. $\dfrac{1}{x^2 + 4x + 5}$

49. $\dfrac{x}{\sqrt{1 - x^2}} + \operatorname{Arcsin} x$

51. $-\dfrac{1}{\sqrt{1 - x^2}}$

53. $2x - y - \sqrt{3} + \dfrac{\pi}{3} = 0$

55. $2\sqrt{3}\, x - 3y + \sqrt{3} + 2\pi = 0$

CHAPTER 14

ARTICLE 14–2

1. $64, 256, 1024; l = 16{,}384, S_8 = 21{,}845$

3. $-1, 5, -25; l = 125, S_7 = 13{,}021/125$

5. $l = 486, S_6 = 728$

7. $r = 3$, or $-4; l = 9$, or 16

9. $a = 36/121; l = 4/1089$

11. $n = 6; S = -126$

13. $a = 625/16, 125/8, 25/4$

15. $n = 9$

17. $\pm 9/4, 3/2, \pm 1$

19. $\pm\sqrt{ab}$

23. 1/81 ft; $26\frac{79}{81}$ ft

25. \$1583

27. Second

ARTICLE 14–3

1. 3/2

3. 64/5

5. $4 + 2\sqrt{2}$

7. 10/3

9. 5/9

11. 64/11

13. $r = 1/7$

15. $16[2 + \sqrt{2}]$

17. 240 ft

ARTICLE 14–4

1. $\log_3 27 = 3$

3. $\log_4 1 = 0$

5. $\log_8 16 = 4/3$

7. $\log_{10} 0.001 = -3$

9. $\log_4 4 = 1$

11. $36^{1/2} = 6$

13. $x = 2$

15. $x = -1$

17. $u = 25$

19. $x = 14$

21. $a = 27/8$

27. $\log_b \dfrac{a + 2}{a - 3}$

29. $\log_a \dfrac{\sqrt{x}}{\sqrt[3]{y^2}}$

31. $\log_a x^5(x - 1)^6$

33. $4 \log_{10} 60.3$

35. $3 \log_{10} 54.3 + \log_{10} 67 - \log_{10} 93.9 - 2 \log 32.5$

ARTICLE 14–5, (1)

1. 0.4099

3. 0.8401

5. 0.6730

7. 0.8373

9. 0.5153

11. 0.8858

13. 2.43

15. 4.12

17. 8.74

19. 1.851

21. 8.374

23. 3.213

ARTICLE 14–5, (2)

1. Characteristic, 1; mantissa, 0.3782

3. Characteristic, −3; mantissa, 0.5728

5. Characteristic, 5; mantissa, 0.8723

7. Characteristic, −4; mantissa, 0.2715

9. 2.5172

11. 3.6747

13. $8.8623 - 10$

15. 6650

17. 267.2

19. 0.003653

ARTICLE 14–5, (3)

1. (a) $9.3629 - 10$ (e) 0.5089

    (b) $9.8457 - 10$ (f) $9.9562 - 10$

    (c) $9.9657 - 10$ (g) $9.5556 - 10$

    (d) $9.8944 - 10$ (h) $9.8954 - 10$

ARTICLE 14–6

1. 32000

3. 34.6

5. 158,800

7. 0.5152

9. 2.642

11. 0.1313

13. 8.52

15. 0.923

17. 79.5

19. 396.1

ARTICLE 14–7

(All problems worked with four-place tables in back of book.)

1. (a) \$295.80, (b) \$297.10, (c) \$297.10 [larger than (b) if more accurate tables were used], (d) \$298.30

3. (a) 11.9 yr
   (b) 11.55 yr

5. $r = 0.3467$

7. (a) -0.2746
   (b) 0.002

ARTICLE 14–8

1. 3.808	3. 2.493	5. 1.947
7. 0.5824	9. 7.052×10^{13}	11. 26.6
13. 2.33	17. 5	19. 3.155
21. 6.14	23. 0.402	25. $\log_e (1 \pm \sqrt{2})$
27. 2/11	29. 1/297	

ARTICLE 14–9

1. $-\dfrac{1}{x}$

3. $-\tan x$

5. $\dfrac{1}{\sin x \cos x}$

7. $\dfrac{1 - \log_e x}{x^2}$

9. $\sec x$

11. $e^x(\cos x - \sin x)$

13. $\dfrac{e^x}{x^2}(x - 1)$

CHAPTER 15

ARTICLE 15–3

1. (a) $\beta = 52°40'$, $b = 319$, $c = 401$
  (b) $\beta = 27°20'$, $a = 1540$, $c = 1730$
  (c) $\alpha = 29°40'$, $\beta = 60°20'$, $c = 6.63$
  (d) $\alpha = 44°40'$, $\beta = 45°20'$, $a = 67.6$
  (e) $\alpha = 38°50'$, $a = 0.522$, $b = 0.648$
  (f) $\beta = 52°20'$, $b = 71.0$, $c = 89.7$
  (g) $\alpha = 33°30'$, $\beta = 56°30'$, $c = 68.7$
  (h) $\alpha = 48°35'$, $a = 2448$, $b = 2160$
  (i) $\alpha = 59°36'$, $\beta = 30°24'$, $b = 3185$
  (j) $\alpha = 23°10'$, $\beta = 66°50'$, $c = 8.320$
  (k) $\alpha = 27°3'$, $b = 1.619$, $c = 1.818$
  (l) $\alpha = 42°37'$, $a = 66.74$, $c = 98.58$
  (m) $\alpha = 42°30'$, $\beta = 47°30'$, $a = 3274$
  (n) $\beta = 65°13'$, $a = 147.0$, $c = 350.8$

3. 313 ft, 19°0′
7. 55°
11. 172 ft

5. 474 sq. in.
9. 7.075 in., 7.075 in., 10.62 in.
13. 78.8 ft

15. 2770 ft   17. 6.30 mi from A, 9.09 mi from B
19. 3195 ft south, 3485 ft west
21. (a) $v = 5$, $\theta = 53°$ (c) $v = 32.9$, $\theta = 119°30'$
    (b) $v = 50$, $\theta = 63°$ (d) $v = 858.2$, $\theta = 296°27'$
23. 56°, 22 ft/sec   25. N 47°0' W
27. (a) $f = 43$, $\theta = 122°$
    (b) $f = 8250$, $\theta = 21°10'$
    (c) $f = 3000$, $\theta = 255°$

ARTICLE 15–5

1. (a) $\gamma = 38°$, $b = 163$, $c = 102$
   (b) $\alpha = 40°26'$, $a = 36.27$, $b = 55.35$
   (c) $\beta = 13°52'$, $a = 270{,}400$, $c = 321{,}000$
   (d) $\alpha = 112°16'$, $a = 30.72$, $c = 26.56$
3. No
5. (a) $\alpha_1 = 91°50'$, $\gamma_1 = 49°30'$, $a_1 = 95.0$
       $\alpha_2 = 10°50'$, $\gamma_2 = 130°30'$, $a_2 = 17.9$
   (b) $\beta = 127°40'$, $\gamma = 7°10'$, $b = 55.0$
   (c) $\alpha = 17°49'$, $\gamma = 14°24'$, $c = 11.96$
   (d) $\alpha = 76°42'$, $\beta = 46°0'$, $a = 6.667$
7. (a) $\beta = 31°19'$, $\gamma = 96°23'$, $a = 28.35$
   (b) $\alpha = 45°50'$, $\beta = 76°30'$, $c = 545$
9. (a) $\alpha = 41°$, $\beta = 56°$, $\gamma = 83°$
   (b) $\alpha = 30°$, $\beta = 63°$, $\gamma = 87°$
15. 29.80 in., 48.52 in.   17. 100 mi, 60 mi
19. 25.5 ft   21. N 79°20' W
23. 148 mi/hr, S 63° E

CHAPTER 16

ARTICLE 16–1

1. Amp 5, period 1   3. Amp 3, period 6
5. Amp 1.5, period $4\pi/3$ 7. Amp 2, period 8π
9. Amp 0.5, period $2\pi/3$ 11. Amp 100, period 200 (approx.)

ARTICLE 16–3

1. Amp 2, period 2π, phase displacement $\pi/6$
3. Amp 5, period π, phase displacement $\pi/16$
5. Amp 1, period 2π, phase displacement 0.25
7. Amp 1, period 2π, phase displacement 1.176
9. Amp 17, period 2π, phase displacement 0.4900
11. Amp $\sqrt{29}$, period 2π, phase displacement 1.1903
13. Period 2π 15. Period 4π 17. Period 2π

ARTICLE 16–4

1. (a) Tangent: $3\sqrt{3}\,x + 6y - \sqrt{3}\pi - 3 = 0$
      Normal: $12x - 6\sqrt{3}\,y - 4\pi + 3\sqrt{3} = 0$
   (b) Tangent: $15\sqrt{3}\,x - 6y - 5\sqrt{3}\,\pi + 9 = 0$
      Normal: $12x + 30\sqrt{3}\,y - 4\pi - 45\sqrt{3} = 0$
5. Where $\theta = 45°$ 7. Increasing 3/25 radians per second
13. Where $\theta = 22°30'$ 15. $13\sqrt{13}$
19. Walk all the way around in least time
    Row to point 2/3 way around and walk the rest in greatest time

ARTICLE 16–5

1. P_x has an x-coordinate, $x = a \cos \omega t$
3. Yes; period π 5. $E = 8 \sin 120\pi t$ 7. $y = 0.001 \sin 800\pi t$

ARTICLE 16–6

1. Amp a
3. $A_0 = 80,\ A_1 = 9.5,\ A_2 = 1.44,\ \alpha_1 = 0.53,\ \alpha_2 = 2.16$

CHAPTER 17

ARTICLE 17–2

7. $(6, 8)$ 9. $(-1, 1)$
11. $(3, 11)$ 13. $(-1/2, -1/2)$
15. $(1, 0)$
17. (a) $13 + 18i$ 19. (a) $-i$
    (b) $3 + 22i$ (b) 1
                                             (c) i
                                             (d) $-i$

ARTICLE 17–3

1. $x^3 - 7x^2 + 17x - 15 = 0$ 3. $2x^3 + 19x^2 + 42x - 26 = 0$
5. $3x^3 - 17x^2 + 27x + 11 = 0$ 7. $4, \pm 3i$
9. $2, 3 \pm \sqrt{2}\,i$

ARTICLE 17–4

1. (a) $2 (\cos 0° + i \sin 0°)$ (e) $2\sqrt{2} (\cos 315° + i \sin 315°)$
   (b) $2 (\cos 180° + i \sin 180°)$ (f) $2\sqrt{2} (\cos 135° + i \sin 135°)$
   (c) $3 (\cos 90° + i \sin 90°)$ (g) $\cos 120° + i \sin 120°$
   (d) $\cos 270° + i \sin 270°$ (h) $\cos 240° + i \sin 240°$
3. (a) $6i$ 5. (a) $\sqrt{3} + i$
   (b) $-4\sqrt{3} - 4i$ (b) $-1 + \sqrt{3}\,i$
   (c) $12i$
   (d) 8

ARTICLE 17–5

1. $64i$ 3. $-4\sqrt{2} - 4\sqrt{2}\,i$

5. $\dfrac{\sqrt{3}}{2} + \dfrac{i}{2}$ 7. 1

9. $-2\sqrt{2} + 2\sqrt{2}\,i,\ 2\sqrt{2} - 2\sqrt{2}\,i$ 11. $1 + \sqrt{3}\,i,\ -2,\ 1 - \sqrt{3}\,i$

13. $\sqrt{3} + i,\ -1 + \sqrt{3}\,i,\ -\sqrt{3} - i,\ 1 - \sqrt{3}\,i$

15. $(\cos 36° + i \sin 36°),\ (\cos 72° + i \sin 72°),\ \cdots$

17. $1,\ i,\ -1,\ -i$

19. $\dfrac{\sqrt{5}+1}{2} + \sqrt{\dfrac{5-\sqrt{5}}{2}}\,i,\qquad \dfrac{1-\sqrt{5}}{2} + \sqrt{\dfrac{5+\sqrt{5}}{2}}\,i,\qquad -2,$

$\dfrac{1-\sqrt{5}}{2} - \sqrt{\dfrac{5+\sqrt{5}}{2}}\,i,\qquad \dfrac{\sqrt{5}+1}{2} - \sqrt{\dfrac{5-\sqrt{5}}{2}}\,i$

CHAPTER 18

ARTICLE 18–2

1. (a) $(x - 2)^2 + (y - 3)^2 = 1$ (c) $(x + \frac{2}{3})^2 + (y - \frac{3}{2})^2 = \frac{1}{16}$

    (b) $(x + 6)^2 + (y - 4)^2 = 36$ (d) $(x - 2\sqrt{3})^2 + (y + \sqrt{2})^2 = 5$

3. $x^2 + y^2 = 41$ 5. $(x - 2)^2 + (y + 2)^2 = 52$

7. $(x - 3)^2 + (y - 2)^2 = 1/10$ 9. $(x - 1)^2 + (y + 1)^2 = 20$

11. $(x - 1)^2 + (y - 5)^2 = 25$ 13. $(x - \frac{19}{6})^2 + (y - \frac{23}{3})^2 = 1445/6$

15. $(x - 6)^2 + (y - 2)^2 = 26$ 17. $(-3, -3)$ and $(-1, 1)$

21. $x - 2y - 4 = 0.$ Yes

27. $(x - 6)^2 + (y - 1)^2 = 25;\ (x + 1)^2 + (y - 2)^2 = 25$

29. Centers $(6, -6)$ or $(126, -126)$

31. $(x - 3)^2 + (y - 3)^2 = 5,\ (x + 1)^2 + (y - 1)^2 = 5$

33. $y = 3x;\ y = 2x;\ \theta = 16°$

35. $2x - 3y + 13 = 0;\ 3x + 2y - 13 = 0$

ARTICLE 18–3

1. Focus $(2, 0)$; directrix $x = -2$; length of latus rectum 8

3. Focus $(0, -1/4)$; directrix $y = 1/4$; length of latus rectum 1

5. Focus $(0, -3/8)$; directrix $y = 3/8$; length of latus rectum 3/2

7. $y^2 = 8x$ 9. $y^2 = -6x$

11. $2y^2 = 9x$ 13. $x^2 - 2xy + y^2 - 8x - 8y = 0$

15. $(y - 4)^2 = 2x - 5$ 17. $A = B = 0$

21. $y^2 + 12x - 36 = 0;\ y^2 - 4x - 4 = 0$

23. $3x - 4y + 13 = 0;\ 3x - 10y + 55 = 0$

ARTICLE 18–4

1. Center $(0, 0)$; foci $(\pm 3, 0)$; major 10, minor 8; eccentricity 3/5

3. Center $(0, 0)$; foci $(\pm\sqrt{3}, 0)$; major $2\sqrt{6}$, minor $2\sqrt{3}$; eccentricity $1/\sqrt{2}$

5. Center $(0, 0)$; foci $(\pm 2/15, 0)$; major 1/6; minor 1/10; eccentricity 4/5

7. $\dfrac{x^2}{13} + \dfrac{y^2}{4} = 1$ 9. $\dfrac{x^2}{36} + \dfrac{y^2}{20} = 1$

11. $\dfrac{x^2}{16} + y^2 = 1$ 13. $\dfrac{x^2}{5} + \dfrac{y^2}{20} = 1$

17. $\dfrac{(x-5)^2}{9} + \dfrac{(y+1)^2}{13} = 1$

19. A, C same sign; $B = 0$

21. $x^2 + 3y^2 = 24$

23. $\dfrac{x^2}{a^2} + \dfrac{y^2}{b^2} = 1$

25. Tangent: $12x + y - 50 = 0$
Normal: $x - 12y + 20 = 0$

27. $x = \dfrac{a^2}{\sqrt{a^2 + b^2}}, \quad y = \dfrac{b^2}{\sqrt{a^2 + b^2}}$

ARTICLE 18–5

1. Center $(0, 0)$; foci $(\pm 10, 0)$; transverse 12, conjugate 16; eccentricity 5/3
3. Center $(0, 0)$; foci $(\pm\sqrt{7}, 0)$; transverse 4, conjugate $2\sqrt{3}$; eccentricity $\sqrt{7}/2$
5. Center $(0, 0)$; foci $(0, \pm 5/12)$; transverse 2/3, conjugate 1/2; eccentricity 5/4

7. $\dfrac{x^2}{9} - \dfrac{y^2}{27} = 1$

9. $x^2 - 4y^2 = 5$

11. $729x^2 - 81y^2 = 4$

13. $y^2 - 3x^2 = 1$

17. $\dfrac{(x-5)^2}{9} - \dfrac{(y+3)^2}{16} = 1$

19. A, C opposite signs; $B = 0$

21. $80y^2 - x^2 = 20$

25. Tangent: $9x + 4y + 19 = 0$
Normal: $4x - 9y + 30 = 0$

ARTICLE 18–7

1. $2x' - 3y' = 0$
3. $x'^2 - 4y'^2 = 4$
5. $x'^2 - y'^2 = 1$ (where $x' = x - 2; y' = y - 2$)
7. $x'y' = 1$ (where $x' = x + 3, y' = y - 7$)
9. $y'^2 = 4x'$ (where $x' = x - 2, y' = y + 1$) cannot eliminate the x term
11. Center $(5, 5)$; vertices $(5 \pm 4, 5)$; foci $(5 \pm 2\sqrt{3}, 5)$; eccentricity $\sqrt{3}/2$
13. Center $(3, 1)$; vertices $(3, 1 \pm 3)$; foci $(3, 1 \pm \sqrt{13})$; eccentricity $\sqrt{13}/3$
15. Center $(1/2, 0)$; vertices $(1/2 \pm 1, 0)$; foci $(1/2 \pm 1/2, 0)$; eccentricity 1/2

ARTICLE 18–8

The new equations when the axes are rotated become:
1. $x'^2 - y'^2 = 16; \theta = 45°$
3. $x'^2 + 2y'^2 = 1, \theta = 45°$
5. $9x'^2 + 4y'^2 = 36, \tan 2\theta = -4/3$
7. $x'^2 = -y', \tan 2\theta = -24/7$
9. $2x'^2 + y'^2 = 26, \theta = 45°$
11. $2(x' + \sqrt{5})^2 + 7y'^2 = 0, \tan 2\theta = 4/3$; point

CHAPTER 19

ARTICLE 19–2

1. $\dfrac{x^4}{4} + 2x^2 + c$

3. $\dfrac{4x^3}{3} - \dfrac{7x^2}{2} + 2x + c$

5. $\dfrac{2x^{3/2}}{3} + \dfrac{3x^{4/3}}{4} + c$

7. $\dfrac{x^3}{3} + 8 \log_e x + \dfrac{6}{x} + c$

9. $x + 2 \log_e x - \dfrac{1}{x} + c$

11. $\dfrac{x^4}{4} - x^3 + \dfrac{3x^2}{2} - x + c$

13. $-\cos x + c$

15. $-\cos x + c$

17. $\dfrac{x^4}{4} - \dfrac{x^3}{3} + x^2 - 2x + c$

19. $\dfrac{x^4}{2} + 2x^3 + 2x^2 + c$

ARTICLE 19–3

1. $\dfrac{(x^2 - 1)^3}{3} + c$

3. $\dfrac{(x^2 - 4)^{3/2}}{3} + c$

5. $\dfrac{2(y^3 + a^3)^{5/2}}{15} + c$

7. $\dfrac{\sin^3 x}{3} + c$

9. $\dfrac{-\cos 3x}{3} + c$

11. $-\log_e (1 - x) + c$

13. $\dfrac{(\log_e x)^3}{3} + c$

15. $x + 2 \log_e (x + 1) + c$

17. $x^2 - 2x + 5 \log_e (x + 1) + c$

19. $\dfrac{x}{2} + \dfrac{\sin 2x}{4} + c$

21. $\dfrac{3x}{2} + 2 \sin x + \dfrac{\sin 2x}{4} + c$

23. $\dfrac{e^{2x}}{2} - 2x - \dfrac{e^{-2x}}{2} + c$

25. $\log_e (e^x - 1) + c$

ARTICLE 19–4

1. $f(x) = \dfrac{x^3}{3} - x + \dfrac{7}{3}$

3. $f(x) = 2\sqrt{x}$

5. $f(x) = 1 - \cos x$

7. $f(x) = \dfrac{x^2}{2} - 2x + 5$

9. $f(x) = x^2 - 4x + 7$

11. $f(x) = -x^2 + 4x - 1$

13. $f(x) = x^3 - 3x^2 + 2x$

15. $h = -16t^2 + 64t$;
at $t = 2$ sec, $h = 64$ ft

17. $5\sqrt{5}$ seconds; $v = 160\sqrt{5}$ ft/sec

19. 16

ARTICLE 19–5

1. 26   3. 1/6   5. 1/2   7. $\log_e 3$

9. $\dfrac{4\sqrt{2}}{3}$ 11. $\dfrac{\sqrt{15}-\sqrt{3}}{2}$ 13. 21   15. 9

17. $3/\pi$ 19. 36   21. 1/6   23. 125/24

25. 13/3   27. 1

ARTICLE 19–6

7. 32/3

9. 0; area between curve and x-axis from -1 to 0 is equal to that from 0 to 1

ARTICLE 19–7

1. 9/2   3. $4\sqrt{3}$ 5. 8/3   7. 4/3

9. 9/2

ARTICLE 19–8

1. 32π 3. $\pi a^3/15$ 5. $4\pi ab^2/3$

9. $\pi(e^4-1)/2$

ARTICLE 19–9

1. 16 inch·pounds   3. $\frac{3}{2}k$ and $\frac{5}{2}k$ 5. $-1000 \log_e 2$

CHAPTER 20

ARTICLE 20–1

1. 4   3. 120   5. 240

7. 1920   9. 60   11. (a) 56,   (b) 64

ARTICLE 20–2

1. 504   3. 585

5. (a) 5040,   (b) 144   7. 5040

9. 103,680   11. 1440

13. 468,000   15. 3780

17. 360   19. $n = 8$

ARTICLE 20–3

1. (a) 35,   (b) 45,   (c) 210   3. 12,650

5. 84,456   7. 18,375

9. 560   11. $384C(36, 6)$

13. (a) 36,   (b) 84   15. 126

17. (a) 28,   (b) 56,   (c) 247   19. $n = 7$

ARTICLE 20–4

  1. (a) 1/6
     (b) 1/3
  5. 1/9

  3. 1/12

  7. (a) 1/221
     (b) 25/102
     (c) 20/221

  9. (a) 28/55
     (b) 14/55

 11. 1/36, 1/216

13. 1/66 if anyone may play with anyone else
    1/36 if men must have women for partners

15. 0.7 (approximate)

ARTICLE 20–5

  1. 1/32
  7. 0.731

  3. 3/100
  9. 0.146

  5. 7/8
 11. 0.034

ARTICLE 20–6

  1. (a) 1/2
     (b) 1/4
  5. (a) 25/72
     (b) 91/216

  3. 0.0081

  7. (a) 12/49
     (b) 9/49
     (c) 12/49

  9. (a) 1/4
     (b) 1/4

APPENDIX

TABLE I
Values of Trigonometric Functions

Degrees	Radians	Sine	Tangent	Cotangent	Cosine		
0° 00′	.0000	.0000	.0000		1.0000	1.5708	90° 00′
10′	.0029	.0029	.0029	343.77	1.0000	1.5679	50′
20′	.0058	.0058	.0058	171.89	1.0000	1.5650	40′
30′	.0087	.0087	.0087	114.59	1.0000	1.5621	30′
40′	.0116	.0116	.0116	85.940	.9999	1.5592	20′
50′	.0145	.0145	.0145	68.750	.9999	1.5563	10′
1° 00′	.0175	.0175	.0175	57.290	.9998	1.5533	89° 00′
10′	.0204	.0204	.0204	49.104	.9998	1.5504	50′
20′	.0233	.0233	.0233	42.964	.9997	1.5475	40′
30′	.0262	.0262	.0262	38.188	.9997	1.5446	30′
40′	.0291	.0291	.0291	34.368	.9996	1.5417	20′
50′	.0320	.0320	.0320	31.242	.9995	1.5388	10′
2° 00′	.0349	.0349	.0349	28.636	.9994	1.5359	88° 00′
10′	.0378	.0378	.0378	26.432	.9993	1.5330	50′
20′	.0407	.0407	.0407	24.542	.9992	1.5301	40′
30′	.0436	.0436	.0437	22.904	.9990	1.5272	30′
40′	.0465	.0465	.0466	21.470	.9989	1.5243	20′
50′	.0495	.0494	.0495	20.206	.9988	1.5213	10′
3° 00′	.0524	.0523	.0524	19.081	.9986	1.5184	87° 00′
10′	.0553	.0552	.0553	18.075	.9985	1.5155	50′
20′	.0582	.0581	.0582	17.169	.9983	1.5126	40′
30′	.0611	.0610	.0612	16.350	.9981	1.5097	30′
40′	.0640	.0640	.0641	15.605	.9980	1.5068	20′
50′	.0669	.0669	.0670	14.924	.9978	1.5039	10′
4° 00′	.0698	.0698	.0699	14.301	.9976	1.5010	86° 00′
10′	.0727	.0727	.0729	13.727	.9974	1.4981	50′
20′	.0756	.0756	.0758	13.197	.9971	1.4952	40′
30′	.0785	.0785	.0787	12.706	.9969	1.4923	30′
40′	.0814	.0814	.0816	12.251	.9967	1.4893	20′
50′	.0844	.0843	.0846	11.826	.9964	1.4864	10′
5° 00′	.0873	.0872	.0875	11.430	.9962	1.4835	85° 00′
10′	.0902	.0901	.0904	11.059	.9959	1.4806	50′
20′	.0931	.0929	.0934	10.712	.9957	1.4777	40′
30′	.0960	.0958	.0963	10.385	.9954	1.4748	30′
40′	.0989	.0987	.0992	10.078	.9951	1.4719	20′
50′	.1018	.1016	.1022	9.7882	.9948	1.4690	10′
6° 00′	.1047	.1045	.1051	9.5144	.9945	1.4661	84° 00′
10′	.1076	.1074	.1080	9.2553	.9942	1.4632	50′
20′	.1105	.1103	.1110	9.0098	.9939	1.4603	40′
30′	.1134	.1132	.1139	8.7769	.9936	1.4573	30′
40′	.1164	.1161	.1169	8.5555	.9932	1.4544	20′
50′	.1193	.1190	.1198	8.3450	.9929	1.4515	10′
7° 00′	.1222	.1219	.1228	8.1443	.9925	1.4486	83° 00′
10′	.1251	.1248	.1257	7.9530	.9922	1.4457	50′
20′	.1280	.1276	.1287	7.7704	.9918	1.4428	40′
30′	.1309	.1305	.1317	7.5958	.9914	1.4399	30′
40′	.1338	.1334	.1346	7.4287	.9911	1.4370	20′
50′	.1367	.1363	.1376	7.2687	.9907	1.4341	10′
8° 00′	.1396	.1392	.1405	7.1154	.9903	1.4312	82° 00′
10′	.1425	.1421	.1435	6.9682	.9899	1.4283	50′
20′	.1454	.1449	.1465	6.8269	.9894	1.4254	40′
30′	.1484	.1478	.1495	6.6912	.9890	1.4224	30′
40′	.1513	.1507	.1524	6.5606	.9886	1.4195	20′
50′	.1542	.1536	.1554	6.4348	.9881	1.4166	10′
9° 00′	.1571	.1564	.1584	6.3138	.9877	1.4137	81° 00′
		Cosine	Cotangent	Tangent	Sine	Radians	Degrees

TABLE I (Continued)
Values of Trigonometric Functions

Degrees	Radians	Sine	Tangent	Cotangent	Cosine		
9° 00′	.1571	.1564	.1584	6.3138	.9877	1.4137	81° 00′
10′	.1600	.1593	.1614	6.1970	.9872	1.4108	50′
20′	.1629	.1622	.1644	6.0844	.9868	1.4079	40′
30′	.1658	.1650	.1673	5.9758	.9863	1.4050	30′
40′	.1687	.1679	.1703	5.8708	.9858	1.4021	20′
50′	.1716	.1708	.1733	5.7694	.9853	1.3992	10′
10° 00′	.1745	.1736	.1763	5.6713	.9848	1.3963	80° 00′
10′	.1774	.1765	.1793	5.5764	.9843	1.3934	50′
20′	.1804	.1794	.1823	5.4845	.9838	1.3904	40′
30′	.1833	.1822	.1853	5.3955	.9833	1.3875	30′
40′	.1862	.1851	.1883	5.3093	.9827	1.3846	20′
50′	.1891	.1880	.1914	5.2257	.9822	1.3817	10′
11° 00′	.1920	.1908	.1944	5.1446	.9816	1.3788	79° 00′
10′	.1949	.1937	.1974	5.0658	.9811	1.3759	50′
20′	.1978	.1965	.2004	4.9894	.9805	1.3730	40′
30′	.2007	.1994	.2035	4.9152	.9799	1.3701	30′
40′	.2036	.2022	.2065	4.8430	.9793	1.3672	20′
50′	.2065	.2051	.2095	4.7729	.9787	1.3643	10′
12° 00′	.2094	.2079	.2126	4.7046	.9781	1.3614	78° 00′
10′	.2123	.2108	.2156	4.6382	.9775	1.3584	50′
20′	.2153	.2136	.2186	4.5736	.9769	1.3555	40′
30′	.2182	.2164	.2217	4.5107	.9763	1.3526	30′
40′	.2211	.2193	.2247	4.4494	.9757	1.3497	20′
50′	.2240	.2221	.2278	4.3897	.9750	1.3468	10′
13° 00′	.2269	.2250	.2309	4.3315	.9744	1.3439	77° 00′
10′	.2298	.2278	.2339	4.2747	.9737	1.3410	50′
20′	.2327	.2306	.2370	4.2193	.9730	1.3381	40′
30′	.2356	.2334	.2401	4.1653	.9724	1.3352	30′
40′	.2385	.2363	.2432	4.1126	.9717	1.3323	20′
50′	.2414	.2391	.2462	4.0611	.9710	1.3294	10′
14° 00′	.2443	.2419	.2493	4.0108	.9703	1.3265	76° 00′
10′	.2473	.2447	.2524	3.9617	.9696	1.3235	50′
20′	.2502	.2476	.2555	3.9136	.9689	1.3206	40′
30′	.2531	.2504	.2586	3.8667	.9681	1.3177	30′
40′	.2560	.2532	.2617	3.8208	.9674	1.3148	20′
50′	.2589	.2560	.2648	3.7760	.9667	1.3119	10′
15° 00′	.2618	.2588	.2679	3.7321	.9659	1.3090	75° 00′
10′	.2647	.2616	.2711	3.6891	.9652	1.3061	50′
20′	.2676	.2644	.2742	3.6470	.9644	1.3032	40′
30′	.2705	.2672	.2773	3.6059	.9636	1.3003	30′
40′	.2734	.2700	.2805	3.5656	.9628	1.2974	20′
50′	.2763	.2728	.2836	3.5261	.9621	1.2945	10′
16° 00′	.2793	.2756	.2867	3.4874	.9613	1.2915	74° 00′
10′	.2822	.2784	.2899	3.4495	.9605	1.2886	50′
20′	.2851	.2812	.2931	3.4124	.9596	1.2857	40′
30′	.2880	.2840	.2962	3.3759	.9588	1.2828	30′
40′	.2909	.2868	.2994	3.3402	.9580	1.2799	20′
50′	.2938	.2896	.3026	3.3052	.9572	1.2770	10′
17° 00′	.2967	.2924	.3057	3.2709	.9563	1.2741	73° 00′
10′	.2996	.2952	.3089	3.2371	.9555	1.2712	50′
20′	.3025	.2979	.3121	3.2041	.9546	1.2683	40′
30′	.3054	.3007	.3153	3.1716	.9537	1.2654	30′
40′	.3083	.3035	.3185	3.1397	.9528	1.2625	20′
50′	.3113	.3062	.3217	3.1084	.9520	1.2595	10′
18° 00′	.3142	.3090	.3249	3.0777	.9511	1.2566	72° 00′
		Cosine	Cotangent	Tangent	Sine	Radians	Degrees

TABLE I (Continued)

449
Values of Trigonometric Functions

Degrees	Radians	Sine	Tangent	Cotangent	Cosine		
18° 00′	.3142	.3090	.3249	3.0777	.9511	1.2566	72° 00′
10′	.3171	.3118	.3281	3.0475	.9502	1.2537	50′
20′	.3200	.3145	.3314	3.0178	.9492	1.2508	40′
30′	.3229	.3173	.3346	2.9887	.9483	1.2479	30′
40′	.3258	.3201	.3378	2.9600	.9474	1.2450	20′
50′	.3287	.3228	.3411	2.9319	.9465	1.2421	10′
19° 00′	.3316	.3256	.3443	2.9042	.9455	1.2392	71° 00′
10′	.3345	.3283	.3476	2.8770	.9446	1.2363	50′
20′	.3374	.3311	.3508	2.8502	.9436	1.2334	40′
30′	.3403	.3338	.3541	2.8239	.9426	1.2305	30′
40′	.3432	.3365	.3574	2.7980	.9417	1.2275	20′
50′	.3462	.3393	.3607	2.7725	.9407	1.2246	10′
20° 00′	.3491	.3420	.3640	2.7475	.9397	1.2217	70° 00′
10′	.3520	.3448	.3673	2.7228	.9387	1.2188	50′
20′	.3549	.3475	.3706	2.6985	.9377	1.2159	40′
30′	.3578	.3502	.3739	2.6746	.9367	1.2130	30′
40′	.3607	.3529	.3772	2.6511	.9356	1.2101	20′
50′	.3636	.3557	.3805	2.6279	.9346	1.2072	10′
21° 00′	.3665	.3584	.3839	2.6051	.9336	1.2043	69° 00′
10′	.3694	.3611	.3872	2.5826	.9325	1.2014	50′
20′	.3723	.3638	.3906	2.5605	.9315	1.1985	40′
30′	.3752	.3665	.3939	2.5386	.9304	1.1956	30′
40′	.3782	.3692	.3973	2.5172	.9293	1.1926	20′
50′	.3811	.3719	.4006	2.4960	.9283	1.1897	10′
22° 00′	.3840	.3746	.4040	2.4751	.9272	1.1868	68° 00′
10′	.3869	.3773	.4074	2.4545	.9261	1.1839	50′
20′	.3898	.3800	.4108	2.4342	.9250	1.1810	40′
30′	.3927	.3827	.4142	2.4142	.9239	1.1781	30′
40′	.3956	.3854	.4176	2.3945	.9228	1.1752	20′
50′	.3985	.3881	.4210	2.3750	.9216	1.1723	10′
23° 00′	.4014	.3907	.4245	2.3559	.9205	1.1694	67° 00′
10′	.4043	.3934	.4279	2.3369	.9194	1.1665	50′
20′	.4072	.3961	.4314	2.3183	.9182	1.1636	40′
30′	.4102	.3987	.4348	2.2998	.9171	1.1606	30′
40′	.4131	.4014	.4383	2.2817	.9159	1.1577	20′
50′	.4160	.4041	.4417	2.2637	.9147	1.1548	10′
24° 00′	.4189	.4067	.4452	2.2460	.9135	1.1519	66° 00′
10′	.4218	.4094	.4487	2.2286	.9124	1.1490	50′
20′	.4247	.4120	.4522	2.2113	.9112	1.1461	40′
30′	.4276	.4147	.4557	2.1943	.9100	1.1432	30′
40′	.4305	.4173	.4592	2.1775	.9088	1.1403	20′
50′	.4334	.4200	.4628	2.1609	.9075	1.1374	10′
25° 00′	.4363	.4226	.4663	2.1445	.9063	1.1345	65° 00′
10′	.4392	.4253	.4699	2.1283	.9051	1.1316	50′
20′	.4422	.4279	.4734	2.1123	.9038	1.1286	40′
30′	.4451	.4305	.4770	2.0965	.9026	1.1257	30′
40′	.4480	.4331	.4806	2.0809	.9013	1.1228	20′
50′	.4509	.4358	.4841	2.0655	.9001	1.1199	10′
26° 00′	.4538	.4384	.4877	2.0503	.8988	1.1170	64° 00′
10′	.4567	.4410	.4913	2.0353	.8975	1.1141	50′
20′	.4596	.4436	.4950	2.0204	.8962	1.1112	40′
30′	4625	.4462	.4986	2.0057	.8949	1.1083	30′
40′	.4654	.4488	.5022	1.9912	.8936	1.1054	20′
50′	.4683	.4514	.5059	1.9768	.8923	1.1025	10′
27° 00′	.4712	.4540	.5095	1.9626	.8910	1.0996	63° 00′
		Cosine	Cotangent	Tangent	Sine	Radians	Degrees

TABLE I (Continued)
Values of Trigonometric Functions

Degrees	Radians	Sine	Tangent	Cotangent	Cosine		
27° 00′	.4712	.4540	.5095	1.9626	.8910	1.0996	63° 00′
10′	.4741	.4566	.5132	1.9486	.8897	1.0966	50′
20′	.4771	.4592	.5169	1.9347	.8884	1.0937	40′
30′	.4800	.4617	.5206	1.9210	.8870	1.0908	30′
40′	.4829	.4643	.5243	1.9074	.8857	1.0879	20′
50′	.4858	.4669	.5280	1.8940	.8843	1.0850	10′
28° 00′	.4887	.4695	.5317	1.8807	.8829	1.0821	62° 00′
10′	.4916	.4720	.5354	1.8676	.8816	1.0792	50′
20′	.4945	.4746	.5392	1.8546	.8802	1.0763	40′
30′	.4974	.4772	.5430	1.8418	.8788	1.0734	30′
40′	.5003	.4797	.5467	1.8291	.8774	1.0705	20′
50′	.5032	.4823	.5505	1.8165	.8760	1.0676	10′
29° 00′	.5061	.4848	.5543	1.8040	.8746	1.0647	61° 00′
10′	.5091	.4874	.5581	1.7917	.8732	1.0617	50′
20′	.5120	.4899	.5619	1.7796	.8718	1.0588	40′
30′	.5149	.4924	.5658	1.7675	.8704	1.0559	30′
40′	.5178	.4950	.5696	1.7556	.8689	1.0530	20′
50′	.5207	.4975	.5735	1.7437	.8675	1.0501	10′
30° 00′	.5236	.5000	.5774	1.7321	.8660	1.0472	60° 00′
10′	.5265	.5025	.5812	1.7205	.8646	1.0443	50′
20′	.5294	.5050	.5851	1.7090	.8631	1.0414	40′
30′	.5323	.5075	.5890	1.6977	.8616	1.0385	30′
40′	.5352	.5100	.5930	1.6864	.8601	1.0356	20′
50′	.5381	.5125	.5969	1.6753	.8587	1.0327	10′
31° 00′	.5411	.5150	.6009	1.6643	.8572	1.0297	59° 00′
10′	.5440	.5175	.6048	1.6534	.8557	1.0268	50′
20′	.5469	.5200	.6088	1.6426	.8542	1.0239	40′
30′	.5498	.5225	.6128	1.6319	.8526	1.0210	30′
40′	.5527	.5250	.6168	1.6212	.8511	1.0181	20′
50′	.5556	.5275	.6208	1.6107	.8496	1.0152	10′
32° 00′	.5585	.5299	.6249	1.6003	.8480	1.0123	58° 00′
10′	.5614	.5324	.6289	1.5900	.8465	1.0094	50′
20′	.5643	.5348	.6330	1.5798	.8450	1.0065	40′
30′	.5672	.5373	.6371	1.5697	.8434	1.0036	30′
40′	.5701	.5398	.6412	1.5597	.8418	1.0007	20′
50′	.5730	.5422	.6453	1.5497	.8403	.9977	10′
33° 00′	.5760	.5446	.6494	1.5399	.8387	.9948	57° 00′
10′	.5789	.5471	.6536	1.5301	.8371	.9919	50′
20′	.5818	.5495	.6577	1.5204	.8355	.9890	40′
30′	.5847	.5519	.6619	1.5108	.8339	.9861	30′
40′	.5876	.5544	.6661	1.5013	.8323	.9832	20′
50′	.5905	.5568	.6703	1.4919	.8307	.9803	10′
34° 00′	.5934	.5592	.6745	1.4826	.8290	.9774	56° 00′
10′	.5963	.5616	.6787	1.4733	.8274	.9745	50′
20′	.5992	.5640	.6830	1.4641	.8258	.9716	40′
30′	.6021	.5664	.6873	1.4550	.8241	.9687	30′
40′	.6050	.5688	.6916	1.4460	.8225	.9657	20′
50′	.6080	.5712	.6959	1.4370	.8208	.9628	10′
35° 00′	.6109	.5736	.7002	1.4281	.8192	.9599	55° 00′
10′	.6138	.5760	.7046	1.4193	.8175	.9570	50′
20′	.6167	.5783	.7089	1.4106	.8158	.9541	40′
30′	.6196	.5807	.7133	1.4019	.8141	.9512	30′
40′	.6225	.5831	.7177	1.3934	.8124	.9483	20′
50′	.6254	.5854	.7221	1.3848	.8107	.9454	10′
36° 00′	.6283	.5878	.7265	1.3764	.8090	.9425	54° 00′
		Cosine	Cotangent	Tangent	Sine	Radians	Degrees

TABLE I (Continued)

451
Values of Trigonometric Functions

Degrees	Radians	Sine	Tangent	Cotangent	Cosine		
36° 00′	.6283	.5878	.7265	1.3764	.8090	.9425	54° 00′
10′	.6312	.5901	.7310	1.3680	.8073	.9396	50′
20′	.6341	.5925	.7355	1.3597	.8056	.9367	40′
30′	.6370	.5948	.7400	1.3514	.8039	.9338	30′
40′	.6400	.5972	.7445	1.3432	.8021	.9308	20′
50′	.6429	.5995	.7490	1.3351	.8004	.9279	10′
37° 00′	.6458	.6018	.7536	1.3270	.7986	.9250	53° 00′
10′	.6487	.6041	.7581	1.3190	.7969	.9221	50′
20′	.6516	.6065	.7627	1.3111	.7951	.9192	40′
30′	.6545	.6088	.7673	1.3032	.7934	.9163	30′
40′	.6574	.6111	.7720	1.2954	.7916	.9134	20′
50′	.6603	.6134	.7766	1.2876	.7898	.9105	10′
38° 00′	.6632	.6157	.7813	1.2799	.7880	.9076	52° 00′
10′	.6661	.6180	.7860	1.2723	.7862	.9047	50′
20′	.6690	.6202	.7907	1.2647	.7844	.9018	40′
30′	.6720	.6225	.7954	1.2572	.7826	.8988	30′
40′	.6749	.6248	.8002	1.2497	.7808	.8959	20′
50′	.6778	.6271	.8050	1.2423	.7790	.8930	10′
39° 00′	.6807	.6293	.8098	1.2349	.7771	.8901	51° 00′
10′	.6836	.6316	.8146	1.2276	.7753	.8872	50′
20′	.6865	.6338	.8195	1.2203	.7735	.8843	40′
30′	.6894	.6361	.8243	1.2131	.7716	.8814	30′
40′	.6923	.6383	.8292	1.2059	.7698	.8785	20′
50′	.6952	.6406	.8342	1.1988	.7679	.8756	10′
40° 00′	.6981	.6428	.8391	1.1918	.7660	.8727	50° 00′
10′	.7010	.6450	.8441	1.1847	.7642	.8698	50′
20′	.7039	.6472	.8491	1.1778	.7623	.8668	40′
30′	.7069	.6494	.8541	1.1708	.7604	.8639	30′
40′	.7098	.6517	.8591	1.1640	.7585	.8610	20′
50′	.7127	.6539	.8642	1.1571	.7566	.8581	10′
41° 00′	.7156	.6561	.8693	1.1504	.7547	.8552	49° 00′
10′	.7185	.6583	.8744	1.1436	.7528	.8523	50′
20′	.7214	.6604	.8796	1.1369	.7509	.8494	40′
30′	.7243	.6626	.8847	1.1303	.7490	.8465	30′
40′	.7272	.6648	.8899	1.1237	.7470	.8436	20′
50′	.7301	.6670	.8952	1.1171	.7451	.8407	10′
42° 00′	.7330	.6691	.9004	1.1106	.7431	.8378	48° 00′
10′	.7359	.6713	.9057	1.1041	.7412	.8348	50′
20′	.7389	.6734	.9110	1.0977	.7392	.8319	40′
30′	.7418	.6756	.9163	1.0913	.7373	.8290	30′
40′	.7447	.6777	.9217	1.0850	.7353	.8261	20′
50′	.7476	.6799	.9271	1.0786	.7333	.8232	10′
43° 00′	.7505	.6820	.9325	1.0724	.7314	.8203	47° 00′
10′	.7534	.6841	.9380	1.0661	.7294	.8174	50′
20′	.7563	.6862	.9435	1.0599	.7274	.8145	40′
30′	.7592	.6884	.9490	1.0538	.7254	.8116	30′
40′	.7621	.6905	.9545	1.0477	.7234	.8087	20′
50′	.7650	.6926	.9601	1.0416	.7214	.8058	10′
44° 00′	.7679	.6947	.9657	1.0355	.7193	.8029	46° 00′
10′	.7709	.6967	.9713	1.0295	.7173	.7999	50′
20′	.7738	.6988	.9770	1.0235	.7153	.7970	40′
30′	.7767	.7009	.9827	1.0176	.7133	.7941	30′
40′	.7796	.7030	.9884	1.0117	.7112	.7912	20′
50′	.7825	.7050	.9942	1.0058	.7092	.7883	10′
45° 00′	.7854	.7071	1.0000	1.0000	.7071	.7854	45° 00′
		Cosine	Cotangent	Tangent	Sine	Radians	Degrees

TABLE II
Logarithms of Numbers

N	0	1	2	3	4	5	6	7	8	9
1.0	.0000	.0043	.0086	.0128	.0170	.0212	.0253	.0294	.0334	.0374
1.1	.0414	.0453	.0492	.0531	.0569	.0607	.0645	.0682	.0719	.0755
1.2	.0792	.0828	.0864	.0899	.0934	.0969	.1004	.1038	.1072	.1106
1.3	.1139	.1173	.1206	.1239	.1271	.1303	.1335	.1367	.1399	.1430
1.4	.1461	.1492	.1523	.1553	.1584	.1614	.1644	.1673	.1703	.1732
1.5	.1761	.1790	.1818	.1847	.1875	.1903	.1931	.1959	.1987	.2014
1.6	.2041	.2068	.2095	.2122	.2148	.2175	.2201	.2227	.2253	.2279
1.7	.2304	.2330	.2355	.2380	.2405	.2430	.2455	.2480	.2504	.2529
1.8	.2553	.2577	.2601	.2625	.2648	.2672	.2695	.2718	.2742	.2765
1.9	.2788	.2810	.2833	.2856	.2878	.2900	.2923	.2945	.2967	.2989
2.0	.3010	.3032	.3054	.3075	.3096	.3118	.3139	.3160	.3181	.3201
2.1	.3222	.3243	.3263	.3284	.3304	.3324	.3345	.3365	.3385	.3404
2.2	.3424	.3444	.3464	.3483	.3502	.3522	.3541	.3560	.3579	.3598
2.3	.3617	.3636	.3655	.3674	.3692	.3711	.3729	.3747	.3766	.3784
2.4	.3802	.3820	.3838	.3856	.3874	.3892	.3909	.3927	.3945	.3962
2.5	.3979	.3997	.4014	.4031	.4048	.4065	.4082	.4099	.4116	.4133
2.6	.4150	.4166	.4183	.4200	.4216	.4232	.4249	.4265	.4281	.4298
2.7	.4314	.4330	.4346	.4362	.4378	.4393	.4409	.4425	.4440	.4456
2.8	.4472	.4487	.4502	.4518	.4533	.4548	.4564	.4579	.4594	.4609
2.9	.4624	.4639	.4654	.4669	.4683	.4698	.4713	.4728	.4742	.4757
3.0	.4771	.4786	.4800	.4814	.4829	.4843	.4857	.4871	.4886	.4900
3.1	.4914	.4928	.4942	.4955	.4969	.4983	.4997	.5011	.5024	.5038
3.2	.5051	.5065	.5079	.5092	.5105	.5119	.5132	.5145	.5159	.5172
3.3	.5185	.5198	.5211	.5224	.5237	.5250	.5263	.5276	.5289	.5302
3.4	.5315	.5328	.5340	.5353	.5366	.5378	.5391	.5403	.5416	.5428
3.5	.5441	.5453	.5465	.5478	.5490	.5502	.5514	.5527	.5539	.5551
3.6	.5563	.5575	.5587	.5599	.5611	.5623	.5635	.5647	.5658	.5670
3.7	.5682	.5694	.5705	.5717	.5729	.5740	.5752	.5763	.5775	.5786
3.8	.5798	.5809	.5821	.5832	.5843	.5855	.5866	.5877	.5888	.5899
3.9	.5911	.5922	.5933	.5944	.5955	.5966	.5977	.5988	.5999	.6010
4.0	.6021	.6031	.6042	.6053	.6064	.6075	.6085	.6096	.6107	.6117
4.1	.6128	.6138	.6149	.6160	.6170	.6180	.6191	.6201	.6212	.6222
4.2	.6232	.6243	.6253	.6263	.6274	.6284	.6294	.6304	.6314	.6325
4.3	.6335	.6345	.6355	.6365	.6375	.6385	.6395	.6405	.6415	.6425
4.4	.6435	.6444	.6454	.6464	.6474	.6484	.6493	.6503	.6513	.6522
4.5	.6532	.6542	.6551	.6561	.6571	.6580	.6590	.6599	.6609	.6618
4.6	.6628	.6637	.6646	.6656	.6665	.6675	.6684	.6693	.6702	.6712
4.7	.6721	.6730	.6739	.6749	.6758	.6767	.6776	.6785	.6794	.6803
4.8	.6812	.6821	.6830	.6839	.6848	.6857	.6866	.6875	.6884	.6893
4.9	.6902	.6911	.6920	.6928	.6937	.6946	.6955	.6964	.6972	.6981
5.0	.6990	.6998	.7007	.7016	.7024	.7033	.7042	.7050	.7059	.7067
5.1	.7076	.7084	.7093	.7101	.7110	.7118	.7126	.7135	.7143	.7152
5.2	.7160	.7168	.7177	.7185	.7193	.7202	.7210	.7218	.7226	.7235
5.3	.7243	.7251	.7259	.7267	.7275	.7284	.7292	.7300	.7308	.7316
5.4	.7324	.7332	.7340	.7348	.7356	.7364	.7372	.7380	.7388	.7396
N	0	1	2	3	4	5	6	7	8	9

TABLE II (Continued)
Logarithms of Numbers
453

N	0	1	2	3	4	5	6	7	8	9
5.5	.7404	.7412	.7419	.7427	.7435	.7443	.7451	.7459	.7466	.7474
5.6	.7482	.7490	.7497	.7505	.7513	.7520	.7528	.7536	.7543	.7551
5.7	.7559	.7566	.7574	.7582	.7589	.7597	.7604	.7612	.7619	.7627
5.8	.7634	.7642	.7649	.7657	.7664	.7672	.7679	.7686	.7694	.7701
5.9	.7709	.7716	.7723	.7731	.7738	.7745	.7752	.7760	.7767	.7774
6.0	.7782	.7789	.7796	.7803	.7810	.7818	.7825	.7832	.7839	.7846
6.1	.7853	.7860	.7868	.7875	.7882	.7889	.7896	.7903	.7910	.7917
6.2	.7924	.7931	.7938	.7945	.7952	.7959	.7966	.7973	.7980	.7987
6.3	.7993	.8000	.8007	.8014	.8021	.8028	.8035	.8041	.8048	.8055
6.4	.8062	.8069	.8075	.8082	.8089	.8096	.8102	.8109	.8116	.8122
6.5	.8129	.8136	.8142	.8149	.8156	.8162	.8169	.8176	.8182	.8189
6.6	.8195	.8202	.8209	.8215	.8222	.8228	.8235	.8241	.8248	.8254
6.7	.8261	.8267	.8274	.8280	.8287	.8293	.8299	.8306	.8312	.8319
6.8	.8325	.8331	.8338	.8344	.8351	.8357	.8363	.8370	.8376	.8382
6.9	.8388	.8395	.8401	.8407	.8414	.8420	.8426	.8432	.8439	.8445
7.0	.8451	.8457	.8463	.8470	.8476	.8482	.8488	.8494	.8500	.8506
7.1	.8513	.8519	.8525	.8531	.8537	.8543	.8549	.8555	.8561	.8567
7.2	.8573	.8579	.8585	.8591	.8597	.8603	.8609	.8615	.8621	.8627
7.3	.8633	.8639	.8645	.8651	.8657	.8663	.8669	.8675	.8681	.8686
7.4	.8692	.8698	.8704	.8710	.8716	.8722	.8727	.8733	.8739	.8745
7.5	.8751	.8756	.8762	.8768	.8774	.8779	.8785	.8791	.8797	.8802
7.6	.8808	.8814	.8820	.8825	.8831	.8837	.8842	.8848	.8854	.8859
7.7	.8865	.8871	.8876	.8882	.8887	.8893	.8899	.8904	.8910	.8915
7.8	.8921	.8927	.8932	.8938	.8943	.8949	.8954	.8960	.8965	.8971
7.9	.8976	.8982	.8987	.8993	.8998	.9004	.9009	.9015	.9020	.9025
8.0	.9031	.9036	.9042	.9047	.9053	.9058	.9063	.9069	.9074	.9079
8.1	.9085	.9090	.9096	.9101	.9106	.9112	.9117	.9122	.9128	.9133
8.2	.9138	.9143	.9149	.9154	.9159	.9165	.9170	.9175	.9180	.9186
8.3	.9191	.9196	.9201	.9206	.9212	.9217	.9222	.9227	.9232	.9238
8.4	.9243	.9248	.9253	.9258	.9263	.9269	.9274	.9279	.9284	.9289
8.5	.9294	.9299	.9304	.9309	.9315	.9320	.9325	.9330	.9335	.9340
8.6	.9345	.9350	.9355	.9360	.9365	.9370	.9375	.9380	.9385	.9390
8.7	.9395	.9400	.9405	.9410	.9415	.9420	.9425	.9430	.9435	.9440
8.8	.9445	.9450	.9455	.9460	.9465	.9469	.9474	.9479	.9484	.9489
8.9	.9494	.9499	.9504	.9509	.9513	.9518	.9523	.9528	.9533	.9538
9.0	.9542	.9547	.9552	.9557	.9562	.9566	.9571	.9576	.9581	.9586
9.1	.9590	.9595	.9600	.9605	.9609	.9614	.9619	.9624	.9628	.9633
9.2	.9638	.9643	.9647	.9652	.9657	.9661	.9666	.9671	.9675	.9680
9.3	.9685	.9689	.9694	.9699	.9703	.9708	.9713	.9717	.9722	.9727
9.4	.9731	.9736	.9741	.9745	.9750	.9754	.9759	.9763	.9768	.9773
9.5	.9777	.9782	.9786	.9791	.9795	.9800	.9805	.9809	.9814	.9818
9.6	.9823	.9827	.9832	.9836	.9841	.9845	.9850	.9854	.9859	.9863
9.7	.9868	.9872	.9877	.9881	.9886	.9890	.9894	.9899	.9903	.9908
9.8	.9912	.9917	.9921	.9926	.9930	.9934	.9939	.9943	.9948	.9952
9.9	.9956	.9961	.9965	.9969	.9974	.9978	.9983	.9987	.9991	.9996
N	0	1	2	3	4	5	6	7	8	9

TABLE III
Logarithms of Trigonometric Functions

Degrees	Log_{10} Sine	Log_{10} Tangent	Log_{10} Cotangent	Log_{10} Cosine	
0° 00′					90° 00′
10′	.4637 −3	.4637 −3	2.5363	.0000	50′
20′	.7648 −3	.7648 −3	2.2352	.0000	40′
30′	9408 −3	.9409 −3	2.0591	.0000	30′
40′	.0658 −2	.0658 −2	1.9342	.0000	20′
50′	.1627 −2	.1627 −2	1.8373	.0000	10′
1° 00′	.2419 −2	.2419 −2	1.7581	.9999 −1	89° 00′
10′	.3088 −2	.3089 −2	1.6911	.9999 −1	50′
20′	.3668 −2	.3669 −2	1.6331	.9999 −1	40′
30′	.4179 −2	.4181 −2	1.5819	.9999 −1	30′
40′	.4637 −2	.4638 −2	1.5362	.9998 −1	20′
50′	.5050 −2	.5053 −2	1.4947	.9998 −1	10′
2° 00′	.5428 −2	.5431 −2	1.4569	.9997 −1	88° 00′
10′	.5776 −2	.5779 −2	1.4221	.9997 −1	50′
20′	.6097 −2	.6101 −2	1.3899	.9996 −1	40′
30′	.6397 −2	.6401 −2	1.3599	.9996 −1	30′
40′	.6677 −2	.6682 −2	1.3318	.9995 −1	20′
50′	.6940 −2	.6945 −2	1.3055	.9995 −1	10′
3° 00′	.7188 −2	.7194 −2	1.2806	.9994 −1	87° 00′
10′	.7423 −2	.7429 −2	1.2571	.9993 −1	50′
20′	.7645 −2	.7652 −2	1.2348	.9993 −1	40′
30′	.7857 −2	.7865 −2	1.2135	.9992 −1	30′
40′	.8059 −2	.8067 −2	1.1933	.9991 −1	20′
50′	.8251 −2	.8261 −2	1.1739	.9990 −1	10′
4° 00′	.8436 −2	.8446 −2	1.1554	.9989 −1	86° 00′
10′	.8613 −2	.8624 −2	1.1376	.9989 −1	50′
20′	.8783 −2	.8795 −2	1.1205	.9988 −1	40′
30′	.8946 −2	.8960 −2	1.1040	.9987 −1	30′
40′	.9104 −2	.9118 −2	1.0882	.9986 −1	20′
50′	.9256 −2	.9272 −2	1.0728	.9985 −1	10′
5° 00′	.9403 −2	.9420 −2	1.0580	.9983 −1	85° 00′
10′	.9545 −2	.9563 −2	1.0437	.9982 −1	50′
20′	.9682 −2	.9701 −2	1.0299	.9981 −1	40′
30′	.9816 −2	.9836 −2	1.0164	.9980 −1	30′
40′	.9945 −2	.9966 −2	1.0034	.9979 −1	20′
50′	.0070 −1	.0093 −1	.9907	.9977 −1	10′
6° 00′	.0192 −1	.0216 −1	.9784	.9976 −1	84° 00′
10′	.0311 −1	.0336 −1	.9664	.9975 −1	50′
20′	.0426 −1	.0453 −1	.9547	.9973 −1	40′
30′	.0539 −1	.0567 −1	.9433	.9972 −1	30′
40′	.0648 −1	.0678 −1	.9322	.9971 −1	20′
50′	.0755 −1	.0786 −1	.9214	.9969 −1	10′
7° 00′	.0859 −1	.0891 −1	.9109	.9968 −1	83° 00′
10′	.0961 −1	.0995 −1	.9005	.9966 −1	50′
20′	.1060 −1	.1096 −1	.8904	.9964 −1	40′
30′	.1157 −1	.1194 −1	.8806	.9963 −1	30′
40′	.1252 −1	.1291 −1	.8709	.9961 −1	20′
50′	.1345 −1	.1385 −1	.8615	.9959 −1	10′
8° 00′	.1436 −1	.1478 −1	.8522	.9958 −1	82° 00′
10′	.1525 −1	.1569 −1	.8431	.9956 −1	50′
20′	.1612 −1	.1658 −1	.8342	.9954 −1	40′
30′	.1697 −1	.1745 −1	.8255	.9952 −1	30′
40′	.1781 −1	.1831 −1	.8169	.9950 −1	20′
50′	.1863 −1	.1915 −1	.8085	.9948 −1	10′
9° 00′	.1943 −1	.1997 −1	.8003	.9946 −1	81° 00′
	Log_{10} Cosine	Log_{10} Cotangent	Log_{10} Tangent	Log_{10} Sine	Degrees

TABLE III (Continued)   455

Logarithms of Trigonometric Functions

Degrees	Log₁₀ Sine	Log₁₀ Tangent	Log₁₀ Cotangent	Log₁₀ Cosine	
9° 00′	.1943 − 1	.1997 − 1	.8003	.9946 − 1	81° 00′
10′	.2022 − 1	.2078 − 1	.7922	.9944 − 1	50′
20′	.2100 − 1	.2158 − 1	.7842	.9942 − 1	40′
30′	.2176 − 1	.2236 − 1	.7764	.9940 − 1	30′
40′	.2251 − 1	.2313 − 1	.7687	.9938 − 1	20′
50′	.2324 − 1	.2389 − 1	.7611	.9936 − 1	10′
10° 00′	.2397 − 1	.2463 − 1	.7537	.9934 − 1	80° 00′
10′	.2468 − 1	.2536 − 1	.7464	.9931 − 1	50′
20′	.2538 − 1	.2609 − 1	.7391	.9929 − 1	40′
30′	.2606 − 1	.2680 − 1	.7320	.9927 − 1	30′
40′	.2674 − 1	.2750 − 1	.7250	.9924 − 1	20′
50′	.2740 − 1	.2819 − 1	.7181	.9922 − 1	10′
11° 00′	.2806 − 1	.2887 − 1	.7113	.9919 − 1	79° 00′
10′	.2870 − 1	.2953 − 1	.7047	.9917 − 1	50′
20′	.2934 − 1	.3020 − 1	.6980	.9914 − 1	40′
30′	.2997 − 1	.3085 − 1	.6915	.9912 − 1	30′
40′	.3058 − 1	.3149 − 1	.6851	.9909 − 1	20′
50′	.3119 − 1	.3212 − 1	.6788	.9907 − 1	10′
12° 00′	.3179 − 1	.3275 − 1	.6725	.9904 − 1	78° 00′
10′	.3238 − 1	.3336 − 1	.6664	.9901 − 1	50′
20′	.3296 − 1	.3397 − 1	.6603	.9899 − 1	40′
30′	.3353 − 1	.3458 − 1	.6542	.9896 − 1	30′
40′	.3410 − 1	.3517 − 1	.6483	.9893 − 1	20′
50′	.3466 − 1	.3576 − 1	.6424	.9890 − 1	10′
13° 00′	.3521 − 1	.3634 − 1	.6366	.9887 − 1	77° 00′
10′	.3575 − 1	.3691 − 1	.6309	.9884 − 1	50′
20′	.3629 − 1	.3748 − 1	.6252	.9881 − 1	40′
30′	.3682 − 1	.3804 − 1	.6196	.9878 − 1	30′
40′	.3734 − 1	.3859 − 1	.6141	.9875 − 1	20′
50′	.3786 − 1	.3914 − 1	.6086	.9872 − 1	10′
14° 00′	.3837 − 1	.3968 − 1	.6032	.9869 − 1	76° 00′
10′	.3887 − 1	.4021 − 1	.5979	.9866 − 1	50′
20′	.3937 − 1	.4074 − 1	.5926	.9863 − 1	40′
30′	.3986 − 1	.4127 − 1	.5873	.9859 − 1	30′
40′	.4035 − 1	.4178 − 1	.5822	.9856 − 1	20′
50′	.4083 − 1	.4230 − 1	.5770	.9853 − 1	10′
15° 00′	.4130 − 1	.4281 − 1	.5719	.9849 − 1	75° 00′
10′	.4177 − 1	.4331 − 1	.5669	.9846 − 1	50′
20′	.4223 − 1	.4381 − 1	.5619	.9843 − 1	40′
30′	.4269 − 1	.4430 − 1	.5570	.9839 − 1	30′
40′	.4314 − 1	.4479 − 1	.5521	.9836 − 1	20′
50′	.4359 − 1	.4527 − 1	.5473	.9832 − 1	10′
16° 00′	.4403 − 1	.4575 − 1	.5425	.9828 − 1	74° 00′
10′	.4447 − 1	.4622 − 1	.5378	.9825 − 1	50′
20′	.4491 − 1	.4669 − 1	.5331	.9821 − 1	40′
30′	.4533 − 1	.4716 − 1	.5284	.9817 − 1	30′
40′	.4576 − 1	.4762 − 1	.5238	.9814 − 1	20′
50′	.4618 − 1	.4808 − 1	.5192	.9810 − 1	10′
17° 00′	.4659 − 1	.4853 − 1	.5147	.9806 − 1	73° 00′
10′	.4700 − 1	.4898 − 1	.5102	.9802 − 1	50′
20′	.4741 − 1	.4943 − 1	.5057	.9798 − 1	40′
30′	.4781 − 1	.4987 − 1	.5013	.9794 − 1	30′
40′	.4821 − 1	.5031 − 1	.4969	.9790 − 1	20′
50′	.4861 − 1	.5075 − 1	.4925	.9786 − 1	10′
18° 00′	.4900 − 1	.5118 − 1	.4882	.9782 − 1	72° 00′
	Log₁₀ Cosine	Log₁₀ Cotangent	Log₁₀ Tangent	Log₁₀ Sine	Degrees

TABLE III (Continued)
Logarithms of Trigonometric Functions

Degrees	Log₁₀ Sine	Log₁₀ Tangent	Log₁₀ Cotangent	Log₁₀ Cosine	
18° 00′	.4900 −1	.5118 −1	.4882	.9782 −1	72° 00′
10′	.4939 −1	.5161 −1	.4839	.9778 −1	50′
20′	.4977 −1	.5203 −1	.4797	.9774 −1	40′
30′	.5015 −1	.5245 −1	.4755	.9770 −1	30′
40′	.5052 −1	.5287 −1	.4713	.9765 −1	20′
50′	.5090 −1	.5329 −1	.4671	.9761 −1	10′
19° 00′	.5126 −1	.5370 −1	.4630	.9757 −1	71° 00′
10′	.5163 −1	.5411 −1	.4589	.9752 −1	50′
20′	.5199 −1	.5451 −1	.4549	.9748 −1	40′
30′	.5235 −1	.5491 −1	.4509	.9743 −1	30′
40′	.5270 −1	.5531 −1	.4469	.9739 −1	20′
50′	.5306 −1	.5571 −1	.4429	.9734 −1	10′
20° 00′	.5341 −1	.5611 −1	.4389	.9730 −1	70° 00′
10′	.5375 −1	.5650 −1	.4350	.9725 −1	50′
20′	.5409 −1	.5689 −1	.4311	.9721 −1	40′
30′	.5443 −1	.5727 −1	.4273	.9716 −1	30′
40′	.5477 −1	.5766 −1	.4234	.9711 −1	20′
50′	.5510 −1	.5804 −1	.4196	.9706 −1	10′
21° 00′	.5543 −1	.5842 −1	.4158	.9702 −1	69° 00′
10′	.5576 −1	.5879 −1	.4121	.9697 −1	50′
20′	.5609 −1	.5917 −1	.4083	.9692 −1	40′
30′	.5641 −1	.5954 −1	.4046	.9687 −1	30′
40′	.5673 −1	.5991 −1	.4009	.9682 −1	20′
50′	.5704 −1	.6028 −1	.3972	.9677 −1	10′
22° 00′	.5736 −1	.6064 −1	.3936	.9672 −1	68° 00′
10′	.5767 −1	.6100 −1	.3900	.9667 −1	50′
20′	.5798 −1	.6136 −1	.3864	.9661 −1	40′
30′	.5828 −1	.6172 −1	.3828	.9656 −1	30′
40′	.5859 −1	.6208 −1	.3792	.9651 −1	20′
50′	.5889 −1	.6243 −1	.3757	.9646 −1	10′
23° 00′	.5919 −1	.6279 −1	.3721	.9640 −1	67° 00′
10′	.5948 −1	.6314 −1	.3686	.9635 −1	50′
20′	.5978 −1	.6348 −1	.3652	.9629 −1	40′
30′	.6007 −1	.6383 −1	.3617	.9624 −1	30′
40′	.6036 −1	.6417 −1	.3583	.9618 −1	20′
50′	.6065 −1	.6452 −1	.3548	.9613 −1	10′
24° 00′	.6093 −1	.6486 −1	.3514	.9607 −1	66° 00′
10′	.6121 −1	.6520 −1	.3480	.9602 −1	50′
20′	.6149 −1	.6553 −1	.3447	.9596 −1	40′
30′	.6177 −1	.6587 −1	.3413	.9590 −1	30′
40′	.6205 −1	.6620 −1	.3380	.9584 −1	20′
50′	.6232 −1	.6654 −1	.3346	.9579 −1	10′
25° 00′	.6259 −1	.6687 −1	.3313	.9573 −1	65° 00′
10′	.6286 −1	.6720 −1	.3280	.9567 −1	50′
20′	.6313 −1	.6752 −1	.3248	.9561 −1	40′
30′	.6340 −1	.6785 −1	.3215	.9555 −1	30′
40′	.6366 −1	.6817 −1	.3183	.9549 −1	20′
50′	.6392 −1	.6850 −1	.3150	.9543 −1	10′
26° 00′	.6418 −1	.6882 −1	.3118	.9537 −1	64° 00′
10′	.6444 −1	.6914 −1	.3086	.9530 −1	50′
20′	.6470 −1	.6946 −1	.3054	.9524 −1	40′
30′	.6495 −1	.6977 −1	.3023	.9518 −1	30′
40′	.6521 −1	.7009 −1	.2991	.9512 −1	20′
50′	.6546 −1	.7040 −1	.2960	.9505 −1	10′
27° 00′	.6570 −1	.7072 −1	.2928	.9499 −1	63° 00′
	Log₁₀ Cosine	Log₁₀ Cotangent	Log₁₀ Tangent	Log₁₀ Sine	Degrees

TABLE III (Continued) 457
Logarithms of Trigonometric Functions

Degrees	Log₁₀ Sine	Log₁₀ Tangent	Log₁₀ Cotangent	Log₁₀ Cosine	
27° 00'	.6570 − 1	.7072 − 1	.2928	.9499 − 1	63° 00'
10'	.6595 − 1	.7103 − 1	.2897	.9492 − 1	50'
20'	.6620 − 1	.7134 − 1	.2866	.9486 − 1	40'
30'	.6644 − 1	.7165 − 1	.2835	.9479 − 1	30'
40'	.6668 − 1	.7196 − 1	.2804	.9473 − 1	20'
50'	.6692 − 1	.7226 − 1	.2774	.9466 − 1	10'
28° 00'	.6716 − 1	.7257 − 1	.2743	.9459 − 1	62° 00'
10'	.6740 − 1	.7287 − 1	.2713	.9453 − 1	50'
20'	.6763 − 1	.7317 − 1	.2683	.9446 − 1	40'
30'	.6787 − 1	.7348 − 1	.2652	.9439 − 1	30'
40'	.6810 − 1	.7378 − 1	.2622	.9432 − 1	20'
50'	.6833 − 1	.7408 − 1	.2592	.9425 − 1	10'
29° 00'	.6856 − 1	.7438 − 1	.2562	.9418 − 1	61° 00'
10'	.6878 − 1	.7467 − 1	.2533	.9411 − 1	50'
20'	.6901 − 1	.7497 − 1	.2503	.9404 − 1	40'
30'	.6923 − 1	.7526 − 1	.2474	.9397 − 1	30'
40'	.6946 − 1	.7556 − 1	.2444	.9390 − 1	20'
50'	.6968 − 1	.7585 − 1	.2415	.9383 − 1	10'
30° 00'	.6990 − 1	.7614 − 1	.2386	.9375 − 1	60° 00'
10'	.7012 − 1	.7644 − 1	.2356	.9368 − 1	50'
20'	.7033 − 1	.7673 − 1	.2327	.9361 − 1	40'
30'	.7055 − 1	.7701 − 1	.2299	.9353 − 1	30'
40'	.7076 − 1	.7730 − 1	.2270	.9346 − 1	20'
50'	.7097 − 1	.7759 − 1	.2241	.9338 − 1	10'
31° 00'	.7118 − 1	.7788 − 1	.2212	.9331 − 1	59° 00'
10'	.7139 − 1	.7816 − 1	.2184	.9323 − 1	50'
20'	.7160 − 1	.7845 − 1	.2155	.9315 − 1	40'
30'	.7181 − 1	.7873 − 1	.2127	.9308 − 1	30'
40'	.7201 − 1	.7902 − 1	.2098	.9300 − 1	20'
50'	.7222 − 1	.7930 − 1	.2070	.9292 − 1	10'
32° 00'	.7242 − 1	.7958 − 1	.2042	.9284 − 1	58° 00'
10'	.7262 − 1	.7986 − 1	.2014	.9276 − 1	50'
20'	.7282 − 1	.8014 − 1	.1986	.9268 − 1	40'
30'	.7302 − 1	.8042 − 1	.1958	.9260 − 1	30'
40'	.7322 − 1	.8070 − 1	.1930	.9252 − 1	20'
50'	.7342 − 1	.8097 − 1	.1903	.9244 − 1	10'
33° 00'	.7361 − 1	.8125 − 1	.1875	.9236 − 1	57° 00'
10'	.7380 − 1	.8153 − 1	.1847	.9228 − 1	50'
20'	.7400 − 1	.8180 − 1	.1820	.9219 − 1	40'
30'	.7419 − 1	.8208 − 1	.1792	.9211 − 1	30'
40'	.7438 − 1	.8235 − 1	.1765	.9203 − 1	20'
50'	.7457 − 1	.8263 − 1	.1737	.9194 − 1	10'
34° 00'	.7476 − 1	.8290 − 1	.1710	.9186 − 1	56° 00'
10'	.7494 − 1	.8317 − 1	.1683	.9177 − 1	50'
20'	.7513 − 1	.8344 − 1	.1656	.9169 − 1	40'
30'	.7531 − 1	.8371 − 1	.1629	.9160 − 1	30'
40'	.7550 − 1	.8398 − 1	.1602	.9151 − 1	20'
50'	.7568 − 1	.8425 − 1	.1575	.9142 − 1	10'
35° 00'	.7586 − 1	.8452 − 1	.1548	.9134 − 1	55° 00'
10'	.7604 − 1	.8479 − 1	.1521	.9125 − 1	50'
20'	.7622 − 1	.8506 − 1	.1494	.9116 − 1	40'
30'	.7640 − 1	.8533 − 1	.1467	.9107 − 1	30'
40'	.7657 − 1	.8559 − 1	.1441	.9098 − 1	20'
50'	.7675 − 1	.8586 − 1	.1414	.9089 − 1	10'
36° 00'	.7692 − 1	.8613 − 1	.1387	.9080 − 1	54° 00'
	Log₁₀ Cosine	Log₁₀ Cotangent	Log₁₀ Tangent	Log₁₀ Sine	Degrees

TABLE III (Continued)
Logarithms of Trigonometric Functions

Degrees	Log$_{10}$ Sine	Log$_{10}$ Tangent	Log$_{10}$ Cotangent	Log$_{10}$ Cosine	
36° 00'	.7692 −1	.8613 −1	.1387	.9080 −1	**54° 00'**
10'	.7710 −1	.8639 −1	.1361	.9070 −1	50'
20'	.7727 −1	.8666 −1	.1334	.9061 −1	40'
30'	.7744 −1	.8692 −1	.1308	.9052 −1	30'
40'	.7761 −1	.8718 −1	.1282	.9042 −1	20'
50'	.7778 −1	.8745 −1	.1255	.9033 −1	10'
37° 00'	.7795 −1	.8771 −1	.1229	.9023 −1	**53° 00'**
10'	.7811 −1	.8797 −1	.1203	.9014 −1	50'
20'	.7828 −1	.8824 −1	.1176	.9004 −1	40'
30'	.7844 −1	.8850 −1	.1150	.8995 −1	30'
40'	.7861 −1	.8876 −1	.1124	.8985 −1	20'
50'	.7877 −1	.8902 −1	.1098	.8975 −1	10'
38° 00'	.7893 −1	.8928 −1	.1072	.8965 −1	**52° 00'**
10'	.7910 −1	.8954 −1	.1046	.8955 −1	50'
20'	.7926 −1	.8980 −1	.1020	.8945 −1	40'
30'	.7941 −1	.9006 −1	.0994	.8935 −1	30'
40'	.7957 −1	.9032 −1	.0968	.8925 −1	20'
50'	.7973 −1	.9058 −1	.0942	.8915 −1	10'
39° 00'	.7989 −1	.9084 −1	.0916	.8905 −1	**51° 00'**
10'	.8004 −1	.9110 −1	.0890	.8895 −1	50'
20'	.8020 −1	.9135 −1	.0865	.8884 −1	40'
30'	.8035 −1	.9161 −1	.0839	.8874 −1	30'
40'	.8050 −1	.9187 −1	.0813	.8864 −1	20'
50'	.8066 −1	.9212 −1	.0788	.8853 −1	10'
40° 00'	.8081 −1	.9238 −1	.0762	.8843 −1	**50° 00'**
10'	.8096 −1	.9264 −1	.0736	.8832 −1	50'
20'	.8111 −1	.9289 −1	.0711	.8821 −1	40'
30'	.8125 −1	.9315 −1	.0685	.8810 −1	30'
40'	.8140 −1	.9341 −1	.0659	.8800 −1	20'
50'	.8155 −1	.9366 −1	.0634	.8789 −1	10'
41° 00'	.8169 −1	.9392 −1	.0608	.8778 −1	**49° 00'**
10'	.8184 −1	.9417 −1	.0583	.8767 −1	50'
20'	.8198 −1	.9443 −1	.0557	.8756 −1	40'
30'	.8213 −1	.9468 −1	.0532	.8745 −1	30'
40'	.8227 −1	.9494 −1	.0506	.8733 −1	20'
50'	.8241 −1	.9519 −1	.0481	.8722 −1	10'
42° 00'	.8255 −1	.9544 −1	.0456	.8711 −1	**48° 00'**
10'	.8269 −1	.9570 −1	.0430	.8699 −1	50'
20'	.8283 −1	.9595 −1	.0405	.8688 −1	40'
30'	.8297 −1	.9621 −1	.0379	.8676 −1	30'
40'	.8311 −1	.9646 −1	.0354	.8665 −1	20'
50'	.8324 −1	.9671 −1	.0329	.8653 −1	10'
43° 00'	.8338 −1	.9697 −1	.0303	.8641 −1	**47° 00'**
10'	.8351 −1	.9722 −-1	.0278	.8629 −1	50'
20'	.8365 −1	.9747 −1	.0253	.8618 −1	40'
30'	.8378 −1	.9772 −1	.0228	.8606 −1	30'
40'	.8391 −1	.9798 −1	.0202	.8594 −1	20'
50'	.8405 −1	.9823 −1	.0177	.8582 −1	10'
44° 00'	.8418 −1	.9848 −1	.0152	.8569 −1	**46° 00'**
10'	.8431 −1	.9874 −1	.0126	.8557 −1	50'
20'	.8444 −1	.9899 −1	.0101	.8545 −1	40'
30'	.8457 −1	.9924 −1	.0076	.8532 −1	30'
40'	.8469 −1	.9949 −1	.0051	.8520 −1	20'
50'	.8482 −1	.9975 −1	.0025	.8507 −1	10'
45° 00'	.8495 −1	.0000	.0000	.8495 −1	**45° 00'**
	Log$_{10}$ Cosine	Log$_{10}$ Cotangent	Log$_{10}$ Tangent	Log$_{10}$ Sine	Degrees

TABLE IV
459

Powers and Roots

No.	Sq.	Sq. Root	Cube	Cube Root	No.	Sq.	Sq. Root	Cube	Cube Root
1	1	1.000	1	1.000	51	2,601	7.141	132,651	3.708
2	4	1.414	8	1.260	52	2,704	7.211	140,608	3.733
3	9	1.732	27	1.442	53	2,809	7.280	148,877	3.756
4	16	2.000	64	1.587	54	2,916	7.348	157,464	3.780
5	25	2.236	125	1.710	55	3,025	7.416	166,375	3.803
6	36	2.449	216	1.817	56	3,136	7.483	175,616	3.826
7	49	2.646	343	1.913	57	3,249	7.550	185,193	3.849
8	64	2.828	512	2.000	58	3,364	7.616	195,112	3.871
9	81	3.000	729	2.080	59	3,481	7.681	205,379	3.893
10	100	3.162	1,000	2.154	60	3,600	7.746	216,000	3.915
11	121	3.317	1.331	2.224	61	3,721	7.810	226,981	3.936
12	144	3.464	1,728	2.289	62	3,844	7.874	238,328	3.958
13	169	3.606	2,197	2.351	63	3,969	7.937	250,047	3.979
14	196	3.742	2,744	2.410	64	4,096	8.000	262,144	4.000
15	225	3.873	3,375	2.466	65	4,225	8.062	274,625	4.021
16	256	4.000	4,096	2.520	66	4,356	8.124	287,496	4.041
17	289	4.123	4,913	2.571	67	4,489	8.185	300,763	4.062
18	324	4.243	5,832	2.621	68	4,624	8.246	314,432	4.082
19	361	4.359	6,859	2.668	69	4,761	8.307	328,509	4.102
20	400	4.472	8,000	2.714	70	4,900	8.367	343,000	4.121
21	441	4.583	9,261	2.759	71	5,041	8.426	357,911	4.141
22	484	4.690	10,648	2.802	72	5,184	8.485	373,248	4.160
23	529	4.796	12,167	2.844	73	5,329	8.544	389,017	4.179
24	576	4.899	13,824	2.884	74	5,476	8.602	405,224	4.198
25	625	5.000	15,625	2.924	75	5,625	8.660	421,875	4.217
26	676	5.099	17,576	2.962	76	5,776	8.718	438,976	4.236
27	729	5.196	19,683	3.000	77	5,929	8.775	456,533	4.254
28	784	5.292	21,952	3.037	78	6,084	8.832	474,552	4.273
29	841	5.385	24,389	3.072	79	6,241	8.888	493,039	4.291
30	900	5.477	27,000	3.107	80	6,400	8.944	512,000	4.309
31	961	5.568	29,791	3.141	81	6,561	9.000	531,441	4.327
32	1,024	5.657	32,768	3.175	82	6,724	9.055	551,368	4.344
33	1,089	5.745	35,937	3.208	83	6,889	9.110	571,787	4.362
34	1,156	5.831	39,304	3.240	84	7,056	9.165	592,704	4.380
35	1,225	5.916	42,875	3.271	85	7,225	9.220	614,125	4.397
36	1,296	6.000	46,656	3.302	86	7,396	9.274	636,056	4.414
37	1,369	6.083	50,653	3.332	87	7,569	9.327	658,503	4.431
38	1,444	6.164	54,872	3.362	88	7,744	9.381	681,472	4.448
39	1,521	6.245	59,319	3.391	89	7,921	9.434	704,969	4.465
40	1,600	6.325	64,000	3.420	90	8,100	9.487	729,000	4.481
41	1,681	6.403	68,921	3.448	91	8,281	9.539	753,571	4.498
42	1,764	6.481	74,088	3.476	92	8,464	9.592	778,688	4.514
43	1,849	6.557	79,507	3.503	93	8,649	9.644	804,357	4.531
44	1,936	6.633	85,184	3.530	94	8,836	9.695	830,584	4.547
45	2,025	6.708	91,125	3.557	95	9,025	9.747	857,375	4.563
46	2,116	6.782	97,336	3.583	96	9,216	9.798	884,736	4.579
47	2,209	6.856	103,823	3.609	97	9,409	9.849	912,673	4.595
48	2,304	6.928	110,592	3.634	98	9,604	9.899	941,192	4.610
49	2,401	7.000	117,649	3.659	99	9,801	9.950	970,299	4.626
50	2,500	7.071	125,000	3.684	100	10,000	10.000	1,000,000	4.642

TABLE V

American Experience Table of Mortality

Age	Number living	Number dying	Age	Number living	Number dying	Age	Number living	Number dying
10	100,000	749	40	78,106	765	70	38,569	2,391
11	99,251	746	41	77,341	774	71	36,178	2,448
12	98,505	743	42	76,567	785	72	33,730	2,487
13	97,762	740	43	75,782	797	73	31,243	2,505
14	97,022	737	44	74,985	812	74	28,738	2,501
15	96,285	735	45	74,173	828	75	26,237	2,476
16	95,550	732	46	73,345	848	76	23,761	2,431
17	94,818	729	47	72,497	870	77	21,330	2,369
18	94,089	727	48	71,627	896	78	18,961	2,291
19	93,362	725	49	70,731	927	79	16,670	2,196
20	92,637	723	50	69,804	962	80	14,474	2,091
21	91,914	722	51	68,842	1,001	81	12,383	1,964
22	91,192	721	52	67,841	1,044	82	10,419	1,816
23	90,471	720	53	66,797	1,091	83	8,603	1,648
24	89,751	719	54	65,706	1,143	84	6,955	1,470
25	89,032	718	55	64,563	1,199	85	5,485	1,292
26	88,314	718	56	63,364	1,260	86	4,193	1,114
27	87,596	718	57	62,104	1,325	87	3,079	933
28	86,878	718	58	60,779	1,394	88	2,146	744
29	86,160	719	59	59,385	1,468	89	1,402	555
30	85,441	720	60	57,917	1,546	90	847	385
31	84,721	721	61	56,371	1,628	91	462	246
32	84,000	723	62	54,743	1,713	92	216	137
33	83,277	726	63	53,030	1,800	93	79	58
34	82,551	729	64	51,230	1,889	94	21	18
35	81,822	732	65	49,341	1,980	95	3	3
36	81,090	737	66	47,361	2,070			
37	80,353	742	67	45,291	2,158			
38	79,611	749	68	43,133	2,243			
39	78,862	756	69	40,890	2,321			

INDEX

INDEX

Minor,
    axis of an ellipse, 354
    of a determinant, 155, 163
Minutes, 49
Modulus of complex numbers, 336
Monomial, 6
Multinomial, 6
Multiple zeros, 228
Multiplication,
    of algebraic expressions, 7
    of fractions, 25
    of radicals, 33

Natural growth, 288
Natural logarithms, 293
Nature of roots, 141
Normal line to a curve, 215
nth roots of complex numbers, 339
Numbers, 1

Oblique triangles, 305
Odd functions, 56
One-dimensional coordinate system, 36
Ordered pairs, 330
Ordinate, 40
Origin, 36
Oscillation, 326

Parabola, 126, 349
Parallel lines, 108
Parenthesis, 6
Pentagon, 73
Period, 63, 313
Periodic decimal, 2, 275
Periodic function, 63
Periodic piecewise continuous curve, 328
Permissible values, 3
Permutation, 401
Perpendicular lines, 108
Phase,
    difference, 315
    displacement, 315
Pi, 2
Point-slope form, 111

Polynomial, 10, 180
Power, 7
    of electric current, 324
Prime numbers, 17
Principal nth root, 28
Principal of superposition, 327
Probability, 406
    of dependent events, 411
    of independent events, 411
    of more than one event, 410
Products, 15
    of ordered pairs, 331
    of zeros of quadratic function, 140
Progressions, 103, 270
    arithmetic, 103
    geometric, 270
    harmonic, 106
Properties,
    of determinants, 159
    of logarithms, 278
Proportion, 146
Protractor, 94
Pure imaginary numbers, 332
Pythagorean Theorem, 43, 305

Quadrantal angles, 66
Quadrants, 41
Quadratic formula, 130
Quadratic function, 126
Quotient, 1
    of ordered pairs, 331

Radian, 50
Radical, 30
    axis, 348
    center, 348
Radicand, 30
Range of a function, 54
Rational function, 180
Rational number, 1
Rational roots, 232
Rationalizing the denominator, 34
Real numbers, 2
Reciprocal functions, 64
Rectilinear motion, 255